2005 Edition

Archer's Bible®

The Ultimate Archery
Reference Guide

Stoeger Publishing Company, Accokeek, Maryland

Stoeger Publishing®
Great Outdoor Books Since 1925

STOEGER PUBLISHING COMPANY
is a division of Benelli U.S.A.

Benelli U.S.A.
Vice President and General Manager:
  Stephen Otway
Vice President of Marketing and Communications:
  Stephen McKelvain

Stoeger Publishing Company
President: Jeffrey Reh
Publisher: Jay Langston
Managing Editor: Harris J. Andrews
Design & Production Director: Cynthia T. Richardson
Photography Director: Alex Bowers
Imaging Specialist: William Graves
National Sales Manager: Jennifer Thomas
Sales Manager Assistant: Julie Brownlee
Publishing Assistant: Christine Lawton
Administrative Assistant: Shannon McWilliams
Proofreader: Celia Beattie

© 2004 by Stoeger Publishing Company.
All rights reserved.

No part of this book may be reproduced or transmitted
in any form or by any means, electronic or mechanical,
including photocopying, recording, or by any information storage and retrieval system, without permission in
writing from the Publisher.

Published by:
Stoeger Publishing Company
17603 Indian Head HIghway, Suite 200
Accokeek, Maryland 20607

BK0403
ISBN:0-88317-288-7
Library of Congress Control Number: 2003116082

Manufactured in the United States of America

Distributed to the book trade and
to the sporting goods trade by:
Stoeger Industries
17603 Indian Head Highway, Suite 200
Accokeek, Maryland 20607
www.stoegerindustries.com

Photography Credits
Mitch Kezar/Windigo: *Title page;*
Alex Bowers: *65, 115, 199, 225, 261, 341, 375;*
Keith de Noble: *331;*
Keith Sutton: *381*

OTHER PUBLICATIONS:
Shooter's Bible
  The World's Standard Firearms
  Reference Book
Gun Trader's Guide
  Complete, Fully-Illustrated
  Guide to Modern Firearms with
  Current Market Values

Hunting & Shooting
Conserving Wild America
Hunting Whitetails East and West
Hounds of the World
The Turkey Hunter's Tool Kit:
  Shooting Savvy
Complete Book of Whitetail Hunting
Hunting and Shooting with
  the Modern Bow
The Ultimate in Rifle Accuracy
Advanced Black Powder Hunting
Labrador Retrievers
Hunting America's Wild Turkey
Taxidermy Guide
Cowboy Action Shooting
Great Shooters of the World
Trailing the Hunter's Moon
Shotgunning for Deer
Hunt Club Management Guide
Tennessee Whitetails

Collecting Books
The Truth About Spring Turkey
  Hunting According to "Cuz"
The Whole Truth About Spring Turkey
  Hunting According to "Cuz"
Sporting Collectibles
The Working Folding Knife
The Lore of Spices

Firearms
Antique Guns
P-38 Automatic Pistol
The Walther Handgun Story
Complete Guide to Compact Handguns
Complete Guide to Service Handguns
America's Great Gunmakers
Firearms Disassembly with
  Exploded Views
Rifle Guide
Gunsmithing at Home
The Book of the Twenty-Two
Complete Guide to Modern Rifles
Complete Guide to Classic Rifles
Legendary Sporting Rifles
FN Browning Armorer to the World
Modern Beretta Firearms
How to Buy & Sell Used Guns
Heckler & Koch: Armorers
  of the Free World
Spanish Handguns

Reloading
The Handloader's Manual of
  Cartridge Conversions
Modern Sporting Rifle Cartridges
Complete Reloading Guide

Fishing
Bassing Bible
Ultimate Bass Boats
The Flytier's Companion
Deceiving Trout
The Complete Book of Trout Fishing
The Complete Book of Flyfishing
Peter Dean's Guide to Fly-Tying
The Flytier's Manual
Flytier's Master Class
Handbook of Fly Tying
The Fly Fisherman's Entomological
  Pattern Book
Fiberglass Rod Making
To Rise a Trout
Fishing Online: 1,000 Best Web Sites
Flyfishning for Trout A to Z
Fishing Made Easy

Motorcycles & Trucks
The Legend of Harley-Davidson
The Legend of the Indian
Best of Harley-Davidson
Classic Bikes
Great Trucks
4X4 Vehicles

Cooking Game
Fish & Shellfish Care & Cookery
Game Cookbook
Dress 'Em Out
The World's Best Catfish Cookbook
Wild About Venison
Wild About Game Birds
Wild About Fresh Water Fish
Wild About Waterfowl
Wild About Seafood

CONTENTS

FOREWORD

I was 12 when I purchased my first bow, an impressive-looking, 62-inch, 45-pound Ben Pearson recurve. It seems I mowed a hundred yards that summer to pay for it at the Western Auto store, the only business in the county in those days that had anything like a sporting goods department.

I'm not saying I'm old or anything, but that wonderful bow—a bow I would shoot for nearly 20 years—set me back a grand total of $65, including six arrows, a quiver, an armguard and a finger tab. It seemed like a fortune. The Western Auto man special-ordered it for me direct from the company, which was then located in my home state of Arkansas.

I stacked hay bales in the backyard, drew circles and bull's-eyes on some paper plates, tucked the plates behind the strings on the bales and started shooting. By the time the sun set the first day, I had broken two of the wooden arrows and lost the other four, including one I shot straight into the sun. Not to fret, though. There were plenty more yards to mow, and the $2.50 I earned for each one would buy five new arrows.

The year after I bought my new bow, a fantastic thing happened. Less than half a mile from my house, an archery range opened. This was no ordinary range, at least not in those days in a small northeast Arkansas town. Twenty targets (hay bales and animals-on-paper targets) were scattered along a half-mile trail through the rolling woodlands, each offering a unique setup to test the archer's skills. At one station, you could shoot from a treestand. Another featured a moving target that passed from right to left or vice versa when your shooting companion cranked a special-made, bicycle-wheel pulley system. There were 10-yard shots and 50-yard shots, shots through the brush, shots in the open, shots up and shots down, and everything in between. In short, for a 13-year-old kid with too much time on his hands, it was heaven. I mowed four yards, paid the $10 annual membership fee and the fun began.

The second year the range was open, I began shooting competitively with the men in the club. And with distinct pleasure, I won more rounds than I lost. The cash prizes meant less time mowing, more time on the shooting range.

This was also the first year I went bowhunting for deer, a pastime I would enjoy for decades to come. When the season opened each October, my hunting buddies and I would load our camping gear and head off for a weekend or week-long hunting trip. We didn't kill many whitetails back then, but those hunting trips are some of the most memorable moments of a long, fulfilling life.

Last month, my 12-year-old son Zach got his first bow—a nice compound made especially for young, just-learning-to-shoot archers. With its pulleys and cables and fiber-optic sights, it's a far cry from the simple recurve I started with more than 35 years ago. He shoots carbon arrows, not wood, and he shoots them not at a paper plate tucked beneath the strings of a hay bale but at a modern target that actually stops the arrows. He hasn't lost one yet.

One thing hasn't changed, though. The magic of archery has as powerful an attraction for Zach as it did for me. A youngster who once came home from school and turned on the computer, the television or a video game now walks in, grabs his bow and arrows and hollers, "Dad, let's go shoot."

That's the best part of all this: I'm out there shooting with him every day. And I do mean every day. Archery has provided a means for us to reconnect—with each other and with the out-of-doors.

In just a few weeks, I've watched Zach's transformation from frustrated novice to proud competitor. His groups are getting tighter and tighter from farther and farther away. And he's looking for new ways to challenge himself. Yesterday, I found him standing on the luggage rack of my van shooting the target from 30 yards instead of his usual ten.

When the sun went down and he came inside, Zach headed straight for the bookcase and pulled out a copy of the Archer's Bible. For the next two hours, flipping through its pages on the kitchen table, we discussed stabilizers and 3-D targets, treestands and shooting releases, peep sights and broadheads. Zach wants it all, and if he finds enough yards to mow, I'm sure he'll soon have it.

I tell you all this because I want you to know why I'm so proud to be the editor of the Archer's Bible. Archery played an incredibly important role in the development of my character. Shooting a bow taught me that patience, diligence and hard work can be rewarded with immeasurable satisfaction. It kept me out of a trouble in a world where trouble was everywhere. And now, it has enabled me to establish a rapport with my son that will make both our lives vastly richer.

The magical sport of archery can transform lives in ways we seldom take time to consider. And a book like the one you now hold in your hands can add spice to this wonderful repast. I hope you enjoy it as much as I've enjoyed putting it together.

Share it with a budding archer, will you? You'll both be glad you did.

—Keith Sutton, Editor

FEATURE ARTICLES

Bowhunting Savvy for Public Lands

by Soc Clay

"Cripes, these climbs are getting tough," I grumbled under my breath as Terry Rohm and I struggled over the trunk of a fallen oak in the Daniel Boone National Forest.

Terry, the public relations manager for Wellington/Tink's, a Georgia company that markets scents for use in hunting, had driven to my east Kentucky home to try for one of the huge whitetail bucks that hide out in the stand-up land Daniel Boone made famous more than two and a half centuries ago. That's back when Native Americans described these game-rich wilds as the "happy hunting ground."

Millions of acres of public lands provide excellent opportunities for bowhunting success.

Rumors of huge bucks being taken and seen abound in the eastern tip of the national forest. In fact, two state-record bucks—one taken by an archer, the other by a black-powder hunter—were found near the national forest's northeastern border. Such notable hunters as TV host Hank Parker and Bill Jordan, founder and president of Realtree Camouflage, have been hunting this area for some time.

"These guys have the resources to hunt anywhere in the world, so it's pretty evident that some huge whitetail are living in these hills," Terry said when we first decided to hunt the 700,000-acre forest.

Kentucky, like many states in America, is blessed with large tracts of public land that provide good opportunities for bowhunters savvy enough to overcome the public-access issue.

"Hunting public lands can offer exciting challenges to archers who develop means of avoiding the main problems with quality hunting in areas with unlimited access—namely pressure and unfamiliar surroundings," Terry explained as we planned our hunt strategy.

In recent years, bowhunting pressure on the Daniel Boone and other public lands harboring big whitetails has in-creased dramatically, especially in the easy-access areas where neophyte archers collect in numbers on opening day and during weekends and holiday periods. That's the reason Terry and I had climbed through a rough section to reach an area two miles from a popular access. Terry thought we would allow the other archers to help drive deer away from the roads and, hopefully, past our stands.

Getting beyond the pressure is a tactic most seasoned archers employ when faced with increased numbers of hunters in the same general area. Terry believes you can solve this issue by simply realizing the average hunter will generally plan a hunt on public lands from an easy-access point, usually meaning a road he or she drives to in a vehicle. Few hunters venture into areas more than a half-mile from parking areas before finding a trail and positioning a stand nearby, he said. For the most part, this type hunter rarely has an opportunity to kill anything other than a yearling buck or a doe. The big boys, the ones with age displayed on their head in the form of large racks, Terry

Still sheathed in velvet, the antlers of this early-season whitetail give promise to a truly magnificent rack. Careful scouting in areas removed from hunting pressure, combined with the right tactics, can still produce trophy bucks on public lands.

Public lands can be exciting places to hunt when bowmen have a plan to avoid locations with heavy hunting pressure.

Savvy bowmen who establish a solid game plan for hunting public lands can find trophy whitetail bucks.

said, will quickly abandon such places as soon as they realize hunters are in the woods.

"Ok," I asked, "How does a bowhunter locate an area on this or other public lands that's likely to produce a quality buck without the hunter having to travel to the far side of Timbuktu?"

Planning a Hunt on Public Lands

Terry, whose job is testing the effectiveness of an entire line of scents made by Tink's for deer, elk and other game species, said hunters should start planning for their hunt a month or more in advance by first contacting the state fish and wildlife agency where the targeted area is located. It's smart, he said, to ask for all available information about deer hunting there with a bow, including deer density and the hunt area's reputation for producing quality bucks.

When a preliminary decision is made to hunt an area, his advice is to obtain the best map available for the location, then fine-tune the actual hunt area with topographical maps. Detailed maps show deer gathering places such as watering holes, woodlots, edge areas, fields and bottom land. Depending on the location, the noted archer's advice is to locate food sources that will be available at the time of the hunt. For instance, edge areas, bottom land and agriculture fields will be best for the early season, while hardwood mast and heavy underbrush areas may be the best later on.

Scouting

Nothing beats a scouting visit to the area, said Terry, who grew up hunting public lands in Pennsylvania. He suggests visiting the area a week ahead of the scheduled hunt to look for fresh sign. In a new location, he recommends following a well-used trail and checking out freshly used cross trails, keeping in mind that intersections nearest the access area are likely to be the most hunted. It's best, he adds, to select as many as five possible stand locations, moving farther away from roads and possible intrusion by others. And, as he reminded me on the rough climb, sometimes the best locations are difficult to access.

Four days before our hunt, we began implementing Terry's game plan. Studying maps and stopping by a half-dozen country stores and gas stations, we pretty well determined where the heaviest hunting traffic occurs in that area of the forest. Then using a topographical map of the section, plus a compass and GPS unit, we planned a route to the far side of the popular access and scouted it for sign.

Preparation

When our hunt area had been determined, Terry recommended several steps to prepare for the day in the field.

Human scents, he said, cause most bowhunters to be unsuccessful. To correct this, he suggested washing ourselves, including our hair, in a nonscented soap the morning of the hunt. All hunting clothing, including caps, backpacks, fanny packs, etc., should be washed in nonscented products and stored outside until hunt day.

Following his advice, we cleaned all equipment of any human or unnatural scent (grease, etc.). And before entering the hunting area, we sprayed on another coating of nonscented.

Terry also recommends wearing rubber or rubber-soled hunting shoes or boots. And he wears an insulated cap to help hold in escaping head vapors.

At the stand location, we sprayed again with a nonscented product (Terry uses Tink's Non Stink). We also applied it to our face, neck and hair, and sprayed our armpits, crotch and the back of our knees. We laid down a cover scent (fox, coon, pine or earth) around the stand. Chewing gum, tobacco products or food items were stored in a locking plastic bag, and we were using lightweight portable tree stands so we could move them if someone was in our chosen spot or if conditions had changed since our scouting trip. Pruning shears allowed us to create clear shooting lanes.

A huge buck examines a scent designed to take its attention from the archer nearby.

Magic X

Establishing Terry's "Magic X" pattern for stand location is an ideal setup for bowhunters. For us, this meant searching out cross trails that met inside chutes or narrow valleys where deer followed paths of least resistance during daily movements. Our stands would be placed so the wind

The edge of a field is always a good place to find deer on public lands.

"The Magic X"

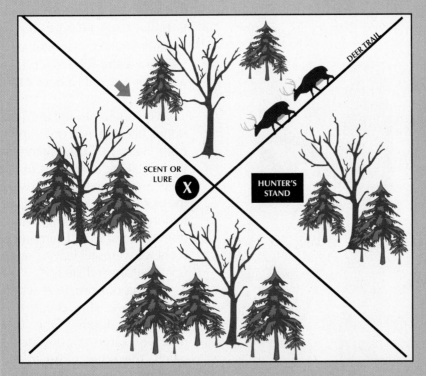

* Locate the intersection of two actively used deer trails.
* Hunter's stand should be on the downwind side of the deer trail intersection.
* Deer lure scent should be placed on the upwind side of the deer trail intersection.
* Place deer scent so deer will smell the lure, not the hunter.
* Important keys to finding the "Magic X":
  * Located deer trail intersection
  * Wind direction
  * Stand placement
* Deer lures for early season:
  * Doe pee
  * Tarsal gland
* Deer lures for the rut:
  * Doe in rut/heat
  * Trophy buck lure

Terry Rohm, a hunting specialist for Wellington/Tink's shows off a trophy buck that fell victim to his "Magic X" bowhunting technique.

would be coming from the direction from which we hoped the deer would come.

The scents we used were placed on the upwind side of our stands, near the intersection of two trails, within accurate bow shooting range. Terry noted that scents are not a "magic bullet," but instead, are an enhancement that might give us a few extra seconds to take a shot or to "pull" a deer a few steps closer.

We opted to place our stands about a half-mile apart, each near well-used intersections. Making judgments of the breeze, we hung the stands on the east side of the "X" junction, figuring the prevailing winds from the west would carry what scent we were still leaving away from the targeted areas.

During our previous scouting trip, we also chose two backup locations. One was near a large honeysuckle patch, the other close to the edge of a clearcut. Terry likes to hunt near known or suspected bedding areas for old bucks. The thick growth would provide the kind of security a big whitetail looks for when the season begins.

Bowhunting Tips for Public Lands

- Start planning in advance, contacting the fish and wildlife agencies in charge of the public area you wish to hunt.

- Obtain as much deer hunting data for the area as possible, including deer density and quality of bucks.

- Obtain topographical maps of targeted hunt area.

- Eliminate as much human or nonnatural scents from body, clothing and equipment as possible.

- Select difficult access routes to avoid other hunters.

- Select a stand area that takes advantage of deer being driven by other hunters.

- Carry lightweight, portable tree stands that are easily moved.

- Erect stands on the downwind side of intersecting trails.

- Place stands so wind blows from incoming deer, not toward deer trails.

- Select three or more stand locations.

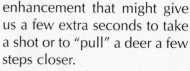

Incredible as it seems, Terry managed to take a heavy-antlered eight-pointer the afternoon of our first day hunting the Daniel Boone. A hanging scent bomb positioned 20 yards from his stand did its work when the big whitetail came down the trail and stopped to nose the scent container. Terry was ready and took the shot.

"When a deer is drawn to the scent, you either take the shot right then or let it pass. Once a deer whiffs the scent, it will be alerted that something is wrong and will usually bolt," he said.

Taking a nice buck with a bow from public lands can take a lifetime of hunting for some, but for savvy archers like Terry Rohm who know how to avoid the pitfalls of public access, the challenge becomes much, much less difficult.

Thousands of archers depend on public lands for a place to hunt deer. While public lands can be extremely productive, bowhunters must have the knowledge to avoid heavy hunting pressure in unfamiliar surroundings.

Why Most Bowhunters Fail to Kill a Deer
by Bruce Ingram

Most bowhunting publications, in most of their articles, detail how to kill big bucks. That's all well and good; I love to read and write about that topic. But the truth is that the success rate for bowhunters across most of the country is extremely low. In fact, we bowhunters seem to have a great deal of difficulty when it comes to killing a deer of either sex.

For example, my two home states of Virginia and West Virginia have success rates of 30 and 25 percent, respectively. In Kentucky, the success rate is a woeful 13 percent, in Tennessee it's 19 percent, and in whitetail-rich Texas, the success rate is just 15 percent.

Some exceptions exist, most notably Mississippi, where archers give evidence of their talent and take advantage of a burgeoning deer herd with a success rate of 88 percent. Most bowhunters, however, fail to kill a deer each season. Here are some reasons why.

Lack of Understanding about Scent Control

A confession that I don't like to make is that the first four years I bowhunted, I failed to kill a deer. When, on opening day of that fifth

Jim Crumley *(below)* **feels that many archers fail to take into account wind direction and current food sources when selecting a site for their stands.**

season, I arrowed a doe shortly after sunrise, I felt as if a miracle had occurred. While I kneeled beside the fallen whitetail and said a prayer of thanks, my self-esteem archerywise was still so low that I wondered if someone else had actually killed the deer and I had stumbled upon it, even though the blood trail had led directly from my stand to the doe.

When I arrived home that morning, my wife, who likewise had little confidence in my bowhunting, asked me why I had returned so early.

"I killed a deer with my bow," I gushed.

"No you didn't," she replied. "Really, why are you home so early?"

I truly believe that the number one reason why I experienced four years of failure—and the main reason why the success rate for other archers is low as well—was/is a lack of understanding about the importance of scent control. If our scent control regimen is lacking, we can employ a rifle and kill a whitetail standing 200 yards away in a field. But if such is the case when we are bowhunting, we will very rarely be able to arrow a deer feeding 20 yards away in a pine thicket.

Many bowhunters fail to practice scent control on their clothes or bodies—a major reason success rates are so low.

My fifth year of bowhunting was the first when I established a routine for keeping myself and my clothes clean, and over the years I have become even stricter about my regimen. Numerous scent-free cleansers exist for our bodies, hair, and clothes; they all have their virtues and should be used. When washing my hunting clothes, I always use scent-free detergent, as well as adding a generous dollop of baking soda to the mix.

Years ago, I stored my freshly laundered hunting garb in black trash bags, which was better than leaving them in a drawer or piled in a corner as too many bowhunters do. Now, I store some of my clothes in a resealable, heavy-duty plastic bag that has a zipper and a valve, and the rest in a Rubbermaid hard plastic container that I bought for about four dollars.

In the field, I primarily employ two cover scents: Nature's Essence of Fall, which I spray on my clothes and on my hair, underarms and groin area, all of which are "high scent" places. Additionally, I apply several drops of Pete Rickard's Acorn Deer Lure (which serves as both a cover scent and an attractant) to my clothes. I also own camouflage that has Scent-Lok technology incorporated within and have found this suit to be helpful in preventing deer from detecting my presence.

This routine works for me. If you are not as successful a bowhunter as you would like to be, consider developing a similar regimen.

During much, if not most, of the early bow season across whitetail country, the number one reason bucks and does travel from place to place is to obtain food. If we are to know where to correctly position our stands, we must understand the major food sources of whitetails.

An error that I used to make a great deal, and still commit somewhat today, is positioning a portable stand where I have seen or arrowed deer in the past. I believe too many bowhunters fail to succeed because they place their stands in the old, familiar places instead of near the hot food source of the moment.

For example, in much of the United States, the favorite food of whitetails is the white oak acorn. When white oaks are dropping their

The first week of deer season, the author believes, is the best time to kill a deer. If you have not been as successful a bowhunter as you would like, consider hunting hard during this time period.

bounty, you should be positioned near them, regardless of whether you live in Vermont, Georgia or Minnesota.

Other major sources of nourishment are the various acorns of the red oaks, such as the northern red, scarlet, pin, black, and blackjack. More important early-season foods are beechnuts, apples, corn and various grain crops.

One of the things I enjoy most about bowhunting is annually figuring out before the season begins—and as it progresses—what the deer are consuming. If you make an effort to do the same in your home woods, then you will greatly increase your chance of success.

I also suggest purchasing a field guide to North American trees and shrubs. I own several such books and refer to them often during archery season.

Lack of Preseason Practice

I used to feel I only needed a few weeks of practice with my compound to prepare for archery season. That misbegotten belief was another reason my fifth season was the first one when I arrowed a deer. A lack of preseason practice also is a major reason why many archers fail to punch a tag.

The truth is, archers must feel totally comfortable with their bows and confident with their shooting ability when a whitetail comes within shooting range. The only way I have found to gain these comfort and confidence levels is through a rigid regimen of preseason practice.

Every year after the Fourth of July, I make a visit to my local archery shop. I have a professional thoroughly examine my compound and release to make sure no parts are worn and nothing needs tightening, fixed or replaced. This activity increases my confidence in my equipment. I then go home and begin a practice schedule that continues until Virginia's season opens the first Saturday in October.

Basically, that regimen involves me shooting nine arrows a session at a target 20 yards away. While doing so, I stand on a chair on my sundeck, which simulates the height I will be shooting from while in a stand. I perform this ritual every other day for three months. Other successful bowhunters I know have different practice schedules. One friend participates in a year-round archery league, another shoots twice

Why the First Week of the Season Is Key to Our Success

Nine out of the past 10 years, I have arrowed a deer either on opening day of Virginia's early archery season or within the first week of it. I have such faith in this time period that I go afield every afternoon after work and stay on stand all day during the Saturday opener.

The primary reason bowhunters, especially those who are not satisfied with their success rates, should spend so much time afield during the initial week is that the deer simply have not yet learned (perhaps relearned is the better word) that they are being hunted. Quite a few of my opening day/week deer have been killed between 10:00 and 2:00, a period generally not regarded as prime time by many archers. The whitetails have not yet adapted to the increased presence of hunters in the woods, an adaptation that often makes them move less during daylight hours.

Over those 10 years, I have also noticed much less deer activity during the second week of the season. Only when the pre-rut period begins does deer movement approach that of the first week of archery season. That time frame is my second most productive period as an archer and is also when a hunter who has hopes of tagging a buck is much more likely to score.

Numerous kinds of cover scents are available: use some of these products and you will likely enjoy higher success rates while bowhunting.

a week year-round behind his house, while a third buddy begins shooting just after spring gobbler season ends. Develop a preseason routine that works for you, and you will kill more deer.

Lack of Composure

The first year I bowhunted, a year-and-a-half-old five-pointer walked by my stand. I was so nervous and flustered I sent an arrow right between his smallish antlers. If I had been a place-kicker, if the sport had been football, and if the deer's antlers had been goal posts, my effort would have been perfect.

The second year, I shot an arrow into an 8-inch-wide sapling I had been too excited to see when a doe walked into range.

The third year, I missed a doe at a distance of just 10 yards when I forgot to look through my peep sight. The arrow buried into the sod beneath the whitetail's feet.

On and on my miseries continued until I finally—mostly—solved my lack-of-composure problem, another issue many bowhunters have that keeps them from being successful. I say mostly solved because I don't personally feel that I will ever totally lose that feeling of anxiety that arises when a deer comes within shooting range. Neither will most other bowhunters. I do believe, however, that we can develop a process that will help greatly settle our nerves at a crucial moment.

Why Stand Sites Fail to Produce

Bowhunting legend and Trebark creator Jim Crumley lives only a few miles from me and has long been my bowhunting mentor. When I told him I was doing a story on why bowhunters often have their efforts go for naught, he urged me to cover the topic of how archers often sabotage their own stand sites.

"One reason success rates are so low is that bowhunters often ruin stands without even knowing they did it," Crumley told me. "They hunt stands too often, when the wind direction is wrong or when the food sources have changed. Deer can become wary around certain stand sites if human scent is constantly in the area. If the wind direction is wrong at a stand, then you simply should not hunt from it if you want the stand to have a chance to be pro-

ductive later in the season. And if the deer have moved on to other food sources, spending time in a stand at the old food source is a big waste anyway."

Crumley also relates that too many bowhunters enter their stands just before dawn and leave right after dark. Make sure, especially in the evening, that all deer have left the immediate area before you climb down. The Virginian has waited as long as an hour after sunset to leave a prized stand, just because several deer remained in the vicinity.

Interestingly, Crumley maintains that mature does have a shared tendency with big bucks in their ability to learn to avoid stand sites. Alarm a mature doe, particularly one with fawns, that is feeding around your stand, and you're not likely to see her again that season.

For instance, when I see a deer approach, I remind myself to do five things: take a deep breath, draw back the bow smoothly, look through the peep sight, focus on the deer's heart/lung area and follow through with the shot. While at full draw, I also remind myself that this is what I have practiced to do for months, and that I know what I am doing—a pep talk, if you will, directed toward myself.

This routine has helped me immeasurably to be a more accurate shooter, and, again, I encourage you to develop your own system for when the proverbial moment of truth arrives.

I believe most of us will never become so composed that we will not ever send an arrow high, wide or low. This past October, for example, I missed a doe standing broadside just 10 yards away, a snafu that still rankles me. But I have come to realize, and rationalize, this is just part of what makes bowhunting such a marvelous and thrilling pastime.

Few archers are hardcore trophy hunters, especially when compared to the many sportsmen who tote rifles, shotguns and muzzleloaders. Many of us would be satisfied if we could annually kill a doe or two for the freezer. Learning better scent control, understanding deer foods, a preseason practice regimen, and controlling our nerves are four ways we can greatly improve our odds of being more successful bowhunters.

Understanding the major food sources for whitetails in your home area can go a long way toward improving your chances of tagging more deer.

(Inset)
Throughout most of the eastern half of the country, various species of white and red oaks provide major sources of food for whitetails. Study the oak varieties in your home area and you will be likely to experience more productive days afield.

The author, at left, begins practicing for the bow season right after the Fourth of July. To increase your chances of success, consider developing a preseason practice routine of your own.

10 Tips for Purchasing Your Next Bow

by Mark Kayser

My optimism went off the charts when I sighted a heavy-antlered buck dogging a doe. The deer were on course to run smack into the tree in which I had my stand, and a stiff wind in my face guaranteed they wouldn't smell me. But as the doe veered from my stand into a dense thicket to browse, my optimism quickly transformed into depression. Even if the pair did pass my stand now, the thick brush prevented an ethical shot.

With nothing to lose, I put my True Talker grunt tube to my lips and aggressively relayed to the buck that he wasn't the only bachelor in the woods. The odds of a buck leaving a female during the rut are slim, but the event unfolding before me illustrated small miracles do happen.

Upon hearing the grunts, the buck paused, then he paralleled the doe on a second, closer trail, offering me several shooting opportunities. My hunting instincts shifted into overdrive as my mind switched to autopilot.

At 18 yards, the buck ran into a wall of estrus scent I sprayed in a nearby shooting lane. Hooked like a catfish on stinkbait, he paused to sample the newfound scent. I drew, aimed and released an arrow into the stalled whitetail.

The buck raced into an open pasture, stopped and began stumbling to his certain doom. Quaking from a high–octane dose of adrenaline, I hung up my bow and calmed myself while eyeing the downed buck in the open field.

I didn't think about my bow at the time, but reflecting back on the day, my choice in bows played a major role in my success. I had chosen a bow that not only was simple and smooth to operate, but which provided the needed kinetic energy to cleanly punch through the buck for his quick end. I had

No matter how you prepare yourself, once an animal enters bow range, your emotions begin to unwrap, leading to trembling, shortness of breath and loss of concentration. If you have overly complicated gear, chances are you'll forget a critical step in your shot process and blow the opportunity.

matched the bow to my body and was able to easily draw it even though temperatures were below freezing and I was dressed like the Michelin Man. Outfitting the bow with simple gear to cater to my autopilot-shooting regime completed my setup.

Today's archery market is flooded with radical-looking new bows that would make Fred Bear scratch his head for a moment as he mulled their designs. I also scratch my head every time I enter a pro shop trying to evaluate the newest bows.

Do you really need all the innovations manufacturers are incorporating into today's bows? If you're in the market for a new bow, use the following tips to transform your bow purchase into a trophy this season.

Educate Yourself

Bow technology is changing almost as fast as computer technology. To drive sales, bow companies need to introduce new equipment each year whether it's needed or not.

To keep up with the new innovations, you need to immerse yourself in every available outlet of archery knowledge. Most major bowhunting publications run reviews and field tests on new models. Check their publications and Web sites for the latest reports, quiz pro shop owners on new models, and converse with local archers at 3-D competitions on their likes and dislikes about new bows. Objective reviews from individuals not aligned through financial obligations offer the best insight.

Objective reviews from individuals offer the best insight. Be sure to scour all available information about bows and their performance reviews before making a final selection.

Hands-on testing is the only way to find the best bow. While magazines and the Web are useful research tools, never purchase a bow without first trying it out.

Buy As Much Quality As Your Budget Allows

Everyone's budget differs, but don't short-change yourself when outfitting for your upcoming hunts. Review your budget, and buy the best-quality bow you can afford.

Generally speaking, higher-priced items usually reflect a higher quality that stands a better chance of surviving a rugged hunt. In the outside chance your bow does break, you also stand a better chance of getting it repaired. Spending more for high-quality equipment buys you easier access to parts and a higher likelihood of finding a trained technician to fix your bow in a remote area.

By researching bows and obtaining professional help from certified pro shops, bowhunters can avoid the mistake of purchasing a bow that doesn't fit their body or shooting style.

Match the Bow to You

It's commonplace for new bow-hunters to try and pull more bow weight than they should. Don't chew off more than you can handle. Seek the advice of pro-shop owners, and follow that advice.

Set the bow at a weight you can comfortably pull. This is especially important for bowhunters in northern latitudes. As temperatures plummet, the amount of weight you can pull decreases. Thick, layered clothing combined with long sits in bone-chilling conditions can impair personal strength.

Buck fever also plays games with your muscles and can make even the strongest bowhunters struggle with their bow when a buck appears. If in doubt, always set your bow several pounds lighter than your peak weight. For wilderness bowhunters, don't forget to take into consideration the bow's overall weight combined with tackle, which increases your backpack load.

Shop for a Single-Cam Bow

One main difference separates 1- and 2-cam bow technology. Wheel synchronization is unnecessary with

1-cam bows, whereas it is critical for smooth shooting with a 2-cam version. On 2-cam bows, the cams must rotate in synchronization or the string may jerk and launch the arrow erratically.

Generally speaking, 1-cam bows using a radical eccentric shoot faster than a standard round-style cam, plus they don't experience the occasional hassles of 2-cam synchronization. Having one less thing to worry about is important for all bowhunters, especially those who hunt in rugged, wilderness conditions.

Look for a Larger Brace Height

Simply put, the brace height is a measurement from the bow's handle to the string and is determined by the riser's design. Bow risers that are radically reflexed or straight place the handle closer to the string, thus increasing the power stroke of the string and shooting the arrow faster. This creates a shorter brace height and gives the arrow less time to straighten out as it leaves the string and passes the arrow rest. The farther the string is from the handle, the larger the brace height, thus decreasing arrow speed, but allowing the arrow more time to straighten out.

As a general rule, bows with a larger brace height have more arrow forgiveness, yet are somewhat slower. Shop for a bow with a brace height from 7 to 8 inches for consistent shooting.

Hunting success comes in the form of a well-matched bow and confidence in shooting.

Long or Short Bow?

Traditionally, longer bows tend to be more easily tuned and are more forgiving. Short bows have long received a bad rap for their diminished weight, shorter brace height, increased vibration and erratic arrow flight. However, new innovations have led to shorter, more maneuverable bows accentuating increased arrow speed with the forgiveness of a longer bow. Inventive riser designs with larger brace heights, anti-vibration technology and the use of parallel limb technology have provided shorter bows many of the same shooting characteristics of their longer counterparts. Visit an archery pro shop and shoot several models side by side before you give the cold shoulder to short bows.

Regular practice is the only way to gain confidence with your archery equipment. Target shooting is the basic step in gaining expertise and confidence with your bow.

Let-Off Update

Most modern bows come standard with 75 percent or higher let-off. Bows with a higher let-off allow a bowhunter the advantage of drawing on an animal and holding only a small percent of the bow's total draw weight at full draw.

Until recently, Pope & Young only allowed the inclusion of animals shot with a bow using 65 percent let-off or less. Late in 2003, the club voted to allow bows with a higher let-off, but any animal taken with a let-off higher than 65 percent will be noted with an asterisk beside the listing.

Shot Placement, Not Arrow Speed

Arrow speed is not nearly as important as arrow placement, especially for bowhunters who only hunt whitetails. Nevertheless, many bowhunters covet fast bows to eliminate yardage estimation mistakes. The average whitetail, however, is shot at 20 yards or less, making yard estimation a moot point.

Remember, as arrow speed increases, bow performance generally decreases, followed quickly by shooting confidence. Matching the bow with the proper arrow spine is the single most important item in shooting performance, not feet per second. A spooked big game animal moves quicker than an arrow released from a modern bow, meaning they can jump the string on a fast bow just as easily as a slow one.

Test-Drive a Bow Before You Buy It

- Without a doubt, the best place to shop for a new bow is at a qualified archery pro shop complete with a shooting range. Check you local Yellow Pages or visit the Web sites of major archery companies for the nearest locations.
- Begin your initial research on the Web or using magazines to narrow your choices on top picks, but forget about shopping on the Web. Would you buy a car without test-driving it? You need to get your mitts on several models for an archery-style test-drive.
- Visit several pro shops offering different models, and shoot the bows to see which fits your body and shooting style. A pro-shop employee will help fit the bow and arrows to your personal measurements. You'll need to determine your draw length, draw weight and eye dominance. Archery professionals can help you get accurate measurements.
- Remember that eye dominance does not necessar-

ily match your right- or left-handed characteristic. Many people are right-handed but left-eye dominant, and vice versa. If you discover this scenario, it's best to adjust your shooting style to match your eye dominance. That may mean becoming a lefty. It's a documented fact that most bowhunters shoot better by switching their bow hands rather than trying to retrain their eyes.

- After noting your personal measurements, pro-shop employees can coach you in correct shooting form and help you determine which accessories might improve your shooting performance. When you whittle your choices down to a couple of models, shoot them side by side and take notes. Look for a bow that comes to full draw smoothly, doesn't jump out of your hand after the shot and offers consistent arrow groups. In the end, only you'll be able to feel the difference between bows and decide which is best for you.

Shooting with Fingers or a Release

Today, more people use a release than shoot with fingers. In fact, more than 75 percent of bowhunters use a release combined with a bow sight and a peep sight.

A release allows the string to be held in one small area and released smoothly at each shot. When fingers are used, they contact the string across a wide area and lessen the chance of consistent smooth releases.

Using your fingers does have its advantages, however. It eliminates the chance of having your release fail or foul, and you don't have to worry about losing your release during a hunt. If you do decide to shoot a compound bow with fingers, choose a bow with a large brace height and a long axle-to-axle length for optimum finger performance.

Add-On Equipment

Because our modern, busy lifestyles have us constantly scrounging for extra time, it pays to use some of today's refined tools for precision shooting. Bow sights and peep sights allow you to sight-in for consistent accuracy. These are much like a riflescope, and when you have your bow sighted-in, the point of aim should never change unless you alter your shooting form. Instead of practicing endlessly to perfect

Accuracy is vital to bow-hunters who pursue white-tails. Selecting the proper arrow spine and matching it to the bow is among the most important elements in shooting performance.

Placing your arrow accurately in the vital zone of a whitetail is more important than arrow speed. Most hunting shots are made at relatively close ranges.

Mark Kayser proudly displays the results of a simple, well–tuned bow with time afield. Kayser's 2003 South Dakota whitetail grossed more than 150 inches and was shot at 18 yards using a combination of whitetail tactics.

instinctive shooting like pioneering bowhunters, you can shoot consistently and accurately using good form.

You may want to investigate other add-on accessories as well. Stabilizers aid in balancing a bow and absorbing bow vibration. Anti-vibration technology can be added to bow limbs to absorb vibration for increased accuracy. A bow-mounted quiver allows quick access to arrows during a hunt.

You'll recognize the perfect bow when you wrap your hands around the grip and shoot it with confidence. If the bow feels like an extension of your arm, you've made the right choice, and it will show in your shooting confidence, and in your grin while admiring a trophy during the upcoming season.

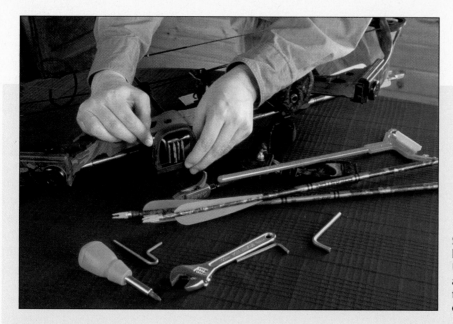

Successful bowhunters should keep their bow setups simple. Uncomplicated, easy-to-use accessories can make the difference between a successful or failed shot.

Keep It Simple

Some of the best bowhunters are good for one reason: they keep their bow accessories to a minimum, thus keeping their bow setups simple. By doing so, they eliminate additional steps or thought processes during bowhunting's adrenaline-charged close encounters. No matter how you prepare yourself, when an animal enters bow range, your emotions begin to unwrap, leading to trembling, shortness of breath and loss of concentration. If you have a complicated shooting style, chances are you'll forget a critical step in your shot process and blow the opportunity.

Even though most archery instructors coach shooters to take their time, aim and concentrate on the target before releasing the arrow, many of today's top bowhunters follow a different coaching style. They practice shooting in the aforementioned, non-rushed style, but they also practice for reality. Few bowhunting situations offer an animal that stands or lingers in one place like a 3-D target. Most opportunities are spur-of-the-moment encounters with only a few seconds of shot opportunity. Today's top bowhunters realize

they must be able to reach full draw in one swift motion and release an instant later.

To be successful in a snap-shooting situation, keep your bow accessories and shooting style simple. That doesn't mean you need to shoot instinctively using your fingers over a release, but it does mean going without some of the fancier gadgets.

First, equip your bow with a large peep sight to give you a large-diameter sight picture for quick aiming, particularly in low light.

Second, purchase a simple bow sight with large fiberoptic pins to firmly plant on your target. Steer clear of pendulum-style quick-click sights that require you to "dial in" before aiming.

Third, if you do use a release, shop for one that attaches easily and firmly without having to look at the process.

Finally, make sure your rest is large enough to firmly hold an arrow without the fear of it falling off in the heat of the encounter.

Keep your shooting equipment and style simple and you'll find success in the fast-paced world of bowhunting.

Think Small for Big Bowhunting Fun

by John T. Uptegrove

Two sets of eyes are always better than one. Taking a buddy on your archery small-game quest is not only more productive, it's just more fun.

The crisp cold front behind the snowstorm left the sky cloudless and blue. The temperature hovered well below freezing, and each footstep made the four inches of fresh, white powder crunch beneath my feet.

Normally, a day like this would be set aside for a lengthy perch high in the tree stand, but the conditions put whitetails on the back burner and gave way to my youthful urges to hunt the little critters. The thought of fried rabbit backs and gravy simmering in a cast-iron skillet offered plenty of determination.

After a short saunter down the road, I approached an aging brush-pile. It was just old enough for my eyes to peer through. Around it, weeds had found plenty of summer growth, and I was fairly sure a

healthy cottontail would be lurking in it. Instead of trudging straight into the heap and kicking brush, I painstakingly stalked around its edge.

I stood silent and gazed through the growth for several minutes. Then I saw it: a small but obvious black dot. Not 15 yards away was the unmistakable glossy, black eye of a rabbit. Only after I picked out the eye did the rest of the rabbit's form take shape.

With a slow and careful motion, I drew back and settled the fletching in the corner of my mouth. It only took an instant before the arrow made a thud and bounced back a few feet. Without the crack of a rifle or boom of a shotgun, the rabbit flipped up and forward, lying perfectly still on its back.

Some folks scoff at the idea of taking a stick and string along on a small-game hunt, but forgoing the gunpowder can make a stellar hunt for any bowhunting fanatic. Believe it or not, bowhunting small game is not out of any archer's reach. If that story is not enough to prove it, the three cottontails in the pan at the end of that day may have changed your mind.

Leaving Big Game Behind

Bowhunters are a strange lot by nature. They go to great measures finding game and even greater lengths preparing for the hunt. In fact, I'd guess that bowhunting blends the greatest efforts of big-game hunters and Olympic archers all into one savvy outdoorsman.

It's best to try shooting from behind natural cover when stalking squirrels. Every step closer increases your odds dramatically for a successful shot.

Most often, bowhunters dream of settling their sight pin behind the shoulder of a bugling bull elk or a swollen-necked whitetail buck. Indeed, these are heart-pounding adventures, but they require more work, planning and time than the average Joe can afford every weekend.

Nevertheless, most of us started out hunting the small game we know so well: rabbits and squirrels. It's not such a far stretch then to imagine chasing these little critters with a bow in hand. Certainly, it's far easier to lug along the trusty .22 rifle and shoot them, or to catch them on the run with a scattergun. But the same can be said for any big–game species, and any avid bowman can attest to the thrill of laying down the rifle and going at it with the stick and string.

The reasons for chasing small game with a bow are practically endless. The seasons are long, and you can get some of the best real world archery practice available. The tasty meals that can be made of small

Taking home a mess of small game is not as difficult as you might think. With a little practice, spotting and stalking can be quite productive.

game are another draw, and you probably have most of the gear you need already.

Practical Pursuits

It's not overly difficult to start hunting squirrels and rabbits by arrow, but conditions must be favorable for increased success. You just can't expect to walk into the woods and start flinging arrows at scampering rabbits or go launching five-dollar arrows into the tops of white oaks.

Aim for the center-of-mass on a small–game animal; this allows you a small margin of error for an imperfect shot or misjudged distance.

Bowhunting small game is an artful display of stalking and spotting.

Squirrels are easiest to start with and also the least wary and most visible. If you've spent any time in a deer stand, you know what I mean. They move about noisily and draw plenty of attention to their activities. In fact, I'd be willing to wager a good percentage of bowhunters have already sent an arrow at a foraging squirrel out of sheer boredom.

Common small-game points are meant to cause instant death by shock rather than penetration. Among the most popular are the Bludgeon by Saunders (*left*), Neet's Small Game Stopper (*center*), and Game Tracker's Shocker (*right*).

To actively pursue squirrels, you'll have to focus all your efforts on the ground because both you and the squirrels will be there. Elevated shots are hardly possible. Shooting at treed squirrels will almost guarantee a miss and a lost arrow. Your shooting form degrades whenever you lean back to shoot at anything much above your line of sight. And it's dangerous to hurl a pointy stick straight above your head and have it heading back your way shortly.

Because squirrels are small targets, they must be close before you shoot. Twenty yards can seem quite far to take a small gray squirrel and not much better for a larger fox squirrel. Your odds for success are increased with every step closer you get.

Start your search in wooded lots where you have seen squirrels in the past, and focus on peak activity times to better your odds. Early morning is good, but evening seems better yet. Walk very slowly, and spend most of your time listening and looking. The trick is to key in on the squirrels' location. Areas heavy with food are squirrel favorites. Trees such as oaks, hickories and pecans provide excellent forage.

Locating the prey may be the least difficult part of the hunt. Stalking into bow range takes patience and practice. Using any available cover to your advantage aids your efforts greatly. Moving with stealth from tree to tree and stopping each time to spend a few minutes observing will get you much closer than you'd think.

When a careful approach gets you within comfortable shooting distance, prepare slowly for the shot. Squirrels standing or sitting on their hind feet are much easier to hit. If they are on all fours rummaging in the leaves, the distance is harder to judge and less of the body is presented for aiming. A simple click of your tongue or gentle whistle will often get them to rise for a look.

Other techniques used by gun hunters seem counterproductive. Using barking squirrel calls is effective for locating squirrels, but the animals tend

The last hour of daylight offers archers their best chance to bag a squirrel with a bow. During the evening, these mischievous creatures come out in droves to wander the forest floor.

Bow Setup and Selection

Going afield for small game doesn't require the latest and greatest gear. Many hunters find it most reasonable to use their big-game setup. This is an easy approach, but the poundage most of us shoot for whitetails and such is overkill for small game. Draw weights from 35 to 45 pounds are the easiest to manage and offer plenty of arrow speed and energy for small targets. In fact, any bow that you feel comfortable with and that you can shoot accurately will be adequate.

There are many options to consider when choosing a small-game setup. Compound bows have the benefit of decreased poundage at full draw, but the low draw weights you'd use for small game make this less of an issue, and you don't often hold at full draw for any length of time.

Modern bows offer other advantages such as peeps, sight pins and stabilizers. This makes them easier to shoot and more accurate for the average shooter. The one major drawback is the hefty weight of most compound bows. The added accessories offer more bulk and catch branches.

Longbows and recurves are very well suited for small game. They are light, simple and less apt to suffer damage when tromping around brush piles and woodlots. In fact, anyone who has ambitions of switching to traditional archery gear may find that pursuing small game with old-fashioned bows is a fantastic way to enter the sport. The small targets and close ranges aid in developing natural shooting instincts.

No matter what bow you choose, it's necessary to focus on making your shots count. Close encounters with a squirrel or rabbit under perfect shot conditions don't happen very often. Practice with small targets like gym socks stuffed with newspaper or even foam rubber balls from your local toy store.

to become alert and nervous, often responding from trees where you can't take archery shots. Dogs definitely don't aid you because the squirrels always are treed.

Hunting rabbits with bow and arrow is one of my favorite pursuits. It's almost a game of wits between hunter and hare. It takes a keen eye and loads of patience to find a motionless rabbit in its brushy hideout. But it can be done, and it's the zenith of small-game accomplishments with a bow.

Timing is crucial for chasing cottontails with a bow and arrow. A mix of snow and sun are ideal. Often, when a snowstorm blankets the countryside, the following day will have clear skies and still winds. This is prime time to pick up your bow and get into hot pursuit. The going gets much tougher when you can't track or use the snow's white background to help you identify your game while it tries to remain well hidden.

Take your time and thoroughly scan the ground. The idea is to spot the rabbit before it makes a break for safety. Hitting a running rabbit is more an act of luck than skill, so it's better to restrain the shot for a static target. To make things even more exciting, rabbits do not always flush easily after a snow, and you may find yourself practically on top of a cottontail before you know it's there.

Start by putting yourself in rabbit-likely places. Areas of thick grasses and piled brush are the most obvious. With fresh-fallen snow, it's not hard to tell if bunnies are nearby because their telltale track will be left all about. Follow the tracks carefully and focus on where they seem to be the most concentrated around the heaviest cover.

Study each spot carefully and approach painfully slow. Look over every clump of grass or sticks and at the base of every bush. If your eyes are sharp, you'll be able to pick out the cottontail in his form. Often the black eye is the first thing you'll recognize, followed by the materializing of the rabbit form. But, you shouldn't just look for the eye. An ear or patch of gray fur sometimes appears first, so be careful not to overlook anything.

Alert ears and a trace of fur reveal the presence of a hidden rabbit. The ability to successfully spot small game comes with experience and a keen eye. Take extra time and always keep your eyes peeled.

If you don't spot your quarry, move slowly and steadily while you keep a watchful eye. At some point, you'll miss a rabbit and it'll flush wildly. Use this to your advantage and find exactly where it was hiding. Remember these places because rabbits will often return if left unmolested for the remainder of the day.

Executing the shot for a well-hidden bunny is no easy task. The ranges are frequently within close quarters, but it's the obstacles such as grass and branches that keep the shot from being perfect. This is something you must contend with, however, and you'll often have to reposition for a good shot. If you spot a cottontail buried deep in the brush, back away slowly and approach from a new angle while keeping your eye focused on the spot so you don't lose sight of your quarry.

Spotting a rabbit buried in cover is plenty tricky, but working an arrow into a thicket can prove to be impossible. To better your odds, back away from your target and get into a better position for a clear shot.

Whether you have visions of squirrels or rabbits in your frying pan, it's not far-fetched that you could fill your game bag with a bow. Archers are persistent and resourceful folks who have a great knack for overcoming the odds and going out of their way to make things more sporting.

Small-game archery is a thrill that's hard to match. Bowhunting big game is as mainstream as it gets. I hardly know a fellow who owns a bow who doesn't chase a whitetail with it, but I know of almost no one who capitalizes on the great resources of small game to make bowhunting a great challenge and a day's worth of rousing adventures.

Take a stroll off the beaten path and put your skills to the test. You'll be in for a lot of fun and many rewards.

Make Your Own Hunting Bow

by Mike Marsh

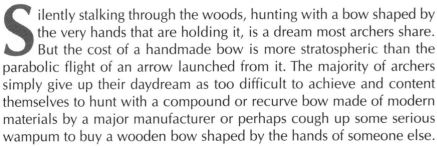

Basil Watts uses the step-through method to string one of his bows. Several other bows are in the rack, ready to be strung and used.

Silently stalking through the woods, hunting with a bow shaped by the very hands that are holding it, is a dream most archers share. But the cost of a handmade bow is more stratospheric than the parabolic flight of an arrow launched from it. The majority of archers simply give up their daydream as too difficult to achieve and content themselves to hunt with a compound or recurve bow made of modern materials by a major manufacturer or perhaps cough up some serious wampum to buy a wooden bow shaped by the hands of someone else.

But, as primitive man learned uncountable centuries ago, bows made from materials at hand are free for the effort of making them and are extremely effective hunting tools. Like those Aborigines, a few modern hunters have learned to gather together to share their knowledge of bow-making skills.

"When I want to make a bow, I hold a bow bee," said bowmaker Basil Watts. "I enjoy making hunting bows so much I want to see the tradition passed on. Not so long ago, you made your own bow if you wanted to hunt. It's easy to make a bow once you learn how."

Watts and his student bowyers have made dozens, perhaps hundreds, of bows by sticking to a simple method. Watts cuts staves and dries them to correct moisture content, then puts out the call to anyone he thinks might be interested in making a bow a month ahead of hunting season.

"The design I use has been around for about 6,000 years," Watts said. "No one has improved upon it. The wood itself tells you how to turn it into a bow."

Watts begins by finding a hardwood tree. Any dense hardwood with a specific gravity above 50 percent will make a bow if the wood is properly dried. The specific gravity of a wood can be found from many library reference sources or online.

"The ideal tree is about 6 to 8 inches in diameter," Watts said. "I cut a 6-foot length and split it into 3-inch wide staves with an ax and wedges. For white woods, I take the bark off. But for a dark wood like Osage, mulberry and locust, I leave the bark on while it's drying. With white woods like hickory, ash and oak, you are going to use the sapwood for the bow and with dark woods, you are going to use the heartwood."

Watts draws a rough profile of the bow on the stave and cuts it out with a band saw. The stave is thicker than the finished bow, about $7/8$ inch at the tips and $1\frac{1}{2}$ to 2 inches at the center.

"The thinner it is, the quicker it dries," Watts said. "I dry up to eight staves at one time in a plywood box that is $6\frac{1}{2}$ feet long, 18 inches wide and 24 inches high. I use two 60-watt bulbs to remove the moisture. The wood is tested with a moisture tester that costs about $35. It takes about three weeks to dry the wood to a moisture content of 10 percent. Then you need to check it every day."

When the stave is dried to 8 percent moisture content, it is worked down a bit and retested. Because only the conductivity of the outside is measured, the inner wood can still be too wet to finish the bow. Flexing a bow that has higher moisture content than 8 percent will cause the wood to set and ruin the bow. "I scrape down the sides with a drawknife, pocketknife or furniture scraper until I get the limbs to 2 inches wide along half their length outward from the center, then make a straight taper to $\frac{1}{2}$ to $\frac{3}{4}$ inch at the tips," Watts said. "With dense woods like Osage, you can take the limbs down to a width of 1 inch, depending upon the style of bow you want."

The bow is cut to a length of 66 to 68 inches. The rule of thumb for bow length is twice the draw length plus 20 percent. The draw length is measured from the point the arrow strikes the bow to the anchor point at the corner of the mouth. Few people under 6 feet tall draw over 28 inches by this method of measurement, and a 28-inch draw length requires a bow length of 67.2 inches.

When the bow is roughly shaped, it is flexed by stringing with an over-length string. A stick with notches in each end is inserted between the string and center of the bow to partially draw the bow to periodically determine the balance of flexibility between the limbs or "tiller" while the bow is being shaped.

"With bows made of dark woods where the heart-

Shooting Your Homemade Wood Bow

Unless a bowhunter starts out hunting with a wood bow, he will have to make some adjustments to develop an accurate shooting style after using a modern bow. All bows cause arrow flex and deflection. But a wood bow, with its absence of a "center-shot" window, casts the arrow away from the side of the bow and top of the knuckle, grip or arrow rest.

Arrow deflection is compensated for by the traditional archer's stance with the bow canted at an angle to the ground, which makes the arrow strike high rather than to the side. This is why archers who shoot primitive bows use the instinctive method for sighting. With the bow shot while in a canted position, the use of a bow sight is difficult.

Each wood bow/archer combination creates a personal shooting bond. When an archer is happy with his bow, he may not honor a request from a fellow archer to shoot it. Overdrawing a wood bow beyond the owner's draw length could result in bow damage. If a request to shoot a wood bow is honored, the shooter should take care to listen to the owner of the bow regarding the proper arrow rest, angle of cant and draw length for shooting that particular bow.

If wood or reed shafts are used, they must be carefully examined for splits and nicks each time they are shot. A damaged arrow can split or shatter when the string is released. The bow should also be examined before and after it is strung before an arrow is nocked. Any splits or cracks are a warning that the bow may "blow" when the string is drawn or released.

Rick Holden made this bow with the help of North Carolina bowyer Basil Watts.

wood will be used, the face of the bow, the side away from the archer, must be taken down to one growth ring or the bow will split," Watts said. "But with white woods where the sapwood is used, the face of the bow can be shaped with a scraper."

With the grip clamped to a flat surface, alternate limbs are lifted and measured at identical distances from the center of the bow. The tiller is measured at different points by looking beneath a straight edge. High spots are marked with a pencil. A wood block or helper's hands can be used to keep limbs flexed while measurements are taken. The limbs are then relieved and the back of the bow scraped to remove wood. The process is repeated until the limbs are balanced, forming identical parabolas from the point they begin flexing near the grip to within 6 inches of the tips. The last 6 inches should have no flex.

The finished grip is about 4 inches long, 1½ inches front-to-back and 1 inch wide, tapering rapidly to the limbs. The goal is to allow the wide sections of the limbs above the grip as much movement as possible

Why Hold a Bow Bee?

Archers who have the dedication and desire to make their own hunting bows from native woods are not large in number. By gathering together, they can share their experiences and help guide novices in developing the skills necessary to make efficient bows.

A group of archers can share the bow-making tools they have and cut costs. A single drying box can remove the moisture from many bow staves at one time. Because it takes at least three weeks to properly dry a stave, drying is the longest step in the bow-making process. Tools such as a moisture tester or hygrometer that are used for testing the moisture content of the wood can also be used by several bowyers.

Each archer develops his own way of shaping and shooting wood bows and brings valuable knowledge to others at a bow bee. Even if he has made only a bow or two, he is still far ahead of most other hunters in his knowledge of the process.

An extra pair of hands is a gigantic help at many steps of the process. With the help of a partner, a job as simple as clamping the bow to a table goes faster. Flexing and marking bow limbs while checking tiller is also easier to accomplish with assistance.

Having others nearby also provides a safety factor while making and shooting new wood bows. Tools such as band saws and razor-sharp scrapers can cause injuries.

A bow bee is primarily about companionship. Lively conversations about making bows and bowhunting help pass the time while building anticipation for the approaching hunting season. Bow-making traditions have likely been passed along in this way since the first bowhunter showed his fellow hunters how he killed a game animal by using two sticks and a twisted bark string.

because that is where the bow's energy is generated.

"The string notch is cut 45 degrees across the sides of the bow, but never into the face of the bow or the bow will break," Watts said. "The notch is cut to half the diameter of the string. Some folks go primitive all the way and make the string of squirrel skin cut to a ¼-inch thickness or twisted plant fibers like dogbane. But I use Dacron, reverse twisted. I don't want to spend a day or two making a bow and have the bow blow up because of a broken string."

The string is stretched for a few shots. Then a nocking point is whipped onto the string. The string length is adjusted while the bow is "shot in." The ideal bracing height is as low as possible in order to impart the maximum amount of energy to the arrow while keeping a minimum of pressure on the bow as the string comes taut after release. But it must be high enough to prevent the string from slapping against the archer's forearm.

The bow can be shot without an arrow rest by laying the arrow against a knuckle. But the top of a piece of rawhide wound around the grip or a piece of deer antler whipped to the bow can serve as an arrow rest.

Basil Watts draws one of his wooden hunting longbows.

"An antler rest needs to be half the thickness of the arrow," Watts said. "To shoot the bow properly, the bow may have to be canted as much as 45 degrees. Without a modern center-shot window, the arrow from a wooden bow has to flex around the bow and deflects away from the grip and rest to some extent. If shot with the bow held perpendicular to the ground, the arrow would deflect away from the bow—to the left for a right-handed archer.

Mike Marsh draws a bead with his homemade, wood hunting bow. Wooden bows must be canted for straight-line arrow flight.

Canting the bow allows the shooter to compensate so that the arrow will strike higher or lower and not to the side. Each bow and each archer are unique. It is the bow that tells the archer how much it must be canted for a straight line-of-arrow flight."

After the archer is satisfied with the way the bow shoots, he can stain the bow any color he chooses or leave it the color of the wood. The bow is finished with several coats of waterproof coating such as polyurethane.

Laminating sinew to the

Crafting a Wooden Bow

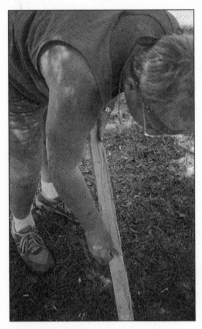

A rough profile of the bow is drawn on a dried wooden stave with a pencil.

Watts uses a band saw to cut out the rough outline of the bow. The bow will then be shaped by hand.

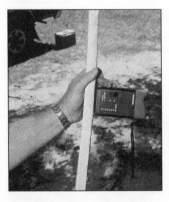

A moisture tester is used to check the moisture content of the stave. The wood must have a moisture content of no more than 10 percent.

An over-length string is used to flex draw the bow limbs to check for uniform flex.

bow will add power because sinew is remarkably resilient for its weight. But adding anything else only reduces power because added weight slows the bow limbs.

"Taking a set" after shooting is a common occurrence for wood bows. However, any bow with less than 2 inches of deflection from the center of the bow to the limb tips when unstrung is considered well made.

All wood bows should be unstrung when not in use. They should also never be left where heat can dry them to below 4 percent moisture content or they will likely break. When a bowhunter invests so much time and effort, he wants his bow to last many seasons.

Watts has taken many game animals with his handmade bows in the forests near his home in the low country along the North Carolina-South Carolina border. He kills several white-tailed deer and wild pigs each season.

"Any bowhunter must know his effective hunting range," Watts said. "I don't shoot past 20 yards. But there are archers who are capable of a high degree of accuracy. Some Native Americans were deadly bowshots at ranges beyond 40 yards."

Watts buys cedar arrow shafts and concedes to using modern fletching and nocks to make his arrows. He also uses modern heads for hunting big game. But several of his apprentices make stone arrowheads and haft them onto homemade reed or wooden shafts with sinew.

"You never know until it's done whether a bow is efficient," Watts said." An interesting tidbit of information is that all efficiently designed wood bows weigh the same, no matter the type of wood or style of bow. The stored energy is in the wood fiber itself, which is the same from bow to bow. A properly shaped wood bow will have draw weights

After locating high spots, Mike Walker uses a drawknife to shape the bow limbs during the "tillering" process.

of 50 to 55 pounds. With a 500-grain arrow and sharp head, it will kill anything on Earth. My bows will shoot a hunting arrow at velocities of around 160 feet per second."

The rule of thumb for calculating the velocity of an arrow shot from an efficient wood bow is to add 100 to the draw weight as measured with a scale at the archer's draw length. For a 55-pound draw, that translates into 155 feet per second.

To achieve the most efficient flight, the arrows must be properly spined for the bow's draw weight. Modern arrows can be shot effectively from a wood bow. But Watts buys cedar shafts and makes arrows just long enough for a hunting broadhead to clear his fingers.

He uses a three-finger leather glove for shooting. But other archers prefer a tab or a thumb button. The most primitive style of release is with bare fingers.

"It is up to the archer how far he goes with the primitive aspects of bowhunting," Watts said. "But with arrows as well as bows, he should take care to learn about his equipment each step of the way. A nicked wood arrow can shatter at release and send a splinter into an arm. That's why a lot of primitive shooters wear a leather wrist cuff that surrounds their forearm."

Some archers take primitive to the limit once they learn how to make bows. Mike Walker fitted his arrows with stone heads.

Mike Walker displays a traditional hand-crafted wooden bow with stone-tipped arrows.

Accessories for Better Bowhunts
by Keith de Noble

"Where is my saw?" I thought as my right hand feverishly groped in the cargo pocket of my camouflage pants. Then my memory suggested it would be in my fanny pack. I unzipped the large pocket where the saw should be, but it wasn't there.

Could I make it back to camp, retrieve my saw, return to this site and get set up before it was too late to make a decent afternoon hunt? Yes—I hoped.

Only moments before this bout of anxiety, I discovered a large, fresh scrape. There were only two possible trees for my climbing stand, and both would need some minor limb trimming. Before making this tempting discovery, I had resigned myself to spending an entire afternoon scouting because all my other hotspots had gotten colder than the front that blew in the day before.

Normally, I'm well prepared when going into the woods. But I wasn't this day. It led me to review my pre-hunt and pre-scouting

An old toothbrush is an excellent tool for cleaning dirt or blood off of broadheads.

process to make sure I was carrying all essential gear, plus comfort equipment to ensure a better bowhunting experience.

Through the years, the equipment I've carried has changed considerably. Technology and invention have been the biggest influences, spurred by advances in bow design and the creation of new and improved archery products. Many improvements are the result of lightweight and space-age materials. Of course, one bowhunter may think a piece of equipment essential, while another may discard it as unnecessary junk.

Like many of the older, long-time bowhunters, I started with traditional equipment. My first bow was a factory-blemish Ben Pearson Cougar recurve. I had six fiberglass arrows; three were tipped with practice points and the others with Ben Pearson Deadhead broadheads. Completing my first bowhunting equipment inventory was a Kwikee Kwiver, an armguard and an archer's finger glove.

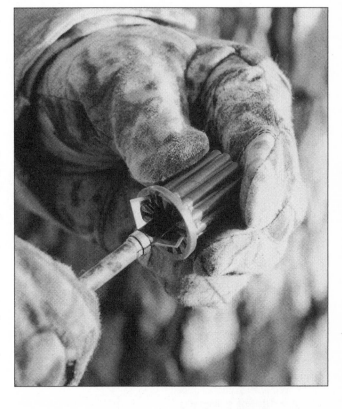

Broadhead wrenches are a must when changing heads or blades. They protect both the blades and the bowhunter's fingers.

At the time, those items were all I needed. And yes, that would have been enough to take a deer. Yet, as I learned more while reading and listening to encouraging words from far more experienced bowhunters, I soon discovered other pieces of equipment.

The last several years have seen a resurgence in traditional equipment. For many, the appeal of going traditional is its simplicity—less equipment, less to go wrong. Hunting with recurve bows or longbows bears the lore of the past, the history of our sport. Yet a few accessories can make it better for the traditional bowhunter.

When I first learned to string a longbow, it was with the step-through, leg-brace technique—not recommended by manufacturers. Fortunately, there are a number of bow stringing devices recommended for stringing, or bracing, traditional bows. They are much safer for the archer and virtually eliminate potential damage to the bow. I keep one in my bow case and another in

Sharpeners can be used on fixed blade broadheads and to touch up replacement blades.

Self-aligning peep sights, with large apertures, work well under hunting conditions. Note the string silencers.

This arrow holding device works well with launcher type rests. A wrist sling is seen just below the arrow rest.

my tackle box.

Have you ever slipped your bow out of the case to discover your string has slipped down the upper limb and fallen off the lower limb nock? After several times of having to deal with that problem, I started using a rubber band to secure the string to the bow. Now, there are a few string keepers on the market. They are easy to use, and probably resemble something used many centuries ago by early archers or Native Americans.

Three types of equipment will always be on my traditional bow: a bow tip protector, brush buttons and a wrist sling.

The tip protector is mounted on the lower limb to help prevent damage when resting the bow tip on the ground, your boot or some other object.

Brush buttons are threaded on to the string and placed close enough to the ends to barely touch the limbs when the bow is braced. Without them, the string and limb work as a collection device for any brush and briars you pass during a walk in the woods.

In my first bowhunting season, I was making a shot at a big doe but had neglected to grip my bow. Upon release of the arrow, the bow left my hand and sailed to the ground, the bottom limb leading the way. It made a spectacular bounce when it flexed against the ground, sailed back up and unstrung itself, all in an instant. I was horrified. Not only had the arrow missed the deer, but I feared the bow was broken. Fortunately, it wasn't.

The next day I was back in the local archery pro shop purchasing a wrist sling, a simple device mounted near the bow grip. Adjusted and used properly, the sling prevents the bow from falling even if the shooter has a completely open hand during the shot.

Two other pieces of equipment that can be used are an arrow holder and string silencers. Some bows are quiet enough, but string silencers will silence bows a bit more. Considering the relatively slower speeds of most recurve bows and longbows, additional quietness is to the hunter's advantage. It may well

eliminate the situation of a deer "jumping the string." Arrow holders are the saving grace of frozen index fingers.

Arrow rests are designed to flip or swing out of the way when the string is pulled back or released. Several different models are available.

Other than tip protectors and brush buttons, all the equipment mentioned thus far works well on compound bows. The complexity of compound bows, however, created a need for specialized equipment to fine-tune and quiet them.

A stand mounted bow holder keeps this hunter's bow ready just inches from his hands.

Stabilizers have been around for years. Recent versions incorporate hydraulics, mechanical devices and dampening materials, all designed to absorb vibration when the bow is shot. Another benefit is to balance the bow in the hand, giving the shooter potentially greater accuracy. The number of stabilizers on the market is staggering, so it's best to try a few at a pro shop to determine the best for your setup.

Similar to stabilizers are counterbalances, another form of stabilizer attached at the base of the limbs on either the face (the side toward the archer) or the back of the bow. The biggest drawback is added weight, but for some shooters, particularly those who use bow quivers, it may be necessary to balance the bow to provide greater accuracy.

One of the more popular and effective innovations in recent years is a limb dampening system. NAP recently introduced the ThunderBlox and now competes directly with LimbSavers. Both systems are designed to absorb and dampen vibration with devices mounted directly on the upper and lower limbs. They are very effective, particularly when used with a stabilizer.

The use of a wrist sling prevents the bow from falling when shot. Note the frayed dental floss above the arrow nock—it should be replaced soon.

If hunting with bow sights, a self-aligning peep sight allows the archer to be more consistently accurate. Several companies offer different designs, and most bowhunters are aware of them. Hunting peep sights should have a large aperture to let in enough light for the low-light situations encountered in the woods.

One of the numerous stabilizers available is this one, which is attached to a knuckle that lets the bowhunter fold the stabilizer up out of the way so the bow can be cased.

These are three of the many wrist sling models available. Though called bow slings by some, they are not to be confused with the bow sling used to carry a bow.

Some bowhunters also use a kisser button, a string-mounted device positioned to touch the corner of the shooter's mouth when at full draw. It assures a consistent anchor point.

Bowhunters may also want to carry several other items while in the woods. Bowstring wax, for example, helps reduce string abrasion caused by walking around in thick cover with your bow. Your bowstring should be well waxed and rubbed regularly with a piece of leather to melt the wax into the strands.

Carry some dental floss to secure a loose peep sight or prevent nock set slippage. It can be tied off with a series of knots or wrapped over a loop with the tag end pulled back under the wraps by pulling on the ends of the loop.

Spare nock sets and nock pliers can be used to secure a loose peep sight or repair the string nock point. Carrying a spare string is also a good idea.

Electrical tape is great repair material. On one trip many years ago, my upper compound limb started showing fiberglass separation. Several wraps of electrical tape around the limb, and a couple of test shots later proved that I could finish the hunt.

Moleskin can be used to reduce noise by application in the sight window around the arrow rest for those times when an arrow falls off the rest. It also helps keep fingers warm when applied around the bow grip.

Bowhunters spend lots of time in the woods in wet weather. Compound bows and tree stands invariably make a squeak at the wrong time. A small tube of petroleum jelly or small bottle of mineral oil helps silence any unwanted noise. I prefer mineral oil because it is odorless and penetrates quickly.

We've discussed equipment on and for the bow. What about the arrow and broadheads?

Most bowhunters use broadheads with replaceable blades. Carry extra blades in a small container that takes up little space. You may also want to carry a broadhead wrench. Replacement blades are razor sharp and can cause painful cuts, especially in cold, damp weather. Use a broadhead wrench and you can avoid the many scars I have on my hands from being a slow learner.

Carrying a small file and sharpener is essential when I'm hunting with fixed broadheads, and I've used them to touch up replaceable blades. A thin coating of petroleum jelly on the blades, edge helps keep them sharp.

One of my arrows is a dedicated practice arrow. Yet, there has been more than one time when it was needed in hunting mode with a new head and blades. A spare broadhead or two comes in handy if one is damaged. A small strip of reflective tape applied between the nock and fletching helps you find an arrow at night.

Blunt arrowheads are very effective on small game. I really enjoy working on swamp rabbits when hunting and scouting in bottom land. Don't forget to take some spare nocks and a nock tool or glue.

Archery gloves, tabs and releases can be lost or damaged when you least expect. A spare allows the bowhunter to finish the hunt.

Many bowhunters do not use armguards. I normally don't. However, with certain clothes, I must either use an armguard or some other device to keep my clothing clear of the string path. The slap of the bowstring on clothing is a sickening sound. It makes for a poor shot and the chance of wounding game is much greater. I carry a few rubber bands that can be used for this or other purposes in a pinch.

Comfort Up a Tree

It didn't take long as a young bowhunter to realize that sitting in a tree stand while holding my bow the entire time was pure drudgery. Many stand manufacturers have designed specific bow holders for their line of stands. Add several choices by other archery suppliers, and a bowhunter can find just the right bow holder for comfort.

One of the simplest holders is a hook screwed into the tree. Placed properly, the bow can be picked up and brought into shooting position with a minimum of movement. Remember, however, it is illegal in many places to damage trees on public and other lands, and screwing objects into a tree constitutes damage.

Fortunately, there are versions of equipment hooks and belts that attach to the tree without penetrating the wood. An equipment belt wrapped around the tree can hold several items hanging from it, ready for the bowhunter's use.

Judging distance from up in a tree is different than on the ground. For many bowhunters it is difficult at best. Some hunters mark various locations around their stand before climbing up for the hunt. However, there are many times when a bowhunter will want to get to the stand as directly as possible without disrupting the surrounding area, particularly if after a wary trophy buck. This is where a rangefinder comes in handy.

Rangefinders come in several models vary in price from tens to hundreds of dollars. I have used both types and found them very effective. More expensive laser models have fortunately gotten lighter, better and have dropped in price. Some are now being incorporated into binoculars, a convenient idea.

Carrying a bow when on long hikes or scouting trips gets old in a hurry. Belt-mounted bow holders are handy, but I prefer a bow sling. A good bow sling hooks to the bow at both ends of the handle section and is slung over the shoulder, letting the bow ride comfortably under the hunter's arm. If properly mounted, the sling allows the bowhunter to shoot without string or cable interference.

Do you want simplicity, or do you want to be prepared for whatever might happen? Either way, there are many fine choices of accessories that help make a bowhunt safe, more comfortable, more fun and overall, a much better experience.

Martin Archery makes a very effective blunt arrowhead. They work well on rabbits and other small game.

Portable bow presses are very handy for working on compound bows in the field. The brackets on the left allow the press to be used on split limb bows.

Two fine choices for self-aligning peep sights.

Packing for the Bowhunt

Rarely do I carry all the equipment I've mentioned in this article. I consider the duration of the hunt, the type of hunt and the proximity to home and shop.

When camping, my gear includes a well-stocked tackle box that contains far more equipment than mentioned thus far. But I can adjust or repair just about anything, regardless what happens.

Accessories not mounted on my bow or tree stand are normally carried in my fanny pack, or backpack, depending on which I use for the hunt. Deciding what to carry depends on the type of stand I'm using, and whether or not I'm using tree steps or carrying cameras. Either way, if properly packed, I'll have what I need.

If I'm out for a half-day or an all-day hunt, there will be minimal equipment. My pack will have blades, a broadhead wrench, a toothbrush, spare tubing for the peep sight, rubber bands, electrical tape, a file, a sharpener, dental floss and normal safety and convenience items.

For long trips, particularly out of state, I take a carefully packed tackle box, lots of extra arrows, a portable bow press and sometimes an extra bow. Equipment in the tackle box includes nock sets, nock pliers, spare sight pins, spare peep sight, bowstrings, string silencers, arrow nocks, broadheads, blades, moleskin, ferrule cement, epoxy glue, fletching cement and lubricants. Along with those items, there is a full range of tools necessary to work on a bow or tree stand.

On a hunt years ago, I lost my compass, and just before climbing down the tree after sundown, my flashlight fell and shattered into pieces when it hit a rock. For that reason, and safety, I always carry two compasses and two flashlights.

Silence Is Golden

by John Sloan

Twenty years ago, at the dawn of the screaming fast bows, I sat 15 feet up a pine tree on the edge of a clearcut in lower Alabama. Across the clearcut, another bowhunter was likewise perched, and as the sun dipped behind the trees, I heard a noise from that direction. Later I learned it had been Tye, the other hunter, shooting at a doe. He missed, his arrow going over the doe's back.

The next day, while shooting a few practice arrows in camp, I realized what the noise was. It was Tye's bow, the loudest bow I have ever heard.

As bows advanced into the realm of the "screamer," they also became louder. Early in this period, some of us, Tye included, had the mindset of "Don't worry about the noise; they can't duck an arrow this fast." We quickly learned how wrong we were. Until a bow can propel

An archer draws a woods-ready bow. This one required only string silencers, a new cable slide and some mole-skin on the shelf.

Practicing in the clothes you will wear to hunt, with an observer watching and listening, is one of the best ways to detect bow noise.

an arrow faster than the speed of sound, noise always will be a consideration.

For me, after more than three decades of shooting arrows at animals, a quiet bow is a must. I will not own or shoot a loud bow. My bow must and will be quiet. Toward this end, I have spent considerable time experimenting with ways to silence loud bows and have discovered just what it is that makes them loud. I'm not an expert and don't know all the technical terms, but my bows are quiet.

I don't have a degree in engineering so I won't be using a lot of technical terms. Some folks could do that, but I'm not one of them. When I say, "cables slap together," I mean cables slap together. I don't know any other term.

I use a four-arrow quiver. One morning, when I was high atop a hardwood ridge in the Tennessee hills, I shot all four arrows at an eight-point buck. All were shot inside 25 yards, and all were shot without the buck running, (I didn't say I was a great shot). I killed the deer with the final arrow, which illustrates why I must have a quiet bow.

A deer can duck the fastest arrow at any distance over 15 yards, maybe less. And right here it must be pointed out that many times it is the sound of the arrow in the air that causes them to duck and spin, not the sound the bow makes. I know of very little that can be done about that other than tuning each arrow, so I will mention it no more. But the bow can be treated to achieve more quiet shots.

Today, many bows are fairly quiet right out of the box. Bow manufacturers, understanding the hunter's needs, began experimenting and making bows quieter. While sound is no big concern to the tournament shooter, it is of paramount importance to the hunter. So big advances have been made in building quiet bows. These advances came in the form of the bow design itself, new string silencers, harmonic dampeners, limb silencers and stabilizers. They all work. But are they enough? Not from my point of view. Not in and of themselves. I find few bows right out of the box quiet enough to suit me.

The first step in silencing a bow is to determine where the sound is coming from. There are many things that cause more noise in a bow than I would like. To discover the cause often is a two-person job. One shoots, the other looks and listens.

Sometimes, it isn't even the bow. After an hour of tinkering with a friend's bow, trying to find the noisy culprit, I started shooting the bow. No noise. I am a finger shooter. The noise was coming from his release. Releases are inherently louder than fingers.

In another instance, a hunter in one of my camps had a bow that made a slapping sound sometimes. We found that it was the string hitting his armguard. I gave him a wool slip-on armguard, and the problem was solved.

On most bows, there can be problem areas to look at in the beginning. The first place I look is at the cables. Cable slap causes noise. Prevent the cables from slapping and the noise is gone.

Cable slap is caused when the two cables contact each other on release. This is caused by the cables being too close together. Some bows are made with plenty of clearance for the cables; some are not. The problem can be corrected in different ways. Changing the cable slide so that the cables have more clearance is the preferred way. I also have corrected it by wrapping tape around one cable near the yoke end, thus tightening it and creating more space.

Have another person watch and listen to your bow to detect unwanted sounds.

From that point, I next look at the cable guard and slide. I like Teflon slides, and I keep my cable guard well lubricated. I'll share a secret with you: the only lubricant I use is the oil from my face. I have found no better cable guard lubricant than body oil. I regularly clean the guard with alcohol. Then lubricate it. If I am hunting in cold or wet weather, I may rub my fingers across my cheeks and nose and then rub the guard several times a day. Beware of the dusty ride on the four-wheeler, too.

I constantly check to make sure my vanes or feathers have plenty of clearance on the cables. Not only is this important for a quiet bow, it is a must for good arrow flight. It may take some experimenting on bows with adjustable cable guards.

Next I look at the arrow rest. Some, by design, are more silent than others. Many of the prong rests can be quickly and easily silenced by simply slipping a sleeve over the prongs or wrapping them with an adhesive, soft-sided wrap. The sound of an arrow screeching across a metal rest is not a sound to be desired. I won't have it. Try to draw on a mature doe at 12 yards and you'll know what I mean.

Up to this point, I have not even begun to add accessories. Until

This bowstring stop is attached to the cable guard and stops the string to eliminate string noise.

now, all I have been doing is shooting at a large butt from just a few feet. I am not concerned with accuracy yet—just sound.

Now I add my sight and quiver attachment. They go on as one piece, the quiver bracket on top of the sight. In the beginning, I add one of the slim rubber gaskets that come with the quiver between the bow and sight, and the sight and the quiver bracket. Then without worrying about sight alignment, I tighten everything down to the max. If it is still quiet, I know I can adjust the sight and keep the silence.

The quiver itself is often a source of sound. I don't shoot with the quiver on the bow. I hang it in the tree when stand hunting, remove it for ground blind hunting and wear a hip quiver when stalking. Arrow/quiver noise is not a problem for me. But for those who shoot with the quiver on the bow, it could be a problem. The quiver must securely attach to the bow with no wiggle or vibration. The arrows must fit tightly in the quiver with no rattle. And the entire unit must be rock solid. This can be done. I just choose to

Up-Front Decisions

Look for the same thing in buying a bow as you would in silencing a bow—a good pro shop with a knowledgeable technician. If you buy a bow from a good shop, the owner should be happy to work with you in selecting and attaching the right accessories to silence that bow and meet your shooting needs. Expect to pay for some of that service.

If possible, shoot the bow several times before leaving the shop in case any adjustments need to be made. The shop should have a good selection of bows for you to try on-site.

Bows today are not inexpensive. Before buying one, stress to the salesman that you want a smooth, quiet bow. Usually the two go hand in hand. If he is worth his salt, he'll steer you in the right direction. Getting a bow that is relatively quiet out of the box is a big plus. Today that is pos-

sible, and it need not require a new mortgage. You shouldn't have to spend the kid's college fund to get a quiet bow.

It is also possible to suitably quiet down an older bow. A good pro-shop technician can help you select new strings, cables and other accessories to make that old family favorite as silent as one hand clapping.

Through the hunting year, no matter what you do, "things" can work loose. I make it a practice to check my bow after each practice session and before each trip to the woods. When possible, even in the dark before daylight, I'll shoot a practice arrow or two dressed in my hunting clothes. If I have something rattling, I want to find it then, not when a trophy walks by.

No Two Bows Are Alike

Even identical bows from the same company may have different "personalities." Therefore, they have to be treated differently.

For example, an accessory that works well to reduce noise on one bow may not perform as well on another bow. But a different accessory, designed to do the same thing, may work great. Sometimes it takes some experimenting.

I have two identical bows, yet to achieve the kind of silence I require took different setups. One has five string silencers and a set of limb vibration reducers. The other has one string silencer and required no limb vibration reducers. Each bow required a different cable guard setting to achieve silent shots.

Many companies make and sell accessories designed to reduce bow noise. There are a lot of products out there. With some bows, it may take some trial-and-error work to get that bow super quiet. Some products will just work better on some bows. But as stated, today, many of the bows are pretty quiet right out of the box.

Companies such as Mathews, Champion, PSE and a host of others are making bows with harmonic dampeners and other devices to reduce limb vibration. And Simms Vibration Laboratory, New Archery products and others make accessories to accomplish that. String silencers abound and most pro shops will have a selection. The same is true for stabilizers.

shoot without the quiver on the bow, thus eliminating that sound aspect.

Now I am ready to get down to the finer points of sound. So far I have only treated the major culprits. You can't really see vibration with the naked eye. But vibration causes sound. Enough vibration and you have a tuning fork. Most vibration comes from two areas, the bow limbs and the string. Both can be treated. Another problem area is the point at which an accessory attaches to the bow.

In recent years, bow manufacturers have begun manufacturing bows with vibration dampeners or eliminators built in, a big advancement. Prior to that, and still selling well, are devices that attach to the limbs to accomplish the same goal. They also work and are perfect for a vintage bow or even a new one as an added measure of vibration prevention. Dampeners are made for both split and solid limb bows. When using these limb silencers, be sure to follow the directions in placement, and be sure the limbs are clean before attaching. Wipe the area down with alcohol or some other cleaner.

I do not use a stabilizer. I just never have, never saw the need for one. But short, properly designed stabilizers can do wonders to help control bow vibration. For many hunters, they are also an aid in accuracy. I subscribe to the K-I-S-S method of hunting. I shoot fingers, one sight pin, no peep sight and no stabilizer. Therefore, I have less to worry with and less possible noise makers.

When convinced I've done all I can for controlling limb vibration, I turn to the string. String silencers come in as many forms as you can think up. Years ago, before there was a wide variety, I often made my own. They worked then, and they still do. Some of the things I used

Each bow is different. The author's two identical bows require different treatments and accessories to make them both hunting quiet.

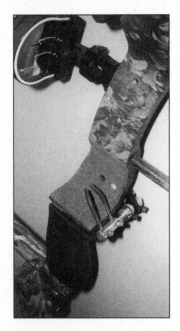

This arrow rest is silenced with soft material and the shelf with moleskin.

There are many types of string silencers. This is a simple one and is effective on many bows.

were black electrical tape, pieces of rubber inner tube and once, quite effectively, a dollop of hot-melt glue.

Today I can buy superior string silencers for the change from a six-pack of soft drinks. One company makes a device that slides over the end of the cable guard and stops the string after the arrow is released. It stops vibration, and it works. Some bows come with built-in string silencers. You may need to experiment with string silencer placement to get your string as quiet as possible. If all else fails, try black electrical tape. It still works.

There are some concerns in the "screaming speed" fraternity that string silencers slow the arrow down. They do. But do you really think it makes a lot of difference to a deer if you miss him at 350 feet per second or 348 feet per second? No matter how fast your bow is, if it is loud, you go to the woods with a handicap. I may be the only bowhunter out there who actually slows my hunting bow down on purpose.

Many years ago, I had an arrow slip off the rest as I was drawing. It clattered against the sight window and shelf, and an opportunity was lost. Since that day, my bows have been well padded with moleskin at any point an arrow might inadvertently touch. I also have used moleskin to make silencing gaskets around sight brackets, and in the dark ages, I wrapped my cables with it. The hunter who is concerned about a quiet bow will always have a supply of moleskin on hand.

Having gone through all of the above drill, I should now have a quiet bow. But I am not finished. Every single attachment and screw must be gone over and retightened. When I have the bow sighted in and have shot a few hundred arrows through it, if it is still quiet, I check all points and add Locktite.

I practice in the exact clothes I will wear hunting. I make sure I have good string clearance on my body. I wear a soft, wool armguard—sometimes two on one arm. And I go to the woods confident I have done all I could, and my bow is quiet enough to suit me.

Now if I could just learn to shoot accurately.

Strategies for Taking Pope & Young Bucks
by Roger B. Hook

Killing a buck big enough to guarantee entry into the Pope & Young record book is a daunting task, but that shouldn't discourage you from trying.

I could feel the tension of the bowstring against the release as the large-bodied whitetail buck inched ever so slowly in my direction. He had just freshened a scrape 60 yards from where I sat perched 20 feet up an oak tree. Several trails crisscrossed the Conservation Reserve Program field below me, leading me to select this particular corner of the field. The large rubs scattered throughout the surrounding timber were his signposts. Or were they?

The first unobstructed view I got of the buck revealed that he was not the nine-pointer I had seen the day before. This was about a 100–inch eight-pointer that had good mass and nice tines. I looked him over closely and logged the sight picture in my mind as he passed directly beneath my stand, thinking he might be next year's Pope & Young target.

Author Roger Hook poses with his nine-point, 138%-inch Pope & Young record whitetail buck. The minimum whitetail antler measurement for a Pope & Young entry is 125 inches.

This wide-racked buck still wears early-season velvet. Big whitetail bucks like this are among the wariest of game animals. To harvest one big enough to make the Pope & Young record book, an archer must use all his cunning to avoid detection by the deer's extraordinarily acute senses.

Moments later, the tension was back on the bowstring. The nine-pointer I had been hoping to see was rubbing his preorbital glands on a limb overhanging the same scrape the smaller buck had just worked. I knew immediately this was the buck I was trying to slip an arrow through. But he headed away from my stand.

Two soft grunts from my ever-present grunt tube got his attention. The body language of a whitetail will always tell you when he hears the call. Head erect, looking over his angled hips, the buck stood glaring. Then, as if on cue, he swapped ends and came straight toward me.

That's when the fear inside me began working overtime. When can I draw? How many yards did I mark the tree he is by? How well have I been shooting lately? A multitude of thoughts jammed the thought processes. And when I drew the bow, he stopped as though he spied me. The buck was standing at a slight angle, facing me. Standing between me and the boilermaker of this Pope & Young buck were two saplings no more than 3 inches in diameter.

The overwhelming urge to bump the trigger on the release was overcome with a moment of reason. I stood there pleading in my mind for the buck to take just a couple of steps, knowing full well that the mental games were the only thing keeping me from blowing an opportunity that had been a long time coming.

The biggest buck of my life was standing a dozen yards away. My nerves were near tilt, and I knew the bell was about to sound. Then the buck moved. And when his right leg went forward for the second step, I released the Gold Tip arrow. The shot was a clean pass-through, traveling through both lungs. The buck piled up in sight.

This was my first Pope & Young buck. More importantly, the experience of harvesting a 138 ⅝-inch whitetail brought new life into deer hunting for me. I had taken many smaller bucks over the years, but the thrill of walking up on another year-and-a-half-old deer was gone. That's when I made a deliberate decision to target mature bucks, especially 125 class and above whitetails.

Some hunters portray "big" bucks as near impossible to harvest with a bow. The task certainly is daunting, but not impossible. The most difficult part, assuming you know where a Pope & Young whitetail hangs out, is getting within 20 yards of such a wary animal. I don't know how many times I've sat in a tree 50 yards from a shooter buck with nothing but a strong desire for him to come my way.

When the scouting is complete, the stand is set and you are ready to hunt a Pope & Young buck, how do you get him in close? The answer has to do with the rut cycle of a deer and whether you are hunting pre-rut, rut or post-rut.

During the pre-rut, I hunt concentrations of rubs. Many times we speak of rubs as though they are found in a straight line. They never seem to be in a line for me. I typically find them in small pockets along ridge tops or in the bottom of draws. When I find a concentration, I log it into the memory bank and hunt it at some point during the pre-rut.

Scrapes also get my attention during the pre-rut. During this time, bucks visit their scrapes with regularity. They anxiously await the estrus cycle of their female counterparts, spending their time laying out territory and checking scrapes for the first indication of a doe nearing her breeding cycle. I find that when a buck begins following and breeding does, he is far less predictable.

An in-depth understanding of pre-rut, rut and post-rut deer behavior is invaluable to the bowhunter, who must bring a deer close to his stand in order to have a chance.

The rut phase can be quite a challenge, especially if you are hunting a particular buck. But, provided you hunt a part of the country where Pope & Young class bucks are commonplace, the rut can offer the best opportunity to harvest a trophy whitetail. Where I hunt, in a state that is mostly hardwood forest and holds few Pope & Young class bucks, the rut can be hit or miss. You might see several bucks chasing or cruising for a willing partner, but your trophy might have picked up a doe at the edge of his territory and moved two miles away.

During the rut, I basically employ two strategies. I hunt areas where I've seen the most does, or I hunt well-worn trails. Finding a good trail in a large hardwood forest isn't easy. Deer can and do travel throughout the area, so I try to locate those magical spots on ridge tops, along the side of the ridge or around a bluff row. These are the natural funnels deer travel. The more deer that pass your location, the greater the likelihood your buck will show up. And every once in a while, a surprise trophy happens by.

Hunting during the post-rut presents the greatest challenge for the bowhunter. Perhaps I should preface that statement with an explanation. The bucks I hunt, when the post-rut hits, have been hunted for three months. The pressure has encouraged nocturnal movement patterns. I see fewer deer during the post-rut, but have on a few occasions observed bucks chasing does. When I do see a buck chasing a doe, I

Finding a Scorer

If you would like to have a buck measured for entry in Pope & Young, you can contact the Pope & Young Club over the Internet. The Web site address is: www.pope-young.org. Click on the RECORD SECTION. Then go to FIND MEASURER. A list of scorers can be located for your state. You can also write the Pope & Young Club at P. O. Box 548, Chatfield, MN 55923

hunt every spare minute in that area hoping I can get a crack at him before she's done with him.

Because I rarely observe breeding during the pre-rut, I concentrate my efforts on hunting food sources. Many experts speak of food sources as though they are as easy to locate as a fast-food restaurant in small town USA. And in certain parts of the country, they are easy to locate. In my neck of the woods, however, there are no agriculture fields. The deer survive on the last few acorns available and what browse they can find. Honeysuckle is one of their favorite food sources, so I fertilize a few of the sweet smelling thickets and focus my late-season hunting efforts in those areas.

Regardless of the time of the rut phase, I take a grunt tube and rattling antlers or a rattle bag to the stand with me. Though I do grunt and rattle blindly at times, I mostly use these tools when I see a mature buck. If a buck moves by your stand too far for a shot, why not grunt to him? Why not tickle the antlers together? I usually wait until I'm certain he isn't going to enter the shooting zone. I grunt to him first. If that doesn't work, I tickle the antlers together. As a last resort, I'll rattle aggressively to him. The trick is to make sure he doesn't notice your movements.

Calling is the most effective way of harvesting a mature buck when bowhunting. Whitetails will come to calling from the time they lose their velvet until they shed their antlers.

You may call to several bucks without a positive response. Don't let that deter you. Many hunters have called to one of those big boys and watched him walk away, or they have grunted to a smaller buck and watched him rapidly exit the scene, and they have allowed the experience to jade their opinion of calling. Don't let that happen. Grunt and rattle to that Pope & Young buck standing in front of you. What do you have to lose if he's already going the other way?

Don't worry about educating the deer, either. Whitetails hear antler banging and other familiar sounds regularly. My only word of caution is that if you hunt the same area frequently, keep blind calling to a minimum. Use grunting and rattling mostly when you are looking at the buck you're hunting.

The most recent Pope & Young buck I harvested was a high-racked eight-pointer with 7-

Hunting areas with concentrations of rubs is a good pre-rut tactic.

inch eye guards. He scored just over 141 Pope & Young inches. The day I took this buck was October 17, which is the time of the pre-rut when I get serious about setting a stand.

The day was clear and cool. I climbed into the stand for only the third time. There was a large concentration of big and small rubs in front of and behind me. I knew they would be there because I'd found the previous year's rubs while turkey hunting in the spring. In fact, during turkey season, I picked the very tree where I located my deer stand.

I would rather leave my bow at home than leave my grunt tube and rattling antlers. This afternoon, for convenience sake, I picked up a small rattling bag and stuck it in my pocket. The strategy was to blind call quite a bit, using mostly light stuff, considering it was early in the season and smack in the middle of the pre-rut.

Rattling antlers are good tools for hunters pursuing Pope & Young class bucks during all phases of the rutting season.

About an hour into the hunt, I offered my best rendition of two bucks sparring with each other, presenting a few short grunts with the rattling. It was my fourth time of the day to call. The sequence must have been a couple of minutes long when I shut it off. Just as I slipped the rattle bag into my pocket, I spotted the buck walking rapidly toward me. His head was high, and he was looking for the intruders in his territory.

The buck never once checked up. He just kept coming, covering the 80 or so yards in long strides. I prepared for the shot hurriedly. As always for me, the eyes and brain were working overtime to determine the openings the buck might walk through and the distances they would be. Finally, he was there, walking between me and a small sapling 24 yards from my stand. The buck paused the moment I bleated with my natural voice, and the arrow flew 23 yards to the old boy's vitals.

Standing over a Pope & Young buck brings to the successful hunter a great sense of accomplishment. Most of us don't get to hunt where you can cull deer that meet the Pope & Young minimum of 125 inches or for bucks that score much higher. Taking a book buck with a bow begins with the decision to harvest only mature deer and ends when the patient hunter has just the right buck in bow range.

Don't worry if it takes several years to harvest your trophy. Each buck you let walk may be next year's Pope & Young whitetail.

Compound Bow Rules Change

A recent change by Pope & Young has a significant impact on bowhunters. The much-debated let-off factor of compound bows has been changed. The 65 percent maximum let-off has been deleted. There is no longer a let-off requirement. The change will apply retroactively.

The minimum typical score for inclusion in the record book is 125 inches. The minimum nontypical is 155 inches.

Crossbows
by Jay Langston

The wind direction began to shift from south to north, which would spell trouble if a buck walked down the main trail I was watching. Before I could reach for my fanny pack to lower it from the tree to vacate the stand, I caught a flicker of movement up the trail I had been watching for nearly an hour.

This time it wasn't a squirrel. The brown form moving through the brush was definitely a whitetail and, hopefully, one of the big-racked bucks that had been leaving sign on every other cedar along the creek bottom. The deer slowly picked its way closer and I caught a glimpse of antler. Raising my binoculars I found the buck and studied his head-gear. The near side of his rack sported a fork and a short brow tine, and as he swiveled his head I saw that the other matched. The buck was not one of the pigs that I was looking for, but a nice offering from the hunting gods. Since I was more interested in punching a tag than hunting for horns, I decided to take the first good shot.

There was only one problem. The buck was working his way down a trail that would put him directly downwind if he continued just 15 more yards into my shooting lane. Just before he got to a point where he would have busted me, he turned and headed straight for my tree. When he was 14 yards away he stopped and looked straight up at me and didn't like what he saw. Frozen in place he tested and retested the wind trying to put all of the pieces together. Turning, he began to walk away from the tree, but stopped broadside while looking up at me. I didn't dare move. Our nerves were equally frayed, but he just didn't have reason enough to turn tale and bolt. Circling my position, he was near an ancient beech tree. Would he pass in front or behind? After several years hunting turkeys, I knew my chance was coming if he walked behind the tree. My luck held as he put the tree between us. I raised a scoped Excalibur Exomag crossbow and held the crosshairs just to the off

Horton's Hunter XS Compound crossbow is rated at 200 lbs draw weight and can accurately center-punch a whitetail at 40 yards.

side of the tree. When the buck stepped clear I squeezed the trigger and watched the bolt disappear in the crease behind the buck's shoulder and stick in the ground beyond.

Predictably, the buck wheeled and streaked away.

Confident of the shot, I lowered my gear and started trailing immediately. The blood trail was faint, but I followed it for 50 yards until it played out. Since I had watched the buck dash beyond the point where I last found blood, I relied on my experience in following up scores of arrowed deer. What the deer have taught me is that mortally wounded animal will often turn toward the side of their body where the arrow entered during the last few seconds that they are mobile. Add to this the experience that deer will often head toward the thickest security cover available.

The Muzzy-tipped bolt had entered the buck's right side, so after another few yards I began looking for places where the buck could cross a deep ditch to the right of his escape trail. I found deep hoof prints on the opposite ditch bank as one possible crossing, so I jumped the ditch and began looking for the deer. Fanning out, I came to another ditch 45 yards further and found the 6-pointer lying in the bottom.

This past fall was my first encounter with crossbow equipment. After 33 years of bowhunting with conventional equipment I gave into my curiosity about this growing aspect of deer hunting. Fifteen years ago when I was Editor of Arkansas Sportsman Magazine, I published numerous articles about successful archers who tagged their bragging-sized bucks with a crossbow. Although it was quite a while in coming, I finally decided to pursue first-hand knowledge of this ancient weaponry.

The use of crossbows for hunting can be traced back for several centuries. When states began regulating hunting about 100 years ago, some early game managers decided that various methods were not "sporting" or safe. That's why we have shotgun-only regulations for deer hunting in many states, or baiting laws that span from anything goes to completely forbidden. These choices were made by small groups of men who were focused on restoring deer populations. Conditions today very different from the first half of the 20th century. Whitetail populations have soared from a low estimate of 200,000 to an approximate 25 million today. Instead of writing regulations to limit the whitetail harvest to facilitate population growth, modern game managers are struggling to add new laws to increase kill numbers to keep deer numbers in check. For this reason many states are relaxing their position on crossbow hunting.

A cocking rope typically gives enough leverage for an average hunter to draw this 200 lb-draw Excalibur Exo Mag. Crank-type cocking devices provide even more leverage.

The recurve crossbow is an equal match to any compound model. It's just a matter of which you choose.

The author with a young buck ready for the freezer.

From an ethical standpoint, I only need to look back to the reason that I began hunting deer with conventional archery tackle. Like many other deer hunters, I wanted to extend my hunting season and opportunities to bag a deer. I didn't start deer hunting as a purist and shun the use of modern firearms. On the contrary, I began hunting deer with a shotgun and switched to a rifle as soon as I mowed enough lawns to pay for it. As much as I enjoy hunting with a recurve or compound, I will always pursue game with any legal method available. For this reason, I have no qualms about hunting with a crossbow.

I picked two popular models to begin my research. The first was a Horton HunterXS compound rated at 200 pounds peak draw weight. Firing a Horton LS2 carbon arrow and a 100-grain Muzzy broadhead, this bow averaged 315 fps across an Oehler chronograph. I mounted a Horton 4x32 Mult-A-Range scope, which has stadia lines corresponding to various ranges in 10-yard increments. This package with attached quiver and bolts tips the scales at approximately 10 pounds. Find out more about Horton crossbows by checking out their website, www.horton mfg.com.

Although compound crossbows have become popular, the recurve models give up little or nothing in the speed department. Excalibur Crossbow Inc., from Ontario, Canada, provided their Exomag model for testing. This model has a 200-pound draw weight and launches a carbon shaft tipped with a 100-grain broadhead at 330 fps. If care is taken when loading this bow to precisely cock the string with the rope cocker, it is capable of tight groups from a bench rest. Flemish twist FastFlight strings, state-of-the-art limbs, and a smooth trigger makes this an accurate rig. Check out Excaliburcrossbow.com for more information about a new 225-pound draw weight bow with a claimed 350 fps peak arrow speed, as well as other products offered.

Recently, changes in crossbow regulations are pending in New York, Tennessee and New Hampshire. As the aspect of the sport's popularity grows, more states will review their regulations for possible inclusion and change.

Crossbow Regulations by State

ALABAMA May be used by the physically challenged during archery season. For more info go to: "http://www.dcnr.state.al.us" www.dcnr.state.al.us

ALASKA May be used for big game or small game during general season. Not permitted during archery-only season. For more info go to: "http://www.state.ak.us" www.state.ak.us

ARIZONA May be used for big game or small game during general seasons and during H.A.M. (Handgun, Archery, Muzzleloader) and fishing. For more info go to: "http://www.gf.state.az.us" www.gf.state.az.us

ARKANSAS Classified and permitted as part of the state's archery deer season. Also permitted for small game, predators and fishing. For more info go to: "http://www. agfc.state.ar.us" www.agfc.state.ar.us

CALIFORNIA May be used for big game during general firearms season. Permitted for small game. For more info go to: "http://www. dfg.ca.gov" www.dfg.ca.gov

COLORADO May be used for big game during general firearms season and for small game birds. "http://wildlife.state.co.us/hunt/index.asp" www.wildlife.state.co.us

CONNECTICUT May be used by the physically challenged during hunting season. For more info go to: "http://dep.state.ct.us" dep.state.ct.us

DELAWARE May be used by the physically challenged for big game during the general firearms season and shotgun season. For more info go to: "http://www.dnrec.state.de.us" www.dnrec.state.de.us

FLORIDA May be used for big game during the general firearms season. Permitted for small game. For more info go to: "http://www.state.fl.us/gfc" www.state.fl.us/gfc

GEORGIA Permitted for use by the physically challenged during archery season. Permitted for fishing. For more info go to: "http://www. dnr.state.ga.us" www.dnr.state.ga.us

HAWAII Permitted for big game and small game on private lands only. For more info go to: "http://www.hawaii.gov/dlnr/dcre/home.htm" www.hawaii.gov/dlnr/dcre/home.htm

IDAHO Permitted during the general firearms season for big game. Permitted for small game and fishing. For more info go to: "http://www.state.id.us/fishgame" www.state.id.us/fishgame

ILLINOIS Permitted for use by the physically challenged during archery season. Permitted for fishing. For more info go to: "http://dnr.state.il.us" dnr.state.il.us

INDIANA May be used during the late archery season. Permitted for fishing. Permitted for use by the physically challenged in the early archery season. For more info go to: "http://www.state.in.us/dnr/fishwild/index.htm" www.state.in.us/dnr/fishwild/index.htm

IOWA Permitted for use by the physically challenged during archery season. For more info go to: "http://www.state.ia.us/dnr/fwdiv.htm" www.state.ia.us/dnr/fwdiv.htm

KANSAS Permitted for use by the physically challenged during archery season. Permitted for small game. For more info go to: "http://www.kdwp.state.ks.us" www.kdwp.state.ks.us

KENTUCKY Permitted for small and big game during crossbow season and general firearms season. For more info go to: "http://www.state.ky.us/agencies/fw/kdfwr.htm" www.state.ky.us/agencies/fw/kdfwr.htm

LOUISIANA Permitted for use by the physically challenged during archery season. For more info go to: "http://www.wlf. state.la.us" www.wlf.state.la.us

MAINE Not recognized as a legal hunting weapon. For more info go to: "http://www.state. me.us/ifw" www.state.me.us/ifw

MARYLAND Permitted for use by the physically challenged during archery season. Also may be used during specified dates during the regular archery season (example: Oct. 1-15, 2003 and Jan. 15-31, 2004) For more info go to: "http://www.dnr.state.md.us" www.dnr.state.md.us

MASSACHUSETTS Permitted for use by the physically challenged by permit only. For more info go to: "http://www.state. ma.us/dfwele/dfw" www.state.ma. us/dfwele/dfw

MICHIGAN Permitted for use by the physically challenged during archery season. For more info go to: "http://www.dnr. state.mi.us" www.dnr.state.mi.us

MINNESOTA Permitted for use by the physically challenged during archery season. For more info go to: "http://www.dnr. state.mn.us" www.dnr.state.mn.us

MISSISSIPPI Permitted for use by the physically challenged during archery season. For more info go to: "http://www.mdwfp.com" www.mdwfp.com

MISSOURI Permitted during regular firearms season and small game seasons. Permitted for fishing. Permitted for use by the physically challenged in archery season. For more info go to: "http://www.conservation.state.mo.us/" www.conservation.state.mo.us/

MONTANA Permitted for regular firearms season. Permitted for small game and predators. For more info go to: "http://fwp.state.mt.us" fwp.state.mt.us

NEBRASKA Permitted for use by the physically challenged during archery and regular firearms seasons. For more info go to: "http://www.ngpc.state.ne.us/" www.ngpc.state.ne.us/

NEVADA Not recognized as a legal hunting weapon. For more info go to: "http://www.state. nv.us/cnr_menu.htm" www.state.nv.us/cnr_menu.htm

NEW HAMPSHIRE Permitted for use by the physically challenged during archery season. For more info go to: "http://www.wildlife. state.nh.us" www.wildlife.state.nh.us

NEW JERSEY Permitted for use by the physically challenged only. For more info go to: "http://www.state.nj.us/dep/fgw" www.state.nj.us/dep/fgw

NEW MEXICO Not recognized as a legal hunting weapon. For more info go to: "http://www.gmfish. state.nm.us" www.gmfish.state. nm.us

NEW YORK Permitted by the physically challenged during archery season. For more info go to: "http://www.dec.state.ny.us" www.dec.state.ny.us

NORTH CAROLINA Permitted for use by the physically challenged during archery season. For more info go to: "http://www.state.nc. us/Wildlife/" www.state.nc.us/Wildlife/

NORTH DAKOTA Permitted for use by the physically challenged during archery season. For more information go to: "http://www. state.nd.us/gnf/hunting/" www.state.nd.us

OHIO Classified as part of the state's archery deer season. Permitted for all legal game except waterfowl. Permitted for fishing. For more info go to: "http://www.dnr. state.oh.us" www.dnr.state.oh.us

OKLAHOMA Permitted for use by the physically challenged during archery season. For more info go to: "http://www.state. ok.us/~odwc" www.state.ok.us/~odwc

OREGON Not recognized as a legal hunting weapon. Permitted for fishing and non-game animals. For more info go to: "http://www.dfw.state.or.us" www.dfw.state.or.us

PENNSYLVANIA Permitted for use by the physically challenged during archery season. For more info go to: "http://www.pgc. state.pa.us" www.pgc.state.pa.us

RHODE ISLAND Not recognized as a legal hunting weapon. For more info go to: "http://www. state.ri.us/dem" www.state.ri.us/dem

SOUTH CAROLINA Permitted during archery and firearms seasons with the exception of areas 1, 2 and 4, and wildlife management areas. For more info go to: "http://www.dnr.state.sc.us" www.dnr.state.sc.us

SOUTH DAKOTA Permitted for use by the physically challenged during archery season. For more info go to: "http://www. state.sd.us/gfp/" www.state.sd.us/gfp/

TENNESSEE Permitted for use by the physically challenged during archery, general firearms and muzzleloader seasons. For more info go to: "http://www.state. tn.us/twra" www.state.tn.us/twra

TEXAS Permitted during general firearms season. For more info go to: "http://www.tpwd. state.tx.us" www.tpwd.state.tx.us

UTAH Permitted for use by the physically challenged. For more info go to: "http://www.nr. state.ut.us" www.nr.state.ut.us

VERMONT Permitted for use by the physically challenged during archery season. For more info go to: "http://www.anr. state.vt.us" www.anr.state.vt.us

VIRGINIA Permitted for use by the physically challenged during archery season. For more info go to: "http://www.dgif.state.va.us/" www.dgif.state.va.us/

WASHINGTON Permitted for use by the physically challenged during archery season. For more info go to: "http://www.dgif. state.va.us/" www.dgif.state.va.us/

WASHINGTON Not recognized as a legal hunting weapon. For more info go to: "http://www. wa.gov/wdfw" www.wa.gov/wdfw

WEST VIRGINIA Not recognized as a legal hunting weapon. For more info go to: "http://www. wa.gov/wdfw" www.wa.gov/wdfw

WISCONSIN Permitted for use by the physically challenged during archery season. Permitted for fishing. For more info go to: "http://www.dnr.state.wi.us" www.dnr.state.wi.us

NEW PRODUCTS

NEW Products: **Arrow Building Components**

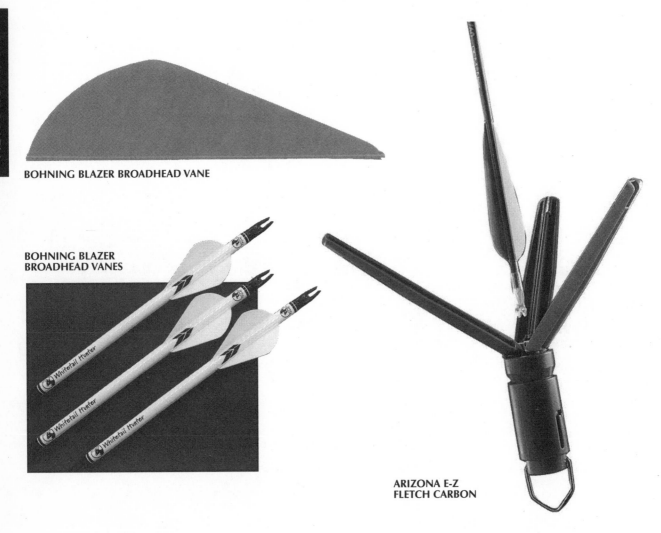

BOHNING BLAZER BROADHEAD VANE

BOHNING BLAZER BROADHEAD VANES

ARIZONA E-Z FLETCH CARBON

ARIZONA RIM COUNTRY

Arizona E-Z Fletch™

With the new Arizona E-Z Fletch for Carbon Shafts, you can fletch a dozen arrow—wood, aluminum and now carbon—exactly the way you want them in less than 30 minutes. It fletches three or four vanes or feathers at the same time. You don't have to depend on someone else to do it, and you can save money while enjoying the process.

The Arizona E-Z Fletch is a compact, lightweight unit that is easy to use, even in the field. The E-Z Fletch Pro automatically adjusts to any size arrow shaft from 2013 to 2613. It comes in straight, straight offset, right or left helical and will also do any style of three or four fletch with nothing extra to buy. The Arizona E-Z Fletch Carbon Arrow model will fletch the smallest carbon shaft up to a 2018 aluminum. This new, patented design ensures precision alignment and includes interchangeable arms.
SRP:..................... **$45**

BOHNING ARCHERY

Blazer Broadhead Vanes

With all the steering capabilities of a 4" vane, The Blazer will amaze you with its silence, accuracy and flight characteristics. All this in a 2" vane that provides maximum accuracy, maximum durability, minimum noise and now maximum steering with minimum weight. Each vane weighs only 5 grains. The bases of all Bohning vanes are chemically treated to promote intense adhesion. No need to clean the bases.

SPECIFICATIONS
Size: 2"
Weight: 5 grains
Colors: Purple, Yellow, Black, Red, Blue, White, Dark Green, Bark Brown, Orange, Hot Pink, Flo Red, Flo Green, Flo Yellow, Flo Orange, Neon Yellow, Neon Orange, Neon Green, Clear
SRP: .... **$12.46 per 100 pack**

NEW Products: **Arrow Building Components**

BOHNING FLETCH-TITE
PLATINUM

BOHNING "X" VANE 1.8"

BOHNING "X" VANE 2.4"

BOHNING "X" VANE 4"

BOHNING QUANTUM
XT ADHESIVE

BOHNING ARCHERY

Fletch-Tite Platinum
Chemically engineered adhesive for
every type of shaft available today:
wood, aluminum and carbon. The
next generation!
SRP: 0.75 oz.. . . . . $2.75
    2 oz.. . . . . $4.58

Quantum XT Adhesive
Instantly bonds nocks, vanes, feathers
and inserts. Extremely impact resistant.
Super strong and super fast. A
"Quantum" leap for instant adhesive
technology. Comes in a 1-oz. bottle.
SRP: $11.66

"X" Vanes
The "X" Vanes, part of Bohning's Target
Series, provide X-treme durability,
X-treme accuracy and minimum noise.
Available in three and 18 colors. The
bases of all Bohning vanes are chemi-
cally treated to promote intense adhe-
sion. No need to clean the bases.
SPECIFICATIONS
Size: 1.8", 2.4" and 4" lengths
SRP: . . . . $12.46 per 100 pack

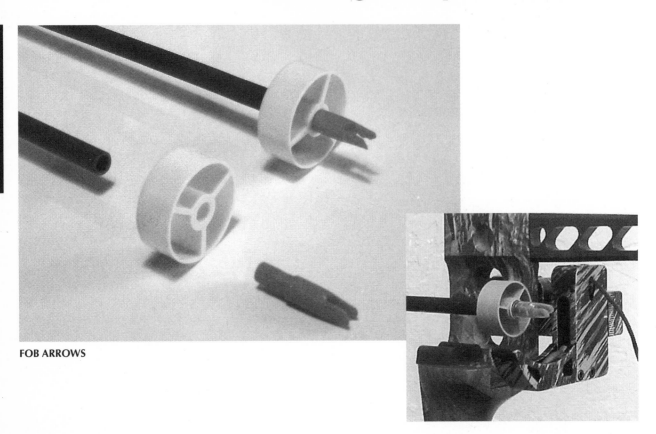

FOB ARROWS

STARRFLIGHT

The FOB™

It's called the FOB™ and looks like something from the aerospace industry, which it is. When an FOB is installed on an arrow shaft in lieu of conventional fletching and shot from a Fall Away Rest, the FOB increases high-speed stability, accuracy and penetration, especially with broadheads.

Wind tunnel and strobe light testing on the FOB showed a 150% increase in low angle stability, 70% reduction in cross wind drift, a 3 fold increase in torque reduction and virtual elimination of arrow shutter when tested against plastic and feather fletching.

As soon as the arrow leaves the string the powerful steering forces of the FOB's ring wing instantly stabilizes the shaft flex paradox. The three powerful turbine struts impart instant spin on the arrow to normalize any shaft straightness tolerances, which allows the arrow to stabilize more rapidly, reducing critical speed robbing, air friction down range. The FOB is especially vital when shooting large broadheads where flight can be a problem. Bottom line, an FOB equipped arrow leaves the bow straighter, stabilizes more quickly, shoots flatter and hits harder.

FOB's are available in two sizes; 1" for target/field use and smaller diameter/mechanical broadheads as well as 1¼" for use with any large diameter broadheads regardless of size. FOB's are simple to install, are made of high impact, weather-resistant space age polymer and will fit standard Internal, component system carbon shafts with a press in nock.

SRP: **$9.95**
    pack of six 1" **$9.95**
    pack of four 1½" **$9.95**

**DROP-TINE
WHISKER BISCUIT**

**DROP-TINE
WHISKER BISCUIT QS**

**DELUXE WHISKER
BISCUIT**

**DELUXE WHISKER
BISCUIT QS**

CAROLINA ARCHERY PRODUTS

Drop-Tine Whisker Biscuit QS

The Drop-Tine Whisker Biscuit Arrow Rest® is now available with a factory-installed Quick Shot Kit. The Quick Shot biscuit will compliment any bow but is perfectly suited to enhance an expandable broadhead setup. The entry slot is tapered to allow quick and easy arrow loading while preventing brush snags when stalking or walking to your stand. The sturdy design means your biscuit will not be bent or twisted and gives you the confidence to know your shot will always be on target. Optional stick-on felt pads are provided for silent arrow loading. Right hand only.
SRP: $51.00

Deluxe Whisker Biscuit QS

The Deluxe Whisker Biscuit Arrow Rest® is now available with a factory installed Quick Shot Kit. The Quick Shot biscuit will compliment any bow but is perfectly suited to enhance an expandable broadhead setup. The entry slot is tapered to allow quick and easy arrow loading while preventing brush snags when stalking or walking to your stand. The sturdy design means your biscuit will not be bent or twisted and gives you the confidence to know your shot will always be on target. Optional stick-on felt pads are provided for silent arrow loading. Right hand only.
SRP: $64.50

NEW Products: **Arrow Rests**

QUICK SHOT KIT

DELUXE QUICK SHOT KIT

CAROLINA ARCHERY PRODUTS

Quick Shot Kit
Upgrade your Original or Drop-Tine Whisker Biscuit Arrow Rest® with the Quick Shot Kit. Provides fast and easy arrow loading. The Quick Shot biscuit will compliment any bow but is perfectly suited to enhance an expandable broadhead setup. The entry slot is tapered to allow quick and easy arrow loading while preventing brush snags when stalking or walking to your stand. The sturdy design means your biscuit will not be bent or twisted and gives you the confidence to know your shot will always be on target. Right or left hand models.
SRP: **$18.00**

Deluxe Quick Shot Kit
Upgrade your Deluxe Whisker Biscuit Arrow Rest® with the Deluxe Quick Shot Kit. Provides fast and easy arrow loading. The Quick Shot biscuit will compliment any bow but is perfectly suited to enhance an expandable broadhead setup. The entry slot is tapered to allow quick and easy arrow loading while preventing brush snags when stalking or walking to your stand. The sturdy design means your biscuit will not be bent or twisted and gives you the confidence to know your shot will always be on target. Right or left hand models.
SRP: **$18.00**

T.K.O. ARROW REST

WHISPER DISK

GOLDEN KEY-FUTURA

T.K.O.

The new T.K.O. is truly a revolutionary Drop-Away Rest that is designed with a sleek, high-tech look with precision adjustments down to the most minute detail. It is clean and uncomplicated with the smoothest drop-away action available today. The features read like a Who's Who of Rests. For starters, it has a simple, adjustable drop-away system that accepts a wide variety of Launcher types with infinite spring adjustment as well as Launcher angle adjustment. The adjustable Launcher also holds your arrow in place even when tilted to the side. The easy to see calibration marks enable in the field, micro-tuning for both vertical and horizontal adjustments while the Anti-Pivot feature locks the Rest down to eliminate any unwanted movement. And if you want to negate the drop-away feature the T.K.O is easily converted to a Fixed or Spring-Loaded Rest, left or right hand.

Smooth and adaptable you bet, but the T.K.O. is also one tough hunting Rest that is manufactured to the tightest tolerances out of Aircraft grade aluminum and stainless steel. You won't find any unnecessary parts or pieces here and you won't find any plastic.

Also available in a new T.K.O. Target model.

SRP: **$49.99**
      Target model: **$54.99**

Whisper Disk

The Whisper Disk is the "silent solution" to arrow falloff, offering easier side-loading and a replaceable shoot-through disk that is designed with the latest in space age closed cell foam. The remarkable disk is quiet, long lasting and absolutely non-abusive to arrow shafts and vanes. The Whisper Disk is also unaffected by weather and is incredibly accurate.

The Whisper Disk is a solid bowhunting rest that will fit left or right hand model bows and is adjustable for vertical and horizontal. It is available for carbon and smaller diameter aluminum shafts and larger diameter shafts.

SRP: **$34.99**

NEW Products: **Arrow Rests**

MUZZY ZERO EFFECT ARROWREST

MUZZY PRODUCTS

Zero Effect Arrowrest™ in Realtree Camo

Muzzy Products Corporation is pleased to announce a new addition to its line of popular Zero Effect Arrowrests. This popular arrow rest system is now available in the versatile Realtree Extra Gray camouflage pattern.

Muzzy Products has perfected the technology to imprint a durable, perfect reproduction of this top-selling camo pattern directly on to the arrow rest system. The Zero Effect Arrowrest in Realtree Extra Gray is the ideal accessory offering enhanced performance for the new fast high tech line of bows available on the market today.

The Zero Effect state-of-the-art technology was developed by Joe Angeloni as a solution to tuning problems associated as offer enhanced accuracy and performance.
SRP:. . . . . $83.25-$116.65

Numbering arrows is a good way to learn which need tuning. But sometimes it's a bit hard remembering which number was performing worse than others. Naming your arrows instead of numbering them may help you remember better. Give each arrow a name and write it on the vane with a waterproof marker. Be creative—names like Heatseeker, Deer Slayer, Razorhead, Viper, etc. With names, it may be easier to keep track of each arrow's performance.

HERITAGE 250

HERITAGE 350

CX CROSSBOLT HUNTER

EASTMAN OUTFITTERS

Heritage™ Hunting Shafts
- Durable carbon composite construction
- Look and feel of classic cedar
- Available in shafts, vanes or 5 barred inch feathers

SPECIFICATIONS
Shafts
Model: W1400
Size/Description: 250/12PK
Grains per Inch: 11.0
Diameter: 0.297"
Straightness: ±.006
SRP:

Model: W1401
Size/Description: 350/12PK
Grains per Inch: 12.0
Diameter: 0.315"
Straightness: ±.006
SRP:

Fletched With Vanes
Model: W1404
Size/Description: 250/12PK
Grains per Inch: 11.0
Diameter: 0.297"
Straightness: ±.006
SRP:

Model: W1405
Size/Description: 350/12PK
Grains per Inch: 12.0
Diameter: 0.315"
Straightness: ±.006
SRP:

Fletched With Feathers
Model: W1407
Size/Description: 250/12PK
Grains per Inch: 11.0
Diameter: 0.297"
Straightness: ±.006
SRP:

Model: W1408
Size/Description: 350/12PK
Grains per Inch: 12.0
Diameter: 0.315"
Straightness: ±.006
SRP:

CX Crossbolt Hunter
- Wrapped carbon composite construction
- Patented Buff Tuff construction
- Available in Realtree Hardwoods Green Camouflage

SPECIFICATIONS
Model: T4061
Size/Description: 20"/6 pack
Grains per inch: 13.7
SRP:

Model: T4062
Size/Description: 20"/36 pack
Grains per inch: 13.7
SRP:

RATCHET-LOC BOW PRESS

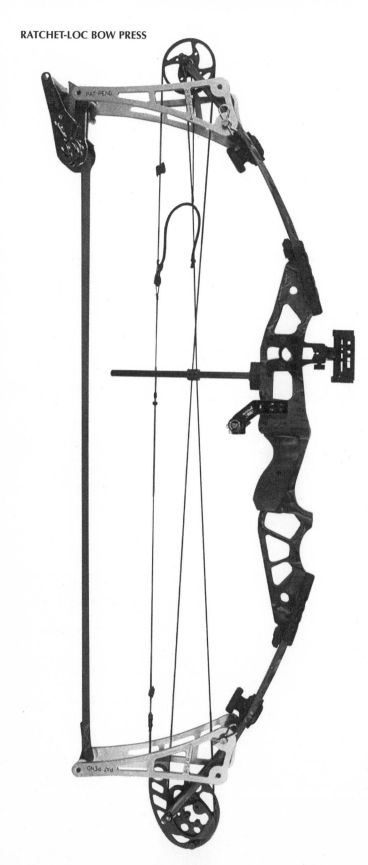

BOW PRESSES

RAM PRODUCTS

Ratchet-Loc Bow Press
New this year from Ram Products is a portable bow press designed for the serious archer. Weighing just 2.5 lbs, The Ratchet-Loc Bow Press is specifically designed for portability, but it is so fast and easy to use that it can replace the bulky bench mounted bow presses used at home and in shops. Because of the strength of the CNC machined, aircraft grade aluminum housings and the incredible strength of the specially designed nylon webbing, this press will easily compress the heaviest bows. Unlike other portable presses on the market, this press will work on any bow and it is up and out of the way to allow for easy access to the strings, cams and limbs. There are no split limb adapters to buy and it comes with its own heavy duty carry case. The Ratchet-Loc Press is designed to accommodate the full range of today's bow designs, including short axle to axle tree stand bows, long radical risers and parallel limb designs.
SRP:. $85

ATV BOW HOLDER

UNIVERSAL BOW HOLDER SYSTEM
BOW HOLDER

UNIVERSAL BOW
HOLDER SYSTEM

UNIVERSAL BOW HOLDER
BMI INTERFACE

CASES, HOLDERS AND SLINGS

ALPINE ARHCERY

Universal Bow Holder System

The number of hunters who take ATVs into the field has risen dramatically and Alpine Archery saw the need for a safe, secure and quiet way to transport their bows. Imagine safely and quietly securing your bow (or rifle) in your vehicle, then mount on your ATV and finally to your treestand. You can with Alpine Archery's newest innovation the Universal Bow Holder System, which is designed to work flawlessly with almost any bow built because of the unique, lightweight Bow Mount Interface (BMI). What this system allows the archer to do, by mounting

the BMI on a bow, is attach that bow and quiver to any of the new Alpine Bow Holders for treestands, ATVs and vehicles. This system ensures your bow will be safely secured to a treestand, transported and protected from vibration on your ATV and mounted securely behind the seat of your vehicle.

Alpine's ATV Bow Holders come in both a handle bar mount or a dovetail version. The versatile dovetail mount works great because the low profile, female portion of the dovetail can be left on your ATV year round and allows for the use of the rack for other duties in the off season. When needed the user can simply install the male dovetail portion of the mount to use either the Bow Mount or optional Long Gun Mount for rifle, shotgun and muzzleloader. This dovetail mount can

be installed on the front or rear rack, or cargo box already installed on some ATVs. All of this is vibration free, only takes seconds to install and is the optimal method of transporting a bow or firearm.

The handle bar mount is easily installed on the tubing members of a front or rear rack on most ATVs. This bar mounted holder sports the same interchangeable features and Flex Strut advantages as the other holders. Regardless of the mounting style preferred the user is assured their hunting equipment will arrive safely in the field.
Minimum advertised price:
ATV Dove Tail Mount. $57.95
ATV Handle bar Mount $32.95
Treestand Bow Holder $16.95

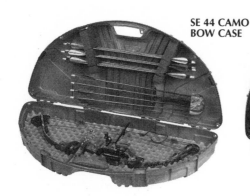

**SE 44 CAMO
BOW CASE**

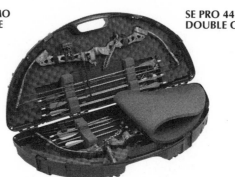

**SE PRO 44
DOUBLE CASE**

CASES, HOLDERS AND SLINGS

DOSKOSPORT

SE 44 and SE PRO 44

DoskoSport™ makes a habit of delivering exactly what sportsmen want. "Case" in point: DoskoSport's all-new SE 44 and SE PRO 44 Bow Cases. DoskoSport conducted extensive consumer research to determine the user-driven features today's archers demand and designed these features and benefits into the new cases. Both products combine all the best ideas at attractive prices.

The cases get their names from their compact 44-inch length, which is ideal for today's shorter bows. They are almost two inches thicker than other cases, giving archers more room for bows and accessories. They are also much wider than competitors' cases, allowing users to leave stabilizers on their bows during storage and transport.

Outside, the all-new SE 44 features a sleek, rugged look with strengthening bodylines and a unique tongue-in-groove hull for added protection against crushing and warping. Four, wide snap-over latches with a recessed design keep the bow case tightly closed, and three padlock tabs offer added security.

The SE 44 also has large, wide-angled feet for a sure footing and an extra-wide recessed handle that makes it easy to carry even while wearing gloves. The case is backcountry tough and comes equipped with additional tabs for strapping it to ATVs, cars and trucks.

Inside, the SE 44 Bow Case offers plenty of space to securely store a bow and several accessories. The extra-wide design leaves room for one

of the SE 44's most consumer-demanded features: internal storage for a fully-loaded quiver. Special screw bosses are included to allow securing a full quiver inside the case without removing the arrows using an additional quiver mount. There's also an all-new arrow retainer design capable of holding 12 additional arrows.

Thick, convoluted foam padding and two sturdy tie-down straps keep the bow in place and protected, while the ribbed, tongue-in-groove hull design provides water and dust resistance.

The new SE PRO 44 Bow Case features all the same design improvements as the SE 44 with several stylish, handy additions. The PRO 44 comes in an exclusive pewter color with attractive PRO 44 emblems. In addition, it includes a unique, removable accessory storage box. This innovative storage box uses convenient quick release hardware to attach to the interior of the case, giving archers the option of securing the box in the lid or in the bottom, beneath the bow strings.

DoskoSport's user-friendly design is evident in the storage box. There are seven removable dividers that can be customized to handle every conceivable accessory, including a unique broadhead holder with a built-in wrench tool. Sturdy, thumb-release snap-over latches keep the lid tightly closed, and the quick release tab secures the accessory box in the case.

SPECIFICATIONS

SE 44 Camo Bow Case
Features:
- New camo "woodsy" look
- Fully loaded quiver storage for in-line or offset quiver (extra mount required, not included)
- Angle locking foam arrow retainers hold 12 arrows
- Secure holding straps for bows and accessories, exterior tabs for padlock or tie-down
- Size (L x W x H): 43.09" x 15.3" x 8"

SRP: **$51.99**

SE PRO 44 Single Bow Case
Features:
- Fully loaded quiver storage for in-line or offset quiver (extra mount required, not included)
- Removable accessory box with built-in broad head tool and adjustable compartments
- Angle locking foam arrow retainers hold twelve arrows
- Secure holding straps for bows and accessories, exterior tabs for padlock or tie-down
- Color: Platinum
- Size (L x W x H): 43.09" x 15.3" x 8"

SRP: **$72.99**

SE PRO 44 Double Case
Features:
- Two bow capacity with foam in between
- Two removable accessory boxes with built-in broadhead tool and adjustable compartments
- Secure holding straps for bows and accessories, exterior tabs for padlock or tie-down
- Size (L x W x H): 43.09" x 15.3" x 8"
- Color: Black

SRP: **$112.99**

CASES, HOLDERS AND SLINGS

KOLPIN OUTDOORS

Deluxe Evolution™ Bow Case Series

Kolpin® Outdoors Inc. has introduced its Deluxe Evolution™ Bow Case Series, a unique collection of three premium bow cases that combine the ultimate in bow protection and carrying convenience. In keeping with Kolpin's mission to provide superior protection, the Deluxe Evolution bow case series offers archery enthusiasts unmatched equipment safety for the fall hunting season.

Constructed with resilient 400-denier water repellent polyester, Kolpin's Deluxe Evolution bow cases provide optimal protection and weather resistance for all types of bows. The ultra-sturdy, triple-density closed cell foam will not compress like open cell foam, and weather-tight polyester lining ensures the bow's protection from harsh conditions or jostling during off-road travel. For added durability, an outer layer of tough Kolpin branded webbing lines the entire length of each case.

Bow hunters will find that reinforced, ballistic nylon web handles with heavy-duty Mud Guard™ zippers and easy-grab Kolpin web zipper pulls allow for secure grip, easy access and trouble-free transportation. Kolpin's Evolution bow cases come equipped with a roomy accessories pocket perfect for carrying game calls, arrows or broadheads, and a large cargo net for securing gear.

Kolpin's Deluxe Evolution series bow cases are available in two-tone Realtree® Hardwoods™ and Tan, and will be available in fall 2004.

SRP:

Bow Case
   (Model #20560), ... $34.99
Bow Case with pocket
   (Model #20550), ... $39.99
Crossbow Case
   (Model #19800), ... $49.99

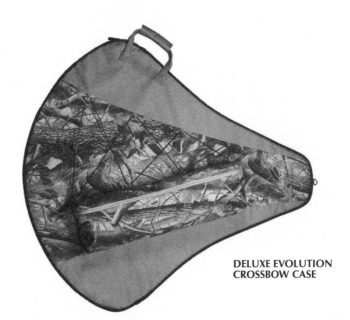

DELUXE EVOLUTION CROSSBOW CASE

DELUXE EVOLUTION BOW CASE WITH POCKET

NEW Products: **Bow Accessories**

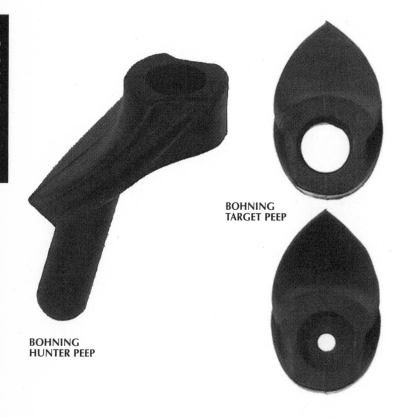

BOHNING TARGET PEEP

BOHNING HUNTER PEEP

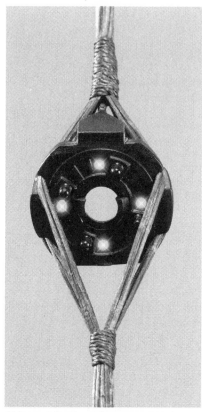

FINE-LINE ULTRA-GLO PEEP SIGHT

SIGHTS AND PEEP SYSTEMS

BOHNING ARCHERY

Hunter Peep
Extra large sight orifice for low light conditions. Includes alignment tube and cable clip.
SRP: **$7.20**

Target Peep
Standard sight orifice. Includes alignment tube and cable clip.
SRP: **$7.20**

FINE-LINE INC.

Ultra-Glo Peep Sight
Fine-Line's Ultra-Glo peep sight is a wide peep featuring adjustable, light-catching fiber optics that pick up ambient light to aid the archer in quickly finding and centering the peep especially in low light conditions. Every shooter will find accuracy improved merely by the addition of the four aperture surrounding points of light, but there is more.

The Ultra-Glo not only combines the advantages of fiber optics that may be adjusted for brightness, but this peep is also wider with a large aperture to aid in focus and concentration for greater accuracy. Two other notable features are the Ultra-Glo is served in with four bowstring sections with a locking tab on the body and will work on any bow with string angles from 30 to 60 degrees. When the Ultra-Glo is served in it will not shift and it will work for all bows, even the short draw bows.

The Ultra-Glo peep sight is made of sturdy composites and weighs no more than other standard peep sights.
SRP: **$16.95**

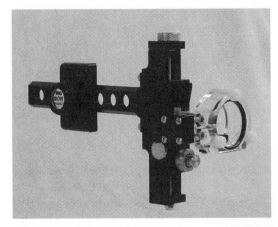

MAG SIGHT MAGNUM

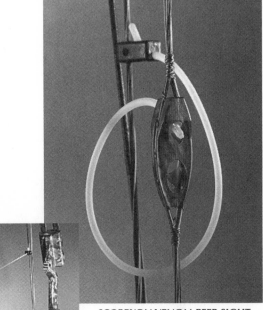

SCORPYON VENOM PEEP SIGHT

SCORPYON VENOM PEEP SIGHT

SIGHTS AND PEEP SYSTEMS

MAG SIGHT PRODUCTS

Mag Sight Magnum
The Mag Sight Magnum round outs Mag Sight Products' current 3-D/ Hunting/Target Scope product line. It's solidly constructed with a magnesium body, delrin slide, acrylic light gathering lens housing, stainless hardware and anodized aluminum. It has been engineered with all of the same integrated options and features that the rest of the product line embodies. The scope offers a near U.V. Light option with the "quiet switch" and others. The scope is sold as a complete unit including lens housing, lockable micro-adjust windage, lockable micro-adjust elevation, rapid elevation adjustment and green or red fluorescent pin.
SRP: $229.95
Light option: $14.95
Lenses: . . . . $29.95-$39.95
Lenses with new Teflon A.R.
    and Crizal A.R. coatings: . . $39.95

SCORPYON TECHNOLOGIES

Venom Peep Sight
The new Venom Peep Sight is a self-aligning system that uses a solid, durable, highly elastic, through-the-peep tether that for the first time allows for a symmetrical peep body with no tether stress points. It is automatically, at the draw, rotated into proper shooting position by using an Everlastomer™, high visibility tether. The peep itself is manufactured from an almost indestructible polycarbonate that features a large .30" diameter aperture and is molded in special Horizon Blue™." Horizon Blue™ is "optically eutropic," or virtually the same color as the atmosphere in pre-dawn and post-sundown light conditions, which are the optimum hunting periods. This color is easy on the eye, allowing the pupil to adjust more rapidly in those critical seconds between the time the peep is drawn to the eye, the target is acquired and the arrow released.

The .30" aperture allows the archer to capture the entire sight guard with all pins inside the peep aperture (centering) rather than a single sight pin, which increases the accuracy of every shot. And the new design for the cable clip is much more secure than anything currently on the market.
SRP:. $15

NEW PRODUCTS

LORE STABILIZER

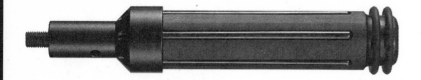

CAMO LORE STABILIZER

DELUXE LORE STABILIZER

STABILIZERS

CAROLINA ARCHERY PRODUCTS

LORE Stabilizer
The LORE Stabilizer's multiphasic fluted damping element is matched to a system of opposed linear springs. This patent pending design provides the greatest damping over the widest range of frequencies. What's more, at only 6¾ inches and 6 oz., the LORE Stabilizer provides all these features in a small package for steady, accurate, effective hunting every time out.
Color: Classic Black
SRP: $37.00

Camo LORE Stabilizer and Deluxe LORE Stabilizer
Carolina Archery Products took the proven LORE Stabilizer design and enhanced it with all the features archers asked for: Mossy Oak Break-Up and Realtree High Definition Camos, built-in articulated base, free custom wrist-sling (perfectly matched to the stabilizer) and a knurled grip for tool-free installation. They also developed Press Pin Technology to install the linear springs and bond them to the base at the atomic level. This produces unmatched vibration damping.
SRP:
Camo LORE Stabilizer: $34
Deluxe LORE Stabilizer: $38

Bowhunter education courses are excellent programs for both beginning and experienced archers. Taking this course can save you years of trial and error in the field. The courses are taught by qualified instructors who will share their knowledge and help you become an effective bowhunter. Contact your local archery club, pro shop or bowhunting association to learn where and when a course will be available in your area.

STABILIZERS

DOINKER

D2 Plus Series

Introducing the all-new Doinker D2 Plus family of patented 360-degree active vibration and noise dampers. The "Plus" means a whole new level of stealth and accuracy, with exclusive ultra-quiet, high-gravitational ITP (interrupted-transfer polymer) and new super-rigid woven carbon rods. Plus, there are three pre-cut, self-adhesive Doinker 4-in-1 CamoSkins—in Realtree Extra Gray, Realtree Hardwoods HD Green and Mossy Oak Break-Up—included with every unit so you can customize your stabilizer to match your bow.

Doinker D2 Plus models include:
TCF5P: Doinker D2 5-inch Fatty Carbon Hunter Plus. The bow hunter's dream come true, with one-inch Doinker D2 Plus and Chubby Hunter Plus weight. 9 oz.
SRP: $55.95

TH3P: Doinker D2 3-inch Chubby Hunter Plus. This tiny heavyweight can act as a stabilizer, back Doinker or both. 7.2 oz.
SRP: $42.95

TH4P: Doinker D2 4-inch Shorty Hunter Plus. Provides greater control and stealth, with less fatigue and noise. 6.5 oz.
SRP: $46.50

TH7P: Doinker D2 7-inch Hunter Plus. Based on Doinker's most famous vibration-eliminating stabilizer for the most powerful draws. 12.5 oz.
SRP: $52.95

TCF10P: Doinker D2 10-inch Fatty Carbon Elite Hunter Plus. This big bruiser features a one-inch carbon rod, one-inch Doinker D2, and internally isolated weight and venting to disperse the energy generated at the riser.
SRP: $135.95

TH7P

TH3P

TCF5P

TCF10P

TH4P

NEW Products: **Bow Accessories**

SA5

SA5L

TCF24

STABILIZERS

Doinker Armored Hunters

The renowned Doinker energy-absorbing powerhouse has gotten even better and lighter. Redesigned to incorporate special thermo-elastomeric compound, ITP, these tough performers soak up noise and shock waves like a sponge.

SPECIFICATIONS
SA5 Doinker: 5-inch Armored Hunter, Black, 7.3 oz.
SRP: **$33.95**
SA5L Doinker: 5-inch Armored Hunter Lite, Black, 6.4 oz.
SRP: **$30.95**

Doinker D2 Fatty Carbon Elite Target Stabilizers

These are the ultimate for shooters who demand unparalleled vibration-dampening on a solid, non-flexing platform. That's because they combine the latest, ITP-charged Doinker D2 technology, stack weights and an all-new ultra-rigid woven one-inch carbon rod. Custom carbon stabilizer lengths are available upon request.

SPECIFICATIONS
TCF24 Doinker D2: 24-inch Fatty Target. 14.5 oz.
SRP: **$205.20**
TCF28 Doinker D2: 28-inch Fatty Target. 15.5 oz.
SRP: **$205.50**
TCF32 Doinker D2: 32-inch Fatty Target. 16.5 oz.
SRP: **$205.20**

TAILORMAID SERVINGS

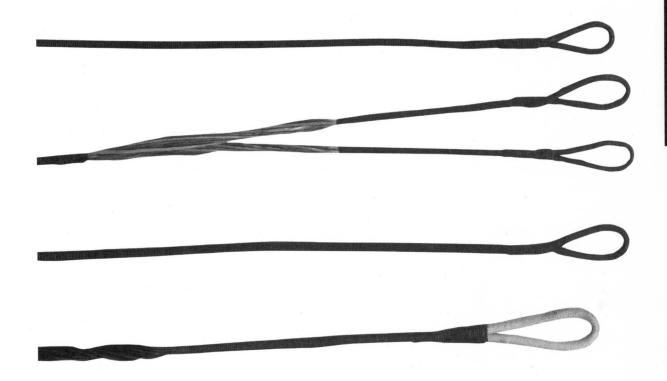

STRINGS AND STRING ACCESSORIES

TAILORMAID ARCHERY PRODUCTS

TailorMaid Servings

Ask any veteran archer where most string wear occurs, and it's not under the center serving. It's at the cams, especially on single cam bows that have abrupt cam angles.

String serving is designed to protect the high-strength miracle fibers used in today's compound bows from the abrasion that can weaken them. But that serving can't do its job if it doesn't stay in place or wasn't made long enough to wrap fully around the cam.

TailorMaid has been able to increase the tightness of its servings to keep them from separating, even where the string makes abrupt transitions off the heel of the cam. And TailorMaid extends the serving further than other manufacturers, so even the largest cams contact only served areas of the string. The string loops are also served where they anchor to the string posts within the cams. This can lengthen string life and it definitely makes it easier for the retailer or shooter to correctly install the string.

For 2004, the upgraded servings are available from TailorMaid for every style of compound bow, including Darton CPS strings, Hoyt Cam strings, cables, one cam bowstrings, two cam strings and Oneida strings.
SRP: . . . . **varies**

NEW PRODUCTS

STINGER FISH ARROW

OSPREY FISH POINT

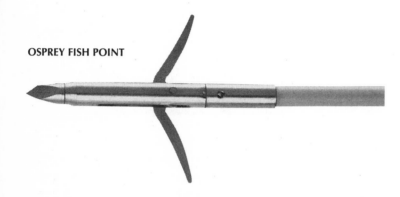

EASTMAN OUTFITTERS

Stinger Fish Arrow
Wrapped fiberglass construction offers the perfect spine for extreme durability.
Model 7033: Stinger Shaft with Osprey Point
SRP:

Model 7035: Stinger Fish Arrow without Point
SRP:

Model 7212: Stinger Wrapped Fish Shaft
SRP:

Osprey Fish Point
Model 7041
• Replaceable trocar tip
• Accepts any style of broadhead for going after tough game fish
SRP:

It's easier to identify a single flawed arrow if you number all your arrows. Use a waterproof marker to write the number on the vane. Now, if arrow 4 continually shoots low, while your other arrows are grouped, you know it's not poor form that is causing the problem, but the arrow. You can then set that arrow aside for later tuning.

H2 PLANTATION JACKET

X SCENT CAMO LONG-SLEEVE T

X SCENT CAMO MOCKNECK T

ARCTICSHIELD

X Scent Garments

X Scent apparel powered by X-STATIC, the Silver Fiber, is an advanced Scent Elimination System (SES) developed for the hunting industry to control body odor in any hunting environment. X Scent apparel uses pure silver to control body odor by binding silver ions to bacteria cells, denatured proteins and ammonia molecules. Ten-plus years of testing and research by several major universities, the medical industry, and the U.S. Military have proven the scent-control effectiveness of X-STATIC.

X Scent apparel is thermodynamic, meaning it will keep you cooler in the summer and warmer in the winter by conducting body heat away from and around your body. X Scent apparel can't fill up like activated-carbon garments, so it never requires reactivation or regeneration, plus it can never wash out like treated fabric. X Scent apparel is highly breathable, skin surface will feel refreshed. No special detergents are needed; wash in a mild scent-free detergent.

H2 Plantation Jacket

The X Scent Plantation is perfect for those bowhunters heading out to the woods on cool mornings when a light jacket equipped with scent control is needed. The Plantation jacket eliminates the source of odor by preventing bacteria growth and regulates body heat with X-STATIC silver-fiber technology. A generous-cut sizing, super quiet Tricot 280-gram outer shell with two slash pockets make this little item a dream-come-true for serious early-season bowhunters.

SPECIFICATIONS
Fabric: 95 percent cotton, 5 percent X-STATIC
Color: Mossy Oak New Break-Up
Sizes: M, L, XL, XXL, XXXL
SRP: $129.95

X Scent Camo Long-Sleeve T

The Long-Sleeve T-shirt has long been a best seller in the hunting industry. X Scent has taken this basic product and combined it with X-STATIC, making it a technologically advanced hunting product.

This high-tech long-sleeve T-shirt eliminates the source of odor by preventing bacteria growth, and regulates body temperature by conducting body heat away from the body with X-STAT-IC silver-fiber technology. Because reactivation or regeneration is never necessary, hunters can take full advantage of this advanced technology while stalking mule deer during early-season hunts out west or as a base layer when the temperature drops during deer season.

SPECIFICATIONS
Fabric: 95 percent cotton, 5 percent X-STATIC
Color: Mossy Oak New Break-Up
Sizes: M, L, XL, XXL, XXXL
SRP: $29.95

X Scent Camo Mockneck T

X Scent's Mockneck Long-Sleeve T-shirt is perfect for those sportsmen who like their neck covered for added warmth and scent control. This long-sleeve T-shirt eliminates the source of odor by preventing bacteria growth and regulates temperature by conducting body heat away from the body with X-STATIC silver-fiber technology.

SPECIFICATIONS
Fabric: 95 percent cotton, 5 percent X-STATIC
Color: Mossy Oak New Break-Up
Sizes: M, L, XL, XXL, XXXL
SRP: $29.95

NEW Products: **Bowhunting Clothing**

X SCENT CAMO
SHORT-SLEEVE T

X SCENT CAMO
LIGHT BIB

X SCENT CAMO
SIX-POCKET PANT

X SCENT CAMO
BUTTON-UP SHIRT

X SCENT FLEECE
PULLOVER

ARCTICSHIELD

X Scent Camo Light Bib
The X Scent Bib is perfect for early-season hunting while adding a layer of odor elimination. This bib is by far the most technologically advanced light weight bib in the hunting industry, considering its ability to eliminate the source of odor by preventing bacteria growth and regulating temperature by conducting body heat away from the body with X-STATIC silver-fiber technology.
SPECIFICATIONS
Fabric: 40/60 cotton-twill outer shell; 95 percent polyester, 5 percent X-STATIC inner liner
Color: Mossy New Oak Break-Up
Sizes: M, L, XL, XXL
SRP: $109.95

X Scent Camo Short-Sleeve T
Just about everyone wears a T-shirt, so why not have one that will control body odor and keep you cool when you head outdoors? This short-sleeve T eliminates the source of odor by preventing bacteria growth, and regulates temperature by conducting body heat away from the body with X-STATIC silver-fiber technology. Because reactivation or regeneration is never necessary you can take full advantage of this advanced technology while hunting in warm weather or as a base layer when the temperature drops late in the season.
SPECIFICATIONS
Fabric: 95 percent cotton, 5 percent X-STATIC
Color: New Mossy Oak Break-Up
Sizes: M, L, XL, XXL, XXXL
SRP: $27.95

X Scent Camo Button-Up Shirt
A camo button-up shirt has a loyal following among certain sportsmen. So if you're that hunter who like button-up shirts, or just want something other than a T-shirt, then here's the solution—X Scent's Camo Button-Up Shirt. Like all X Scent garments this eliminates the source of odor by preventing bacteria growth, and regulates temperature by conducting body heat away from the body with X-STATIC silver-fiber technology.
SPECIFICATIONS
Fabric: 60/40 cotton twill outer shell, 95 percent polyester, 5 percent X-STATIC inner liner
Color: Mossy Oak New Break-Up
Sizes: M, L, XL, XXL, XXXL
SRP: $79.95

X Scent Camo Six-Pocket Pant
The X Scent Six-Pocket Pant is perfect for early-season hunting or everyday use while adding a layer of odor elimination. This pant is by far the most technologically advanced in the hunting industry, considering its ability to eliminate the source of odor by preventing bacteria growth and regulating temperature by conducting heat away from the body with X-STATIC silver-fiber technology.
SPECIFICATIONS
Fabric: 60/40 cotton twill outer shell, 95 percent polyester, 5 percent X-STATIC inner liner
Color: Mossy Oak New Break-Up
Sizes: M, L, XL, XXL
SRP: $87.95

X Scent Fleece Pullover
X Scent's 3/4-Zip Pullover is something you won't want to put away when hunting season is over. This pullover is by far the most technologically advanced in the hunting industry, considering its ability to eliminate the source of odor by preventing bacteria growth and regulating temperature by conducting heat away from the body with X-STATIC silver-fiber technology.
SPECIFICATIONS
Fabric: 95 percent cotton, 5 percent X-STATIC
Color: Green
Sizes: M, L, XL, XXL, XXXL
SRP: $59.95

X SCENT BASE LAYER T

X SCENT BASE LAYER PULL-ON PANT

X SCENT HEAD COVER

X SCENT LIGHT GLOVES

X SCENT BOOT SOCKS

ARCTICSHIELD

X Scent Base Layer T

The Long-Sleeve T-shirt has long been a best seller in the hunting industry. X Scent has taken this basic product and combined it with X-STATIC, making it a technologically advanced hunting product.

This high-tech long-sleeve T-shirt eliminates the source of odor by preventing bacteria growth and regulates body temperature by conducting body heat away from the body with X-STATIC silver-fiber technology. Because reactivation or regeneration is never necessary, hunters can take full advantage of this advanced technology while remaining worry free on hunts.

SPECIFICATIONS
Fabric: 95 percent cotton, 5 percent X-STATIC
Color: Green
Sizes: M, L, XL, XXL, XXXL
SRP: **$29.95**

X Scent Base Layer Pull-On Pant

The basic base layer hunting garment has now been made into an effective hunting garment. X Scent's Base Layer Pull-On Pant eliminates the source of odor by preventing bacteria growth and regulates body temperature by conducting body heat away from the body with X-STATIC silver-fiber technology.

SPECIFICATIONS
Fabric: 95 percent polyester, 5 percent X-STATIC
Color: Green
Sizes: M 32-34, L 36-38, XL 40-42, XXL 44-46
SRP: **$29.95**

X Scent Boot Socks

Foot odor can be difficult to control on a personal level and is critical from a hunting perspective. X Scent has the only real answer to foot odor while hunting. These socks are by far the most technologically advanced in the hunting industry, considering their ability to eliminate the source of odor by preventing bacteria growth and regulating temperature by conducting heat away from the body with X-STATIC silver-fiber technology.

X Scent Boot Socks have been proven effective by the U.S. Military and are used by U.S. soldiers all over the world to protect their feet from harmful bacteria for days under all conditions and environments.

SPECIFICATIONS
Fabric: 95 percent cotton, 5 percent X-STATIC
Colors: Green, Gray, and Oatmeal
Styles: 13-inch crew and 18-inch calf
Sizes (men's): M 5-9½, L 10–12, XL 12½-14
SRP: **$14.99**

X Scent Head Cover

X Scent's Head Cover is by far the most technologically advanced in the hunting industry, considering its ability to eliminate the source of odor by preventing bacteria growth and regulating body temperature by conducting heat away from the body with X-STATIC silver-fiber technology.

SPECIFICATIONS
Fabric: 95 percent cotton, 5 percent X-STATIC
Color: Green
SRP: **$19.95**

X Scent Light Gloves

X Scent Lightweight Knit Gloves provide a complete scent-control system for early season hunters who want to eliminate odor on their hands. They eliminate the source of odor by preventing bacteria growth and regulating temperature by conducting heat away from the hand with X-STATIC silver-fiber technology.

SPECIFICATIONS
Color: Green
Sizes: M/L, L/XL
SRP: **$19.95**

NEW Products: **Broadheads and Arrow Points**

ARROWDYNAMIC GOBBLER GUILLOTINE

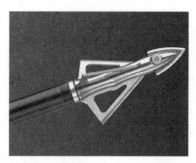

BARRIE SUPREME XP

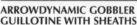

ARROWDYNAMIC GOBBLER GUILLOTINE WITH SHEATHS

BARRIE TURBO

ARROWDYNAMIC SOLUTIONS

Gobbler Guillotine

Arrowdynamic Solutions introduces the first razor-sharp, four-bladed broadhead invented solely for the purpose of hunting big game birds. The Gobbler Guillotine line of broadheads features the world's largest cutting width ever in a fixed-bladed design with lethal cutting widths up to four inches by four inches.

Point of aim for birds is now the much larger and more prominent head/neck region, the same area shotgun hunters aim for. The wide cutting width and razor-sharp blades provide the most accurate, lethal and humane manner of killing a bird ever invented for the bow hunter. The Gobbler Guillotine broadheads are engineered to work by understanding and incorporating the aerodynamics that others have designed around.

The aerodynamic sheaths, via their round shapes, eliminate lift generated by the flat blade surfaces as they fly thru the air from bow to bird. Thus they eliminate the problems ("steering effect" or "broadhead planing") that lead to typical fixed bladed broad-

heads having a different point of impact than your target tips. Simply sight in with the respective target tip weight, screw on the Gobbler Guillotine and go hunt. The blades cut through the plastic sheaths like a hot knife thru butter and continue on to lop the head/neck off the bird and kill it instantly, ethically and humanely. The Gobbler Guillotine:

- Increases the "kill zone" target area
- Provides for greater margin of error in shot placement
- Virtually eliminates shaft loss
- Saves meat
- Decreases tracking time, fly-offs and bird loss

Available in two sizes: 125 grain 4" x 4" and 100 grain 2.5" X 2.5" fixed bladed designs
SRP: . . . $38.50 per package of three

BARRIE ARCHERY

Supreme XP™

The Supreme XP™ from Barrie Archery is a super tough, 100-grain, three-blade broadhead that is designed with a razor sharp, stainless steel blade insert tip that slices on impact. The

replaceable tip blade is held in place by a stainless steel point that won't rust. It is followed by three .030" thick stainless steel main blades that are locked securely in an aircraft quality aluminum body by the patented Self-Centering collar system. It sports an aggressive 1⅛" cutting diameter. All blades are easily replaced making this another user-friendly broadhead that will penetrate deep.
SRP: . . . . $19.99 per three pack

Turbo

The 3 blade, 100-grain Turbo™ incorporates a Bi-Directional™ Blade Design that allows the hunter to angle the offset blades either right or left wing to match arrow fletching. This offset blade design provides a compliment to the arrow fletching for increased rotational stability improving accuracy.

The Turbo features a one-piece, stainless steel body with a Tri-Cut Tip that won't rust. It sports an aggressive 1⅛" cutting diameter with thick .030" stainless steel vented blades. The blades are held tight in part by 3 set screws. Each Turbo comes pre-assembled.
SRP: . . . . $21.99 per three pack

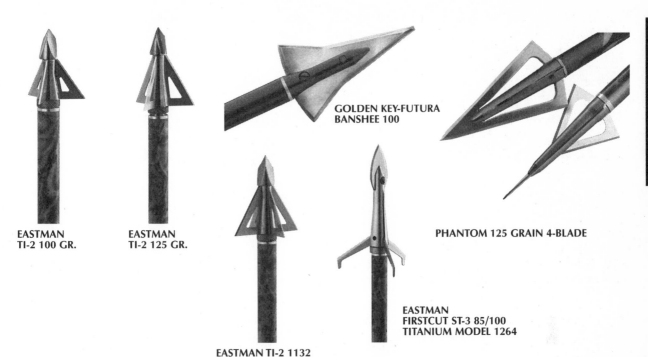

EASTMAN
TI-2 100 GR.

EASTMAN
TI-2 125 GR.

GOLDEN KEY-FUTURA
BANSHEE 100

PHANTOM 125 GRAIN 4-BLADE

EASTMAN
FIRSTCUT ST-3 85/100
TITANIUM MODEL 1264

EASTMAN TI-2 1132

NEW PRODUCTS

EASTMAN OUTFITTERS

Ti-2 Extreme Titanium Broadheads
Titanium Coated Ferrule:
- One piece for extra strength and penetration
- More durable than standard steel
- Resists bending
- 1⅛" Cutting Diameter
- ¹⁷/₁₀₀" Razor sharp stainless steel blades

SPECIFICATIONS
Model: 1123
Weight: 100 gr.
Cutting Diameter: 1"
Blade Thickness: ¹⁷/₁₀₀"
Blade Style: Solid 3-Blade
SRP:

Model: 1124
Weight: 125 gr.
Cutting Diameter: 1⅛"
Blade Thickness: ¹⁷/₁₀₀"
Blade Style: Solid 3-Blade
SRP:

Model: 1132
Weight: 125 gr.
Cutting Diameter: 1⅛"
Blade Thickness: ¹⁷/₁₀₀"
Blade Style: Solid 4-Blade
SRP:

FirstCut™ ST-3 85/100 Titanium
Cut-on contact 3-blade expandable broadhead for extreme penetration.
SPECIFICATIONS
Model: 1264
Weight: 85/100 gr.
Cutting Diameter: 1⅓"
Blade Thickness: ³¹/₁₀₀₀"
Blade Style: 3-Blade Mechanical
SRP

GOLDEN KEY-FUTURA

Banshee 100
The Bansee 100 is a super-tough, highly efficient, 100 grain, cut-on-impact head that features a resharpen-able/replaceable .048" thick stainless steel blade. The new design of the head's tapered point greatly increases initial penetration while the swept wing, rear section widens out to give a large wound channel for quick game recovery. This new blade shape elimi-nates windplaning and the non-vented design is ultra quiet while being unbe-lievable strong. The slim taper of the leading edge uses virtually 'zero' foot pounds of the coveted kinetic energy to start penetration making the Bansee the perfect choice for lower draw weight bows. The Banshee 100 comes

pre-sharpened in a ready to hunt three pack.
SRP: . . . . **$21.99 per three pack**

PHANTOM BROADHEADS
Phantom is pleased to introduce new broadheads to its popular line. The new 100-grain 4-blade and 125 grain 4-blade broadheads are designed for those who want a heavier broadhead for increased kinetic energy. The Phantom's leading blade design starts working the instant it makes contact, and the bleeder blade follows with a secondary cut, making blood trails short and to the point. The primary blades on these new broadheads can be resharpened for years of depend-able service.

For bowhunters seeking speed and the flatter trajectory that comes from a faster, lighter arrow, Phantom offers the 105-grain 2-blade (125 grain with-out the secondary blade) and an 80 grain 2-blade (100 grain without the secondary blade). Both the 2-blade and the 4-blade Phantom broadheads deliver increased penetration, elimina-tion of turbulence and decreased drag for maximum flight control.
SRP: **$19.99**

NEW Products: **Bows**

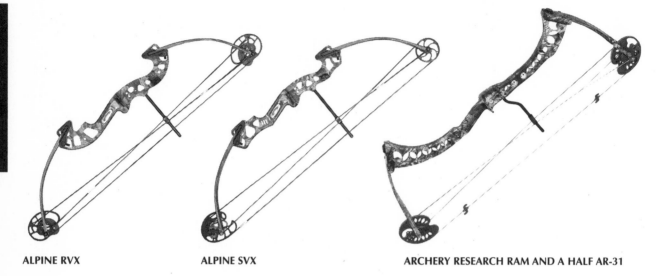

ALPINE RVX   **ALPINE SVX**   **ARCHERY RESEARCH RAM AND A HALF AR-31**

ALPINE ARCHERY

RVX

The RVX from Alpine Archery is short, light and performs with the best, most expensive bows made today only with a lighter price tag. It features a light, reflexed riser design with cutting edge limb pockets and a choice in either the hot Twin Force Cam or the industry standard, the patented Fast Trac One Cam. Both feature increased speed, up to 15 fps, draw length adjustability without the need of a bow press and both have the patented Fast Trac Ball Bearing Technology. The limbs are Bi-Flex composite with Inter-Loc Limb Mounting System and a torque free two-piece wood panel grip.

SPECIFICATIONS

Finish: Realtree Hardwoods Green HD
Axle-to-Axle Length: 35"
Let-Off: 65 or 80%
Brace Height: 6.5"
Draw Weights: 50, 60 and 70 lbs.
Length: 26" through 30"
Weight: 3.8 lbs.
Minimum advertised price: $459

SVX

The SVX from Alpine Archery is a great looking bow that comes with Bi-Flex composite limbs secured in Alpine's cutting edge VX Series Limb Pockets and the patented Fast Trac Single Cam Series with an increase in arrow speed of up to 15 fps. This remarkable Cam Series has a rotating draw length element that allows for an amazing five inches of adjustment without the need of a bow press. The SVX also comes with a comfortable two-piece grip for torque free shooting and Alpine's legendary riser geometrics for outstanding balance, accuracy and shooting characteristics.

SPECIFICATIONS

Finish: Realtree Hardwoods Green HD
Axle-to-Axle Length: 35"
Let-Off: 65 and 80%
Brace Height: 7.5"
Draw Weights: 50, 60 and 70 lbs.
Length: 27" through 31"
Weight: 3.4 lbs.
Minimum advertised price: $439

ARCHERY RESEARCH

RAM And A Half™ Cam Bows

Archery Research is proud to introduce the new RAM and a Half™ Cam system, available on the AR-31, AR-34 and AR-37 riser platforms. The RAM and a Half™ Cam system is the first "straightline" style hybrid cam available on the market. Pushing the technological envelope even further, the RAM and a Half™ Cam system offers draw length adjustment using modules that have been optimized for each individual size, providing the ultimate performance at every draw length.

The RAM and a Half™ Cam is the smoothest hybrid cam available. With a synchronized cam at each end of the bow, the RAM and a Half™ provides uncompromised performance and incredibly straight nock travel throughout the entire range of draw-lengths. While sharing similar looks and the smooth feel of the RAM Cam, the RAM and a Half™ incorporates numerous features sought by discerning archers. Precision machined components and sealed ball bearings provide hassle-free performance. Draw length adjustments are managed with carefully designed modules providing up to five inches of draw length adjustment. Multiple string post attachments allow an additional ±³/₈" of draw length adjustment for a total range of 26" to 30 ³/₄". Clearly marked stop adjustments are also incorporated for both high and low let-off options.

SPECIFICATIONS

AR-31 RAM and a Half™
Speed: 300 fps
Finish: Mossy Oak BreakUp Camo Only
Axle-to-Axle Length: 31"
Let-Off: 70% effective, 65% actual
Brace Height: 8-¹/₂"
Draw Weights: 26-30" 60# and 70# (sold as 29" only)
Mass Weight: 3.7 lbs.
SRP: $499

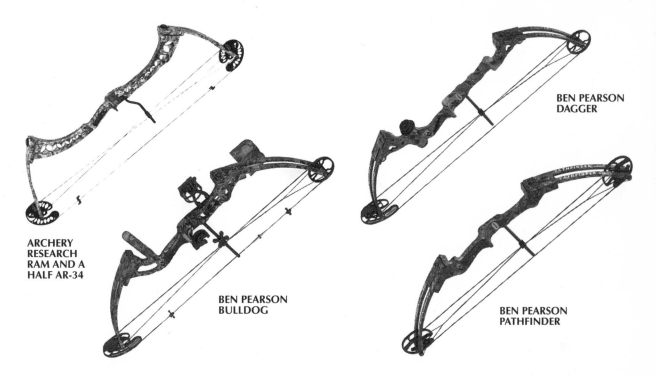

ARCHERY RESEARCH RAM AND A HALF AR-34

BEN PEARSON BULLDOG

BEN PEARSON DAGGER

BEN PEARSON PATHFINDER

ARCHERY RESEARCH

AR-34 RAM and a Half™
Speed: 309 fps
Finish: Mossy Oak BreakUp or Blade Comp
Axle-to-Axle Length: 34"
Let-Off: 70% effective, 65% actual
Brace Height: 8"
Camo Draw Weights: 26-30" 60# and 70# (sold as 29" only)
Blade Target Blade Competition Draw Weights: 26-30" 50# and 60# (sold as 29" only)
Mass Weight: 3.8 lbs
SRP: $499

AR-37 RAM and a Half™
Speed: 312 fps
Finish: Mossy Oak BreakUp or Blade Comp
Axle-to-Axle Length: 37"
Let-Off: 70% effective, 65% actual
Brace Height: 7"
Camo Draw Weights: 26-30" 60# and 70# (sold as 29" only)
Blade Target Blade Competition Draw Weights: 26-30" 50# and 60# (sold as 29" only)
Mass Weight: 3.8 lbs.
SRP: $599

BEN PEARSON ARCHERY

Bulldog
If you are looking for a compact speed bow that tunes easy and shoots smooth, look no farther than the new Pearson Bulldog. Short, fast and rugged, this powerhouse is ideal for a deer camp or stalking icy creeks for Kodiak bears.
SPECIFICATIONS
Speed OTB: 310 fps
Let-off: 75 %
Draw Lengths: 25–30"
Draw Weights: 50, 60 or 70 lbs.
Axle to Axle: 31½"
Brace Height: 7¾"
Cam: KinetiCam
String: 85"
Cable: 35"
SRP: $459

Dagger
The all-new Dagger features a "frequency–rigged" riser that is precision sculpted from a solid billet of aluminum. This new riser design focuses vibration along an angular crest to promote vibration-free shooting. The Dagger's lightweight Quadra-Flex Limbs are anchored in lockable, pivoting limb pockets which, coupled with the new riser, promote rock-solid fit

for consistent shooting.
SPECIFICATIONS
Speed OTB: 312 fps
Let-off: 75%
Draw Lengths: 25–30"
Draw Weights: 50, 60 or 70 lbs.
Axle to Axle: 32⅜"
Brace Height: 7½"
Cam: KinetiCam
String: 86½"
Cable: 35½"
SRP: $589.99

Pathfinder
A wide draw length range allows you to fit this bow to shooters of an age. The Pathfinder is available in two styles, a twin-cam system and a single cam system. Short draw shooters can develop their technique on the range and then graduate to deer and small game with the same bow.
SPECIFICATIONS
Draw Length: 18–28"
Draw Weight: 20, 30, 40, 50 or 60 lbs.
Axle to Axle: 30¼"
Brace Height: 5¾"
Cam: Pathfinder Twin Cam with Rotatable modules.
VM1 jr Single Cam with 5 separate modules.
SRP: $295

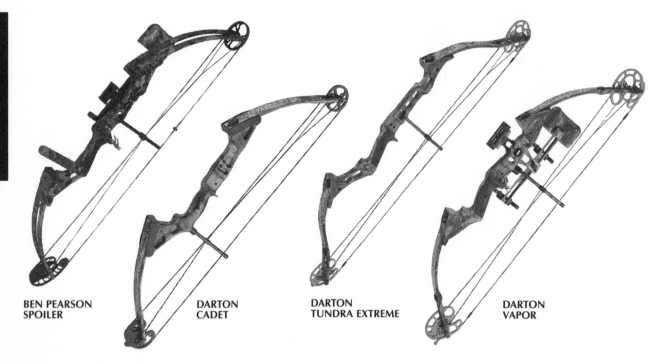

BEN PEARSON
SPOILER   DARTON
                 CADET   DARTON
                                TUNDRA EXTREME   DARTON
                                                        VAPOR

BEN PEARSON ARCHERY

Spoiler

For 2004, history repeats itself. Strength, Performance and Tradition are found in the Spoiler. Fast, lightweight and powerful, the Spoiler is a handful of bowhunting success just waiting to happen.

SPECIFICATIONS
Speed OTB: 305 fps
Let-off: 75%
Draw Lengths: 24–31"
Draw Weights: 50, 60 or 70 lbs.
Axle to Axle: 33"
Brace Height: 7⁷/₈"
Cam: Z 4
String: 86¹/₄"
Cable: 36³/₄"
SRP:..................$389

DARTON

Cadet™

The all new Cadet was designed specifically to fit the young archer who is getting into the sport for the very first time. This bow will ensure they start out right, shoot their best from the start and grow with them for a great archery experience.

The Cadet is a light, 2.8-lb. shooter with a short 32³/₄" axle-to-axle length with an easy to draw peak weight of only 35 lbs (45 lbs. is optional) with 35% let-off. It is also adjustable down to 15 lbs enabling even the smallest person to comfortably shoot.

Always ahead of the innovation curve, DARTON technology has eliminated the need for specific draw length adjustments, offering a smooth, useable draw length valley of 19" - 26" so the Cadet will easily fit a wider range of archers. Other high-quality features include optional higher let-off modules and an adjustable, positive draw stop to ensure the safe use of short arrows. The Cadet is available in Realtree Hardwoods Green HD® or Black Riser with Camo Limbs.
SRP:..................$229

Tundra™ Extreme

The all new Tundra shares many of the same quality features as the Maverick Recurve, only with a longer deflexed machined riser that includes provisions for our optional VSS integral dampening system. This creates a smooth shooting, accurate and forgiving bow for the 27"- 32 _", longer draw archer. The comfortable 7 _" brace height and efficient cam/limb design combine to make this model one sweet shooting, versatile bow for FITA, 3D or bowhunting. Available in Competition Green or Realtree Hardwoods Green HD®.
SRP:.................$679.99

Vapor

Darton has done it again with their introduction of the new, hot shooting Single Cam steamer, the Vapor. This bow features a great looking, lightweight machined riser with Darton's popular C/P/S Force 9 Hybrid Cam System to combine head snapping speed, easy holding let-off and the simplest set up available for pinpoint tuning. The Vapor also has an innovative ONE adjustable draw length module that maintains good performance from 26-30" in half inch increments.

The VAPOR is 35¹/₈" axle-to-axle, 75% let-off, draw lengths of 26" to 30", 50, 60 and 70 lbs. peak weights and a comfortable 7" brace height. Available alone or as a complete package with Fiber Optic Sight, Camo Bow Quiver and Launcher Rest in Realtree Hardwoods Green HD®.
SRP:.................$429.99

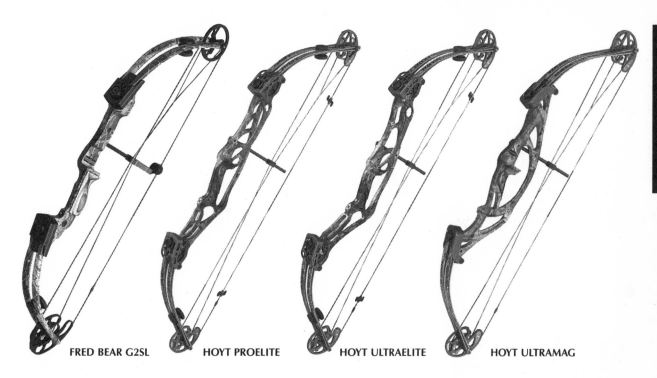

FRED BEAR G2SL   HOYT PROELITE   HOYT ULTRAELITE   HOYT ULTRAMAG

FRED BEAR
G2SL

At 3 lbs, 300 fps IBO speed and 30"
axle-to-axle, the G2SL is the shortest,
lightest and quietest Buckmasters ever
built by this company. Consider these
exceptional features:

- Sims Stealth Limb Savers uses
  Dacay Time Modification technology
  and NAVCOM material providing
  optimal noise and vibration
  reduction.
- Shock Stop system cancels noise
  and vibration by as much as 40%.
- High-tech, precision-machined
  aluminum titanium riser guarantees
  strength and superior accuracy.
- Revolutionary, patented CarbonAir
  Quad limbs, the quietest, fastest and
  most durable limbs available.
- Limb damping system featuring
  high-tech, vibration-eliminating
  polymer pocket insert.
- Buckmasters Modular Perimeter
  OneCam for 300 fps IBO speeds,
  75% let-off.
- Smooth, friction-free ball bearing
  idler wheel.

SPECIFICATIONS

Draw length: 27"-29" (optional
modules allow for draw length
adjustment of 24" to 31")
Draw weight: 50-60 lbs. and 60-70 lbs.

Let-Off: 75%
(optional modules 65% let-off)
Brace height: 7¹/₂"
Axle to axle: 30"
Mass weight: 3 lbs.
Limbs: Compression molded quad
straight
Riser: machined 6061-T6 Aluminum
Cam: Modular Perimeter OneCam
String: 84.25" TechTwist
Grip: Checkered laminate wood
Camo: Custom Realtree Hardwoods
Bow Speed: IBO fps 300; AMO fps 228
SRP:.....................$420

HOYT

ProElite

Bow Specifications: ProElite
AMO Draw Length: 26- to 32-inch.
Draw Weights: 30#, 40# and 80#
Bow Speed: IBO fps = 296
Axle-to-Axle: 38 inches
SRP:.....................$860
UltraElite

The Elite Series Shoot-Thru bows feature the innovative TEC Shoot-Thru
design that increases the lateral stiffness and balance of the riser while
achieving the highest level of consistency and accuracy. They also feature
Hoyt's new Triax Pocket Stabilization

System for unmatched pocket toler-
ances. The Elite Series models include
the UltraElite, patterned after the ever-
popular UltraTec and the ProElite,
which incorporates the deflex geome-
try of the traditional ProTec.
Bow Specifications: UltraElite
AMO Draw Length: 25-to 31-inch
Draw Weights: 30#, 40# and 80#
Bow Speed: IBO fps = 310
Axle-to-Axle: 37 inches
SRP:.....................$860

UltraMag

The UltraMag™. Features new 3D
Ribbing Technology engineered into
the riser to allow for greater strength
and stiffness while reducing the over-
all mass weight of the bow. The grip
has been reduced to minimize hand
torque and create greater accuracy.
Hoyt's revolutionary Cam & ¹/₂
Performance System and high per-
formance XT 2000 5-layer laminated
limb come standard on the new
UltraMag.
Bow Specifications: UltraMag
AMO Draw Length: 24- to 30-inch
Draw Weights: 30#, 40# and 80#
Bow Speed: IBO fps = 305
Axle-to-Axle: 36 inches
SRP:.....................$459

UltraTec

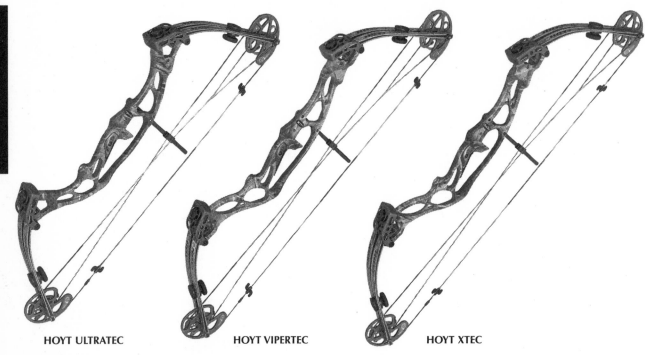

HOYT ULTRATEC   **HOYT VIPERTEC**   **HOYT XTEC**

The UltraTec™ incorporates the new Triax Pocket Stabilization System machined into the riser. This provides for an increase in strength and stability to the pocket area and overall bow design resulting in even greater accuracy and consistency. Add the Cam & ½ Performance System and you've got a world-class bow archers and bow-hunters. This configuration is standard for UltraTec XT2000 Cam & ½. UltraTec also available in Spiral Cam & ½ and XT3000 limb.

BOW SPECIFICATIONS: ULTRATEC
AMO Draw Length: 25- to 31-inch
Draw Weights: 30#, 40# and 80#
Bow Speed: IBO fps = 308
Axle-to-Axle: 37 inches
SRP: XT2000 . . . . $759
SRP: XT3000 . . . . $829

ViperTec
The new 32-inch ViperTec's longer riser and shorter limb design allows for superior balance, an increased sight window, and substantially reduced recoil for a smooth and quiet shot. The contoured lines machined throughout the aluminum riser also make this bow look as good as it shoots.

BOW SPECIFICATIONS: VIPERTEC
AMO Draw Length: 24- to 30-inch
Draw Weights: 30#, 40# and 80#

Bow Speed: IBO fps = 300
Axle-to-Axle: 32 inches
SRP: $700

XTEC
The XTEC is powered by Hoyt's revolutionary Cam & ½ Performance System making for an incredibly fast, forgiving and quiet bow. The TEC riser design now incorporates the new Triax Pocket Stabilization System, which increases the breadth of contact between the dowel and the riser providing the strongest and most stable pocket and riser design on the market.

BOW SPECIFICATIONS:
AMO Draw Length: 24- to 30-inch
Draw Weights: 30#, 40# and 80#
Bow Speed: NA
Axle-to-Axle: 35½ inches
SRP: $659

JENNINGS ARCHERY

CK Bows
Jennings Archery introduces a new age of technology with the CK bows with Carbon Kinetics. Every CK bow has Carbon Kinetic energy chambers engineered into the bow limbs. The CK bows feature these patented com-

pression-molded limbs that are short, powerful and resistant to torque. The Carbon Kinetic Chamber stores greater energy with a patented carbon fiber design, producing better performance, superior durability and overall increased kinetic energy to the core of the bow. The patent pending Carbon Kinetic Chamber limbs also balance the stress, ensuring continuous cross-sectional stability.

The CK limbs are anchored in polyurethane, taper lock precision-machined aluminum limb cups to help prevent any movement or noise, further enhancing performance.

The carbon fiber limb design, seen in the ellipse on each bow limb, incorporates multiple layers of carbon fiber for enduring strength. This carbon fiber design once found only in high-performance jets and race cars now is the signature feature for the Jennings CK bows.

The CK lineup includes:

CK 4.0. A faster, silent and more accurate bow with a high 70% let-off. The new bow is simply a technically superior arrow-launching platform. This 40-inch bow delivers a clean, powerful release with total impact and increased speed efficiency. Speed is 300 fps IBO.

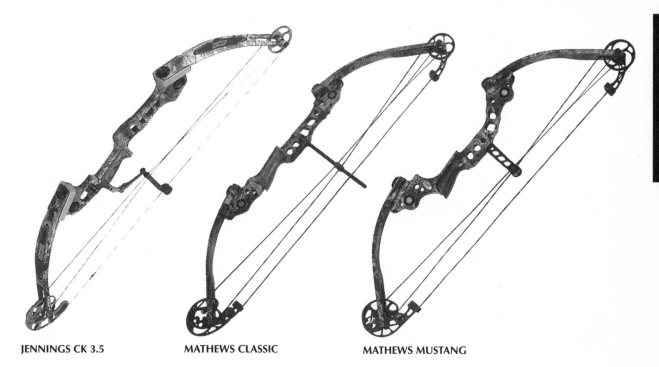

JENNINGS CK 3.5 **MATHEWS CLASSIC** **MATHEWS MUSTANG**

CK 3.5. A short, light and powerful bow designed to maximize performance characteristics found in World Class hunting equipment. The 35-inch bow, with unmatched overall performance, is ideal for maneuverability and consistent accuracy. Speed is 308 fps IBO.

CK 3.3. A compact, efficient bow perfect for deep in the woods performance hunting. This 34-inch bow is shorter and more lightweight than the 35-inch model, yet it still consistently delivers a powerful, accurate release. Speed is 302 fps IBO.

Additional CK bow features include:
• Balanced TechTwist string
• Factory-installed speed buttons
• Machined Perimeter Weighted Modular OneCam
• Available in Custom Realtree Hardwoods camo
• Limited Lifetime Warranty
SRP:

MATHEWS

Classic
The new Mathews Classic is fast, compact and, at 3.6 lbs., it's as light as a feather. And, it features some of Mathews latest technology, such as the all-new InLine Grip, which is ergonomically superior and has a wood inlay that shows the center of the grip to establish centershot; and two vibration-quelling technologies—Harmonic Damping and String Suppressors™ for smooth, quiet shooting. The Harmonic Damping System™ places weights at either end of the riser that float in elastic to eat up riser vibration. String Suppressors are tiny "fingers" that reach out and actually touch the bowstring so, upon release, vibration is further reduced.

Like all Mathews bows, the Classic comes equipped with a Zebra® ZS Twist™ bowstring. By twisting the strands in two bundles in the opposite direction and then counter-twisting the two bundles, peep rotation is virtually eliminated.

The Mathews Classic measures 36" axle-to-axle, features the new REAL-TREE® Hardwoods HD camo and is available in both a 65% and 80% let-off. For information on the Classic and the full line-up of Mathews bows, log on to www.mathewsinc.com.
SRP:.....................$589

Mustang™
Now shooters with short draw lengths (19" to 26") can shoot a Mathews™. The new Mathews Mustang™ may be short when it comes to draw length, but it's not short on Mathews™ innovation.

Available with draw lengths from 19" to 26" (including 24½" and 25½"), and peak draw weights from 20 lbs. to 50 lbs., the new Single Cam Mustang™ features Harmonic Dampers, String Suppressors™, a Roller Guard and a StraightLine perimeter-weighted cam with ball bearings, the same technology you'll find on other Mathews™ bows.

The Mustang™ is (approx.) 32" axle to axle and weighs (approx.) 3¼ lbs. Let-off is 70% which is Pope & Young legal.

Also, Mustang™ owners will be able to update draw length and draw weights through an exchange program at authentic Mathews™ dealers.
SRP:.....................$549

NEW for 2005: **Bows**

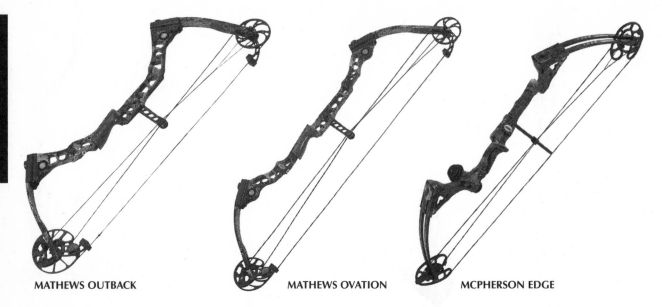

MATHEWS OUTBACK   **MATHEWS OVATION**   **MCPHERSON EDGE**

Outback™

Whether you hunt behind the barn, out back behind the cabin or back in the far reaches of the mountains, plains or tundra, the new Mathews OUTBACK™ has shorter, more parallel limbs that make the OUTBACK extremely quiet and maneuverable. When combined with other recoil suppressing features like Perimeter Weighted Technology™, the OUTBACK is one remarkably quiet bow.

The OUTBACK is also shorter than any bow Mathews offers. Another completely new introduction on the OUTBACK is the new ergonomically superior InLine grip with a defined centerline. It features a wood inlay that indicates the center of the grip to more easily establish your centershot.

The 80% let-off OUTBACK (65% also available) features the HP (High Performance) Cam, the least complex, most advanced cam ever available. The V-LOCK™ Zero Tolerance Limb Cup System features a perfectly machined V-shaped "limb pocket" that guides the V-shaped limb into place for a snug, zero-tolerance fit. The "fingers" of the OUTBACK's String Suppressors™ reach out and touch the bowstring so, upon release, string vibration is reduced. Vibration is even further reduced by the Harmonic Damping System™, which places weights on either end of the riser.

The OUTBACK features the new

REALTREE® Hardwoods camo. The bow comes in draw lengths from 26"–30v (including half sizes) and draw weights of 40–70 lbs.
SRP:. **$729**

Ovation

Loaded with new innovations, the Mathews Ovation is the ultimate bow for when a tournament is on the line.

The new Ovation comes fully loaded with Mathews innovations that will help put more competitors on more podiums. It features the new ergonomically superior InLine Grip, with a wood inlay that shows the center of the grip in order to better establish centershot. The Ovation features a Ball-Bearing Idler Wheel and the StraightLine HP (High Performance) Cam for the least complex and smoothest shooting performance of any cam ever designed.

Also incorporated in the new Ovation is the V-LOCK™ Zero Tolerance Limb Cup System, featuring a perfectly machined V-shaped "limb pocket" that guides the V-shaped limb into place for a snug, zero-tolerance fit.

Vibration is significantly reduced by both the Harmonic Damping System™, which places weights on either end of the riser that float in elastic, and String Suppressors™ with "fingers" that reach out and touch the bowstring to further reduce vibration upon release.

The Ovation measures 40" axle-to-axle, features the new REALTREE® Hardwoods HD camo, and is available with both a 65% and 80% let-off.
SRP:. **$749**

MCPHERSON ARCHERY

EDGE

Fast, silent and deadly. The McPherson Edge riser is precision sculpted from a solid billet of aluminum. This new riser's frequency-ridge design effectively manages the path of vibration. Equipped with new lockable pivoting limb pockets and new Magneto Cam System, the Edge will prove itself as a stable and effective shooting platform.

SPECIFICATIONS
Speed: 310 fps
Let-off: 75 %
Draw Lengths: 25–30"
 Draw Weights: 50, 60 or 70 lbs.
Axle to Axle: 34"
Brace Height: 7⅝"
Cam: Magneto
String: 56"
Buss Cable: 35¼"
Control Cable: 37"
SRP: **$600-699**

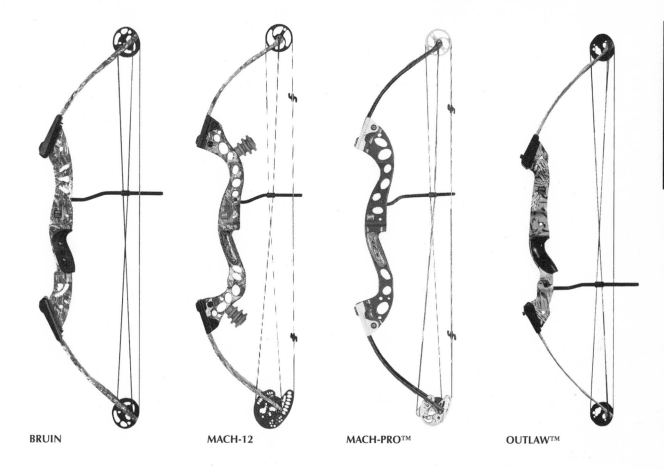

BRUIN   MACH-12   MACH-PRO™   OUTLAW™

PSE

Bruin™ Synergy 8™
The Bruin™ Synergy 8 features PSE's Integrated Cam-Lock™ cable guard and comes with a fully machined aluminum riser (in the same price class the competition settles for a cast riser). The Bruin has three cam options for any shooting style

Bruin
BOW SPECIFICATIONS:
AMO Draw Length:
Draw Weights: Let-Off: 65% actual 70% effective
Bow Speed: I.B.O. Speed: 298 fps
Axle-to-Axle: 36 inches
SRP:

Bruin™ Lightning 3™
BOW SPECIFICATIONS:
One Cam
AMO Draw Length:
Draw Weights: Let-Off: 80% 65% adjustable

Bow Speed: I.B.O. Speed: 290 fps
Axle-to-Axle: 36 inches
SRP:

Bruin™ Rimfire™
BOW SPECIFICATIONS:
AMO Draw Length:
Draw Weights: Let-Off: 65% actual 70% effective
Bow Speed: I.B.O. Speed: 295 fps
Axle-to-Axle: 35 inches
SRP:

Mach-12
When Pete Shepley designed the original Mach-One™ bow in 1982, his purpose was to blow away the archery world with speed, accuracy and unmatched quality in craftsmanship. The 2004 Mach 12™ carries on Pete's tradition with some of the most advanced features and technology ever produced.
BOW SPECIFICATIONS
AMO Draw Length:
Draw Weights: Let-off: 80% (65% adj.)

Bow Speed: I.B.O. Speed: 318 fps
Axle-to-Axle: 38 inches
SRP:

Mach-Pro™ Rimfire Cam™
BOW SPECIFICATIONS:
AMO Draw Length:
Draw Weights: Let-Off: 65% actual / 70% effectiv
Bow Speed: I.B.O. Speed: 300 fps
Axle-to-Axle: 37 ½ inches
SRP:

Outlaw™ Synergy-4™
The Outlaw features and incredible 5 ½ inches of draw-length adjustment and machined aluminum components The Perfect bow to get young people involved in archery!
SPECIFICATIONS:
AMO Draw Length:
Draw Weights: Let-Off: 65%
Bow Speed: I.B.O. Speed: 210 fps
Axle-to-Axle: 32½ inches
SRP:

NEW Products: **Bows**

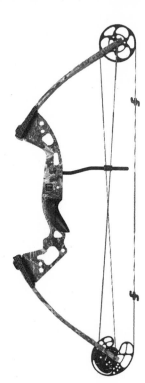

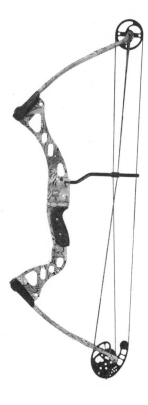

SCORPION NRG ™   **TRITON NRG™ ONE-CAM**   **TYPHOON™ LIGHTNING 3™**   **KINGFISHER RECURVE BOW**

Scorpion NRG ™

The Skorpion features PSE's Phase III™ Grip System and comes with removable Vibracheck® HD Harmonic Disruptors™. Offered in Mossy Oak® Obsession™ Camo. 70# offered in MossyOak® Obsession™ only.

BOW SPECIFICATIONS
AMO Draw Length:
Draw Weights: Let-Off: 80% / 65% adjustable
Bow Speed: I.B.O. Speed: 305 fps
Axle-to-Axle: 33 inches
SRP:

Triton NRG™ One-Cam

The Venom offers high-end features at an affordable price featuring parallel limb design and a torque-reducing grip. String leeches are included.

BOW SPECIFICATIONS
AMO Draw Length: able
Draw Weights: Let-Off: 80% / 65% adjust
Bow Speed: I.B.O. Speed: 300 fps
Axle-to-Axle: 32 inches
SRP:

Typhoon™ Lightning 3™ One-Cam

PSE has harnessed one of nature's most powerful forces in the all-new Typhoon™. No other bow offers so many high-end features at such a low-end price. 70# offered in MossyOak® Forest Floor™ only

BOW SPECIFICATIONS
AMO Draw Length:
Draw Weights: Let-Off: 80% / 65% Adjustable
Bow Speed: I.B.O. Speed: 298 fps
Axle-to-Axle: 33 inches
SRP:

Venom NRG™ One-Cam

The Venom features sleek and lightweight risers and comes with PSE's patented Limb Isolation System and Cam-Lock™ cable guard. The Venom is equipped with the new NRG Cam™. Offered in Mossy Oak® Obsession™ Camo. 70# offered in MossyOak® Obsession™ only

BOW SPECIFICATIONS
AMO Draw Length:

Draw Weights: Let-Off: 80% / 65% adjustable
Bow Speed: I.B.O. Speed: 305 fps
Axle-to-Axle: 35 inches
SRP:

KINGFISHER RECURVE BOWS

PSE's new bowfishing bow is finished in Mossy Oak™ Forest Floor Camo Finish.
Draw Weight: 40#, 45# and 50#
Length: 60-inches
SRP: $139.99

EXCALIBUR
EXOMAX

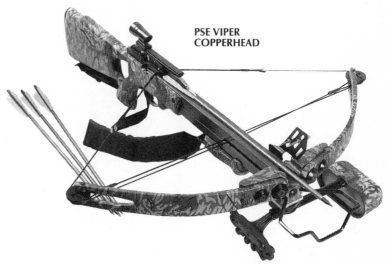

PSE VIPER
COPPERHEAD

EXCALIBUR CROSSBOW INC.

ExoMAX

Excalibur Crossbow Inc. is proud to announce the introduction of its latest crossbow, the ExoMAX. This is the first production crossbow with a 225-pound draw weight, producing arrow speeds up to 350 fps using recurve limbs. Excalibur's proven recurve limb design and ongoing innovations and technology accomplish this amazing speed and power without sacrificing reliability and accuracy. The ExoMAX comes finished in Realtree Hardwoods camouflage using the new Kolorfusion process for the most detailed and realistic camo finish ever. It has quick detach sling swivels and a fiber-optic front sight. It is also drilled and tapped to accept Excalibur's optional scope and quiver mounts.

SPECIFICATIONS
Velocity @ 350 Grain: 350 fps
Draw Weight: 225 lbs.
Power Stroke: 16.5"
Mass Weight: 6.5 lbs.
Overall Length: 39.5"
Arrow Length: 20"
Arrow Weight: 350 gr. minimum
String Type: Flemish Fast Flight
SRP:

PSE

Viper Copperhead Crossbow

The new Viper Copperhead Crossbow features an anodized machined aluminum barrel with a heavy duty steel foot stirrup and thumbhole-grip stock in all season camouflage. The Viper has an ambidextrous safety lever that automatically engages safety when the crossbow is cocked. Sights consist of a cross-hair style rear peep sight and front sight with two brass pins. The draw weight is 150 lbs.
SRP **$229**

DOUBLE BULL BS5

**EASTMAN
CARBON VENTURE BLIND**

**EASTMAN
CARBON VENTURE BLIND
WITH SAFARI SYSTEM**

BLINDS

DOUBLE BULL ARCHERY

BS5

All Double Bull products are manufactured with the archer in mind. The company starts with the finest blend of blind fabrics available, silent window systems and a patented cam lock framework that carries an unconditional life-time warranty. These blinds are designed to give the archer the room they need at the height they want.

The BS5 is the most advanced ground blind available. The 45" of pass-through netting is a whitetail hunter's dream. Spot, prepare, follow and make the shot through the netted corner. If the critter circles, just drop the interior curtain and open one of the additional six shooting ports. Four Prostaff viewing windows wrap the walls, allowing the advanced ground pounder the shot of a lifetime. Comes standard with a black-backened interior, aluminum hubs, 5" scent/light flap, 8 points of stakedown and carrying

case. Each BS5 includes Double Bull's "Part IV" video.

The BS5G model makes use of Double Bull's patent pending "GTI" technology to beat the whitetail and his mythical six sense. "Ghost Trap Interiors" capture and remove all the demons lurking in your head, thus eliminating all predator-type pheromones alerting the wary whitetail to your hide.

SPECIFICATIONS
Center Height: 5' 7"
Shooting Diameter: 6' 4" (76")
Floor Space: 5' X 5'
Cased Size: 44" X 10"
Weight: 19 lbs.
Big Screen: 45" Wide X 19" Netted Face
6 Additional Shooting Ports: 7" X 15" Tall
4 Prostaff Viewing Ports: 6" X 15" Tall
Available in Recurve Height: 6' 2"
Available w/ optional waterfowl zippers: $25.00 ea.
SRP: . . . . $299-$446

EASTMAN OUTFITTERS

Carbon Venture Blind
Features:
- RiverBottom Pattern
- Sets up in seconds
- V-style door
- 8 windows
- Heavy-duty aluminum hubs
- Heavy-duty water resistant polyester shell with scent eliminating interior coating
- Reduces airborne human scent
- ExScent carbon coating (see below)
- Automatically activated when exposed to direct sunlight, even in the cold winter months
- Convenient carrying-case with padded shoulder straps
- Available with and without Safari System® (see below) for added versatility

SPECIFICATIONS
Model 9736: Carbon Venture Blind with Safari System®
Model 9735: Carbon Venture Blind
Size: W-60" x L-60" x H-69"
Weight: 14 lbs.
SRP:

CARBON POP-UP 9712

CARBON POP-UP 9713

BLINDS

EASTMAN OUTFITTERS

Carbon Pop-Up RiverBottom Hunting Blinds
FEATURES:
- Lined with scent eliminating carbon (ExScent; see below)
- Available with and without Safari System® (see below)
- Pops open instantly
- Sets up in less that 30 seconds
- Pull down shoot-through mesh windows
- D-style door
- Guide ropes
- Includes carrying bag with back-pack straps
- Available with and without Safari System
- Instructional Video Included

SPECIFICATIONS
Model#9712RB
- Lined with scent eliminating carbon
- Pops open instantly
- Sets up in less than 30 seconds
- Folded 24" disc and 3" thick
- Size: W-57" L-57" H-64"
- 9.5 lbs

Model #9716
- 25% larger than standard pop-up blinds
- Size: W-66" L-66" H-71"
- 16.5 lbs

Model# 9713
- Patented Pending Safari System®
- Lined with scent eliminating carbon
- Pops open instantly
- Sets up in less that 60 seconds
- Folded 24" disc and 3" thick
- Size: W-57" L-57" H-64"
- 11.5 lbs

Model #9714
- 25% larger than standard pop-up blinds
- Perfect for the hunter who needs that extra room
- Size: W-66" L-66" H-71"
- 19 lbs

ExScent Carbon Scent Eliminator Systems
Eastman Outfitters provides a scent elimination systems with their blinds at a much more economical cost than competitors do with carbon lined cloth.

BLIND FEATURES:
- Carbon lining eliminates odor completely by absorbing scent.
- Doesn't absorb scent in storage and handling.
- Sunlight and heat reactivates Carbon lining, even during the winter.
- Instructional video included.
- Black Silhouette Block interior prevents shadows and conceals hunters from sight as well as smell.
- Water repellent.
- Shoot-through windows

Safari System®
- New Safari System® offers a removable, realistic 3-D blending system (Patent Pending)
- Easily installs within minutes
- Packs away in minutes in blind carrying-case

BUCK STOP ALURE

BUCK STOP FIVE

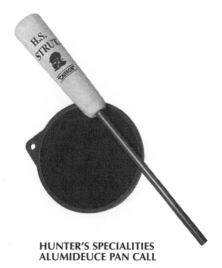
HUNTER'S SPECIALITIES
ALUMIDEUCE PAN CALL

CALLS, SCENTS AND ATTRACTORS

Buck Stop Lure Company

Alure™

Buck Stop Lure Company has developed a new, popularly priced blended lure it calls Alure™.

Alure™ starts with Rutting Buck and Doe-In-Heat® urines and blends in additional ingredients to calm and attract deer. Because natural urine is a major component of the new scent, Buck Stop bottles Alure™ in a flip-top, plastic container. The specially formulated plastic allows the scent to breath and prevents the build-up of game-spooking off odors. The product comes with a money-back guarantee. Any hunter not happy with results in the field can send Buck Stop the sales slip to obtain a refund of the purchase price.
SRP:

Five™

Buck Stop Lure Company had to work long and hard to come up with a hunting scent more effective than its urine-based sex scents. Since the late 1990s, the family-owned firm has been experimenting with powerful blended scents

that could appeal to more of a buck's basic instincts. Years of field tests helped it identify the most effective blend for the 2004 product introduction of FiveTM. FiveTM starts with a blend of Rutting Buck Urine and Doe-In-Heat® Urine from Buck Stop's whitetail herd. Then the company mixes in a calming agent, curiosity link and enhancer. While FiveTM is designed for pre-rut and rut use, these added ingredients help it attract deer whether or not they have mating on their minds.

This concentrated lure comes in a 2 ounce flip-top bottle and is boxed along with directions for its use.
SRP:

Code Blue

Standing Estrous Urine

Code Blue announces the pinnacle of deer scents with the new Standing Estrous Urine, the only deer lure on the market that already has attracted a buck. Standing Estrous is taken from does in estrous immediately after they are observed "standing" for the test buck. That means this urine is from an animal that is ready to be bred, as opposed to simply in "estrous," like all other estrous scents. And, like all

Code Blue urines, it is single-source, meaning that in each bottle of Code Blue, you get the urine from a single animal, never a blend of urines from different animals.
SRP: $37.99

Hunter's Specialties

Alumideuce™ Pan Call

Hunter's Specialties new Alumideuce™ pan call allows hunters to make high-pitched, long distance yelps, cuts and purrs. The aluminum over glass surface produces all the sounds of the hen turkey to bring gobblers running. The calls are built on the same pan as the "Li'l Deuce" which is one of the favorites of five-time World Friction Calling Champion and Hunter's Specialties Pro Staff member, Matt Morrett.

The aluminum surface comes ready to use and never needs sanding. The call comes packaged with a carbon striker that allows it to work in any weather.

With the new Alumideuce Call in your vest this spring, you will be ready to play the sounds gobblers love to hear.
SRP: $14.99

NEW Products: **Hunting and Shooting Accessories**

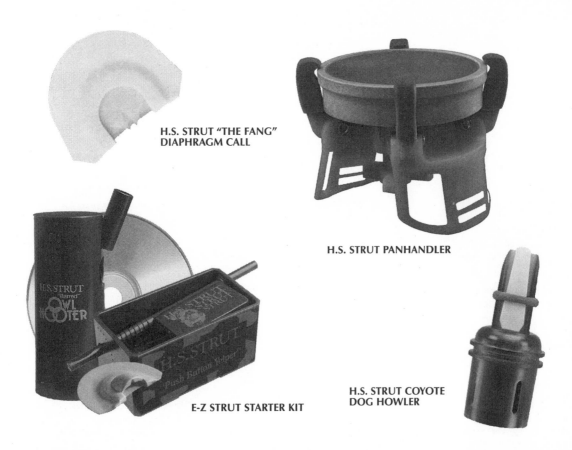

H.S. STRUT "THE FANG" DIAPHRAGM CALL

H.S. STRUT PANHANDLER

E-Z STRUT STARTER KIT

H.S. STRUT COYOTE DOG HOWLER

CALLS, SCENTS AND ATTRACTORS

HUNTER'S SPECIALTIES

H.S. Strut® Coyote Dog Howler

Locator calls are an important part of every spring turkey hunter's gear. Sometimes the turkeys just won't gobble and you need something that will "shock" them into giving away their location. Many hunters have recently discovered the effectiveness of using coyote sounds as a locator call.

With the new Coyote Dog Howler from H.S. Strut®, you can fool that wary old Tom into telling you where he is. The sturdy "bite style" open reed call features an adjustable band for consistent tuning. The call not only lets you reproduce realistic coyote howls, it can also make barks, whines and yelps. With a little practice, you can also use it to call in coyotes during the off-season.
SRP: **$8.99**

E-Z Strut Starter Kit

Hunter's Specialties has packaged some of their most effective and user-friendly calls together to help novice turkey hunters join the sport. Included in the E-Z Strut Starter Kit is a Push-Button Yelper, Tone Trough "Starter Double Reed" Diaphragm Call, Owl Hooter and the popular "So You Want To Be A Turkey Hunter" instructional video on DVD, which contains plenty of turkey hunting tips and tactics, along with how to properly use locator and hen calls.

Whether you are a beginner or an experienced hunter, the E-Z Strut Starter Kit contains everything you need to be successful this spring.
SRP: **$27.99**

H.S. Strut® "The Fang" Diaphragm Call

Hunter's Specialties "The Fang" diaphragm call features three ultra-thin reeds with a split top reed. The tough, thin reeds are strong enough to hold up to hours of calling. The Fang is built to satisfy the most experienced callers, yet is easily blown by beginners.

The split top reed allows hunters to get super raspy yelps and cutts with ease. The Gold Premium Flex™ Frame ensures unsurpassed call-to-call consistency.
SRP: **$5.99**

H.S. Strut® Panhandler

The new H.S. Strut® Panhandler makes it easier than ever to run your favorite pan call while keeping your bow ready for a shot at a strutting tom. The Panhandler features an adjustable 4-prong "claw" that holds your call firmly in place. To use, simply loosen the nut on the bottom to open the claw, drop in your call, then tighten the nut with light finger pressure and the call is securely held in place while you hunt. The base of the Panhandler is molded to fit comfortably against your leg and is held in place with an adjustable strap with a quick release buckle.

The Panhandler allows hunters to change calls throughout the day to find the one that works best, while always remaining ready to take the shot.
SRP: **$14.99**

NEW PRODUCTS

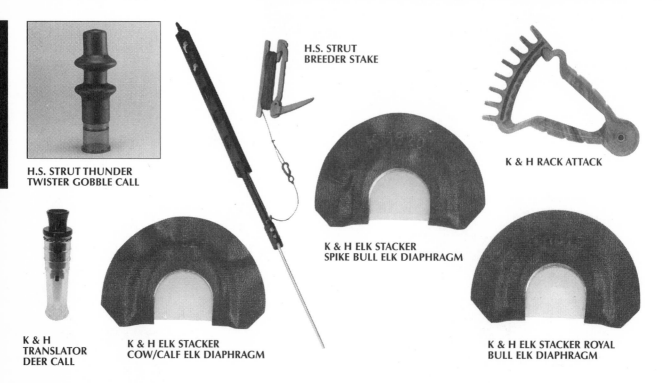

H.S. STRUT THUNDER TWISTER GOBBLE CALL

H.S. STRUT BREEDER STAKE

K & H RACK ATTACK

K & H ELK STACKER SPIKE BULL ELK DIAPHRAGM

K & H TRANSLATOR DEER CALL

K & H ELK STACKER COW/CALF ELK DIAPHRAGM

K & H ELK STACKER ROYAL BULL ELK DIAPHRAGM

CALLS, SCENTS AND ATTRACTORS

HUNTER'S SPECIALTIES

H.S. Strut® Thunder Twister Gobble Call

Hunter's Specialties has taken their popular Twister Gobble Call and made it even better for 2004. A larger baffle gives the call deep thunderous volume and better tone to fool even the wariest gobbler. The patented twist-on Silencer Plus™ feature allows hunters to silence the call by turning the open end 180°. This eliminates unwanted sounds while moving through the woods. The tough latex diaphragm is built to hold up under the toughest hunting conditions.
SRP: $16.99

H.S. Strut® Breeder Stake

The new Breeder Stake from Hunter's Specialties adds lifelike motion to your hen decoy to help bring gobblers running to your setup. The sturdy stake replaces the one that comes with your hen decoy. The new collapsible stake can be raised and lowered with the attached cord to simulate a hen moving into the breeding position. This motion will convince even the most wary gob-

bler that your decoy is the real thing.
The new Breeder Stake works with virtually all commercially available decoys (sold separately) and comes with 60 feet of line.
SRP: $12.99

KNIGHT & HALE

Rack Attack

This unique rattling unit allows hunters to create lifelike big-buck fighting sounds with only the minimal movement of one hand, leaving the other hand free to hold the gun in position or use a grunt tube to add realism to the scenario. All it takes is a squeezing motion like that of the old hand and forearm exercise device.
SRP: $19.95

Translator Deer Call

Knight & Hale announces the introduction of a new standard in deer calls, the Translator, which makes all effective deer sounds from a single call. The Translator Deer Call allows hunters to make sounds from a fawn bleat to a buck grunt simply by sliding the bottom portion of the call.
SRP: $14.95

Elk Stacker Cow/Calf Elk Diaphragm

Because of the design, the reeds on Knight & Hale's new Stacker Diaphragms never stick together, ensuring consistent, true calling time after time. The Stacker Cow/Calf Elk Diaphragm features a moon cut for the nasally, realistic pitch of an elk cow or calf.
SRP: $7.30

Elk Stacker Spike Bull Elk Diaphragm

The ultra-thin latex on this elk diaphragm produces high, whiney bugles. The Stacker Spike Bull Diaphragm accurately reproduces the bugle of a young, satellite bull.
SRP: $7.10

Elk Stacker Royal Bull Elk Diaphragm

One of the frames on this Stacker Royal Bull Diaphragm call holds two reeds and the other frame holds a single reed with a moon cut to produce a deep, throaty bugle of a big bull elk. This diaphragm makes awesome, loud bugles and aggressive chuckles.
SRP: $7.00

NEW Products: Hunting and Shooting Accessories

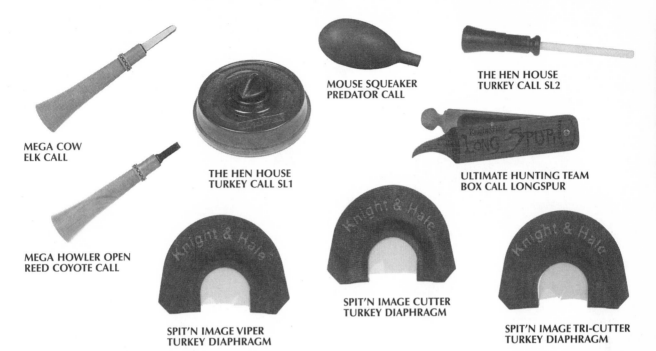

MEGA COW ELK CALL

THE HEN HOUSE TURKEY CALL SL1

MOUSE SQUEAKER PREDATOR CALL

THE HEN HOUSE TURKEY CALL SL2

ULTIMATE HUNTING TEAM BOX CALL LONGSPUR

MEGA HOWLER OPEN REED COYOTE CALL

SPIT'N IMAGE VIPER TURKEY DIAPHRAGM

SPIT'N IMAGE CUTTER TURKEY DIAPHRAGM

SPIT'N IMAGE TRI-CUTTER TURKEY DIAPHRAGM

Mega Cow Elk Call

Knight & Hale's new Mega Cow Open Reed Elk Call is an easy-to-use call with the kind of volume hunters need in mountains and windy conditions. Open-reed, "bite-down" calls are notoriously easy to use, and the big extended bell shape on the Mega Cow throws the sound way out there. This is a great call for all cow and young bull sounds.
SRP: **$15.90**

Mega Howler Open Reed Predator Call

Knight & Hale's new Mega Howler Open Reed predator call pulls in coyotes and bobcats from "way out there." The bell end piece throws the high-pitched squeals with the volume needed to predator hunt on windy days or rough, hilly terrain. Open-reed, "bite-down" calls are notoriously easy to use, so this call is perfect for beginners as well as accomplished callers.
SRP: **$15.90**

Mouse Squeaker Predator Call

Knight & Hale's new Mouse Squeaker is an easy-to-use bellows call that makes the panicked sound of a distressed mouse. An all-around effective predator call for foxes, bobcats, coyotes and others, the Knight & Hale

Mouse Squeaker's loud sound brings them in from a long distance.
SRP: **$6.50**

The Hen House Turkey Call

The new Hen House gives every turkey hunter the ability to make at least three distinct volume and tone level calls simply by turning the dial on the bottom of the call. And, the striker included was matched to the call by Knight & Hale's Ultimate Hunting Team. Now, callers can go from a quiet, natural-sounding tree call to a loud, raspy yelp with just a turn of the dial.
SRP: **$23.90**

Spit'n Image Viper Turkey Diaphragm

Multi-World and Grand National Turkey Caller Chris Parrish designed Knight & Hale's new Spit'n Image line of diaphragms to be extremely easy to use and super-realistic. The Viper is a 2-reed call with the sound of a triple reed.
SRP: **$6.48**

Spit'n Image Tri-Cutter Turkey Diaphragm

Knight & Hale Spit'n Image diaphragms take advantage of a thin prophylactic top layer to create a 3-reed call that

blows as easy as a 2 reed, and sounds as good as a 4-reed. The Tri-Cutter is a triple-reed call with awesome raspy tones.
SRP: **$6.48**

Spit'n Image Cutter Turkey Diaphragm

All Spit'n Image diaphragms are laser engraved, so the print doesn't wash off in your mouth. That way, you'll always be able to identify your favorite call. The Cutter is a 3-reed call that sounds like an advanced 4-reed.
SRP: **$6.48**

Ultimate Hunting Team Box Call Longspur

It's the only box call worthy of the Ultimate Hunting Team. The top-of-the-line Long Spur features a solid, one-piece base of medium-heavy grain mahogany and a lid of exotic heavy grain African babinga wood. These two wood types combine to create awesome, unique and super-natural-sounding calls. The Ultimate Hunting Team Long Spur also features a handsome wood stain and a turkey "spur" handle that provides added lid control as well as a stylish look. Includes a Silencer Strap.
SRP: **$47.90**

**THE SQUEEZE BOX
TURKEY BOX CALL**

**LOHMAN SASSY HEN
TURKEY CALL**

**LOHMAN DYNAMITE
KEG CALL**

**LOHMAN MINI-PUMP
ACTION YELPER**

**LOHMAN MINI-PUMP
COW/ELK CALL**

KNIGHT & HALE

The Squeeze Box Turkey Box Call

Finally, a box call that requires minimum hand movement to create realistic calls. Knight & Hale's new Squeeze Box is a true one-hand call, allowing hunters to take advantage of the sweet turkey music inherent in box calls while keeping one hand on the gun. The base of this waterproof call is machined from a single piece of wood for a smooth sound.

SRP: **$21.90**

KOLPIN OUTDOORS

Lohman® Dynamite Keg Call

Kolpin Outdoors Inc. introduces a new concept in keg-type deer calls with the Lohman® Dynamite Keg Call. Producing sounds with the mere push of a button, the Dynamite Keg Call emits perfect doe Estrus bleats to attract deer for hunters and wildlife photographers alike.

The Dynamite Keg Call design features a push-down plunger, making it quick and easy to achieve the social bleat and estrus bleats of a doe. Eliminating the need to blow into the call, or turn the call over and upright again, the Dynamite Keg Call is the ultimate in user-friendly designs. A perfect all-season call, Dynamite Keg Call sounds appeal to a variety of deer including whitetail and mule deer.

The compact Dynamite Keg Call conveniently fits in a gear bag or case pocket. Made of durable material and designed for freeze-proof operation,

the Dynamite Keg Call is able to withstand a variety of outdoor conditions and rough travel.

SRP: **$11.99**

Lohman® Mini-Pump™ Action Yelper

The new Mini-Pump™ Action Yelper from Kolpin® Outdoors provides mouth-call quality sound in a pocket-sized, easy-to-operate mechanical unit. The latest addition to the Lohman® game calls line, the Mini-Pump Action Yelper produces exceptionally realistic turkey calls with an easy push of the pump.

The Mini-Pump Action Yelper is small enough to fit in a hunter's pocket, and features easy, one-hand operation. Through its patent-pending Pump-Action™ technology, the Mini-Pump allows both amateur and professional hunters to master realistic yelps and excited clucks with the simple push of a pump. Weather resistant, injection-molded and easy-to-adjust, the Mini-Pump Action Yelper is ideal for the hunter on the go, providing a durable, user-friendly turkey call with high quality diaphragm sound.

SRP: **$16.99**

Lohman® Mini-Pump™ Cow/Elk Call

The new Mini-Pump™ Cow/Elk Call from Kolpin® Outdoors introduces the newest concept in elk calls. The latest addition to the Lohman® game calls line, the Mini-Pump Cow/Elk Call produces perfect mews and chirps with an easy push of the pump.

The Mini-Pump Cow/Elk Call is small enough to fit in a hunter's pock-

et, and features easy one-hand operation. The latest addition to Lohman's patent-pending Pump-Action™ series, the Mini-Pump Cow/Elk Call is perfect for novice and experts alike. Weather resistant, injection-molded and easy-to-adjust, the Mini-Pump Cow/Elk Call is ideal for the hunter on the go, providing a durable, user-friendly call that easily produces incredibly realistic elk cow and calf calls.

SRP: **$22.99**

Lohman® Sassy Hen™ Turkey Call

The Lohman® Sassy Hen™ from Kolpin® Outdoors provides incredibly realistic and effective hen calls with an easy-to-operate, one-hand design. Designed to keep excess movement and noise to a minimum, the Sassy Hen will fool even the wisest tom, and ensure a successful turkey hunt.

The Sassy Hen box friction call produces high-pitched hen calls with incredible volume, and features an easy-to use, one-hand design. The Sassy Hen is compact and convenient, fitting perfectly in a jacket pocket or gear bag. The Sassy Hen requires minimal movement to operate, and is equipped with an innovative lock-down mechanism to ensure a quiet carry. Individually custom-crafted for superior quality, each Sassy Hen is made of American Black Walnut, Cherry and Birch hardwood.

SRP: **$13.99**

MONTANA—GROUP

MONTANA DECOY

Mating Turkey Decoy
Weighing a light one-pound, this two sided, photo realistic image of a pair of mating turkeys is made of a durable polyester fabric that is portable, light, quiet and sets up in seconds to help hunters or photographers bring the prized birds in close.
SRP: **$39.95**

Jake Decoy
Montana Decoy now offers a new Jake decoy to go with their Full Strut and Mating Pair Decoys that are so realistic they will fool even the most skittish of turkey. Each is a perfect size and shape so the profile/silhouette is accurate with a state-of-the-art photographic finish on both sides of each decoy so the look is completely natural and lifelike. Each decoy folds into a small, compact, lightweight, easily portable unit for travel and carry to the field where they are quickly and effortlessly set in place.
SRP: **$29.95**

Cow Moose Decoy
This new decoy is the ultimate in realism. It is not only perfect in size and shape so the profile/silhouette is accurate but the state-of-the-art photographic finish on both sides bring this decoy to life, guaranteed to fool even the most sharp-eyed bull. By using a combination of calls and decoy the new Cow Moose is no match for the big bulls. And like all Montana Decoys, this one also folds into a small, compact, lightweight, easily portable unit for travel and carry to the field where each is quickly, effortlessly set in place.
SRP: **$109.95**

Frontal Cow Elk III Decoy
Montana Decoy now offers this incredibly realistic decoy to go with their Cow Elk Rump and side secoys that are so realistic they will fool even the most eagle eyed bull. By strategically placing these decoys either singularly or in groups, the smart hunter can cover every angle for enticing the bulls in close. Each is a perfect size and shape so the profile/silhouette is accurate with a state-of-the-art photographic finish on both sides of each decoy so the look is completely natural and lifelike. Each decoy folds into a small, compact, lightweight, easily portable unit for travel and carry to the field where each is quickly, effortlessly set in place.
SRP: **$99.95**

**SCRAPE JUICE
BOWHUNTER'S SET-UP**

**SCRAPE JUICE SUPER ODOR
ELIMINATOR**

WIZARD SCENT WIZARD

SCRAPE JUICE

Bowhunter's Set-Up

Hunters know that the most acute sense a deer has is that of smell. Deer use their phenomenal sense of smell to detect danger, locate breeding mates and food. Bowhunter's Set-up from Scrape Juice focuses on the deer's sense of smell with a proprietary formula that will bring the bucks in.

Bowhunter's Set-Up is a true attractant that works on deer any time during the season. The successful combination of gland extracts and a secret trapper's formula offers a unique lure that deer can't resist. Available in an easy-to-use 2 oz. vapor mist spray, Bowhunter's Set-Up should be in every hunter's pocket.
SRP: $9.95

Super Odor Eliminator

With deer season in full swing, hunters across the country are taking to the woods in hopes of filling their tag. To increase the odds of success, beat the deer's number one defense – their sense of smell.

A large part of a deer's brain is used for odor reception. Studies show that deer smell at a level 20 times better than humans. Scrape Juice offers Super Odor Eliminator, which eliminates hunters' natural scent. This proprietary formula has been proven to be more effective than the leading brands for eliminating human and all other odors.

Designed for easy, quick and effective application, the specially designed pump bottle provides a continuous spray. Super Odor Eliminator is available in an 8-ounce bottle and a 32-ounce economy refill bottle at retailers nationwide.
SRP: . . $6.95 (8 oz.), $12.99 (32 oz.)

WIZARD OUTDOOR PRODUCTS

Scent Wizard™

When combined with Wizard Outdoors' innovative "Do-It-Yourself" reusable, sealed scent cartridges, the Scent Wizard™ is the best scent dispensing system in the market today. Features such as the ability to use any commercial or homemade scent, weatherproof construction that enables the user to still disperse scent in rain or snow, and quick scent changing capabilities place the Scent Wizard™ head and shoulders above any competitors. Four AA batteries power a high-speed fan that forces molecules of your favorite scent over a wide area. Scent Wizard™ can also be used with Wizard Outdoor Products' new all natural Insect Repelling Beads to create the best mosquito, flea, tick and biting fly repellent available.
SRP: $34.95

NEW Products: **Hunting and Shooting Accessories**

ARCHERY SHOOTER SYSTEMS
HAMMER TWO BOW HANGER

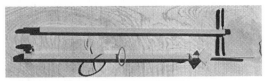

ARCHERY SHOOTER
SYSTEMS HAMMER SIX
BOW HANGER

HAMMER SIX BOW HANGER

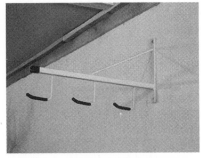

ARCHERY SHOOTER SYSTEMS
HAMMER THREE BOW WALL HANGER

FIELD LOGIC
BLOCK
BULLSEYE
TARGET

WIZARD
ARCHERY
STAND-BY
ULTIMATE BOW
STAND

TARGETS AND RANGE EQUIPMENT

ARCHERY SHOOTER SYSTEMS

Hammer Bow Hangers

Archery Shooter Systems felt there was a need for products that can help archers keep their valuable equipment off the ground to avoid being damaged. The company's bow hangers have a slide hammer action that allows the hangers to be self driven, as well as removed, in just seconds. This eliminates the need to drive nails into trees or dig holes around tree roots because the Hammer Hanger can be put into the ground virtually anywhere.

This is the first self-driving bow hanger on the market. Use it in hunting blinds, tree stands, backyards, 3D tournaments, on the beach or at campsites. It's the fastest, most versatile hanger you'll ever use.

SPECIFICATIONS

Single Bow Hanger
- 2-in-1 design, great for treestands and ground blinds

SRP: **$29.99**

Two Bow Hanger
- Designed with a ring for holding arrows
- Great for the backyard shooter, schools and youth events

SRP: **$29.99**

Six Bow Hanger
- Folds for easy transport and storage
- Hang bows at all types of outdoor archery shoots

SRP: **$49.99**

Three Bow Wall Hanger
- Perfect for pro shops, at home or on an indoor archery range

SRP: **$19.99**

FIELD LOGIC

BLOCK Bullseye Target

The Bullseye has a built in FITA design; no more hassle with paper targets. This is the perfect target for schools and organizations like 4H, Scouts and archery clubs.

Field Logic's patented "open layer" design stops arrows with friction, not force. The arrow slides between compressed layers of foam which creates heat and friction that literally "grabs" the arrow, stopping it with virtually no damage to the target. The new BLOCK Bullseye is even more portable with the sturdy, yet lightweight stand with wheels. Transporting the target is safe, simple, and easy.

SPECIFICATIONS
Size: 36 x 36 x 11 inches
Weight: 40 lbs.
SRP: **$179.99**
  Two Wheel Stand. $49.99

WILDWOOD INNOVATIONS

Archery Stand-By Ultimate Bow Stand

New from Wildwood Innovations, the Archery Stand-By Ultimate Bow Stand incorporates an adjustable block and pin that will easily accommodate conventional compound, parallel limb and even recurve bows. The Archery Stand-By is specifically designed to be a secure and convenient place to set your bow while retrieving arrows indoors and out.

SRP: **$39.95**

NEW PRODUCTS

**TWO PERSON
OUTFITTER
LADDER STAND**

**OUTFITTER LOUNGER
LADDER STAND**

TREESTANDS

GORILLA TREESTANDS

Outfitter Lounger Ladder Stand
Two Person Outfitter Ladder Stand
Gorilla Incorporated presents two new
Treestand Manufacturers Association
certified, state-of-the-art ladder stands
at the forefront of their product line
this season.

First, the Outfitter Lounger Ladder
Stand offers the serious hunter a
stable, sturdy stand including a flip-up
footrest, removable padded arm rests,
padded shooting rail and a thick
padded backrest, with flip-up AirRide
cushion seat that provides more room
on the oversized, 17.5" x 26" platform.

Next, the Two Person Outfitter
Ladder Stand features two comfortable
AirRide cushion seats with back rests
that flip up to provide more room for
both hunters on the extra-large 48" x
33" platform. In addition to all-welded
steel and aluminum construction,
which is standard on all Gorilla
Treestands, this stand offers the flip-
down footrest and flip-back padded
shooting rail. The Outfitter Two Person
Ladder Stand is 16 feet from seat to
ground and can accommodate any
Outfitter Ladder Stand accessories.

TMA certified Full Body Safety
Harnesses are included with all
Gorilla Treestands. A safe treestand
hunting video is also included.

Gorilla products incorporate
features that you won't find on most
treestands, including Easy-Cinch dual
claw straps for quick, easy and secure
tree attachment from either side of the
tree, as well as cam-action platforms
that firmly bite into the tree, locking
the stand in place. Gorilla also uses
nylon bushings and washers at all pivot
points, eliminating metal-to-metal
contact, the leading cause of squeaks.

SPECIFICATIONS
Outfitter Lounger Ladder Stand
Model: 42018
Base weight: 56.4 LBS
Weight: 69 LBS with accessories
Height: 15' from seat to ground
Weight limit: 300 lbs
Seat Size: 19" x 12"
Padded backrest: 12" x 19"
Platform Size: Extra large 17.5" x 26"
SRP: **$159.99**

**Two Person Outfitter
Ladder Stand**
Model: 43020
Weight: 158 lbs.
Height: 16' from seat to ground
• Weight limit 500 lbs.
Seat Size: (2) 19" x 12"
Platform Size: Extra large 48" x 33"
SRP:

*Many hunting accidents occur when a limb breaks as the hunter is climbing to
or descending from a treestand. It's best never to use limbs to climb into your stand.
Instead, install a few extra tree steps or use climbing sticks. A limb below your regular
stand that once was green and solid can die and therefore break,
sending you helplessly to the ground.*

THE DEERVIEW MIRROR

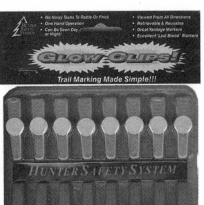

HUNTER SAFETY SYSTEM GLOW CLIPS

**HUNTER SAFETY SYSTEM
SILENT SYSTEM**

OTHER ACCESSORIES

BOHNING ARCHERY

Broadhead Wrench
Works with any blade configuration. Protects from sharp edges and is handy to carry in the field. Individually packaged.
SRP: **$1.60**

DEERVIEW INC.

The DeerView Mirror™
This unique innovation allows you the ability to see 360 degrees while hunting. What you can't see over your shoulders, you can see in the DeerView Mirror™.
FEATURES:
- Shatter-resistant adjustable panoramic mirror
- 28 inches of rigid, yet flexible, tubing
- Molded with quality, very light weight plastic
- Not effected by heat, cold, water or ice
- Weighs less than 1? pounds
- Easily disassembles into 3 pieces to conveniently fit in your backpack
- Safety feature: Allows you to see other hunters approaching from the rear.
SRP: **$29.95**

HUNTER SAFETY SYSTEM

Glow Clips
Finally, a trail-marking device that easily allows the hunter to find his/her way through the woods during the day or night. No need to stop and set down your bow each time you mark your trail with these handy clips. One hand operation allows the hunter to quickly and simply attach a Glow Clip to a branch while leaving the other hand free to carry a bow or other necessities to the stand.

With Glow Clips, there are no tacks to rattle or prick as you walk. Viewed from all directions, this product makes great yardage markers as well as "last blood" indicators when tracking wounded deer.

Glow Clips are easily retrieved and reusable. A bright red/orange color makes them easily seen during the day, while a reflective marker located on each side lights up the trail regardless of whether you're coming or going to your deer stand.
SRP: . . . . **$6.99 per 16 pack**

Silent System
No more noisy treestands. At last, a quick and easy-to-use product that eliminates game spooking noise from metal treestands. Simply peel and stick strips of "SILENT SYSTEM" to the metal bars of your treestand to silence it while making it slick resistant as well. The Hunter Safety System's newest product, Silence System, is waterproof, warm to the touch and comes in a camouflage pattern that makes the entire treestand disappear in the trees.
SRP: **$15.95**

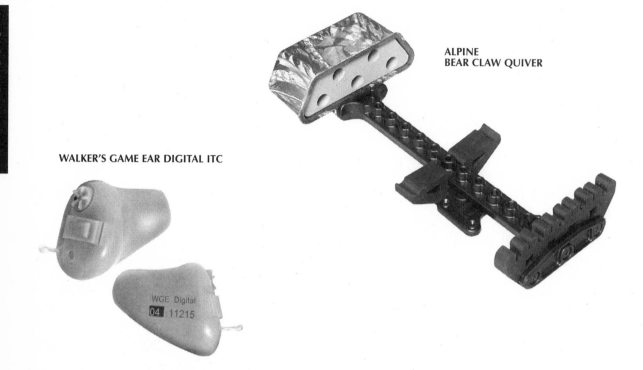

ALPINE
BEAR CLAW QUIVER

WALKER'S GAME EAR DIGITAL ITC

WALKER'S GAME EAR

Walker's Game Ear Digital ITC

Walker's Game Ear, the leader in hearing protection and enhancement, continues to set the standard with the introduction of the new Walker's Game Ear Digital ITC. This new device fits snugly inside the ear canal, making it virtually invisible. The state-of-the-art two-channel digital sound technology allows the user to hear more clearly and to easily separate the various noises encountered in the field.

The new Walker's Game Ear Digital ITC amplifies sound up to four times with an amazing 30dB of power with a maximum output of 110 dB SPL. This new unit offers an extended high frequency range, allowing users the ability to detect sounds previously omitted. Additionally, a 1.3-volt button-cell long life battery powers this small in-the-ear unit. A battery is included with the unit.

While the hearing enhancement offered from the Walker's Game Ear Digital ITC is unsurpassed, more importantly the unit also provides hearing protection. By incorporating

an advanced Sound Activated Compression (SAC) circuit, this unit instantly suppresses loud sounds such as muzzle blasts. This new in-the-ear unit packs a lot of power and protection in a very small, comfortable unit.

Designed to fit most ears, the Walker's Game Ear Digital ITC has been made from a soft shell, providing comfort to the user. For an exact fit, two different units, one for each ear, have been carefully designed to meet the needs of the outdoorsman. For greater amplification and better directionality, a binaural set (left and right ear) is recommended, but not necessary. If ordering one unit, be sure to specify the right or left ear.

Weighing less than $\frac{1}{4}$ ounce, this new state-of-the-art digital hearing enhancement/protection device comes ready to use with batteries and carrying case.
SRP:. **$529**

ALPINE ARCHERY

Bear Claw Quiver

Alpine Archery's new Bear Claw Quiver stands apart from all others in that it is a lightweight quiver system designed for the treestand hunter. A great fit on any bow, the five-arrow Bear Claw conveniently carries any size or material arrow shaft with any point from field tip to standard or mechanical broadheads. Thanks to the unique, new mounting system, once in your treestand the Bear Claw detaches from the bow and is easily mounted to Alpine's new Treestand Quiver Mount so your arrows are in easy reach but not on your bow.

Other features that make the Bear Claw the quiver to own include the wide range of vertical adjustments for perfect bow mounting and the vibration dampening spacer to move quiver away from bow if needed. The Bear Claw is available in RealTree X-tra Gray, Hardwoods Green HD, Hardwoods HD (Mathews) and Mossy Oak New Break-Up and Obsession.
Minimum advertised price: . . **$24.95**

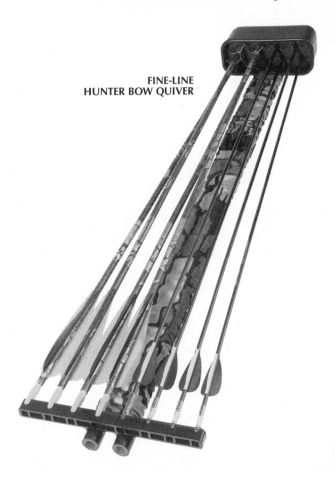

FINE-LINE
HUNTER BOW QUIVER

ARCHERY RESEARCH
ADJUSTABLE TWO-PIECE QUIVER

ARCHERY RESEARCH
Adjustable Two-Piece Quiver

Adding to its growing product line, Archery Research proudly unveils the new Adjustable Two-Piece Quiver that is sure to be an enormous success with bowhunters. This new quiver features a molded hood that can be mounted in multiple locations allowing the archer to change the position and angle of the rack of arrows relative to the bow, as well as being able to accommodate different length arrows. The unique extended arrow clip holds five arrows at a slight angle, allowing them to be contained within the profile of the bow for protection. This quiver also has the ability to position the arrows as close to the riser as possible to improve the balance of the bow by optimizing its center of gravity. Another innovative feature is the adjustable rubber gripper on the machined aluminum clip that can use any diameter carbon or aluminum

arrow. The AR quiver uses a unique reverse collet locking system, making it the fastest two-piece detach quiver on the market today. This high quality quiver offers ultimate stability for years of rugged use.
SRP:

FINE-LINE INC.

Hunter Bow Quiver

The Fine-Line Hunter Bow Quiver features a unique telescoping center bar that is adjusted to fit the length of the arrows. This is necessary because each arrow is captured firmly in place by not only inserting the point into the foam filled hood but also at the nock end. Unlike ordinary bow quivers which utilize a set of rubber grippers to hold the arrows at mid point, the Hunter features a Nock Bar onto which each arrow, nock end, is snapped into place. This feature

provides extra lateral strength to the arrow but actually protects the nocks from damage and debris while hunting. The Nock Bar also eliminates vibration, arrow noise, slippage and arrow loss common with the gripper-style quivers.

Arrow removal is accomplished quickly by pushing the arrow up into the deep hood and then pulling down and out. This also allows for No-Eyes movement from quiver to string because the cock vane is always up.

The Hunter Bow Quiver weighs a light 12 oz, adapts to fit all size/length/make of arrow from the thickest wood and aluminum to the smallest diameter Carbon shaft. The Hunter also features a Quick Detach Center Locking System for easy removal and a choice of three replaceable camouflage sleeves. A Quiver Lock Extension Bar is available as an accessory to allow single unit sight and quiver mounting and removal.
SRP: $36.95

NEW Products: **Release Aids**

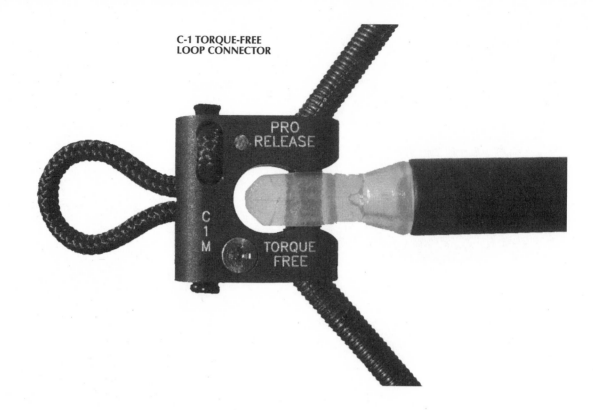

**C-1 TORQUE-FREE
LOOP CONNECTOR**

PRO RELEASE INC.

C-1 Torque-Free Loop™ Connector

The C-1 Torque-Free Loop™ Connector attaches to the bowstring to provide a convenient, superior connection between the archer, release aid, arrow and bowstring. It's designed as a positive way to eliminate bowstring torque for increased accuracy. It combines some of the best features of a nock device, a string loop and a rotating-head Release. It allows up to 180-degrees rotation of the release aid behind the arrow without any affect on the shot or flight path of the arrow.

The 'C-1' is a precision made, quality product that eliminates torque, keeps the arrow on the string at full draw, eliminates serving wear and maintains perfect peep/sight alignment for the most accurate shooting possible. It's made of durable, anodized aluminum with high quality polyester loop material. It installs quickly and easily, comes in two throat sizes and works with all loop-compatible release aids.
SRP: $19.95

*"So long as the new moon returns in heaven a bent, beautiful bow,
so long will the fascination of archery keep hold in the hearts of men."
—Maurice Thompson, The Witchery of Archery, 1879*

COMPOUND BOWS

Alpine Archery Compound Bows

1 CAM

INFERNO CAM

FATAL IMPACT

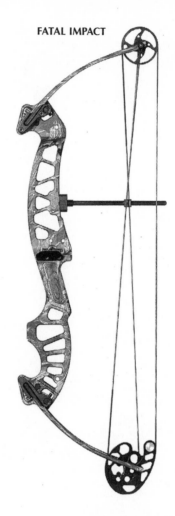

CHALLENGER

The Challenger bow offers the same features as Alpine's Stealth Force but is also outfitted with a standard 1-Cam or Inferno cam system. The Challenger's features include: split limbs, two-piece wood checkered grip panels and a machined Inverse twin limb mounting system. This bow weighs 3.5 pounds and is coated with Mossy Oak Forest Floor camouflage.

BOW SPECIFICATIONS: CHALLENGER

AMO Draw Length: 26- to 31-inch in 1-inch increments with Inferno Cam; begins at 27- inch with the One-Cam system

Draw Weights: 50#, 60# and 70#, 80% let-off standard and 65% let-off optional with standard cam; Note

that only 65% let-off is offered with Inferno cams

Bow Speed: NA

Axle-to Axle: 39 inches

SRP: with Inferno cams. $459
      with the 1-Cam system $489

Fatal Impact

Alpine's Fatal Impact successfully combines speed with quiet, smooth and relatively shock and vibration free shooting. This bow is part of the VX line of high performance risers that feature a parallel limb design and Alpine's new Bi-Polar Riser dampening and Inter-Loc Limb Mounting System. This unique system is designed to stop the limbs from moving during the shot sequence, which will quiet the shot

and reduce vibration. An innovative limb-pocket acts to dampen the shock and vibrations of each shot. The Fatal Impact delivers outstanding perform-ance and control with a long reflexed riser for a longer field of view than most bows today. This bow has a mass weight of 4.2 pounds, is 34" axle-to-axle. It is available in Realtree Hardwoods Green HD camo with a two-piece wood grip.

BOW SPECIFICATIONS

AMO Draw Length: 27-, 28-, 29-, 30- and 31-inches

Draw Weights: 50, 60 and 70 pounds with 65 or 80% let-off

Bow Speed: NA

Axle-to Axle: 34 inches

SRP:. $415

IMPACT X-TREME

MICRO

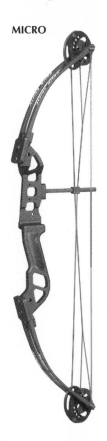

RAVAGE

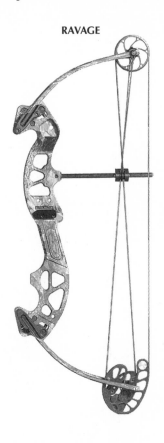

IMPACT X-TREME

The Impact X-Treme was designed to be a lightweight machined riser bow equipped with factory-selected accessories. The Impact features a very slim, two piece grip that allows a glove to be worn in cold weather without making the bow torque when shot. It is fitted with a Soft Loc 5-arrow Mossy Oak camo quiver, fiber optic sight, Whisper Flite rest and Pro Flex stabilizer with bow sling. The bow weighs 2.4 pounds, uses Inverse Twin limb mounting and is available with Stalker II cams or Alpine's 1-Cam system.

BOW SPECIFICATIONS: IMPACT X-TREME
AMO Draw Length: 23- to 30-inch with Stalker cams; 26- to 30-inch in 1-inch increments in the 1-Cam version
Draw Weights: 50#, 60# and 70# with 80% let off standard (65% let-off optional). Note that 65% let-off is the only option with Stalker cam models
Bow Speed: NA
Axle-to Axle: 34 inches
**SRP: for Stalker models $309
   for 1-Cam models $369**

MICRO

The Micro is the choice for starting serious young shooters. All of the hardware and riser are completely CNC machined aluminum. The Micro sports adult bow features such as Alpine's split limb technology, two panel ABS grips, and carbon cable guard rod. Another feature is the easy-adjust Stalker II Cam with 8-inch draw adjustment. The bow's draw length is adjusted by removing one screw and rotating the take-up side of the cam. Each hole is one inch of draw and about two pounds of peak weight gained or lost depending on whether you lengthen or shorten the draw. No bow press is required and the adjustment only takes minutes. This cam is perfect for growing children and weighs only 2¼ pounds. The Micro is available in black finish only.

BOW SPECIFICATIONS: MICRO
AMO Draw Length: 21- to 28-inch
Draw Weights: 30#, 40# and 50#; 65% let off
Bow Speed: NA
Axle-to Axle: 32 inches
SRP: $189

RAVAGE

The Alpine bow's design is a top example of today's technology with its aggressive VX riser and Bi-Polar dampeners. Another new feature is Inter-loc limbs with a nylon dampening system. The Ravage model also advances parallel limb technology to a new higher level to deliver a very short and compact bow. This bow's design was the result of an application of state-of-the-art computer modeling software. Other features of this bow include: Fast Trac cam system with wide body technology, Bi-Flex composite limbs, a cable guard and a two-piece wooden grip. This bow weighs 4 pounds, has a 7½-inch brace height and is offered in Realtree's Hardwoods Green High-Definition camouflage finish.

BOW SPECIFICATIONS: RAVAGE
AMO Draw Length: 25- to 29-inch in 1-inch increments
Draw Weights: 50#, 60# and 70# with 80% let-off standard (65% let-off optional)
Bow Speed: NA
Axle-to Axle: 28 inches
SRP: $675

Alpine Archery Compound Bows

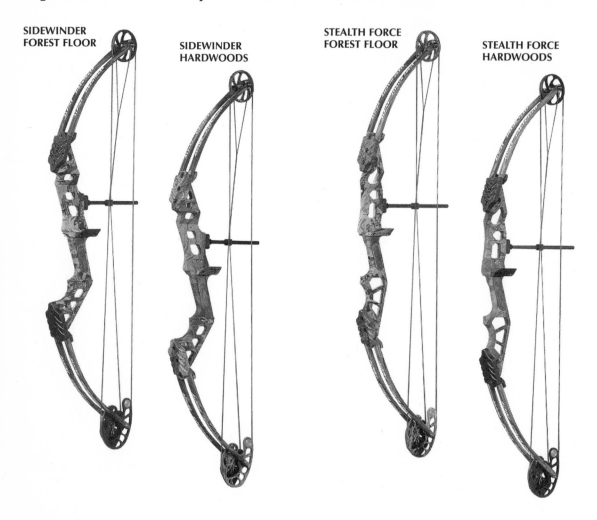

SIDEWINDER
FOREST FLOOR

SIDEWINDER
HARDWOODS

STEALTH FORCE
FOREST FLOOR

STEALTH FORCE
HARDWOODS

SIDEWINDER

The Sidewinder is the fastest bow in Alpine's Fast Trac Series. It is designed for the shooter who demands a quality fit and finish in a technically advanced arrow shooting machine. Speed, accuracy and reliability are maintained without sacrificing smooth, quiet shooting characteristics. This bow utilizes the ultra reflex riser with a two panel, checkered wood grip. The Sidewinder is for the more seasoned shooter that is comfortable with reflexed risers. Other features include a four- point Bearing Control System (patent pending) and Wide Body Cam Technology to make this Fast Trac Series bow the most technically advanced reflexed bow on the market. This bow is available in Realtree Hardwoods and Mossy Oak Forest

Floor camouflage dipped finish. This bow weighs 3.5 pounds, has split limbs and a 6-inch brace height.

BOW SPECIFICATIONS: SIDEWINDER
AMO Draw Length: 26 to 30 inches in 1-inch increments
Draw Weights: 50#, 60# and 70# with 80% let off standard (65% optional)
Bow Speed: NA
Axle-to Axle: 36 inches
SRP: **$589**

STEALTH FORCE

The Stealth Force combines Alpine's Fast Trac technology with a higher brace height than many of the bows. The Stealth Force comes in two axle-to-axle lengths, with the shorter version producing the greater arrow velocity. The bow's riser is designed for balance and has a two piece,

checkered wood panel grip and a full-view sight window cutout. The straight, carbon cable guard and Teflon slide provide a smooth draw and whisper-quiet operation. The bow uses perimeter-weighted cams and Bi-Flex composite limbs set in machined pockets. Other features include: Alpine's Fast Trac Four Point Bearing Control System, Wide Body Cam Technology and split limbs.

BOW SPECIFICATIONS: STEALTH FORCE
AMO Draw Length: 27- to 31-inch (down to 26 for the shorty models) in 1-inch increments
Draw Weights: 50#, 60# and 70# with 80% let-off standard (65% let-off optional)
Bow Speed: NA
Axle-to Axle: 39 or 36 inches
SRP: **$549**

TETON LITE

Alpine's Teton Lite compound bow has all of the features of the company's Sidewinder model, but is offered with either the standard perimeter weighted 1-Cam or Inferno cam systems. The Teton Lite is covered in Mossy Oak Forest Floor camo. This bow uses silicone imbedded Bi-Flex composite limbs and an Inverse twin limb mounting system.

BOW SPECIFICATIONS: TETON *Lite*
AMO Draw Length: 25- to 30-inch in 1-inch increments with Inferno
CamDraw Weights: 50#, 60# and 70#, 80% let-off standard and 65% let-off optional withstandard cams. Note that 65% let-off is the only option with Inferno cams
Bow Speed: NA
Axle-to Axle: 36 inches
**SRP: for Inferno cam models. . . $489
for 1-Cam models. $519**

TETON LITE

"A good way to train correctly is to place your target ten feet from you at first, and shoot at it at that distance until you can hit a four-inch ring every shot; then remove it ten feet further and repeat the practice till you keep inside the ring; move again ten feet and so on until you are shooting sixty or one hundred feet. You may then increase the distance daily, say three feet, till you can show good work at sixty or one hundred yards."
—Maurice Thompson, The Witchery of Archery, 1879

COMPOUND BOWS

Bass Pro Shops Compound Bows

COMPOUND BOWS

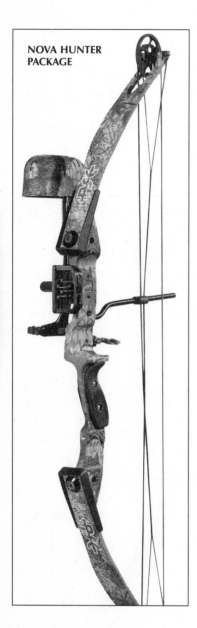

NOVA HUNTER PACKAGE

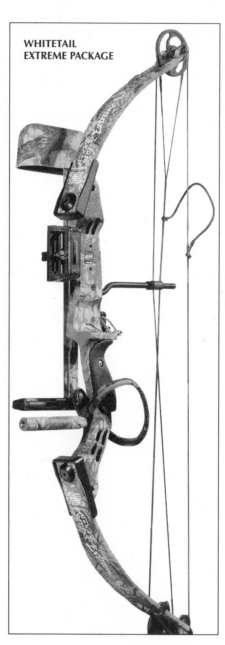

WHITETAIL EXTREME PACKAGE

NOVA HUNTER PACKAGE

This bow and matching components begins with PSE's Nova compound bow as a base. The bow's features include a solid machined aluminum riser, solid Magnaglass limbs, and Vector-4 machined aluminum cams. The add-ons include: fiber optic sight, arrow rest and Mongoose six-arrow quiver in PSE's Brush camouflage finish to match the bow.

BOW SPECIFICATIONS:
NOVA HUNTER PACKAGE
AMO Draw Length: 25-27, 27-29, 28-30 and 29-31 inches
Draw Weights: 40# to 50#, 50# to 60# and 60# to70# with 75% let-off
Bow Speed: NA
Axle-to Axle: 39 inches
SRP: **$199.99**

WHITETAIL EXTREME PACKAGE

This hunting bow assembly starts with PSE's short Whitetail compound bow which features solid limbs, a machined aluminum reflex riser and the Arson OneCam system. The bow has a black molded grip and cable guard. The accessories include: FX Hunter 3-pin sight with pin guard, 5-inch stabilizer, camo wrist sling, peep sight and quiver that holds six arrows. The package is ready for hunting with PSE's Brush camouflage coating.

BOW SPECIFICATIONS:
WHITETAIL EXTREME PACKAGE
AMO Draw Length: 28, 29 and 30 inches
Draw Weights: 50# to 60# and 60# to 70# with 70% let-off
Bow Speed: NA
Axle-to Axle: 34 inches
SRP: **$299.99**

Bass Pro Shops Compound Bows

WHITETAIL QUEST

This bow is similar to the Whitetail Vision model and uses an aluminum Super Cam. It has a solid riser, stylish molded grip and matching black limb pockets. The bow is available in six right-hand models and three left-hand versions. The accessories include a 3-pin fiber optic sight with a level attached and a quiver for arrows. The bow is camouflaged by Realtree Hardwoods.

BOW SPECIFICATIONS: WHITETAIL QUEST
AMO Draw Length: 28, 29 and 30 inches
Draw Weights: 50# to 60#, 60# to70# with 75% let-off
Bow Speed: NA
Axle-to Axle: 34½-inches
SRP: $249.99

WHITETAIL VISION PACKAGE

This Bass Pro exclusive compound bow is manufactured by Bear Archery and begins with a machined aluminum reflexed riser and then adds on solid compression molded carbon/glass limbs. The bow moves arrows with a Perimeter OneCam system. Other features include a wood two-piece grip, cable guard and inter-changeable modules to adjust the draw length. Accessories include: quick detach 4-arrow quiver, 3-pin fiber optic sight, arrow rest, peep sight and string silencers. Left- and right-hand models are available and all bows are coated with Realtree's Hardwoods High- Definition camo pattern.

BOW SPECIFICATIONS: WHITETAIL VISION PACKAGE
AMO Draw Length: 28 to 30 inches
Draw Weights: 60# to 70# with 75% let-off
Bow Speed: NA
Axle-to Axle: 34 inches
SRP: $399.99

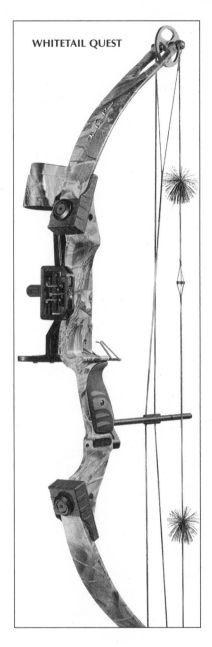

WHITETAIL QUEST

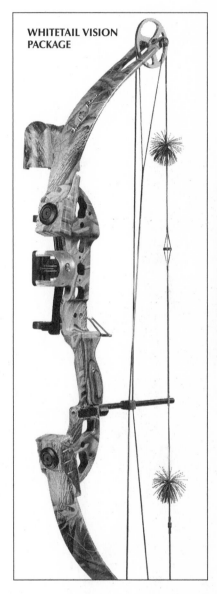

WHITETAIL VISION PACKAGE

COMPOUND BOWS

"The history of the bow and arrow is the history of mankind."
—Fred Bear

Compound Bows • **121**

Bear Archery Compound Bows

BADGE

BADGE

This Bear Archery bow is designed for young and small framed archers. Its features include a rugged, lightweight riser with integral grip and limb pockets. Other features include solid carbon recurve limbs and 20 pound adjustable draw weight range. This bow is only available as a right-hand model and in Hardwoods High Definition camouflage.

BOW SPECIFICATIONS: BADGE
AMO Draw Length: 21 or 25 inches
- adjustable range for 21-inch is 20 to 23 inches
- adjustable range for 25-inch is 24 to 27 inches

Draw Weights: 15-25# or 35-45# with 65% let-off
Axle-to Axle: 34.875 inches
Weight in hand: 2 lbs., 15 oz.
SRP: . . . . **Starting at $159**

Arrow straightness is very important for accuracy. When shooting field points and especially broadheads, the straightness of the arrows influences how well they group. Good straight arrows can increase effective shooting distance and provide better hits on close shots. Thus, it's important to buy the straightest arrows you can afford.

EPIC XTREME

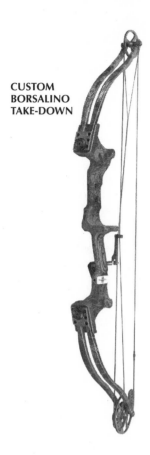

**CUSTOM
BORSALINO
TAKE-DOWN**

**CUSTOM
WHITETAIL
PINNACLE**

COMPOUND BOWS

CUSTOM BORSALINO TAKE-DOWN

This technologically advanced compound bow folds in half and sets up again in less than a minute. It can be easily transported in an optional soft-sided carrying case. Other features include bronzed hardware, draw length adjustable OneCam system and a Realtree Hardwoods camouflage finish. This compound bow incorporates the Shock Stop noise and vibration elimination system and is available as a right-hand only model. A tip of the famous Fred Bear Borsalino hat is offered to the company on the creation of this bow.

BOW SPECIFICATIONS:
CUSTOM BORSALINO TAKE-DOWN
AMO Draw Length: 25- to 33-inch
Draw Weight: 60-70#
Bow Speed: IBO fps = 321;
AMO fps = 237
Axle-to Axle: 381/4 inches
Weight in hand: varies by selection of cams and other options
SRP: **$749**

CUSTOM WHITETAIL PINNACLE

This advanced design bow is custom built to owner specifications at the North American Archery Group's Gainesville, Florida, facility. Its features include the innovative ZenCam that produces virtually no hand shock and a superbly energy efficient design that reduces limb travel. This bow is available in Realtree Harwoods High Definition camouflage and left- and right-hand models. This is one of the few offerings in the archery industry where you can have a custom hunting compound bow built to your specifications.

BOW SPECIFICATIONS:
CUSTOM WHITETAIL PINNACLE
AMO Draw Length: 28- to 31-inch
Draw Weights: 50-60# and 60-70# with let-off dependant upon cam selection
Bow Speed: IBO fps = 298;
AMO fps = 233
Axle-to Axle: 38 inches
Weight in hand: varies
SRP: **$499**

EPIC XTREME

This hunting compound bow utilizes a modular weighted OneCam that permits eight inches of draw length adjustment and one inch of micro adjustment. The stylish bronze anodized and brass weighted dampening system contrasts against the bow's Realtree Hardwoods High Definition camouflage finish. The machined aluminum riser offers a 7½-inch brace height and is available in left- or right-hand models with a checkered laminated wood grip complete with an inlaid compass. This model has a swing-arm cable guard and a distinct Fred Bear signature inset on the riser.

BOW SPECIFICATIONS: EPIC XTREME
AMO Draw Length: 28-, 29- and 30-inch; adjustable range from 24 to 31 inches.
Draw Weights: 50-60# and 60-70# with 75% let-off (65% let-off optional)
Bow Speed: IBO fps = 303;
AMO fps = 234
Axle-to Axle: 32 inches
Weight in hand: 3 lbs., 15 ozs.
SRP: **$399**

Bear Archery Compound Bows

FRED BEAR TRX32

FRED BEAR FAMILY BOW

FRED BEAR TRX32

This Fred Bear TRX32 bow offers a Perimeter weighted One-cam. Other features include four Carbon Quad straight limbs, a 6061 T-6 machined aluminum riser and a vibration-suppressing grip. This bow is coated with Advantage camouflage and has a string shock stop system attached to the tip of the cable guard. The bow's riser has quiver-mounting holes and speed buttons are factory installed on the TechTwist bowstring. The limb pockets are a unique gold color.

BOW SPECIFICATIONS
AMO Draw Length: 28, 29 and 30 inches adjustable ranges from 24 to 31 inches
Draw Weights: 40-50, 50-60 and 60-70 pounds with 75% let-off, 65% optional
Bow Speed: 303 fps IBO and 234 fps AMO
Axle-to Axle: 32 inches
SRP: $399.95

FRED BEAR FAMILY BOW

A unique compound bow that's designed to be used by every archer at any level of experience. This bow has no specific draw length, has 48½-inch string and weighs approximately 2 pounds. It is offered in right hand models only and is a blue and granite color.

BOW SPECIFICATIONS
AMO Draw Length: 14 to 28 inches
Draw Weights: 20 pounds adjustable
Bow Speed: NA
Axle-to Axle: 33 inches
SRP: $129.99

LITTLE DELTA

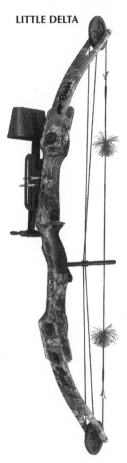

TRX

VAPOR 300

LITTLE DELTA

The Little Delta was designed to help kids step into the archery arena in adult-like style. Features include a Mossy Oak Break-Up camouflage finish, magnesium riser, carbon solid straight limbs and the use of solid composite modular cam. This model includes a cable guard and all weather composite grip. Left- and right-hand versions are available and the bow will accommodate accessories.

BOW SPECIFICATIONS: LITTLE DELTA
AMO Draw Length: 25 inches, adjustable 24 to 27 inches
Draw Weight: 25-35# or 40-50#
Axle-to Axle: 34.625 inches
Weight in hand: 3 lbs., 10 oz.
SRP: **$129**

TRX

This special-edition Fred Bear 100th Birthday Anniversary commemorative Team Realtree bow wears a Realtree Hardwoods High Definition finish on the machined 6061-T-6 aluminum riser and four carbon recurve limbs. Other features include a Shock Stop tipped cable guard and checkered laminated wood grip with inlaid compass. The TRX is available in left- and right-hand versions with a 94¾-inch long Tech Twist string and gold colored accents on the limb pockets, idler wheel and cam.

BOW SPECIFICATIONS: TRX
AMO Draw Length: 28-, 29- or 30-inch: adjustable range from 24 to 31 inches
Draw Weights: 40-50#, 50-60#, or 60-70#; 70% let-off (65% let-off optional)
Bow Speed: IBO fps = 305; AMO fps 230
Axle-to Axle: 35.875 inches
Weight in hand: 3 lbs., 15 oz.
SRP: . . . . **Starting at $399**

VAPOR 300

This high-tech 4-limb compound bow was designed to assist bowhunters on the hunt. Features of the Vapor 300 include a machined aluminum riser, powerful V-Tech OneCam and a vibration dampening Elasto-Polymer grip. Other features include an adjustable cable guard and tan/olive Tech Twist string. This bow is coated in Realtree Hardwoods High Definition camo and the left-hand model has a checkered laminated wood grip.

BOW SPECIFICATIONS: VAPOR 300
AMO Draw Length: 28-, 29- and 30-inch; adjustable range from 24 to 31 inches.
Draw Weights: 40-50#, 50-60#, 60-70#; 75% let-off (65% let-off optional)
Bow Speed: IBO fps = 302; AMO fps = 223
Axle-to Axle: 34.25 inches
Weight in hand: 4 lbs., 6 oz.
SRP: **$279**

COMPOUND BOWS

Ben Pearson Archery Compound Bows

440 QUAD KIT

ANACONDA

440 QUAD KIT

The 440 has been the work horse bow in the Pearson line for five years. In 2002, Pearson offered the 440 Quad Kit which includes the bow and all the accessories. The 440 Quad features: 15½-inch quadra-flex split limbs, wide track idler wheel, Z3 catapult PhD Cam, soft-feel thermo grip, velvet antler finish in rest area, and Superflauge camo.

The accessories include: bow with fiber optic sight, stabilizer, release aid, string silencer, peep, arrow rest, quiver and four arrows.

BOW SPECIFICATIONS: 440 QUAD KIT
AMO Draw Length: 25- to 32-inch
Draw Weights: 50#, 60# and 70# with 75% let-off
Bow Speed: IBO fps= 303
Axle-to Axle: 36¾-inches
Weight in hand: 3.6 lbs.
SRP:. **$469**

ANACONDA

The machined aluminum riser on the Anaconda has withstood the torture of over 100 dry fires. This bow has a 20-degree bio grip slant handle—a "must have" requirement by a growing number of experienced hunters—and an IBO speed of 310 fps. Other features include: a wood grip; 15½-inch quadra-flex split limbs, Z3 weighted catapult PhD cam, and Superflauge camo.

BOW SPECIFICATIONS: ANACONDA
AMO Draw Length: 25- to 32-inch
Draw Weights: 50#, 60# and 70# with 75% let-off
Bow Speed: IBO fps= 310
Axle-to Axle: 36¼-inches
Weight in hand: 3.6 lbs.
SRP:. **$489**

Ben Pearson Archery Compound Bows

CHEROKEE

This bow is similar to Pearson's Warrior model and is designed for young bowhunters. It features a 16-inch straight raiser design with velvet antler finished shelf, 12½-inch quad limbs, and a wide track idler wheel. Other features are a cable guard with slide and molded grip. The Cherokee is backed with a lifetime guarantee.

BOW SPECIFICATIONS

AMO Draw Length: 22 to 26 inches with modular adjustments
Draw Weights: 25, 35 or 45 pounds
Bow Speed: NA
Axle-to Axle: 29½ inches
SRP:...................$299

COLT KIT

A complete package that includes the bow, quiver, sights and arrow rest—all you need to add is a young archer or small-framed shooter. The Colt bow has a CNC machined riser, Two-Cam system and quad limbs. It comes equipped and camouflaged with Superflage camo.

BOW SPECIFICATIONS

AMO Draw Length: 19-21 or 22-24 inches
Draw Weights: 20, 30, 40, or 50 pounds
Bow Speed: NA
Axle-to Axle: 29 5/16 inches
SRP:...................$299

CHEROKEE

COLT KIT

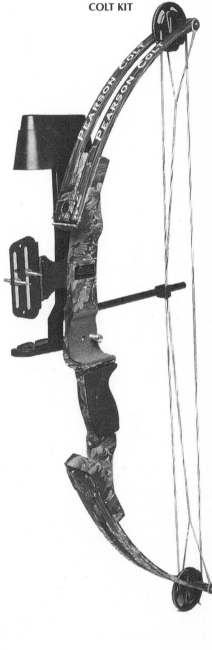

Carbon or aluminum? Both arrow shaft materials have advantages. Carbon arrows are lightweight and therefore will shoot faster. Carbon shafts also are extremely durable. Aluminum arrow shafts are normally straighter, and their heavier weight can result in better penetration.

Ben Pearson Archery Compound Bows

COMPOUND BOWS

DIAMONDBACK VX

DIVA VX

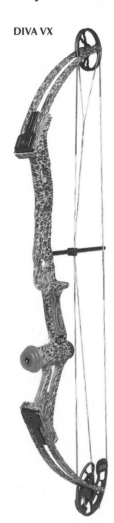

FREEDOM

DIAMONDBACK VX

This hunting compound bow features the VIB-X noise and vibration reduction module in a pocket on the riser. Other features include the Laser cam and Accu-Trac idler wheel, both with ball bearings. The Diamondback has 14½-inch limbs and a lifetime guarantee. This bow has a 7⅞-inch brace height and is covered with Lynch Worldwide's Superflage.

BOW SPECIFICATIONS

AMO Draw Length: 24 to 31 inches, modular adjustments

Draw Weights: 50, 60 or 70 pounds, with 85% standard and 65% or 75% let-off optional

Bow Speed: 302 fps IBO

Axle-to Axle: 31⅜ inches

SRP: $599

DIVA VX

The unique and flashy leopard—caged cat camo—skin finish on this compound bow will be the first thing that you notice. The Diva features an 85% pet-off Laser PhD cam and an Accu-Trac idler wheel. The machined riser has the VIB-X noise and vibration reduction module built in. This system works unlike any other and is a plus at reducing felt hand vibration upon arrow launch. This bow has a 6⁹/₁₆-inch high brace height,

BOW SPECIFICATIONS

AMO Draw Length: 24 to 31 inches adjustable with modulars

Draw Weights: 30, 40, 50, 60 or 70 pounds

Bow Speed: 303 fps IBO

Axle-to Axle: 35 ⅜ inches

SRP: $619

FREEDOM

The Freedom has 42-degree limb pockets, the Vib-X noise and vibration reduction system installed in the riser and a Z-Cam with PHd (perfect horizontal delivery). The cam and the Accu-Tracidler wheel are based on ball bearings and the quad limbs are 12½ inches long. This bow has a wooden grip and 6¹¹/₁₆-inch brace height. The shelf is covered with a factory installed velvet antler finish. This bow has a lifetime guarantee and is covered with Superflage Freedom camouflage.

BOW SPECIFICATIONS

AMO Draw Length: 23 to 30 inches, modular adjustments

Draw Weights: 50, 60 or 70 pounds

Bow Speed: 315 fps IBO

Axle-to Axle: 35³/₁₆ inches

SRP: $699

FREEDOM PRO

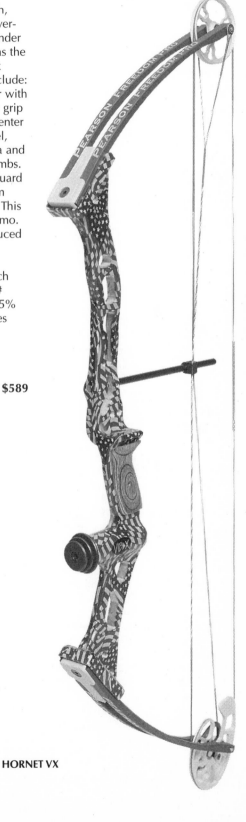

FREEDOM PRO

The Freedom Pro features a red, white and blue patriotic All-American color scheme. Beyond this, the Freedom Pro has 42-degree limb pockets, the Vib-X noise and vibration reduction system installed in the riser and a Z-Cam with PhD (perfect horizontal delivery). The cam and the idler wheel are based on ball bearings and the quad limbs are 14½-inches long. This bow has a wooden grip and 8⅝-inch brace height.

BOW SPECIFICATIONS

AMO Draw Length: 26 to 33 inches, modular adjustments
Draw Weights: 50, 60 or 70 pounds
Bow Speed: 303 fps IBO
Axle-to Axle: 37⅛ inches
SRP: **$739**

HORNET VX

With a 31-inch axle-to-axle length, this "shortie" is powerful, maneuverable, lightweight and a top contender for treestand hunters. This bow has the VIB-X vibration dampening shock below the grip. Other features include: a machined aluminum reflex riser with a full sight window, below center grip that puts the arrow in the exact center of the bow, wide track idler wheel, velvet antler finish in the rest area and four 14½-inch quadra-flex split limbs. The Hornet VX also has a cable guard with slide and uses the single cam design with a Whisper PhD cam. This bow is finished in Superflauge camo. The new Hornet VX was reintroduced in 2002.

BOW SPECIFICATIONS: HORNET VX

AMO Draw Length: 24- to 31-inch
Draw Weights: 50#, 60# and 70# with 85% let-off (and 65% and 75% let-offs are possible when modules are purchased and installed)
Bow Speed: IBO fps= 302
Axle-to Axle: 31½-inches
Weight in hand: 3.7 lbs.
SRP: **$589**

A point worth remembering: bows with a long axle-to-axle length and long brace height are physically more forgiving and easier to shoot.

HORNET VX

Ben Pearson Archery Compound Bows

COMPOUND BOWS

MARK XII

MCPHERSON
38 SPECIAL

PENTRATOR VX

MARK XII

This compound bow has an 87% let-off—one of the highest in the archery industry. It has similar design features and components to the other McPherson bows. It uses the Thruster PhD cam and Widetrack idler wheel system. The bow is camouflaged, has a wooden grip and a cable guard with slide. The Mark XII has an aluminum riser and split limbs. For any archer with shoulder pains, this could be the bow for you with its high let-off rating.

BOW SPECIFICATIONS: MARK XII
AMO Draw Length: 26- to 33-inch
Draw Weights: 50#, 60# and 70# with 87% let-off
Bow Speed: IBO fps= 301
Axle-to Axle: 35⁷/₁₆-inches
Weight in hand: 3.5 lbs.
SRP:. $399

MCPHERSON 38 SPECIAL

The lower part of the riser on this compound hunting bow features the new VIB~X noise and vibration reduction system. The chamber on this under-the-grip section incorporates a specially engineered polymer-Vibasorb that virtually eliminates vibration, noise and hand shock. Other features include: a machined aluminum riser and limb pockets; low torque wood grip; Pearson's exclusive velvet antler finish in the arrow rest area; all aluminum retainers; four 14½-inch quadra-flex split limbs tested to 300,000 cycles; catapult weighted Thruster cam with PhD—perfect horizontal delivery—single cam technology; wide track idler wheel and a new yellow and black string and harness assembly. The bow is coated with Lynch World Wide's Superflauge camo pattern.

BOW SPECIFICATIONS:
MCPHERSON 38 SPECIAL
AMO Draw Length: 25- to 32-inch
Draw Weights: 50#, 60# and 70# with 75% let-off (and 65% and 85% let-offs are possible when modules are purchased and installed)
Bow Speed: IBO fps= 310
Axle-to Axle: 38 inches
Weight in hand: 3.9 lbs.
SRP:. $759

PENTRATOR VX

The Penetrator, new in 2002, comes straight from the Pro Shop at Pearson Archery with enough accuracy for the 3-D archer and enough stored energy for the largest of big game species. The Penetrator features a 36½-inch axle-to-axle length, 6½-inch brace height, the VIB~X noise and vibration reduction system. This bow has a straight aluminum riser, four-limb design and a Thruster PhD single cam. It also has a cable guard and wood grip.

BOW SPECIFICATIONS: PENTRATOR VX
AMO Draw Length: 24- to 31-inch
Draw Weights: 50#, 60# and 70# with 85% let-off
Bow Speed: IBO fps= 310
Axle-to Axle: 36⁹/₁₆-inches
Weight in hand: 3.7 lbs.
SRP:. $579

Ben Pearson Archery Compound Bows

PREDATOR VX

PIRANHA

PIRANHA

The Piranha will fit adult archers or those much smaller in size. This bow can provide growing youngsters a bow that will give them many years of shooting pleasure thanks to the Var-max PhD single cam, the most adjustable cam in the archery industry. Other features include: a machined aluminum riser; soft-feel thermo grip, velvet antler finish in the rest area, 14¼-inch quadra-flex split limbs, wide track idler wheel and Superflauge camo.

BOW SPECIFICATIONS: PIRANHA
AMO Draw Length: 24- to 32-inch
Draw Weights: 40#, 50#, 60# and 70# with 75% let-off
Bow Speed: IBO fps= 287
Axle-to Axle: 30½-inches
Weight in hand: 3.2 lbs.
SRP:................... **$399**

PREDATOR VX

The quad limb compound bow has a wooden grip, cable guard with slide and the VIB-X noise and vibration reduction system. The shelf is covered with a factory installed velvet antler finish. Other features include a laser cam with PhD and cable guard with slide. This hunting bow is covered with Superflage camouflage.

BOW SPECIFICATIONS
AMO Draw Length: 225 to 32 inches with modular adjustments
Draw Weights: 50, 60 and 70 pounds with 85% let-off stock and 65% or 75% optional
Bow Speed: 304 fps IBO
Axle-to Axle: 34½ inches
SRP:................... **$599**

It's a fact: the closer the bow string is to the riser (low brace height), the greater the likelihood that the string will hit your forearm. So, if your bow is chewing your arm off, this may be the problem. There isn't much you can do to correct this, but you can try removing the grip from the riser and replacing it with a thin wrap. Or change up your shooting style.

Ben Pearson Archery Compound Bows

SCREAMER

SPOILER LITE

STINGER

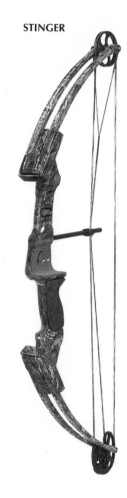

SCREAMER

This McPherson compound bow uses a 2½-inch wide track idler wheel and Thruster PhD cam to propel arrows. Other features include: a machined aluminum riser, low torque wood grip, velvet antler finish at the arrow rest area; all aluminum retainers, 14½-inch quadra-flex split limbs, and Superflauge camo. Special features include 65% let-off modules for the Pope and Young minded archer or 85% let-off modules for the archer wanting a higher let-off capability. The modules are sold separately. This bow has a cable guard with slide.

BOW SPECIFICATIONS: SCREAMER
AMO Draw Length: 23- to 30-inch
Draw Weights: 50#, 60# and 70# with 75% let-off (65% and 85% let-offs optional)
Bow Speed: IBO fps= 318
Axle-to Axle: 33¼-inches
Weight in hand: 3.6 lbs.
SRP:. **$519**

SPOILER LITE

In 2002, the Spoiler returned to Pearsons line as the Spoiler Lite. While its legacy as a shorter more compact bow lives on, its previous cam has been replaced with a hybrid—the new and advanced Whisper PhD cam. This cam provides more speed, ease of draw, and better shooting perform-ance. Other features include: a wood grip; Pearson's exclusive velvet antler finish at the arrow rest, a wide track idler wheel for straight string travel and Superflauge camo.

BOW SPECIFICATIONS: SPOILER LITE
AMO Draw Length: 24- to 31-inch
Draw Weights: 50#, 60# and 70# with 85% let-off
Bow Speed: IBO fps= 307
Axle-to Axle: 33½-inches
Weight in hand: 3.6 lbs.
SRP:. **$519**

STINGER

This bow was designed for small frame archers, ladies and youth. The Stinger features: a machined aluminum riser, soft-feel thermo grip, velvet antler finish in rest area, all aluminum retainers, 12½-inch split limbs and a Superflauge camo finish. This bow has the same design and features of many of their adult versions, including a cable guard with slide and single-cam system.

BOW SPECIFICATIONS: STINGER
AMO Draw Length: 20- to 26-inch
Draw Weights: 20#, 30#, and 40# with 75% let-off
Bow Speed: IBO fps= NA
Axle-to Axle: 28⅞-inches
Weight in hand: 2.8 lbs.
SRP:. **$309**

Browning Compound Bows

MIRAGE 33

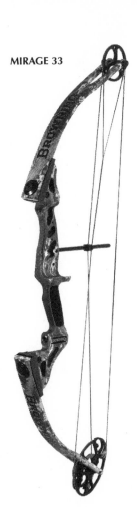

ADRENALINE 33

ADRENALINE SX

ADRENALINE SX COMPETITION

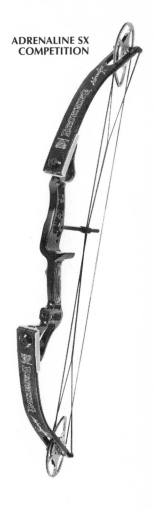

33 CLASS BOWS

This trio of bows—Mirage 33, Adrenaline 33 and Impulse LS—offer value for hunters seeking top-of-the-line components in an affordable one-cam compound bow. All bows feature forged/machined aluminum 33 risers (machined aluminum riser in the Impulse), Dynaflite strings and strong 450 Plus cables. The Mirage and Adrenaline models have 15-inch Contour XP limbs, integral cable guard, contoured two-piece foam grip and locking limb bolts and aluminum fixed position limb pockets. The lighter Impulse weighs 2.6 lbs. and has a 31½-inch axle-to-axle length and IBO speed of 277 fps. The Mirage uses the Cyber-Cam SX system to propel arrows and the Adrenaline and Impulse use Lightning cams and

have 70% let-off. All of the bows are available in Mossy Oak Break-Up camouflage.

BOW SPECIFICATIONS:
MIRAGE AND ADRENALINE 33
AMO Draw Length: varies.
Draw Weights: varies; 75% let-off and 65% optional
Bow Speed: IBO fps = 300 (Mirage), 305 (Adrenaline)
Axle-to Axle: 33 inches (Mirage) and 33¼-inches (Adrenaline)
Weight in hand: 3.9 lbs.
SRP:. **$499**
Impulse **$299**

ADRENALINE SX

This Browning compound bow uses the company's Lightning cam system along with solid Contour XP limbs. Other features include a two-piece

wooden grip, machined aluminum riser and cable guard with slide. The Adrenaline is finished in Mossy Oak camouflage.

BOW SPECIFICATIONS
AMO Draw Length: 24-27, 27-29 and 29-31 inches
Draw Weights: 40-50, 50-60 and 60-70 with 70% let-off
Bow Speed: 305 fps
Axle-to Axle: 33 inches
SRP:. **$745**

ADRENALINE SX COMPETITION

This is a competition version of the Adrenaline with the option of a blue or red riser. The components and design are similar and this bow has chromed cams and idler wheels.
SRP: **$799.95**

COMPOUND BOWS

Browning Compound Bows

ECLIPSE SLX

ECLIPSE ZLX

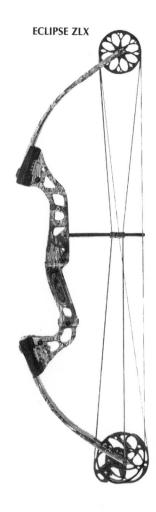

ECLIPSE ZLX COMPETITION

ECLIPSE SLX

This leader of the Browning pack of bows features a machined aluminum reflex riser that incorporates a machined self-grip with laminated wood insert panels. The riser makes the bow more comfortable to shoot. Other features include Radial-Lok pivoting limb pockets that are dampened with ImpacStop vibration dampening inserts. The limbs also assures positive limb to pocket alignment.

The Eclipse can be adjusted over a 3-inch draw length span and from 65% to 75% let-off. It has 15½-inch Contour XP limbs, an integral aluminum/carbon cable guard, two-piece wood grip, 8125 string and 450 plus cables and raised dome limb graphics. The idler wheel has a sealed ball bearing system. This compound bow is available in Mossy Oak Break-Up camouflage.

The Browning Eclipse SL 36 has a similar riser, limb and design as Eclipse SLX, including the use of Cyber-Cam SX system, and has a 36-in axle-to-axle length. This bow's limb pockets do not have the Radial Lok vibration system and the SL 36 has molded foam grip inserts.

BOW SPECIFICATIONS: ECLIPSE SLX
AMO Draw Length: varies.
Draw Weights: varies; 75% let-off and 65% optional
Bow Speed: IBO fps = 310
Axle-to Axle: 36 inches
Weight in hand: 4.3 lbs.
SRP:. $745
    (add $16 for LH models)
SL 36 . . . . $545

ECLIPSE ZLX

This new model compound bow by Browning features the Split harness system with its unique one cam and counter rotating twin idlers. The split harness supports the bottom limb tip to provide adjustability to balance the limb fork load. Other features include a machined aluminum riser, Cyber ZX cam, adjustable let-off, Radial-Lok pivoting limb pockets and Impact-stop vibration dampening pocket inserts. This bow has custom two-piece grips and is camouflaged with Mossy Oak Break Up.

BOW SPECIFICATIONS
AMO Draw Length: 27 to 31 inches
Draw Weights: 50-60 and 60-70 pounds with 65% or 75% let-off
Bow Speed: 302 fps
Axle-to Axle: 36 inches
SRP:. $799

ECLIPSE ZLX COMPETITION

A compound bow similar to the Eclipse ZLX but this bow has glossy black limbs, chromed cams and idler wheels and a dark blue riser. This bow is also available in red.
SRP: $849

MIRAGE ZX

MICRO ADRENALINE COMBO

MICRO ECLIPSE COMBO

MIDAS 2 COMBO

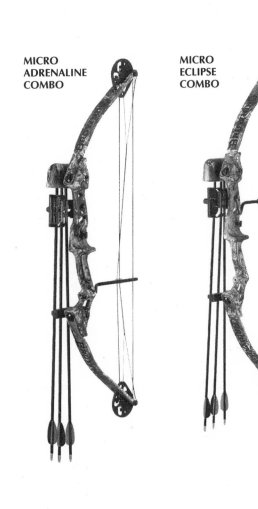

MICRO CLASS COMBOS

These youth-oriented bows—Micro Adrenaline, Micro Eclipse and Midas 2—are available in a complete combo that will have any young shooter increasing their skills and accuracy in record time. All bows have a 6¼-inch brace height, approximately 32-inch axle-to-axle length and Taperflex limbs. Other items offered in the combo package include: quivers, sights with pins, three matching carbon arrows, and a two-piece wood grip (foam only on the Midas 2). Each bow weighs slightly more than 2½-pounds and propels arrows at approximately 270-plus fps IBO. The Adrenaline and Midas 2 have under-the-grip cable guards and the

Eclipse has an upper cable guard. All bows have dual cams (the Eclipse is single cam with idler wheel) and are camouflaged for hunting. The Midas has a black riser. All of these bows are available without the combo package for $70 less.

BOW SPECIFICATIONS: MICRO ADRENALINE, MICRO ECLIPSE AND MIDAS 2 COMBOS
AMO Draw Length: varies and can be adjusted approximately 6 inches.
Draw Weights: varies; 65% let-off (60% for the Adrenaline model)
Bow Speed: IBO fps = 270-plus
Axle-to Axle: approximately 32 inches
Weight in hand: 2.7 lbs.
SRP: Adrenaline and Eclipse . . . $335
Midas 2 . . . . $265

MIRAGE ZX

A bow that utilizes Browning's new Split Limb harness One-Cam technology and twin idler. The Mirage provides 5 inches of draw length adjustment and has two-piece wooden grips. This bow has 15-inch Contour XP limbs, pivoting machined limb pockets and Impact stop limb pocket inserts to reduce vibration. The Mirage weighs 3.8 pounds and has a 7½-inch brace height.

BOW SPECIFICATIONS
AMO Draw Length: 26 to 30 inches
Draw Weights: 50-60 and 60-70 with 75% or 65% let-off
Bow Speed: 300 fps
Axle-to Axle: 33 inches
SRP:. $749

Browning Compound Bows

MIRAGE ZX COMPETITION

RAGE

MIRAGE ZX COMPETITION

This bow is similar to the standard camouflaged Mirage but has chromed limb pockets, cam and idler, plus a choice of red or blue riser. The competition model also has a cable guard and wooden grip.

SRP:. **$799**

RAGE

A bow designed for hunters on a budget, this compound has a machined aluminum riser and HyperMax cam system that permits 10 inches of adjustment. Other features include Contour XP limbs, a one-piece grip and cable guard with slide. The Rage weighs 3.9 pounds and is covered with Mossy Oak Break Up camouflage. This bow is offered as a package with a two-piece quiver, sight, three fiber optic pins and an arrow rest for $399

BOW SPECIFICATIONS

AMO Draw Length: 21-31 inches
Draw Weights: 45-55 and 55-65 with 70% let-off
Bow Speed: 292 fps
Axle-to Axle: 35 inches
SRP:. **$319**

"You will discover that to be a good shot is not the half of what it takes to make a tolerable bird slayer."
—Maurice Thompson,
The Witchery of Archery, 1879

COMPOUND BOWS

Browning Compound Bows

TORNADO COMBO

AMBUSH COMBO

SINGLE-CAM COMBOS

Browning takes the guess work and search out of finding the right accessories to perfectly match your hunting bow with the Tornado and Ambush combos.

The Tornado's accessories include: a seven-arrow one-piece Twist-Lok quiver in Mossy Oak Break-Up, TM Hunter arrow rest, 4½-inch solid tapered stabilizer, fiber optic sight with three metal sight pins and Whisper string silencers. This package also has an adjustable braided nylon sling, sight peep and nock. The Tornado bow has a machined aluminum riser, Contour XP limbs, molded grip with wood inserts and Dynaflite string. This bow's Cyber-Cam 5 provides 5 inches of draw length adjustability in half-inch increments and let-off that's adjustable from 65% up to 80%.

The Ambush combo includes: a two-piece quiver that will hold up to six arrows, a fiber optic sight, Toughman arrow rest, stabilizer, Whisper string silencers and a sling. A nock point and sight peep are included in the package to assist with accuracy when shooting. The Ambush has a unique black powder-coated machined aluminum riser and soft rubber grip with wood inserts. Other features include: a cable guard, Ignitor 3 cam and Dynaflite string. This bow also has solid Contour XP limbs coated with Ambush camouflage.

The Tornado and Ambush bows have a bold Browning logo on the limbs in black letters.

BOW SPECIFICATIONS:
AMBUSH AND TORNADO COMBOS
AMO Draw Length: varies.
Draw Weights: varies; 80% let-off adjustable to 65% (Tornado) and 75% let-off Ambush
Bow Speed: IBO fps = 292 (Tornado) and 280 (Ambush)
Axle-to Axle: 36 inches
Weight in hand: 3.9 lbs.
SRP: Tornado combo. $445
Ambush XB combo. $299
Ambush separately $229

CYBER-CAM 5

COMPOUND BOWS

Compound Bows • **137**

Browning Compound Bows

MIRAGE SX   ADRENALINE SX

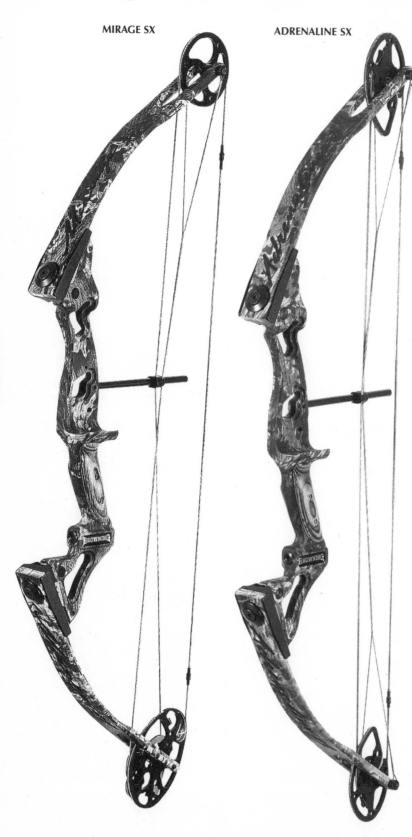

SX Class Bows

The two offerings in Browning's SX Class bows are the Mirage and Adrenaline. The Mirage has a forged/machined aluminum SX riser, Cyber-Cam SX system, adjustable let-off module with 65% or 75%, 15-inch Contour XP limbs and intergral aluminum/carbon cable guard. This bow's Radial-Lok pivoting machined aluminum limb pockets have ImpacStop vibration dampening pocket inserts. Other features include locking limb bolts, raised, domed limb graphics and 8125 string with 450 Plus cables. SX Class bows have two-piece wood grips and are camouflaged for hunting by a hand-dipped application of Mossy Oak Break-Up.

The Adrenaline SX compound bow features Lightning cams, a 6½-inch brace height, 70% let-off and the same axle-to-axle length and mass weight. Both SX bows have a Browning logo embedded in the riser under the grip.

Bow Specifications: Mirage SX
AMO Draw Length: varies.
Draw Weights: varies; 75% let-off and 65% optional
Bow Speed: IBO fps = 302
Axle-to Axle: 33 inches
Weight in hand: 3.9 lbs.
SRP: **$675**
Adrenaline **$675**

CYBER-CAM SX

Browning Compound Bows

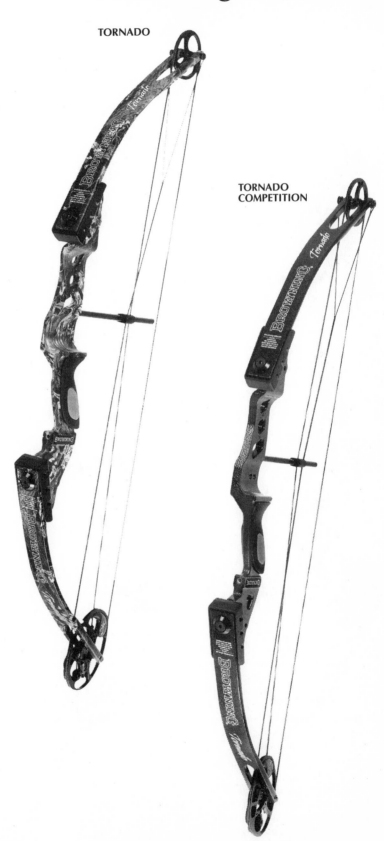

TORNADO

TORNADO COMPETITION

TORNADO

An ergonomically designed bow with a moderately reflexed machine riser with a one-piece logo grip. The Tornado uses Contour XP limbs and the Cyber5 cam system. The tips of the 15½-inch limbs fit into pockets. This bow is camouflaged with Mossy Oak and uses a Dynaflite 97-inch string. This bow is also available in a package complete with quiver, sight, rest, stabilizer and sling for $539.

BOW SPECIFICATIONS
AMO Draw Length: 24-28 and 27-31 inches
Draw Weights: 50-60 and 60-70 with 80% let-off and 65% let-off optional
Bow Speed: 292 fps
Axle-to Axle: 37 inches
SRP: **$439**

TORNADO COMPETITION

A competition version of the Tornado compound bow by Browning. This bow is only available in blue and has black limbs. All other components are similar in design and color and the performance and specifications are the same.
SRP: **$479.95**

"The bowman, to be successful as a hunter, must learn to perfection the habits of his game."
—Maurice Thompson, The Witchery of Archery, 1879

Buckmasters Compound Bows

G2

HYPERTECH

Bow Speed: IBO fps = 292;
AMO fps = 220
Axle-to Axle: 39½-inches
Weight in hand: 4 lbs., 10 oz.
SRP:. $279

G2

Representing the next generation of bows, the lightweight G2 incorporates Sims LimbSaver technology to cancel recoil, vibration and noise. Other features include a ball bearing mounted idler wheel, TechTwist string, lightweight carbon cable guard and a custom checkered hardwood grip. Special polymer wedges around the base ends of the Carbon Quad limbs help absorb shock and reduce noise. The G2 is available in right- and left-hand models with a Realtree Hardwoods camo finish. This hunting bow has a machined aluminum riser and a perimeter weighted cam.

BOW SPECIFICATIONS: G2
AMO Draw Length: 28-, 29- and 30-inch; adjustable range 28 to 30 inches
Draw Weights: 40-50#, 50-60# and 60-70# with 70% let-off (65% available)
Bow Speed: IBO fps = 309;
AMO fps = 232
Axle-to Axle: 31 inches
Weight in hand: 3 lbs., 9 oz.
SRP:. $499

HyperTech

The 34-inch axle-to-axle HyperTech features a perimeter weighted cam, Carbon Quad straight limbs and a Realtree Hardwoods camouflage finish. The right-hand model has an Elasto-Polymer grip and the left-hand version has a checkered laminated wood grip. Other features include a machined 6061-T-6 aluminum riser, solid cable guard and red-and-black TechTwist string.

BOW SPECIFICATIONS: HYPERTECH
AMO Draw Length: 27-, 28-, 29-, 30 and 31-inch; adjustable range 24 to 31 inches
Draw Weights: 50-60# and 60-70# with 70% let-off (65% optional with available modules)
Bow Speed: IBO fps = 298;
AMO fps = 221
Axle-to Axle: 34 inches
Weight in hand: 4 lbs., 7 oz.
SRP:. $299

2000

This performance oriented bow features a machined 6061-T-6 aluminum riser that provides a 7.375-inch brace height for its left- or right-hand versions. Other features include compression molded CarbonAir limbs, a synthetic string and the use of a SuperCam. Left-hand models feature a checkered laminated wood handle and the right-hand model has an elasto-polymer non-skid grip. It's available in Realtree Harwoods camouflage finish and with a solid cable guard equipped with a slide.
BOW SPECIFICATIONS: 2000

AMO Draw Length: 28-, 29- and 30-inch; adjustable range 26 to 32 inches
Draw Weights: 50-60# and 60-70# with 75% let-off (65% available)

Buckmasters Compound Bows

ULTRA MAG SET

This Buckmasters compound hunting bow arrives complete with sights, arrow rest and two-piece quiver. It's available in left- and right-hand versions with a black all-weather composite grip nestled against a magnesium riser. Other features include a Realtree Hardwoods camouflage finish, carbon quad limbs and a solid cable guard. Technology and matching accessories meet here to create a bow package that's ready for the hunt after you add arrows.

BOW SPECIFICATIONS: ULTRA MAG SET
AMO Draw Length: 28-, 29- and 30-inch; adjustable range 24 to 30 inches
Draw Weights: 50-60# and 60-70# with 75% let-off (65% available)
Bow Speed: IBO fps = 291; AMO fps = 223
Axle-to Axle: 35.5 inches
Weight in hand: 4 lbs.
SRP:. $249

YOUNG BUCKS

This feature packed bow is designed to introduce novice shooters to archery and bowhunting in an affordable package. The bow weighs less than 2 pounds, has adjustable draw weights and numerous high let-off options to make the bow compatible with growing arms and muscles. Other features include Realtree Hardwoods camouflage finish, sight, two piece quiver and arrow rest. The Young Bucks bow is available in right-hand version only.

BOW SPECIFICATIONS: YOUNG BUCKS
AMO Draw Length: 20-, 21- and 22-inch
Draw Weights: 17 to 22# with 65% let-off
Axle-to Axle: 30 inches
Weight in hand: 1 lb., 9 oz.
SRP: bow only $99
    package costs additional

"If you can shoot only one arrow a day, but concentrate with full focus on that one arrow, I believe it will do you more good than shooting 100 arrows ... Your goal is to develop the feel, mentally and physically, of a perfect shot, to build ... the subconscious controls and recognition points."
—Bryon Ferguson, Become the Arrow, 1994

COMPOUND BOWS

Cabela's Compound Bows

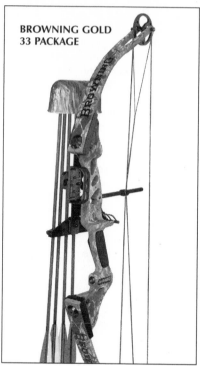

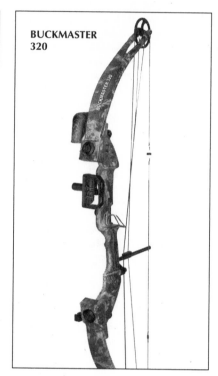

BROWNING BUCKMARK PACKAGE

This bow and accessory kit starts with Browning's popular Buckmark bow with the solid Contour XP limbs and Cyber Cam SX one-cam system. Other features of the bow include a molded riser and ergonomic grip. The Buckmark is coated with Ambush camouflage.

The package components include: a camouflaged two-piece quiver that hold six arrows, Lightning sight with three fiber optic pins, Huntsman Toughman rest and four carbon arrows along with the bow. All items are selected and designed to compliment the bow's in-the-field performance. The bow can be obtained in right- and left-hand models.

BOW SPECIFICATIONS: BROWNING BUCKMARK PACKAGE
AMO Draw Length: 28- to 30- inch
Draw Weights: 50/60# and 60/70# with 65% to 75% adjustable let-off
Bow Speed: IBO fps= 290, AMO fps= 224
Axle-to Axle: 36 inches
SRP: **$299.99**

BROWNING GOLD 33 PACKAGE

This kit is similar to the Browning Buckmark package and uses the Cyber Cam 5 system which delivers five full inches of draw length adjustment without taking the bow to a pro shop. This bow has limb pockets for the solid limbs, single cam, carbon cable guard with slide and a molded grip. The bow is coated with Ambush camouflage. The kit that accompanies the bow includes: a TL seven arrow quiver, adjustable arrow rest, Lightning sight and four Browning arrows. This bow is offered in RH models only.

BOW SPECIFICATIONS:
BROWNING GOLD 33 PACKAGE
AMO Draw Length: 26- to 30-inch
Draw Weights: 50/60# and 60/70# with 65% or 80% adjustable let-off
Bow Speed: IBO fps= 300, AMO fps= 234
Axle-to Axle: 33³⁄₈-inches
SRP: **$399.99**

BUCKMASTER 320

This exclusive Cabela's bow has a short axle-to-axle length and a Perimeter OneCam system. Its compression molded carbon straight limbs are anchored in Quiet Tech limb cups to reduce game spooking noise and annoying vibrations. Other features include a radically reflexed machined aluminum riser, two-piece checkered wood grip and Posi-lock cable guard. This hunting bow is coated with Advantage Timber camouflage and has a 6-inch brace height. This bow is available as a left- or right-hand model.

A kit is offered for this bow that includes: a matching three-pin fiber optic sight with level, two-piece arrow quiver in matching camo, a Golden-Key Huntsman arrow rest, peep sight, and Whiskers string silencer.

BOW SPECIFICATIONS: BUCKMASTER 320
AMO Draw Length: 28-, 29- and 30-inch
Draw Weights: 60# to 70# with 65% let-off
Bow Speed: IBO fps =320, AMO fps= 236
Axle-to Axle: 35¼-inches
SRP: **$299.99**
bow with kit **$349.99**

Cabela's Compound Bows

DARTON MUSTANG PACKAGE

This package is recommended for beginning or economically inclined archers and is big on features and low on price. The bow's features include: Darton's Post Feed Cam (PFC) single-cam technology, a solid die-cast riser, cable guard and molded grip. The package includes the bow, arrow rest, quiver and fiber optic sight with four pins. The entire assembly is covered in Superflage camo.

BOW SPECIFICATIONS:

DARTON MUSTANG PACKAGE

AMO Draw Length: 27- to 30-inch
Draw Weights: 50/60# and 60/70# with 75% let-off
Bow Speed: IBO fps= 277, AMO fps= 220
Axle-to Axle: 38¾-inches
SRP: **$199.99**

DARTON STRIKER PACKAGE

This Cabela's Exclusive package starts with a Striker compound bow by Darton and adds on an arrow rest, quiver and fiber-optic sight with pins. The bow features a solid riser with built-in overdraw, PFC single-cam system, molded grip and Superflage camo finish. There is a considerable savings by purchasing this package when compared to purchasing the parts separately.

BOW SPECIFICATIONS:

DARTON STRIKER PACKAGE

AMO Draw Length: 27- to 30-inch
Draw Weights: 50/60# and 60/70# with 75% let-off
Bow Speed: IBO fps 277, AMO fps= 220
Axle-to Axle: 38¾-inches
SRP: **$229.99**

PSE BABY-G PACKAGE

One of PSE's top selling models is now available with a top-notch accessory package to make the trip from home to treestand much quicker and less stressful. Features of this bow include a split-harness string system to prevent the wheel from leaning, a Lightning One-Cam with positive draw stop, and a machined 6061 aluminum riser. The PSE Baby-G also has a wooden grip, solid Magnaglass limbs and Brush camouflage finish. The package components incorporate an FX sight, Mongoose arrow rest, stabilizer and peep, plus a one-piece quiver stocked with 4 carbon arrows.

BOW SPECIFICATIONS:

PSE BABY-G PACKAGE

AMO Draw Length: 28-, 29- and 30-inch
Draw Weights: 50/60# and 60/70# with 80% let-off
Bow Speed: IBO fps= 315, AMO fps= 246
Axle-to Axle: 36 inches
SRP: **$399.99**

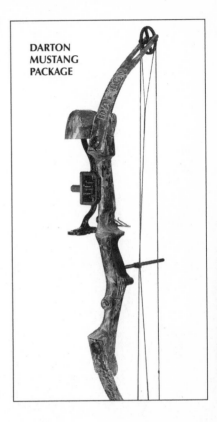

DARTON MUSTANG PACKAGE

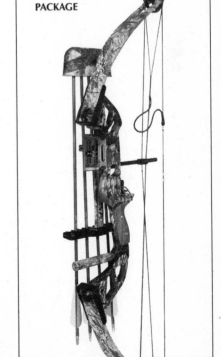

PSE BABY-G PACKAGE

COMPOUND BOWS

"Robin's favorite mark was a small willow staff or wand (made white by peeling off the bark) stuck in the ground at one hundred yards' distance. This he is represented rarely ever to have missed."
—Maurice Thompson, The Witchery of Archery, 1879

Custom Shooting Systems Compound Bows

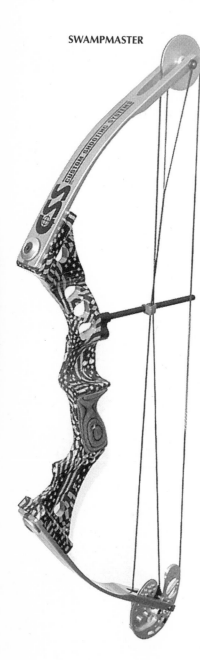

SWAMPMASTER

CHALLENGER

This CSS bow has a machined aluminum riser and soft touch molded grip or optional walnut grip. Other features for this bow include: Gordon thermal composite limbs, pro shop adjustable let-off and Mossy Oak Break-Up camo. This bow weighs 4 pounds and has a single-cam design.

BOW SPECIFICATIONS: CHALLENGER

AMO Draw Length: 25- to 33-inch

Draw Weights: 40#, 50#, 60#, 70#+ Max and Big game 80#+. Offers an adjustable let-off from 60% to 75%

Bow Speed: 310 fps IBO

Axle-to-Axle: 38, 40, 42 and 44 inches

SRP:. $625

Tournament Models Starting at . . $700

CONTENDER

The Contender has similar features and parts of the Challenger model. This bow has a deflex style riser and is offered in the same colors as the Challenger.

BOW SPECIFICATIONS: CONTENDER

AMO Draw Length: 26- to 35-inch

Draw Weights: 40#, 50#, 60#, 70#+. The pro shop adjustable let-off ranges from 60% to 75%

Bow Speed: 290 fps IBO

Axle-to-Axle: 38, 40, 42 and 44 inches

SRP: Starting at $700

Tournament Models Starting at . . $700

ECLIPSE

This bow is based on the Swampmaster. Features include: a T-6061 machined aluminum reflex riser, soft-touch one-piece grip, Gordon thermal composite limbs and Perimeter 1 cams. The Eclipse weighs 4 pounds and has a 7¹⁄₂-inch brace height. It is available in Mossy Oak Break-Up camouflage. A walnut wood grip is optional for an additional $10.

BOW SPECIFICATIONS: ECLIPSE

AMO Draw Length: 25- to 33-inch

Draw Weights: 40#, 50#, 60# and 70#+ Max. The let-off can be adjusted at the pro shop and ranges from 60% to 75%

Bow Speed: 305 fps IBO

Axle-to-Axle: 38 inches (optional 40 inches)

SRP: Starting at $625

Tournament Models Starting at . . $700

SYSTEM

Features include perimeter 1 cam, adjustable let off, a 7¹⁄₄-inch brace height and composite solid limbs. This bow is offered in Mossy Oak Break-Up.

BOW SPECIFICATIONS: SYSTEM

AMO Draw Length: 24- to 34-inch

Draw Weights: 40#, 50#, 60#, 70#+ Max and Big Game 80#. The pro shop adjustable let- off ranges from 60% to 75%

Bow Speed: 300 fps IBO

Axle-to-Axle: 38, 40, 42 and 44 inches

SRP:. $595

Tournament Models Starting at . . $670

SWAMPMASTER

This CSS compound hunting bow is offered only in Mossy Oak camo and is the company's flagship hunting bow. It has a T-6061 machined aluminum reflex riser, soft-touch grip, Gordon Thermal composite solid limbs and uses the perimeter 1-cam system to propel arrows. The Swampmaster weighs 3.7 pounds, has a cable guard and has a 6⁷⁄₈-inch brace height.

BOW SPECIFICATIONS: SWAMPMASTER

AMO Draw Length: 24- to 30-inch

Draw Weights: 40#, 50#, 60#, 70#+; pro shop adjustable let off from 60% to 75%

Bow Speed: 300 fps IBO

Axle-to-Axle: 32 and 34 inches

SRP:. $565

TALON

This hunting bow has the standard CSS riser, grip, cable guard and solid composite limbs with reinforced tips. It uses the perimeter 1 cam system and is offered only in Mossy Oak camo. The bow wears a distinct CSS logo on the limbs. The Talon has a 7¹⁄₂-inch brace height and a longer axle-to-axle length. Optional "green".

BOW SPECIFICATIONS: TALON

AMO Draw Length: 24- to 31-inch

Draw Weights: 40#, 50#, 60#, 70#+. The pro shop adjustable let-off ranges from 60% to 75%

Bow Speed: 285 fps IBO

Axle-to-Axle: 36 inches

SRP:. $395

DARTON'S PREMIER PRO SERIES

CYCLONE EXPRESS '3D'

Darton's Cyclone Express '3D' is designed for 3-D tournaments and bowhunting. This model incorporates a Deflexed machined riser and short limbs along with the C/P/S Express single-cam system. Its long axle-to-axle length makes it a good choice for finger shooters. Other features include limb pockets, cable guard and molded black grip. This bow is available in Superflauge camo and weighs 4.2 pounds.

BOW SPECIFICATIONS:
CYCLONE EXPRESS '3D'
AMO Draw Length: 27- to 31½-inch
Draw Weights: 50#, 60# and 70# with 80% let-off
Bow Speed: IBO fps= 304, AMO fps= 234
Axle-to Axle: 38 inches
SRP: **$619.99**
Tournament Models Starting at . . **$730**

CYCLONE EXPRESS 'LD'

The Express 'LD' –Long Draw—shares many of the same features as Darton's Maverick Recurve, only with a longer deflexed machined riser. Other features include an 8-inch brace height, efficient cam/limb design, cable guard and molded grip. Available in Superflauge camouflage.

BOW SPECIFICATIONS:
CYCLONE EXPRESS 'LD'
AMO Draw Length: 28- to 34¼-inch
Draw Weights: 50#, 60# and 70# with 80% let-off
Bow Speed: IBO fps= 300, AMO fps= 232
Axle-to Axle: 41¼-inches
SRP: **$659.99**
Tournament Models Starting at . . **$770**

EXECUTIVE VEGAS

This bow features a long axle-to-axle measurement and the proven C/P/S 'SD' Single Cam System. Other specifications for this bow (model No. 9627) include a 9½-inch brace height—one of the archery industry's tallest—and weight of 4.3 pounds.

BOW SPECIFICATIONS: EXECUTIVE VEGAS
AMO Draw Length: 27- to 31-inch
Draw Weights: 50# and 60# with 75% let-off
Bow Speed: IBO fps= 275, AMO fps= 211
SRP: uperflage camo **$659.99**
Tournament Models Starting at . . **$770**

EXECUTIVE VEGAS SD

The Vegas SD bow by Darton has shorter limbs and a shorter axle-to-axle length than the standard model and is available in a Superflage camo finish for hunting. Another feature of this bow is the proven C/P/S 'SD' single cam system. This model has an 8½-inch brace height, cable guard, molded black grip and weighs 4.3 pounds.

BOW SPECIFICATIONS:
EXECUTIVE VEGAS SD
AMO Draw Length: 27- to 31-inch
Draw Weights: 40#, 50#, 60# and 70# with 75% let-off
Bow Speed: IBO fps= 275, AMO fps= 211
Axle-to Axle: 41¼-inches
SRP: **$749.22**

CYCLONE EXPRESS

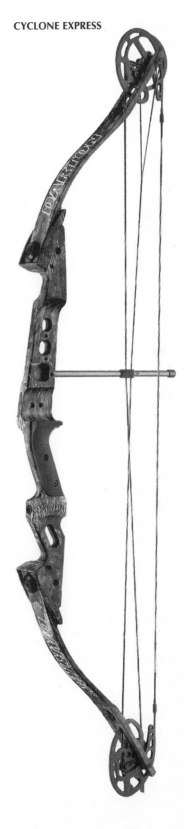

Darton Archery Compound Bows

RAMPAGE EXPRESS

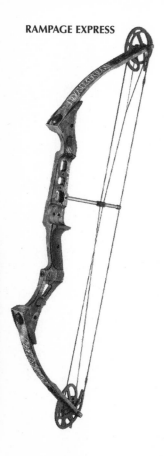

AVALANCHE EXTREME

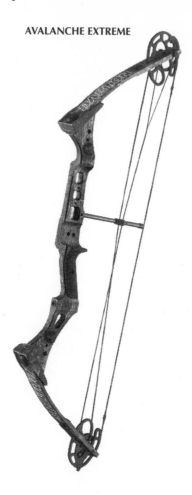

MAGNUM EXTREME

RAMPAGE EXPRESS

The Rampage has a reflex machined riser with a brace height of slightly less than 7 inches. Other features include short FlexPower Limbs and the C/P/S 'Express' single-cam system. Available in Darton's Superflauge camo.

BOW SPECIFICATIONS: RAMPAGE EXPRESS
AMO Draw Length: 25½- to 31¾-inch
Draw Weights: 50#, 60# and 70# with 80% let-off
Bow Speed: IBO fps= 310,
AMO fps= 240
Axle-to Axle: 37¼-inches
SRP: $629.99
Tournament Models Starting at . . $740

DARTON'S PREMIER ASSAULT SERIES

AVALANCHE EXTREME

The Avalanche Extreme combines Darton's new C/P/S Extreme cam system and reflex machined riser for a high-energy producing power stroke.

The 7½-inch brace height helps provide overall shootability while the highly efficient UltraFlexPower Limbs, with their unique mounting angle, and the new Integral Dampening System makes a fast shooting bow. This bow is available in both right- and left-hand models.

BOW SPECIFICATIONS
AMO Draw Length: 26½ inch to 30½ inch with 70 or 80% let-off
Draw Weights: 50, 60 and 70 pounds
Bow Speed: 308 IBO
Axle-to Axle: 34⅜ inch
SRP: $630

MAGNUM 33

The Magnum 33 spits out arrows at over 300 fps. Construction of the Magnum 33 starts with the C/P/S Express cam system matched with a pair of short, energy-efficient limbs utilizing high strength modulus materials. Other features include a forged aluminum riser, 7⅞-inch brace

height, limb pockets and black molded grip. This hunting bow is available in Darton's Superflauge pattern and weighs 3.4 pounds.

BOW SPECIFICATIONS: MAGNUM 33
AMO Draw Length: 26¼- to 31⅜-inch
Draw Weights: 50#, 60# and 70# with 80% let-off
Bow Speed: IBO fps= 302,
AMO fps= 237
Axle-to Axle: 33 inches
SRP: $549.99
**Magnum Extreme
(camouflage only)** $569.99

MAGNUM EXTREME

The Magnum Extreme begins with the new C/P/S Extreme cam system for power, performance and accuracy. It is then outfitted with a pair of matched UltraFlexPower energy efficient limbs utilizing high strength modulus materials. To complete this impressive package it all comes together on a redesigned version of the Maverick forged aluminum riser with new Integral Dampening System. The Magnum Extreme is available in both right and left hand models, has a 6½-inch brace height, is axle-to-axle, and weighs 3.4 lbs.

BOW SPECIFICATIONS
AMO Draw Length: 25½ to 30 inches
Draw Weights: 50 to 70 pounds with 70% or 80% let-off
Bow Speed: 312 IBO fps
Axle-to Axle: 32⅝ inches
SRP: $469

MAVERICK EXPRESS RECURVE

The Maverick Express 'Recurve' is a compound bow that features Darton's C/P/S Express single-cam system. The lightweight bow–under 3.6 lbs.–has magnesium limb pockets attached to a 7075-T6 forged riser. Other features include a lightweight set of narrow, composite Recurve limbs, cable guard, and molded grip. Available in Superflauge camo and Darton's competition colors.

BOW SPECIFICATIONS:
MAVERICK EXPRESS RECURVE
AMO Draw Length: 25½ to 33 inches
Draw Weights: 50#, 60# and 70# with 80% let-off
Bow Speed: IBO fps= 314, AMO fps= 244
Axle-to Axle: 38 inches
SRP: $579.99
Tournament Models Starting at . . **$690**

MAVERICK RECURVE REW

This Maverick model features REW (Round Energy Wheels) technology and includes a machined forged riser and FlexPower recurve limbs. Other features include a 7-inch brace height, cable guard, and molded grip. The Maverick Recurve REW weighs 3.7 pounds. Available in Superflauge pattern.

BOW SPECIFICATIONS:
MAVERICK RECURVE REW
AMO Draw Length: 25¾- to 32⅝-inch
Draw Weights: 50#, 60# and 70# with 80% let-off
Bow Speed: IBO fps= 279, AMO fps= 219
Axle-to Axle: 44 to 44½-inches
SRP: $569.99
Tournament Models Starting at . . **$650**

DARTON'S TROPHY SERIES

EXCITER

Darton's Exciter compound bow is designed for kids around a rugged and dependable machined aluminum riser matched up with a pair of machined pultruded fiberglass limbs and versatile Short Draw P/F/C single-cam system. It is available in a draw weight range suitable for bowhunting and with the Short Draw P/F/C single cam and four interchangeable modules. It can be adjusted to fit the growing archer. The bow comes in either SuperFlage camo or black as a single unit or as a package with camouflaged bow quiver, 3-pin fiber optic sight and arrow rest. The Exciter is available in both right and left hand models, has a 6⅝-inch brace height and weighs a light 2.8 pounds.

BOW SPECIFICATIONS
AMO Draw Length: 21½ to 25½inches
Draw Weights: 20 to 45 pounds with 80% let-off
Bow Speed: NA
Axle-to Axle: 32⅝ inches
SRP: $279.99
  camouflaged $279.99
  black. $249.99

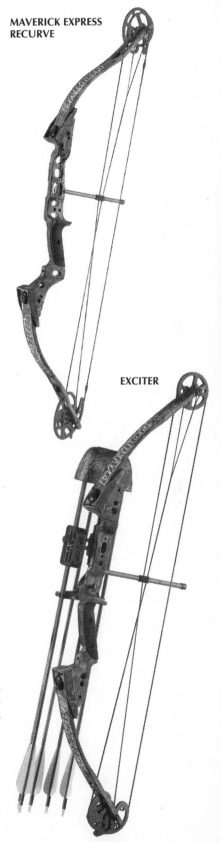

MAVERICK EXPRESS RECURVE

EXCITER

Darton Archery Compound Bows

EXPLORER

FURY EXPRESS

STORM

EXPLORER

Built with a solid lightweight, tough 20K magnesium riser, the Explorer features reliable, high quality Gordon fiberglass camouflaged limbs and easy-to-draw molded eccentric wheels. Buyers have a choice of two different peak weights and adjustable Tri-Draw molded wheels.

The Explorer II has a 35# draw weight and slightly longer draw length along with 65% let-off. Both models weigh 2.4 pounds.

BOW SPECIFICATIONS: EXPLORER
AMO Draw Length: 18- to 20-inch
Draw Weights: 25# with 65% let-off
Bow Speed: NA
Axle-to Axle: 32⅛ inches
SRP: Explorer. $129.99
Explorer II. $139.99

FURY EXPRESS

This single-cam compound uses a lightweight, machined riser along with Darton's C/P/S Express single-cam system. Other features include: interchangeable and adjustable draw length modules, cable guard and a molded grip. The Fury Express is also offered as a complete package with fiber-optic sight, bow quiver, launcher arrow rest and arrows. This model is available in TimberTop camouflage, weighs 3.8 pounds and has a 6⅛-inch brace height.

BOW SPECIFICATIONS: FURY EXPRESS
AMO Draw Length: 25⅜- to 31⅝-inch
Draw Weights: 50#, 60# and 70# with 80% let-off
Bow Speed: IBO fps= 301, AMO fps= 235
Axle-to Axle: 35⅛ inches
SRP: $429.99

FURY SD

The Fury SD is another unique design that makes Darton's C/P/S technology available to shorter draw archers. This lightweight model weighs 3.6 pounds and has a 6⅜-inch brace height. This shorter axle-to-axle length bow is available by itself or as a complete package with fiber optic sight, bow quiver, launcher rest and arrows.

BOW SPECIFICATIONS: FURY SD
AMO Draw Length: 21⅝- to 26½-inch

Draw Weights: 50#, 60# and 70# with 75% let-off
Bow Speed: NA
Axle-to Axle: 34¾-inches
SRP: $429.99

PIONEER

Manufacturing of the Pioneer starts with a solid, lightweight 20K Magnesium riser, pultruded fiberglass limbs and versatile short-draw PFC single-cam technology. The Pioneer arrives with 4 interchangeable modules and it can be made to fit the growing archer for years of shooting fun. Other features include: solid limbs, a cable guard and camouflage finish. To make things complete, a package with bow quiver, 3-pin sight and arrow rest can be added.

The Pioneer II has similar components and is available in 45# draw weight, 80% let-off and slightly longer draw length. It's designed for slightly larger built young archers. This bow weighs 2.8 pounds and has a 6-inch brace height.

BOW SPECIFICATIONS: PIONEER
AMO Draw Length: 21- to 24½-inch
Draw Weights: 35# with 75% let-off
Bow Speed: NA
Axle-to Axle: 33 inches
SRP: Pioneer $169.99
Pioneer II $199.99

STORM

Darton's Storm compound bow is a design achievement that utilizes short pultruded fiberglass limbs and a PFC single-cam system. This bow comes complete with four interchangeable draw length modules and has a cable guard and molded grip. A unique feature is camouflaged limb pockets. The Storm bow is available by itself or as a complete package with fiber-optic sight, bow quiver, launcher rest and arrows. This bow is available in TimberTop camo.

BOW SPECIFICATIONS: STORM
AMO Draw Length: 27- to 30-inch
Draw Weights: 50#, 60# and 70# with 75% let-off
Bow Speed: IBO fps= 290, AMO fps= 225
Axle-to Axle: 33½-inches
SRP: $349.99

Firebrand Technologies Compound Bows

DISCOVERY BOW

The first thing you'll notice about this bow is no cams or wheels and the two-piece limbs. The bow has an aluminum riser and wooden two-piece grip. The let-off is adjustable over a wide range by moving a single set screw. Other features include: a cable guard and finish options that include Illusion and Fall Special camouflage and flat black.

BOW SPECIFICATIONS: DISCOVERY BOW
AMO Draw Length: 25 to 27, 28 to 30, and 30 to 32 inches, adjustable by 3 inches
Draw Weights: 25# to 45# or 50# to 70# with let-off from 0% to 90%
Bow Speed: up to 260 fps IBO
Tip-to-Tip: 39 inches (does not have axles and cams)
SRP:. **$375**

INTENSITY

The most noticeable feature about this compound bow is the ribbed riser —featuring Shadow Cast technology— that's crafted from aircraft grade aluminum and heat treated to a T-6 hardness. The riser ribs help add strength and increase the camouflage effectiveness of the bow. Other bow features include: carbon limb pockets, carbon composite limbs, machined walnut grip, weight forward riser, Saunders roller cable slide and 20-strand Dyneema cables. The Intensity by Forge has an extra wide sight window and up to 7-inch brace height. The bow is covered under an unconditional five-year warranty.

BOW SPECIFICATIONS: INTENSITY
AMO Draw Length: 25 to 27, 28 to 30, and 30 to 32 inches
Draw Weights: 25# to 45# or 50# to 70#
Bow Speed: up to 300 fps IBO
Tip-to-Tip: 43 inches (does not have axles and cams)
SRP:. **$429**

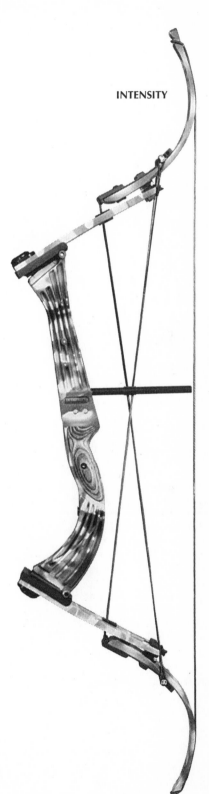

INTENSITY

Placing scent wicks around your stand can help you know for sure if a game animal is within your shooting range. Place several wicks in a circle around your stand, all positioned at a certain distance, say 20 yards. You can now judge an animal's distance by its position relative to the wicks. Don't place the scent wicks too far, though. This can cause a buck to get hung up on the scent wick and not come close enough for a good shot.

COMPOUND BOWS

Forge Bow Company Compound Bows

COMPOUND BOWS

DUSTER HP

F2 AND F2XL

FIRESTORM

DUSTER HP AND DUSTER HB

Forge's Duster compound has a anti-vibe one-piece comfort grip, integrated cable guard and modular draw length adjustment. It has a machined aluminum riser and is available in LH and RH versions with an Autumn Leaf camo finish. The HP model has fiberglass limbs and the HB model has compression molded limbs.

BOW SPECIFICATIONS:
DUSTER HP AND DUSTER HB
AMO Draw Length: 25- to 30-inch with HP; 27- to 31½-inch with HB system
Draw Weights: 50#-60#, 60#-70# w/HP (note HB model is offered in 60#-70# only). Both styles offer 65% or 80% let-off versions.
Bow Speed: 305 fps IBO with HP; 290 fps IBO with HB
Axle-to-Axle: 32 inches with HP; 32½-inches with HB
SRP: $459

F2 AND F2XL

This F2 has a hybrid aluminum riser with billets, cable guard and anti-vibe one-piece grip. Other design features include perimeter mass cam technology and vertical energy transfer technology. This bow offers one of the archery industry's largest draw weight adjustment ranges and longest draw lengths. This bow is available in left- and right-hand models and with a camouflaged coating.

BOW SPECIFICATIONS: F2 AND F2XL
AMO Draw Length: 26- to 31-inch with F2; 27- to 32-inch with F2XL system
Draw Weights: 50#-70# with F2 (Note: F2XL is offered in 55#-70# only). Both styles offer 65% or 80% let-off.
Bow Speed: 309 fps IBO with F2; 300 fps IBO with F2XL
Axle-to-Axle: 38 inches with F2; 40 inches with F2XL
SRP: $569
Tournament Models: F2 . . . . $649
      F2XL $539

FIRESTORM

This model is similar to the Lightning Strike and has a longer axle-to-axle length. Other features include compression molded carbon and glass limbs, modular draw system, cable guard and molded grip. This bow is available in LH and RH options, in a camo finish and with a single cam or dual cam design.

BOW SPECIFICATIONS: FIRESTORM
AMO Draw Length: 25- to 28½-inch with single cam; 26- to 30-inch with double cams
Draw Weights: 40#-50#, 50#-60# with one-cam system (Note: the double cam model offers an additional 60#-70# option). Both styles offer 65% or 80% let-off options.
Bow Speed: 280 fps IBO w/ one cam; 305 fps IBO w/dual cam design
Axle-to-Axle: 35 inches one-cam; 36 inches w/dual cam
SRP: single cam $329
    double cam system $299

Forge Bow Company Compound Bows

LIGHTNING STRIKE

F34 AND PF36

X/STAR

LIGHTNING STRIKE

Forge's Lightning Strike comes with a $50 plus S&H limb exchange offer so that the bow can grow with the shooter or be upgraded without having to purchase an entire new bow. This bow features a machined aluminum riser, choice of one-cam or dual-cam layout, hardened stainless steel axles and a two-piece grip. The Lightning Strike weighs less than 3 pounds, is available in left- and right-hand models and has a camouflaged finish.

BOW SPECIFICATIONS: LIGHTNING STRIKE
AMO Draw Length: 23½- to 27½-inch with single cam; 22- to 28-inch with double cam
Draw Weights: 20#-30#, 30#-40#, 40#-50# (note double cam offers additional 50#-60#)
Bow Speed: NA
Axle-to-Axle: 33 inches one-cam, 33½-inches w/dual cam
SRP:.....................$299

PF34 AND PF36

This Forge compound bow is offered in two axle-to-axle lengths—34 and 36 inches—and is based on an aluminum machined riser that provides a taller sight window—up to 8-inches on the PF36—and a larger grip area with the comfort grip system installed. Other features include a Forge cam and idler wheel, perimeter mass technology and cable guard. This bow offers a wider poundage adjustment range than other models. The main differences in the models are the PG fiberglass limbs on the PF34 and compression molded limbs on the PF36. Available in LH or RH and with a camo finish.

BOW SPECIFICATIONS: PF34 AND PF36
AMO Draw Length: 25½- to 30-inch with PF34; 27- to 31¼-inch with PF36 system
Draw Weights: 45#-60#, 55#-70# with PF34 (note the PF36 model is available in 55#-70# range only). Both bows offer 65% or 80% let-off.
Bow Speed: NA
Axle-to-Axle: 34 inches with PF34; 36 inches with PF36
SRP:.....................$539
Tournament Model $619

X/STAR

Forge's X-Star series permits changing of a cable or bow string in the field without a press by alternately loosening the limb bolts. Warning: do not try this with other Forge bows or other compound bows from other manufacturers to avoid serious injury, per the company information. Forge set out to serve the tall archer with a longer draw length through the X/Star and it's mission accomplished. This bow has a 43-inch axle-to-axle length. Other features include anti-vibe grip, integrated cable guard, one-cam system and PG fiberglass limbs. This model has an 8¼-inch brace height and is offered in LH or RH models with the company's Autumn Leaves camo finish.

BOW SPECIFICATIONS: X/STAR
AMO Draw Length: 27½- to 33½-inch
Draw Weights: 50#-65#, with 58%, 65% or 80% let-off
Bow Speed: 284 fps IBO
Axle-to-Axle: 43 inches
SRP:.....................$529

Golden Eagle Compound Bows

BRAVE SCOUT

BRAVE SPORT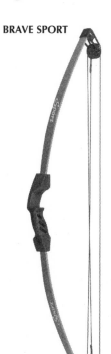

BRAVE WARRIOR

TITAN 38

CARBON TITAN EXPRESS

BRAVE SCOUT

This lightweight composite bow from Golden Eagle accommodates matching accessories to provide adult-scale satisfaction. It's available as a right-hand only model with Mossy Oak's Break-Up camouflage or black finish. This bow has an eye-catching yellow logo on its limb along with a cable guard and profiled grip. Buyers can sometimes spot this bow in mass merchandise retail stores but it is not a toy and should be used under adult supervision.

BOW SPECIFICATIONS: BRAVE SCOUT
AMO Draw Length: 20- and 22-inch
Draw Weight: 17-22# with 65% let-off
Axle-to Axle: 30 inches
Weight in hand: 1 lbs., 12 oz.
SRP:. **$39**

BRAVE SPORT

The Brave Scout is an entry-level basic compound bow with two lightweight composite wheels attached to the ends of limbs with brackets. Other features include a composite riser and fiberglass limbs. This bow is offered in a right-hand only model, and it arrives with two matched aluminum arrows

and a paper target. The bow's color is appropriately Robin Hood Hunter Green. This and all youth bows should be used under adult supervision and guidance.

BOW SPECIFICATIONS: BRAVE SPORT
AMO Draw Length: 19-, 20- and 21-inch
Draw Weight: 15# with 50% let-off
Axle-to Axle: 30 inches
Weight in hand: 15 oz.
SRP:. **$35**

BRAVE WARRIOR

This threshold bow's 80% let-off means youngsters can use it to successfully learn about archery without a struggle. The bow's features include a Mossy Oak Break-Up finish, solid cams, cable guard and solid composite limbs and riser. It's available in a right-hand only model and as a solid black version for those opting to forgo camouflage.

BOW SPECIFICATIONS: BRAVE WARRIOR
AMO Draw Length: 23-, 24- and 25-inch, adjustable 23- to 28-inch
Draw Weight: 30-40# with 80% let-off
Axle-to Axle: 33 inches
Weight in hand: 2 lbs., 3 oz.
SRP:. **$99**

CUSTOM TITAN EXPRESS/ TITAN 38

The Titan Express is one of the industry's longest bows with a 42.5-inch axle-to-axle length. This could be great news for finger shooters and tall archers with longer arms. This bow's features include a SwingArm II cable guard and solid 5% TurboTech cam. The Titan 38—a shorter model—utilizes a Controlled Power System that features level nock travel, Shock Stop vibration dampening technology and an all-synthetic string and harness system. Both bows feature laminated wood grips, a Realtree Hardwoods High Definition camouflage finish and are only available in right-hand models.

BOW SPECIFICATIONS: CUSTOM TITAN EXPRESS/TITAN 38
AMO Draw Length: 29 to 33-inch
Draw Weights: 65-75# (Titan 38 has 60-70#) and let-off varies
BOW SPEED: IBO FPS= 293;
AMO FPS= 231
Axle-to Axle: 42.5 inches
Weight in hand: varies
SRP:. **$429**

CUSTOM Z-FIRE

EVOLUTION XTR

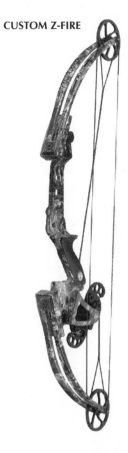

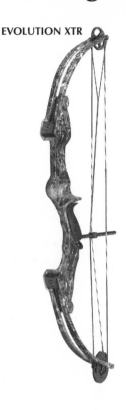

CUSTOM Z-FIRE

This futuristic compound bow is designed to the purchaser's specifications at the Golden Eagle plant. Features of the Custom Z-Fire include the use of a 65% let-off ZenCam, angled natural reflex riser and four limbs. This model is available in left- and right-hand versions with Mossy Oak Break-Up camouflage. Many of the features are based upon customer selection. Price and weight may vary. This is one of the few places in the archery industry where you can have a custom hunting compound bow built to your specifications and with the components that you like.

BOW SPECIFICATIONS: CUSTOM Z-FIRE
AMO Draw Length: 28- to 30-inch;
Draw Weights: 50-60# and 60-70# with let-off dependant upon selections
Bow Speed: IBO fps = 288; AMO fps = 230
Axle-to Axle: 34.5 inches
Weight in hand: varies
SRP:................$449

EVOLUTION GOLD SET

This unique hunting bow package includes the company's carbon quad recurve limbs, magnesium riser, Gold Dot Perimeter Weighted cam system, plus sights, arrow rest, cable guard and a two-piece quiver. It's available in a right-hand only model and with the Mossy Oak Break-Up camouflage finish.

BOW SPECIFICATIONS:
EVOLUTION GOLD SET
AMO Draw Length: 30-inch; adjustable range 28 to 31 inches
Draw Weights: 50-60# and 60-70# with 75% let-off (65% optional with modules)
Bow Speed: IBO fps = 291; AMO fps = 227
Axle-to Axle: 38.5 inches
Weight in hand: 4 lbs., 5 oz.
SRP:................$349

EVOLUTION XTR

The Evolution by Golden Eagle incorporates a powerful MachOne OneCam with a unique tunnel design built into a magnesium riser. Other features include: carbon quad straight limbs, all-weather composite grip and a Mossy Oak Break-Up finish. This bow is offered in a right-hand model only. The Evolution series has included many models over the years and has a strong following among bowhunters.

BOW SPECIFICATIONS: EVOLUTION XTR
AMO Draw Length: 28-, 29- and 30-inch
Draw Weights: 50-60# and 60-70# with 65% let-off
Bow Speed: IBO fps= 290; AMO fp = 218
Axle-to Axle: 35.125 inches
Weight in hand: 4 lbs., 2 oz.
SRP:................$199

Golden Eagle Compound Bows

MOSSY OAK 32

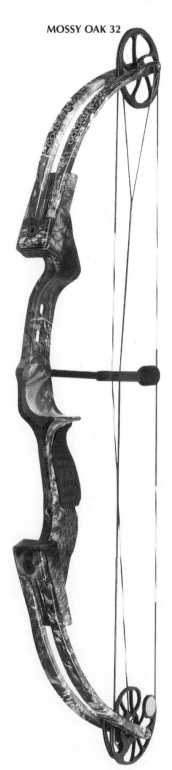

MOSSY OAK 36

MOSSY OAK 32

Golden Eagle's new Mossy Oak 32 offers a 75% let-off with a Gold Dot Perimeter weighted One-cam. Other features include four Carbon Quad straight limbs, a straight 6061 T-6 machined aluminum riser and an elasto-polymer grip. This bow is coated with Mossy oak camouflage and has a string shock stop system. The bow's riser has quiver-mounting holes pre-bored and you can install optional Adjustable Dampening System brass weight rings to reduce vibration. This bow is offered in right-hand models only.

BOW SPECIFICATIONS

AMO Draw Length: 28 and 29 inches adjustable with modules to range from 27 to 31 inches
Draw Weights: 50-60 and 60-70 pounds
Bow Speed: 284 fps IBO and 226 fps AMO
Axle-to Axle: 32 inches
SRP: $399

MOSSY OAK 36

This compound bow is similar in design to the Mossy Oak 32 but has a longer 36-inch axle-to-axle length thanks to longer limbs. This bow weighs 4 pounds, 2 ounces and is designed for finger shooters.

BOW SPECIFICATIONS

AMO Draw Length: 28 and 29 inches adjustable with modules to 28 to 32 inches
Draw Weights: 50-60 and 60-70 pounds with 75 or 65% let-off
Bow Speed: 284 fps IBO and 226 fps AMO
Axle-to Axle: 36 inches
SRP: $399

OBSESSION

RAPTOR

OBSESSION

The Obsession features precision engineering and the unique ShockStop string suppressor. Other features include a machined reflex riser equipped with a two-piece checkered hardwood grip with an interior leather wrap. The straight carbon cable guard is located above the grip and it can be located below the grip if desired. The Obsession also has the Gold Dot Perimeter One Cam system and compression molded CarbonAir Qud limbs and a four-inch ball bearing mounted idler wheel. This bow is available in left- and right-hand models and is coated with new Mossy Oak Break Up camouflage.

BOW SPECIFICATIONS

AMO Draw Length: 27, 28 and 29 inches adjustable with modules
Draw Weights: 40-50, 50-60,and 60-70 pounds with 75% let-off and 65% let-off optional
Bow Speed: 284 fps IBO, 226 fps AMO
Axle-to Axle: 34 inches
SRP:. **$499**

RAPTOR

The Raptor utilizes one-cam efficiency, a machined aluminum riser and CarbonAir quad limbs. The limbs are anchored in a Split-Loc limb box to eliminate noise and vibration. The raptor is coated with new Mossy Oak Break Up camouflage and is offered in right-hand only. This bow has a 6.8-inch brace height and weighs 3 pounds, 10 ounces.

BOW SPECIFICATIONS

AMO Draw Length: 29 inches plus/minus 1 inch
Draw Weights: 50-60 and 60-70 pounds with 65% let-off
Bow Speed: 292 fps IBO and 229 fps AMO
Axle-to Axle: 36 inches
SRP: **$249.65**

SPARROWHAWK

This compact bow was developed for short-draw archers and young shooters. This model is legal for hunting in most states and is a great choice for small-framed beginning hunters. The Sparrowhawk's design features include power-packed carbon quad limbs, 75% let-off and the solid RapidCam system. It's available in right- and left-hand models with numerous draw lengths. This bow has a solid cable guard, magnesium riser and Mossy Oak Break-Up finish and uses a 52-inch Tech Twist string.

BOW SPECIFICATIONS: SPARROWHAWK

AMO Draw Length: 25-, 26-, 27-, 28-, 29- and 30-inch
Draw Weights: 30-40# and 40-50# with 75% let-off
Bow Speed: IBO fps= 281; AMO fps= 220
Axle-to Axle: 36.5 inches
Weight in hand: 4 lbs., 6 oz.
SRP:. **$159**

Golden Eagle Compound Bows

SPARROWHAWK II

SPLITFIRE 32 XTR

SPLITFIRE 36

SPARROWHAWK II

Golden Eagle created this bow with the short draw archer in mind. The riser is computer designed and machined from aluminum and has a large 7-inch brace height. Other features include straight CarbonAir quad limbs, Rapid Cam twin cams, molded grip and cable guard with slide. This bow is offered in right-hand models only and is camouflaged with Mossy Oak Break Up.

BOW SPECIFICATIONS
AMO Draw Length: 24, 25, 26, 27 and 28 inches
Draw Weights: 30-40 and 40-50 pounds with 75% let-off
Bow Speed: 278 fps IBO and 218 fps AMO
Axle-to Axle: 36½ inches
SRP:. **$199**

SPLITFIRE 32 XTR

This 4-limb compound bow has an adjustable dampening system and unique 15-degree angled natural aluminum riser and modular Gold Dot cam. Ergonomic grip utilizes all-weather composite cover and is available in a right-hand model only. Other features include carbon quad straight limbs and Mossy Oak Break-Up camouflage finish.

BOW SPECIFICATIONS: SPLITFIRE 32 XTR
AMO Draw Length: 28-, 29- and 30-inch; adjustable range 27 to 31 inches
Draw Weights: 50-60# and 60-70# with 75% let-off
Bow Speed: IBO fps= 284; AMO fps= 226
Axle-to Axle: 32.75 inches
Weight in hand: 4 lbs., 4 oz.
SRP:. **$379**

SPLITFIRE 36

This bow combines a lightweight aluminum riser with high-tech carbon limbs. Other features include a high-mount cable guard for maximum fletch clearance and a 15-degree angled Natural Series riser complete with an all-weather composite grip. The Splitfire 36 utilizes a Modular Perimeter OneCam and is covered under Golden Eagle's Solid Gold Assurance Plan. It's available as a right-hand model only in Mossy Oak Break-Up camouflage.

BOW SPECIFICATIONS: SPLITFIRE 36
AMO Draw Length: 28-, 29- and 30-inch; adjustable range 28 to 31 inches
Draw Weights: 50-60# and 60-70# with 70% let-off
Bow Speed: IBO fps = 284; AMO fps = 226
Axle-to Axle: 36 inches
Weight in hand: 4 lbs., 5 oz.
SRP:. **$249**

BRUTE ELITE

This High Country compound model has 16-inch VFA limbs and standard limb pockets attached to the semi-reflexed forged and machined MR9 riser. Other features include an 8-inch brace height, one-piece grip and cable guard. These bows weigh approximately 4 pounds and are available with three cam options: Perimeter Weighted MX1 cam, Perimeter XD and D/S Hatchet cam systems. All models are available in Mossy Oak or High Country's Advanced 3-D camouflage.

BOW SPECIFICATIONS: BRUTE ELITE
AMO Draw Length: 26- to 30-inch
Draw Weights: 60# to 70#
Bow Speed: NA
Axle-to Axle: 36 inches
SRP: $455.99

CARBON 4-RUNNER AND 4-RUNNER EXTREME

These high-tech bows feature High Country's XCR1 stealth carbon riser, Vibra Damp limb pockets and the Vibra Flex V-Split limbs with LET limb stabilization technology. All models have a two-piece gray wooden grip. The shorter Extreme has 14-inch limbs and the standard 4-Runner models have 16-inch limbs. Numerous cam styles can be included with both groups of bows. All models are available in Mossy Oak or Advanced 3-D camouflage.

CARBON FORCE EXTREME

This bow has a CR2 carbon riser with a semi-reflex riser geometry and 14-inch Vibra Flex Armor V-Split limbs set in Vibra Damp limb pockets. Multiple cam options are available and the grip is a two-piece hardwood low-wrist style. HCA's Carbon Force Extreme weighs less than 3 pounds and has a 7-inch brace height. This model is available with Perimeter Weighted MX1 cams and Perimeter XD cams. All models are available in Mossy Oak or Advanced 3-D camouflage.

The Carbon Force bow is similar design and components with 29- to 33-inch draw length, 16-inch split limbs and the CR2 riser. This model weighs approximately 3 pounds and is available with the Perimeter Weighted MX1 cam, Perimeter XD and D/S hatchet cam systems. These systems

provide a 39-inch axle-to-axle length.
BOW SPECIFICATIONS:
CARBON FORCE EXTREME
AMO Draw Length: 27- to 31-inch
Draw Weights: 60# to 70#
Bow Speed: NA
Axle-to Axle: 35 inches
SRP: $645.99

LITE FORCE

The Lite Force was introduced in 2000 and is geared for ladies and young shooters. Features include the MR9 forged and machined riser with a split hardwood grip attached. The bow has 14-inch split limbs with a lifetime warranty and uses Mini Xtra-Draw one cams with XD or XL style cams. The Lite Force weighs 2.7 pounds and is coated in Mossy Oak Break-Up or Advanced 3-D camouflage.

BOW SPECIFICATIONS: LITE FORCE
AMO Draw Length: 22- to 26-inch
Draw Weights: 40# and 50#
Bow Speed: NA
Axle-to Axle: 31 inches
SRP: $357

4-RUNNER, 4-RUNNER EXTREME AND 4-RUNNER MONSTER

These bows have the same style and cam options as the Carbon 4-Runners but are based on a forged and machined X-Rad1 riser. Of special interest is the 4-Runner Monster that can produce 80, 90 and 100 draw weights with the round wheel-like Pro Cam and 16-inch V-Split limbs. Draw lengths range from 24 to 30 inches. SRPs for these bows start at $500.

SPECIFICATIONS
AMO Draw Length: 26 to 30 inches, and 25 to-29 inches on the Extreme style
Draw Weights (lbs.): 60 to 70, and 50, 60 and 70 with D/S hatchet cams
Bow Speed: NA
Axle-to Axle: 36 inches, and 31 inches on the Extreme models
SRP: Both models starting at . . . $635

BRUTE ELITE

COMPOUND BOWS

MAX-XTREME

MICRO QUAD

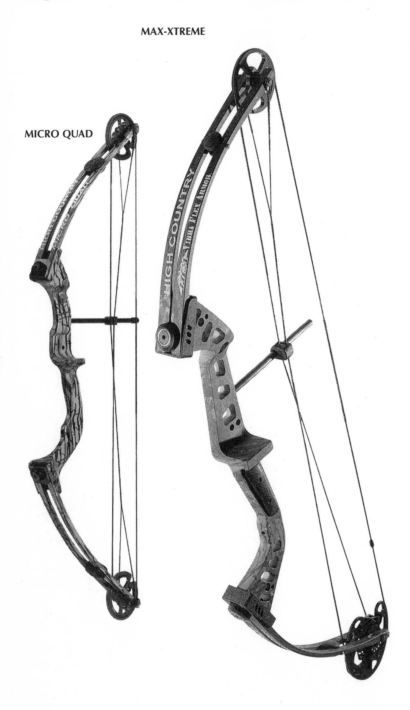

Max-Xtreme

The new Max-Xtreme Carbon compound bow is light—just over 2 pounds and will handle any arrow from lightweight carbon to heavy aluminum. This bow has a weatherproof, military grade carbon riser that features a semi-reflex riser and the L.E.T. System, (Limb Equalization Timing) with Solid Vibra Damp S-D Tech bushing system that reduces noise and vibrations. The Quad Loc Pockets with Super S-D Tech Pad also aid in shock reduction. The Max-Xtreme is available in three cam configurations and with 14- or 16-inch Vibra Flex Armor V-Split limbs. It is coated with Mossy Oak camouflage. It is protected by a lifetime warranty.

BOW SPECIFICATIONS
AMO Draw Length: varies widely
Draw Weights: 60- to 70 pounds
Bow Speed: up to 375 fps
Axle-to Axle: 32 or 37 inches
SRP:. $815

MICRO QUAD

This youth and lady's bow is centered around the cast aluminum reflex designed AT2 riser by High Country. Other features include 14-inch Power Glass quad limbs, and the option of three cam systems: Perimeter Xtra-Draw, Mini XL or Pro Cam. This bow weighs less than 3 pounds and is coated with HCA standard camo colors.

BOW SPECIFICATIONS: MICRO QUAD
AMO Draw Length: 22- to 26-inch with Perimeter cams; 22- to 29-inch with the Pro Cam system
Draw Weights: 30#, 40# and 50#
Bow Speed: NA
Axle-to Axle: 31 inches
SRP: Perimeter cams. $238
Pro Cam model $152

High Country Archery Compound Bows

PerFX Cam

HCA's new PerFX CAM can cover six draw lengths ranging from 24 to 32 inches and has three peak weight ranges from 25 to 80 pounds in two let-offs. The features include a new two-track system, lighter cam with more velocity and improved tracking to keep the string and harness completely in line while eliminating side pressure. This bow system delivers a full 35-pound weight range.

Bow Specifications
AMO Draw Length: ranges from 24 to 29 inches, 225 to 30, 26 to 31 and 27 to 32 inches
Draw Weights: 45, 50, 60, 70 and 80 pounds with 65 or 80% let-off
Bow Speed: NA
Axle-to Axle: dependant upon setting with cam module
SRP: $865

Power Force X1

This bow utilizes a FR1 solid forged and machined riser and 16-inch solid power glass limbs to propel arrows. The power Force X1 is offered with three cam series: Perimeter Xl, D/S Hatchet and Pro cams. An optional accessory package that custom fits the bow includes sight, quiver and peep. All models are available in Mossy Oak or Advanced 3-D camouflage.

Bow Specifications: Power Force X1
AMO Draw Length: 23- to 33-inch
Draw Weights: 60# to 70#, and 50#, 60# and 70# with the Pro cams; 80% and 65% let-off based on cam selection
Bow Speed: NA
Axle-to Axle: 38 inches
SRP: $238

Quad Runner

This bow is similar to the Lite Force and has an MR10 style riser and 14-inch quad limbs and the same cam options.

Bow Specifications: Quad Runner
AMO Draw Length: 22- to 26-inch
Draw Weights: 30#, 40# and 50#
Bow Speed: NA
Axle-to Axle: 31 inches
SRP: Starting at $346

Supreme Extreme

This HCA compound bow utilizes a patented, forged and machined MR11 riser along with 14-inch Vibra Flex Armor V-Split limbs set in Vibra Damp limb pockets and equipped with the L.E.T. limb stabilizing system. Multiple cam options are available and the bow has the center line idler wheel layout and a 7-inch brace height. Available cam systems include Perimeter Weighted MX1, Perimeter XD (Xtra Draw) and Perimeter XL (Xtra Lite). This bow includes a cable guard and wooden grip. All models are available in Mossy Oak or Advanced 3-D camouflage, weigh approximately 3.4 pounds and the limbs have a lifetime warranty.

Bow Specifications: Supreme Extreme
AMO Draw Length: 25- to 29-inch
Draw Weights: 60# to 70#
Bow Speed: NA
Axle-to Axle: 31 inches
SRP: $569.99

Ultra Extreme

This HCA bow series is based on a forged and machined FRM1 semi-reflexed riser and 14-inch VFA split limbs. The bows weigh approximately 3.7 pounds and are offered in two cam choices: the single-cam Perimeter XD Xtra Draw and dual cam D/S Hatchet. Both models are available in Mossy Oak or Advanced 3-D camouflage.

Bow Specifications: Ultra Extreme
AMO Draw Length: 24- to 30-inch
Draw Weights: 60# to 70#
Bow Speed: NA
Axle-to Axle: 36 inches
SRP: $390

POWER
FORCE X1

ULTRA
EXTREME

PERFX CAM

High Country Archery Compound Bows

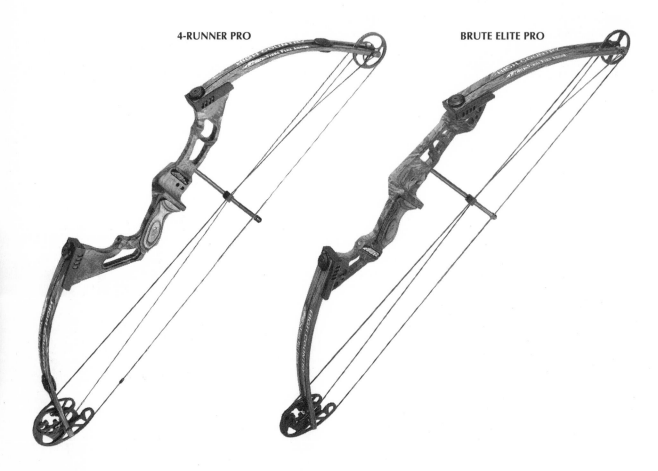

4-RUNNER PRO   BRUTE ELITE PRO

THE PRO SERIES

4-RUNNER EXTREME PRO AND 4-RUNNER PRO

These bows are similar to Carbon 4-Runner series except this group uses the forged and machined X-Rad1 riser instead of the carbon. Other features include: center line idler wheel, split limbs with the Lib Equalization Timing system, cable guards and wood grips. The Extreme Pro uses 16-inch limbs and yields a 7-inch brace height and the standard Pro has 14-inch limbs with a 6½-inch brace height. Cam options include HCA's Perimeter Xtra-Draw one cam and Perimeter Xtra-Lite one cam series.

The 4-Runner Pro models have 60# and 70# draw weight and a draw length ranging from 25 to 29 inches.

BOW SPECIFICATIONS:
4-RUNNER EXTREME PRO
AMO Draw Length: 25- to 29-inch
Draw Weights: 60# and 70#
Bow Speed: more than 300 fps IBO
Axle-to Axle: 31 inches on the Extreme models
SRP: $635.99

BRUTE ELITE PRO

This bow's Vibra Damp Limb pockets are fastened to an MR9 forged and machined riser. Features of the Brute Elite Pro include LET system, Perimeter Xtra-Lite one cam, 8-inch brace height and 16-inch split limbs. This bow was introduced as a new model in 2001 and is available in Mossy Oak or Advanced 3-D camouflage.

BOW SPECIFICATIONS: BRUTE ELITE PRO
AMO Draw Length: 28- to 38-inch
Draw Weights: 60# and 70# with 65% or 80% let-off
Bow Speed: nearly 300 fps IBO
Axle-to Axle: 36 inches
SRP:. $460

CARBON 4-RUNNER PRO AND 4-RUNNER EXTREME PRO

These high-tech bows feature High Country's XCR1 stealth carbon riser,

Vibra Damp limb pockets and the Vibra Flex V-Split limbs with LET limb stabilization technology. These bows use HCA's ball and socket limb mount bolts. All models have a two-piece gray wooden grip. The shorter Extreme Pro has 14-inch limbs and the standard 4-Runner Pro models have 16-inch limbs. All models use Perimeter XL cams, weigh approximately 2.6 pounds and are available in Mossy Oak or Advanced 3D camouflage.

The Carbon 4-Runner Pro has a 36-inch axle-to-axle length as a result of 16-inch limbs. It yields a 26- to 30-inch draw length and has similar components and design features of the upscale 4-Runner Extreme Pro.

BOW SPECIFICATIONS:
CARBON 4-RUNNER EXTREME PRO
AMO Draw Length: 25- to 29-inch
Draw Weights: 60# and 70#
Bow Speed: more than 300 fps IBO
Axle-to Axle: 31 inches on the Extreme models
SRP: Starting at $613.99

High Country Archery Compound Bows

CARBON FORCE PRO AND CARBON FORCE EXTREME PRO

These bows have a CR2 carbon riser with a semi-reflex riser geometery and V-Split limbs set in Vibra Damp limb pockets. The bows weigh less than 3 pounds. Both models use Perimeter XL cams and are available in Mossy Oak or Advanced 3-D camouflage.

The Carbon Force Pro bow is similar design and components with 16-inch split limbs and the CR2 riser. This system provides a longer 39-inch axle-to-axle length and yields a draw length ranging from 29 to 33 inches.

BOW SPECIFICATIONS:
CARBON FORCE EXTREME PRO
AMO Draw Length: 27- to 31-inch
Draw Weights: 60# to 70#
Bow Speed: more than 300 IBO
Axle-to Axle: 35 inches
SRP:. **$642**

PREMIER EXTREME PRO AND PREMIER PRO

These bows are based on the forged and machined MR5 riser and feature wood grips and cable guards. Other features include Vibra Damp Pockets, center line sealed bearing idler wheels and split limbs.

The Premier Pro uses 16-inch limbs and offers a longer 38-inch axle-to-axle length. It also has 60# and 70# draw weights and a 29 to 33 inch draw length and is offered in three cam styles.

BOW SPECIFICATIONS:
PREMIER EXTREME PRO
AMO Draw Length: 22- to 31-inch
Draw Weights: 50#, 60# and 70# with Perimeter XD and XL cams
Bow Speed: more than 300 fps IBO
Axle-to Axle: 36 inches
SRP: **$535.99**

ULTRA EXTREME PRO

This High Country Archery compound bow was introduced in 2001 and works from an FRM1 riser with split limbs attached via the standard limb pockets. The LET limb vibration dampening system is installed and other features include a cable guard and molded one-piece grip. This bow uses the Perimeter Xtra-Lite one-cam, provides a 6½-inch brace height, and it's offered in the company's standard camouflage choices.

BOW SPECIFICATIONS: ULTRA EXTREME PRO
AMO Draw Length: 26- to 30-inch
Draw Weights: 60# and 70# with 65% or 80% let-off
Bow Speed: NA
Axle-to Axle: 36 inches
SRP: **$356.99**

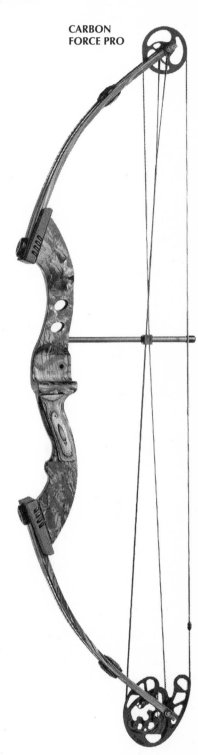

CARBON FORCE PRO

COMPOUND BOWS

"An archer wants to see how far away from the target he can get and still hit it. A bowhunter wants to see how close he can get to his target before he shoots."
—Dr. Mark Timney

Hoyt Compound Bows

BANSHEE

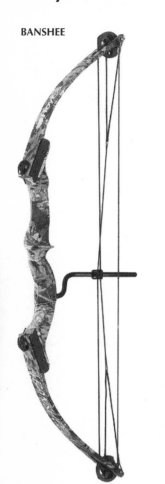

CYBERTEC XT2000

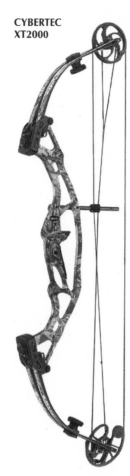

HAVOCTEC XT2000

HAVOCTEC ZR200

BANSHEE

This bow is built specifically for young archers. The Banshee wheel is designed to be extremely easy to shoot and is adjustable to keep pace with growing young shooters. This bow is available in camouflage with a two-wheel configuration and cable guard. The Banshee has a 6¾-inch brace height.

BOW SPECIFICATIONS: BANSHEE
AMO Draw Length: adjustable
Draw Weights: 20# to 50#
Bow Speed: NA
Axle-to Axle: 32 inches
SRP: . . . . varies

CYBERTEC

The CyberTec compound bow uses shorter XT2000 limbs to provide greater vertical stability, and the bow's 36-inch axle-to-axle length makes it very accurate. The CyberTec also incorporates Hoyt's patented TEC design in the riser, which works like a bridge's truss to completely dampen shot vibration throughout the bow. The result is a vibration free and whisper quiet shot. Other bow features include a choice of standard, Excel cam (medium) or VersaCam (hard) to suit the shooter's preference. The CyberTec is available in Mossy Oak camouflage.

BOW SPECIFICATIONS: CYBERTEC
AMO Draw Length: From 21- to 31-inch dependant upon cam selected
Draw Weights: 40# to 80#
Bow Speed: Up to 309 fps dependant upon cam selection
Axle-to Axle: 36 inches
SRP: . . . . varies by selection

HAVOCTEC

This lightweight (3.25 pounds), short axle-to-axle bow shoots like a dream and is patterned after the ever-popular Havoc while incorporating the patented Hoyt TEC riser design. This innovative design dampens vibration in the bow by channeling it through the truss and away from the hand. The result is an extremely quiet, smooth and accurate shot. This bow has a 7½-inch brace height and split-limb design with chrome or standard limb pockets.

BOW SPECIFICATIONS: HAVOCTEC
AMO Draw Length: 21- to 31-inch dependant upon cam and limb selection
Draw Weights: 40# to 80#
Bow Speed: From 270 to 300 fps IBO dependant upon cam and limb selection
Axle-to Axle: 31½-inches
SRP: . . . . varies by selection.

Hoyt Compound Bows

HYPERTEC XT2000

MAGNATEC XT2000

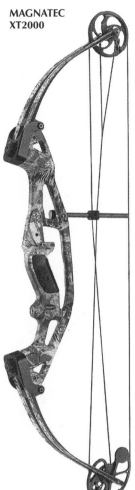

MAGNATEC ZR200

MT SPORT ZR200

COMPOUND BOWS

HYPERTEC

The HyperTec features a shorter brace height to provide the long power stroke required for fast arrow speeds. The riser is stiff and lightweight with virtually no recoil or vibration at release. The HyperTec has a 6-inch brace height. This is a bow designed for advanced archers, so consult your local dealer to see if it's right for you.

BOW SPECIFICATIONS: HYPERTEC

AMO Draw Length: 24- to 30-inch dependant upon cam selection

Draw Weights: 40# to 80#

Bow Speed: 320 fps IBO

Axle-to Axle: 33 inches

SRP: . . . . varies

MAGNATEC

The lightweight MagnaTec was built with the bowhunter in mind and incorporates Hoyt's patented TEC design. The MagnaTec delivers a quiet and recoil-free shot. This bow is only available as a hunting bow in Mossy Oak Break Up and has a 7-inch brace height. Models available in Hoyt's XT2000 and ZR200 configurations.

BOW SPECIFICATIONS: MAGNATEC

AMO Draw Length: 21- to 32-inch based upon cam and limb selection

Draw Weights: 40# to 80#

Bow Speed: Up to 305 fps IBO.

Axle-to Axle: 35¹⁄₂-inches

SRP: . . . . varies

MT SPORT

The lightweight and affordable MT Sport also incorporates Hoyt's patented TEC engineering. This bow's shorter axle-to-axle length also makes it a more maneuverable bow in all hunting conditions. This bow is only available in Mossy Oak camo. The MT Sport utilizes Accuwheels and the company's ZR200 layout.

BOW SPECIFICATIONS: MT SPORT

AMO Draw Length: Available from 22 to 34 inches

Draw Weights: 40# to 80#

Bow Speed: Up to 286 fps IBO

Axle-to Axle: 34¹⁄₂-inches

SRP: . . . . varies

Hoyt Compound Bows

PROTEC
XL2000

PROTEC
XL PRO

PROTEC
XL3000

RAZORTEC

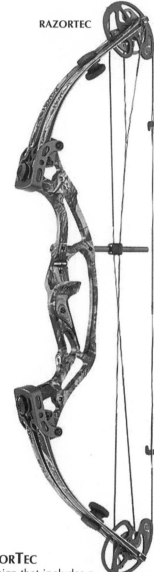

PROTEC

Hoyt's ProTec combines proven deflex geometry with a longer and stiffer riser along with the company's TEC design. This bow is available with Accuwheels, Excel cams and Versacams and with LXPRO, XT3000 and XT2000 limbs and styles. The bow's finish choices include Mossy Oak camouflage.

BOW SPECIFICATIONS: PROTEC
AMO Draw Length: 25- to 34-inch
Draw Weights: 40# to 80#
Bow Speed: Up to 290 fps IBO
Axle-to Axle: 38 to 46 inches
dependant upon cam selection
SRP: . . . . **varies**

RAZORTEC

A design that includes a new technology that permits both cams to work together without timing. Other features include a dual locking limb pocket design, cable guard with a Pro cable guard slide, and quiver attachment holes. This bow continues Hoyt's odd-looking TEC multi-cut riser design that reduces vibration. Sims Limb Savers are factory installed and the riser has a stainless steel stabilizer bushing installed. This camouflaged model has wooden panel grip inserts.

BOW SPECIFICATIONS
AMO Draw Length: 25 to 31 inches
Draw Weights: 50, 60 and 70 pounds
Bow Speed: 302 fps
Axle-to Axle: 31½ inches
SRP:. **$665**

SAPPHIRE
ZR200

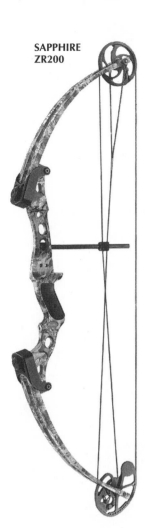

VORTEC
ZR200

ULTRATEC
XL2000

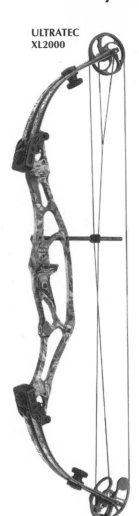

ULTRATEC
XL3000

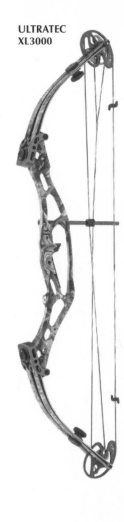

COMPOUND BOWS

SAPPHIRE

This bow is designed for women and short-draw shooters. The Sapphire fully utilizes its moderately reflexed riser to provide superior speed. The specially-designed grip accommodates smaller hands and virtually eliminates hand-torque to improve shot accuracy. Available systems to move arrows include: Accuwheels, Excel and VersaCams. This bow has a standard riser (solid) and molded grip, plus a split-limb design. The Sapphire is available in Mossy Oak.

BOW SPECIFICATIONS: SAPPHIRE
AMO Draw Length: 21- to 28-inch
Draw Weights: 40# to 60#
Bow Speed: Up to 277 fps IBO
Axle-to Axle: 34³/₄-inches
SRP: . . . . **varies**

ULTRATEC

The UltraTec's longer axle-to-axle length and shorter XT2000 limbs make this bow a solid performer. This bow is available in camouflage and has a 7-inch brace height. Models are available with Accuwheels, Excel cams, VersaCams and Hoyt's exclusive Redline cams and with XT3000 and XT2000 limb layouts.

BOW SPECIFICATIONS: ULTRATEC
AMO Draw Length: 22- to 33-inch dependant upon cam selection
Draw Weights: 40# to 80#
Bow Speed: Up to 305 fps IBO dependant upon limb and cam selection
Axle-to Axle: 38 inches
SRP: . . . . **varies**

VORTEC

The VorTec features Hoyt's patented TEC riser design, which dampens shot vibration. Other features include wood grip, vibration dampening system and multiple cam options. This bow is available in Mossy Oak camouflage finish only with black limb pockets and ZR200 limb configuration. The VorTec opened the door for Hoyt's innovative risers and much of today's high-tech looks in bow design. Other cam system choices for the VorTec include Excel and VersaCam options.

BOW SPECIFICATIONS: VORTEC
AMO Draw Length: 22- to 33-inch dependant upon cam selection
Draw Weights: 40# to 80#
Bow Speed: Up to 300 fps IBO dependant upon cam selection
Axle-to Axle: 36 inches
SRP: . . . . **varies**

Jennings Compound Bows

CARBONMASTER
XTREME

CMX

CARBONMASTER XTREME
This 4-limb hunting bow has a solid cable guard and micro-adjustable brass spool in the cam for fine tuning precision. Other features include: a 93.75-inch Tech Twist string, Carbon Quad Straight limbs and a Perimeter Weighted Cam II system to propel the arrows. The Carbonmaster Xtreme uses the Shock Stop noise and vibration elimination system. This bow is available with a Realtree Hardwoods finish and in left- or right-hand versions with an all-weather composite grip.

BOW SPECIFICATIONS:
CARBONMASTER XTREME
AMO Draw Length: 27-, 28-, or 29-inch: adjustable range from 24 to 31 inches
Draw Weights: 40-50#, 50-60#, or 60-70# with 70% let-off (65% let-off optional)
Bow Speed: IBO fps= 298; AMO fps= 224
Axle-to Axle: 35.375 inches
Weight in hand: 4 lbs.
SRP: Starting at **$229**

CMX
The CMX (Carbon Master Extreme) has a vibration-suppressing grip and machined riser that will accept the optional Adjustable Dampening System with brass weights. Other features include the unique blue-and-black twist tech string, high mount carbon cable guard, and Perimeter Weighted OneCam. This bow is camouflaged has solid carbon limbs. It weighs 3 pounds, 8 ounces.

BOW SPECIFICATIONS
AMO Draw Length: 27, 28 and 29 inches adjustable up to 32 inches with modules
Draw Weights: 40-50, 50-60 and 60-70 pounds
Bow Speed: 300 fps IBO, 228 fps AMO
Axle-to Axle: 37½ inches
SRP: **$299**

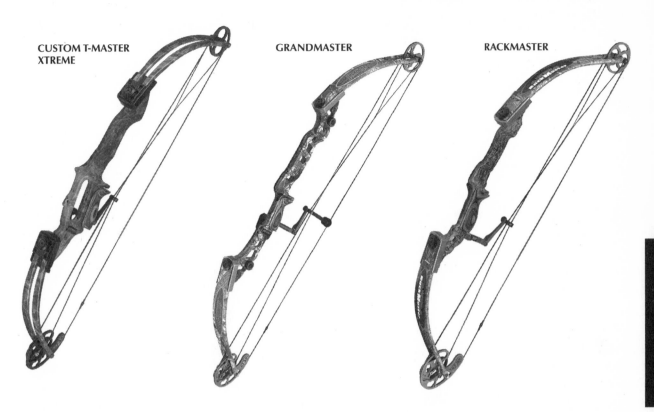

CUSTOM T-MASTER XTREME

GRANDMASTER

RACKMASTER

CUSTOM T-MASTER XTREME

Here's a rare chance to have a 4-limb compound bow made to your specifications by the North American Archery Group plant in Gainesville, Florida. This custom bow's features include: a No-Torque pivoting wood grip, idler wheel mounted on ball bearings and the modular OneCam system that permits multiple draw length adjustments. Other construction features include left- or right-hand versions with the total-silence, vibration dampening limb pockets and a Mossy Oak Break-Up finish.

BOW SPECIFICATIONS:
CUSTOM T-MASTER XTREME
AMO Draw Length: 24- to 31-inch
Draw Weights: 60-70# with let-off dependant upon design selected features
Bow Speed: IBO fps= 311; AMO fps= 239
Axle-to Axle: 33½-inches
Weight in hand: varies
SRP:. **$599**

GRANDMASTER

This high-tech bow was designed as a 3-D shooter and dons a camo skin in the hunting version. It has a 23-inch precision machined aluminum/titanium riser, modular cam that provides up to 8 inches of draw length adjustment and a 1-inch micro adjustment for a precision draw. The GrandMaster has Carbon Twill limbs and an adjustable dampening system that can use either a brass or titanium anodized weights to tame torque, dampen vibration and eliminate noise. This bow utilizes a SwingArm cable guard.

Available in Realtree Hardwoods and left- and right-hand versions.

BOW SPECIFICATIONS: GRANDMASTER
AMO Draw Length: 27-, 28-, or 29-inch: adjustable range from 26 to 33 inches
Draw Weights: 40-50#, 50-60#, or 60-70# with 70% let-off (65% let-off optional)
Bow Speed: IBO fps = 300; AMO fps= 223
Axle-to Axle: 40½-inches
Weight in hand: 4 lbs., 5 ozs.
SRP: Starting at **$599**
Marble finish **$699**

RACKMASTER

This lightweight compound bow has a micro-adjustable SwingArm cable guard. Other features include the modular weighted OneCam system, ball bearing mounted idler wheel and a custom checkered hardwood grip. The riser design provides a 7½-inch brace height. The RackMaster is available in Realtree Hardwoods camouflage finish only.

BOW SPECIFICATIONS: RACKMASTER
AMO Draw Length: 27-, 28- and 29-inch; adjustable range from 24 to 31 inches.
Draw Weights: 40-50#, 50-60#, 60-70# with 70% let-off (65% let-off optional)
Bow Speed: IBO fps= 302; AMO fps= 230
Axle-to Axle: 34.375 inches
Weight in hand: 3 lbs., 10 oz.
SRP:. **$399**

Jennings Compound Bows

RACKMASTER LITE

TROPHYMASTER

RackMaster Lite

This hunting bow is designed for hunters with short draw lengths. Its features include: solid carbon-matrix limbs, titanium-styled Jennings hardware and a Perimeter OneCam. This bow uses a distinct blue/black Tech Twist string, has an all-weather comfort foam grip and has a solid cable guard. The Rackmaster Lite provides a 6¼-inch brace height on a machined 6061-T-6 aluminum riser. It's available in right- and left-hand versions and in Realtree Hardwoods camouflage finish.

BOW SPECIFICATIONS: RACKMASTER LITE
AMO Draw Length: 24-, 25- and 26-inch; adjustable from 22 to 26 inches.
Draw Weights: 20-30#, 30-40#, and 40-50# with 75% let-off
Bow Speed: IBO fps= 255
Axle-to Axle: 31½-inches
Weight in hand: 2 lbs., 12 oz.
SRP: $229

StarMaster

This four-limb bow utilizes a perimeter weighted cam, carbon quad limbs and machined aluminum riser to provide premium hunting performance. Other bow features include: a Mossy Oak Break-Up camouflage finish, checkered wood laminated grip and swinging cable guard. The StarMaster is available in right- and left-hand versions. This bow could be considered a top value that offers lots of technology at a bargain price.

BOW SPECIFICATIONS: STARMASTER
AMO Draw Length: 27-, 28- and 29-inch; adjustable from 25 to 32 inches.
Draw Weights: 40-50#, 50-60#, and 60-70# with 75% let-off (65% optional)
Bow Speed: IBO fps= 313;
AMO fps= 234
Axle-to Axle: 38 inches
Weight in hand: 4 lbs., 10 oz.
SRP: $449

TrophyMaster

This compact hunting bow uses Carbon Twill limbs and a modular cam to provide results oriented performance. The bow's features include: an adjustable dampening system, SwingArm cable guard, machined aluminum riser and titanium-anodized hardware. It has a checkered laminated wood grip and is available in left- and right-hand models and in Realtree Hardwoods camouflage.

BOW SPECIFICATIONS: TROPHYMASTER
AMO Draw Length: 27-, 28-, and 29-inch; adjustable range from 24 to 31 inches.
Draw Weights: 40-50#; 50-60#; and 60-70# with 70% let-off
Bow Speed: IBO fps = 308;
AMO fps = 232
Axle-to Axle: 35.375 inches
Weight in hand: 4 lbs., 1 oz.
SRP: Starting at $499
marble finish $549

MARTIN'S PRO SERIES

ALTITUDE

Martin's Altitude compound bow is designed with the rigors of treestand hunting in mind. The short axle length is easily maneuvered through the woods and makes treestand hunting easier and more comfortable. The Altitude riser's compact design—machined from a solid aluminum block—also uses center line riser technology that allows you to hold steady and make better shots. Other features include solid limbs nestled in limb pockets and a black molded rubber grip. This bow weighs 3 pounds, 10 ounces and is available in Mossy Oak Break-Up and in right- or left-hand models.

BOW SPECIFICATIONS: ALTITUDE
AMO Draw Length: 24- to 29-inch
Draw Weights: 50#, 60# and 70# with 75% let-off (65% optional)
Bow Speed: 301 fps IBO
Axle-to Axle: 30 ³/₈-inches
SRP: Starting at $626.64
Tournament Models Starting at . . $687

JAGUAR

The affordable Jaguar has a die cast riser and a short axle length. Other features include straight glass composite limbs set in limb pockets and a molded grip on this dual-cam bow. Martin's Jaguar is available in Advantage Timber, Cherry Red, or Deep Blue. This bow is offered in right-hand only.

The Jaguar Magnum is similar in design and uses the Fuzion single-cam system. This bow has wood panel grips. It's available in Mossy Oak Break-Up. The Jaguar Magnum is offered in right-hand only.

BOW SPECIFICATIONS: JAGUAR
AMO Draw Length: 25- to 31-inch
Draw Weights: 40# to 70# with 75% let-off (65% let-off optional)
Bow Speed: 291 fps IBO
Axle-to Axle: 36 ³/₈-inches
SRP: Starting at $419.42
Tournament Models
Starting at $479.42

BOW SPECIFICATIONS: JAGUAR MAGNUM
AMO Draw Length: 25- to 30-inches
Draw Weights: 50#, 60# and 70# with 75% let-off (65% optional)
Bow Speed: 310 fps IBO
Axle-to Axle: 33 ¹/₄-inches
SRP: Starting at $457.42
Tournament Models
Starting at $517.42

JAGUAR

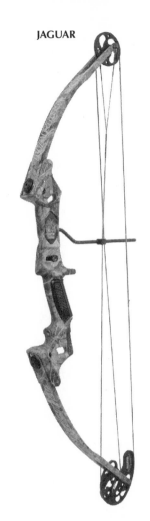

ALTITUDE

COMPOUND BOWS

Martin Archery Compound Bows

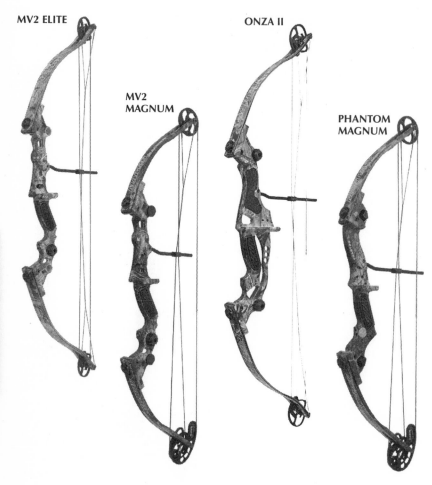

MV2 ELITE

MV2 MAGNUM

ONZA II

PHANTOM MAGNUM

ONZA II

The Onza II has a unique riser with its long shelf and grip with a brace. It is available in three styles: Elite, Straight and SE. The cam options are Fury, Fury-X and Fusion. Color options include Advantage Timber or standard carbon, and the target series can be acquired in sunburst yellow, blue fade to red, platinum and Procat burgundy.

BOW SPECIFICATIONS
AMO Draw Length: 26 to 32 inches and varies by cam selection.
Draw Weights: 50, 60 and 70 pounds
Bow Speed: 305 fps
Axle-to Axle: 32 inches in the SE, 36⅜ inches for the Straight and 39⅞ inches for the Elite model
SRP:.......$1,131.12 to $1,263.12

PHANTOM

Martin's economical Phantom has a riser that is machined from a solid block of aluminum. It's available with Z-cams and Fuzion cams. Other features include solid limbs and wood panel grips. This bow weighs 3 pounds, 15 ounces and has a 6¾-inch brace height. The Phantom is coated with Martin Archery's own Phantom camouflage and is available in right- or left-hand models.

The Phantom bow is available in three styles. The Phantom Elite model uses Fury cams and has a long 38-inch axle-to-axle length. The Phantom Fusion uses a single cam design and has a rubber molded grip. The Phantom Magnum uses the Fusion single-cam system and has a 33-inch axle-to-axle length.

BOW SPECIFICATIONS: PHANTOM
AMO Draw Length: 25- to 32-inch
Draw Weights: 50#, 60# and 70# with 75% let-off (65% optional)
Bow Speed: 285 fps IBO
Axle-to Axle: 37¼-inches
SRP: Phantom Fuzion and Magnum,
starting at $506.64
Tournament Models $566.64
Phantom Elite with Fury cams,
starting at $785.06
Tournament Models $895.06

MV2 ELITE

The recently introduced MV2 Elite has proven itself. At the 2001 National Indoor Championships. The MV2 uses Quick-Loc accessories and the VEM (Vibration Escape Module) system with dampners attached on the riser. The MV2's unique accessory attachment system makes it easier than ever to mount all your favorite hunting gear. The Quick Pin quiver system gives you a super-solid, rattle-free attachment to your bow with any Martin Direct Mount Quiver. The Lever-Loc Sight System allows the use of most any sight and permits a secure lock to The MV2 riser. Sights can be removed and replaced without affecting settings thanks to a double-pin alignment system. The quiver pin plugs into a receptacle on the riser and a knob on the opposite side is tightened to lock it into place. The quiver easily separates

from the bow. This permits users to quickly and quietly detach the quiver in a treestand without alerting game. This dual-wheel bow is available in Advantage Timber. The MV2 Elite is available in right- or left-hand models.

The MV2 Magnum bow is similar in design and uses a single cam system. It has a slightly shorter axle-to-axle length and slightly faster IBO rating and is available in Mossy Oak camouflage. This bow has an SRP less than the MV2 Elite.

BOW SPECIFICATIONS: MV2 ELITE
AMO Draw Length: 25- to 33-inch
Draw Weights: 40# to 70# with 75% let-off (65% let-off optional)
Bow Speed: 296 fps IBO
Axle-to Axle: 39⅞-inches
SRP: Starting with the Fury cams
.... $1036.42
Tournament Models Starting at
.... $1096.42

Martin Archery Compound Bows

SCEPTER II ELITE   COUGAR   COUGAR ELITE   COUGAR MAGNUM

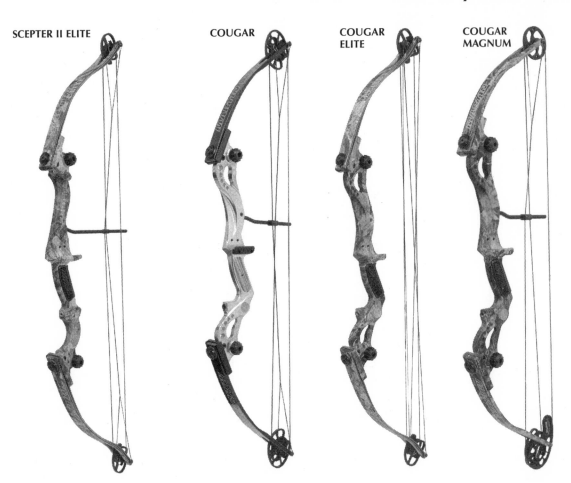

SCEPTER II ELITE

The Scepter II Elite is available with standard Fury cams or Fury-X cams. The Scepter II Elite benefits from no limb tip torque, cam lean or cable friction. This solid limb bow is available in red, blue, or custom colors. Available in right- or left-hand models.

BOW SPECIFICATIONS: SCEPTER II ELITE
AMO Draw Length: 26- to 34-inch
Draw Weights: 40# to 80# with 75% let-off (65% let-off optional)
Bow Speed: 290 fps IBO
Axle-to Axle: $42\frac{7}{8}$-inches
SRP: Approximately $1244.78
Tournament Models
   Starting at $1304.78

SPEED FIRE MAGNUM

Martin's Speed Fire Magnum incorporates technological advancements such as the V.E.M. (Vibration Escape Module) and the Elevated Stabilizer Wing to improve the bow's feel and accuracy. Other features

include: a single-cam Fuzion system, solid limbs and a molded grip. This bow is available in Mossy Oak Break-Up and in right- or left-hand models.
BOW SPECIFICATIONS:
SPEED FIRE MAGNUM
AMO Draw Length: 25-to 30-inch
Draw Weights: 50#, 60# and 70# with 75% let-off (65% let-off optional)
Bow Speed: 301 fps IBO
Axle-to Axle: 32 inches
SRP: Starting at $702.20

MARTIN'S GOLD SERIES

COUGAR

Martin's Cougar has a long, sleek reflexed riser that's made from 6061-T6 aluminum. Other features include the V.E.M. (Vibration Escape Module), solid limbs set in pockets and a molded grip. The Cougar is available in two camouflage patterns, Advantage Timber and the new

anodized Phantom camouflage. Fury Cams are available in high let-off and 65% let-off. This bow is also offered in right or left hand models.

The Cougar is also available in Elite, Fury-X, Fuzion and Magnum models. The Fury model uses the soft Fury Dual cam system and solid limbs and has a 42-inch axle-to-axle length. The Cougar Fuzion uses the Fuzion hard-cam system and has a 40-inch axle-to-axle length. The Magnum uses 14-inch limbs with tip reinforcements and a one-cam system. This model is available in Mossy Oak Break-Up camouflage.

BOW SPECIFICATIONS: COUGAR
AMO Draw Length: 24- to 32-inch and variable by cam selection
Draw Weights: 40# to 70# with 75% let-off (65% let-off optional)
Bow Speed: up to 310 fps IBO
Axle-to Axle: $40\frac{1}{8}$-inches and varies by limbs and model selection
SRP: $710.86

Martin Archery Compound Bows

TIGER

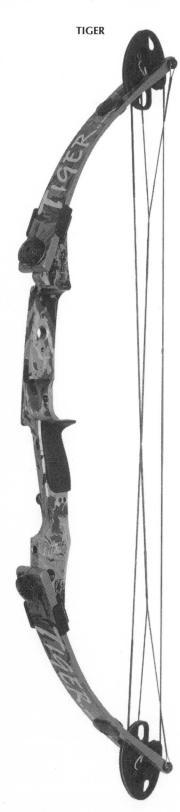

PANTHER MAGNUM

Martin's Panther Magnum is built around a solid, machined aluminum riser. Combined with solid 14-inch limbs the result is a very compact 33-inch axle-to-axle length. This bow has a black molded grip, weighs 3.7 pounds and has a 7¼-inch brace height. The Martin Fuzion single-cam system powers the bow that is available in Mossy Oak Break-Up. Specify right- or left-hand.

BOW SPECIFICATIONS: PANTHER MAGNUM
AMO Draw Length: 26- to 31-inch and variable by cam selection
Draw Weights: 50#, 60# and 70# with 75% let-off (65% optional)
Bow Speed: 300 fps IBO
Axle-to Axle: 33⅙
SRP: Approximately $524.48
Tournament Model Approximately
. $762.20

TIGER

The Martin Tiger offers young archers equipment that is as enjoyable to shoot as a full sized bow. The Tiger's solid machined riser and Mini Z-Cams propels arrows to the target at more than 200 feet per second. Each Tiger compound bow comes complete with a full set of draw length modules that allow adjustment of draw over a 17- to 23-inch range. Other features include a solid cams and limbs plus a black molded grip. This bow is available in either anodized Reality camouflage and in right- or left-hand versions. The Tiger weighs approximately 2.3 pounds.

BOW SPECIFICATIONS: TIGER
AMO Draw Length: 17- to 24-inch adjustable
Draw Weights: 20#, 30# and 40# with 65% let-off
Bow Speed: 300 fps IBO
Axle-to Axle: 31½-inches
SRP: $270.70
Tournament Model $337.70

Always inspect your compound bows thoroughly before each season to check for wear and tear. Carefully go over your bow and look for cracks, warped limbs, bent cam-axles causing cam tilt, dirt and other debris, and anything that looks out of the ordinary. Tighten all loose screws. Replace strings and cables that have broken strands. If you are not confident you can do a thorough inspection yourself, have a pro at your local bow shop check things out.

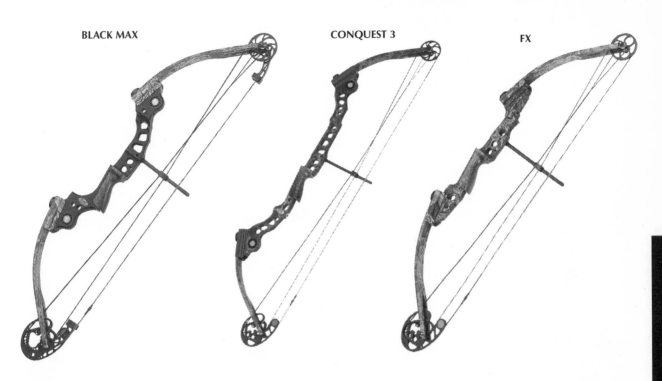

BLACK MAX   **CONQUEST 3**   **FX**

BLACK MAX

This lightweight compound, single-cam bow boasts possibly the fastest speed of any bow—a whopping 330 fps IBO. It utilizes the MaxCam system and has a flat black riser, solid limbs, cable guard and wooden grip. The bow's limbs are camouflaged with Trebark to offer a refreshing appearance in the market or they are offered as solid black limbs to match the riser.

BOW SPECIFICATIONS: BLACK MAX
AMO Draw Length: 25- to 30-inch
Draw Weights: 40# to 70# with 65% let-off
Bow Speed: 330 fps IBO; 252 fps AMO
Axle-to-Axle: 36 inches
SRP:. **$699**

CONQUEST 2

This bow has a noticeably long riser and even with parallel limbs it pushes a 41-inch axle-to-axle length. Other specs include: a competition one-piece grip, original MaxCam, Harmonic dampening, cable guard, a ball bearing idler wheel and Zebra Twist string. The Conquest 2 is available in Realtree Xtra camouflage.

BOW SPECIFICATIONS: CONQUEST 2
AMO Draw Length: 28- to 32-inch; 24- to 29-inch with MiniMax

cams and 28- to 32- inch with the SuperSoft cams
Draw Weights: 40# to 70# with 80%, 65% or 60% let-off
Bow Speed: 310 fps IBO; 236 fps AMO
Axle-to-Axle: 41 inches
SRP:. **$429**
Tournament Model **$749**

CONQUEST 3

This compound bow features the new V-lock limb tips and pockets, plus harmonic damping system and a wooden competition grip. It is coated in camouflage and has a standard cable guard with slide. This bow weighs 4.4 pounds.

BOW SPECIFICATIONS
AMO Draw Length: 28 to 32 inches
Draw Weights: 40 to 70 pounds with 80, 65 or 60% let-off
Bow Speed: 310 fps IBO, 236 AMO
Axle-to Axle: 41 inches
SRP: **$749**

FX

Lightweight and short overall length best describe the FX. This Mathews creation weighs a scant 3.3 pounds and features a cable guard, solid limbs, competition one-piece grip and the original MaxCam system with

weighted single cam. The riser is more standard in appearance than other Mathews' risers. The FX is offered in Realtree camo and with patented Zebra Twist strings.

BOW SPECIFICATIONS: FX
AMO Draw Length: 27- to 31-inch; 23- to 28-inch with MiniMax cams
Draw Weights: 40# to 70# with 80% or 65% let-off
Bow Speed: 308 fps IBO; 235 fps AMO
Axle-to-Axle: 34 inches
SRP:. **$749**

GENESIS

This Mathews bow was geared to help beginning archers learn the basics without working through complex measurements. The bow has zero let off and is adjustable from 10 to 20 pounds draw weight. Kids can't outgrow it! It features split limbs, single cam with idler wheel, limb pockets, molded grip, arrow rest and cable guard. This bow has a Realtree Xtra camouflage finish.
SRP: starting at. **$160**

Mathews Compound Bows

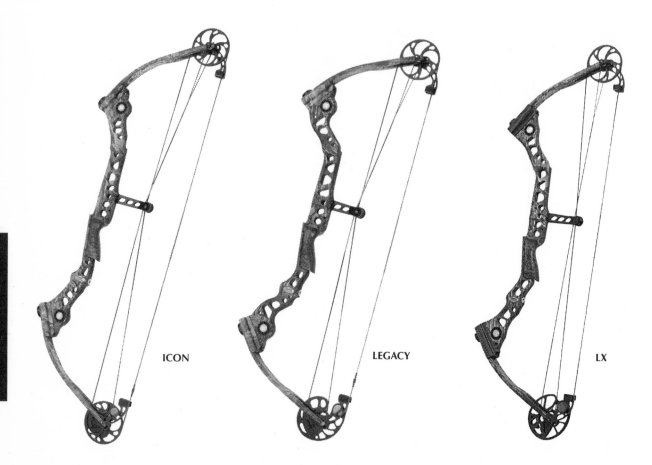

ICON

LEGACY

LX

ICON

This bow uses the concentric SoloCam—a round cam—for arrow energy. Other features include a ball-bearing idler wheel, Mathews' competition grip, Harmonic dampeners in plastic bushings, string suppressors, solid one-piece limbs and the innovative roller guard. The Icon is coated in Realtree Xtra camouflage and utilizes the parallel limb design. It also has threaded brass bushings to accept accessories such as a stabilizer below the grip. This bow has a 7⅝-inch brace height and weighs 4.45 pounds.

BOW SPECIFICATIONS: ICON

AMO Draw Length: 24- to 30-inch, 27½- to 29½-inch half sizes

Draw Weights: 40# to 70# with 70% let-off

Bow Speed: 300 fps IBO; 225 fps AMO

Axle-to-Axle: 37 inches

SRP:. $749

LEGACY

The Mathews Legacy compound bow incorporates the latest company technology including string suppressors to reduce string vibration and noise, the roller guard that replaces the traditional cable guard and parallel limb design which was started in 1996. This bow has a wooden grip and is coated in Realtree camouflage. This flagship bow for Mathews uses the Harmonic dampening system—brass or aluminum discs inserted into the ends of the riser. The Legacy has a 7½-inch brace height and weighs approximately 4.35 pounds.

BOW SPECIFICATIONS: LEGACY

AMO Draw Length: 24- to 30-inch, 27½- to 29½-inch half sizes

Draw Weights: 40# to 70# with 70% let-off

Bow Speed: 308 fps IBO; 235 fps AMO

Axle-to-Axle: 34 inches

SRP:. $699

LX

This compound bow by Mathews has the company's V-Lock zero tolerance limb system where the v-shaped limb tip fits into a specially designed V-shaped limb cup. Other features include the HP (high performance) single cam, string suppressors at the cams, a ball bearing roller guide instead of a cable guard, and parallel limb design. The cams incorporate perimeter-weighted technology and the bow has a Zebra Zs twist string. It features a wooden grip, harmonic damping system and camouflage coating. The LX weighs 4½ pounds.

BOW SPECIFICATIONS

AMO Draw Length: 25 to 30 inches

Draw Weights: 40 to 70 pounds with 80 or 65% let-off

Bow Speed: 315 fps IBO

Axle-to Axle: 35 inches

SRP: $719

Mathews Compound Bows

MQ1

The MQ1 has the parallel limb design, straightline cam, a ballbearing mounted idler wheel, solid limbs and a cable guard. Other features include a wooden grip and camouflage finish. This bow weighs 3.75 pounds and has a 7½-inch brace height.

BOW SPECIFICATIONS: MQ1
AMO Draw Length: 24- to 30-inch; 27½- to 29½-inch half sizes
Draw Weights: 40# to 70# with 80% or 70% let-off
Bow Speed: 308 fps IBO; 235 fps AMO
Axle-to-Axle: 37 inches
SRP:. $659

MQ-32

This bow grabbed Field & Stream's Best-of-the-Best award. The MQ-32 features a short riser and resulting short 32-inch axle-to-axle length. Other features include: straightline MaxCam, wooden grip, cable guard, Zebra twist string and solid limbs. This bow weighs only 3¼-pounds and is coated with a Mathews' camo finish.

BOW SPECIFICATIONS: MQ-32
AMO Draw Length: 24- to 30-inch; 27½- to 29½-inch half sizes
Draw Weights: 40# to 70# with 80% or 70% let-off
Bow Speed: 303 fps IBO; 228 fps AMO
Axle-to-Axle: 32 inches
SRP:. $599

Q2

Mathews rates the Q2 as one of their best selling bows of all time. Features of the Q2 include: parallel limb design, Straighline MaxCam 2, Harmonic dampening system, cable guard, competition grip, and threaded brass bushings to accept accessories. It's available in Realtree Xtra camo.

BOW SPECIFICATIONS: Q2
AMO Draw Length: 23- to 30-inch; 26½- to 29½-inch half sizes
Draw Weights: 40# to 70# with 70% let-off
Bow Speed: 308 fps IBO; 235 fps AMO
Axle-to-Axle: 34 inches
SRP:. $689

Q2XL

Similar to the Q2 but is based on a longer 27-inch riser—compared to Q2's 23-inch riser—and made for finger shooters or those with longer draw lengths.

BOW SPECIFICATIONS: Q2XL
AMO Draw Length: 24- to 31-inch; 27½- to 30½-inch half sizes
Draw Weights: 40# to 70# with 70% let-off
Bow Speed: 308 fps IBO; 235 fps AMO
Axle-to-Axle: 38 inches
SRP:. $699

RIVAL PRO

The Mathews Rival Pro uses a smaller MaxCam and mini idler wheel to control the string and launch arrows. Other features of this parallel limb designed bow include: long 27-inch plus riser, wooden grip, cable guard and Zebra twist string. It is camouflaged for hunting and has an 8-inch brace height.

BOW SPECIFICATIONS: RIVAL PRO
AMO Draw Length: 25- to 30-inch
Draw Weights: 40# to 70# with 65% let-off
Bow Speed: 308 fps IBO; 232 fps AMO
Axle-to-Axle: 40 inches
SRP:. $699

SPORTSMAN

This bow was developed with bow-fishermen and upland hunters in mind. It uses the fin or feather cam with perimeter weighting to create a low let off. The bow can be smoothly released at full draw or half draw without feeling a discernable let off "bump." There is no specific draw length for this bow and the same bow can be used by a wide group of shooters. Other features include Mathews' competition zebra twist string and solid limbs. The bow is coated in Realtree camo only and weighs 3.3 pounds.

BOW SPECIFICATIONS: SPORTSMAN
AMO Draw Length: 20- to 32-inch
Draw Weights: 40# to 70# with 70% let-off
Bow Speed: NA
Axle-to-Axle: 34 inches
SRP:. $429

Q2

SPORTSMAN

COMPOUND BOWS

Mathews Compound Bows

SQ2

SQ2

This Mathews compound bow has a short 31-inch axle-to-axle length and uses the Harmonic dampening system. Other features include: a competition grip, cable guard, Straightline MaxCam 2, and a ball bearing idler wheel. The bow is offered in Realtree camo, has an 8¹⁄₂-inch brace height and weighs 3.3 pounds.

BOW SPECIFICATIONS: SQ2

AMO Draw Length: 23- to 30-inch, 26¹⁄₂- to 29¹⁄₂-inches half sizes

Draw Weights: 40# to 70# with 70% let-off

Bow Speed: 305 fps IBO; 230 fps AMO

Axle-to-Axle: 31 inches

SRP:. **$659**

ULTRA 2

This Mathews bow has features similar to the SQ2 but uses the Original MaxCam along with solid limbs and a cable guard. It's offered in Realtree camo and has a 6¹⁄₈-inch brace height and tips the scale at 3.7 pounds.

BOW SPECIFICATIONS: ULTRA 2

AMO Draw Length: 23- to 30-inch; 22- to 27-inch with MiniMax cams

Draw Weights: 40# to 70# with 80% or 65% let-off

Bow Speed: 320+ fps IBO (one of the industry's highest!); 245 fps AMO

Axle-to-Axle: 36 inches

SRP:. **$629**

ULTRA 2

When you sight-in your bow during the off season, be sure to check the penetration depth of your arrows at your farthest shooting distance. If you are not getting adequate penetration at this distance, you need to keep moving closer to your target until you get good penetration. Set this distance as your maximum shooting range. Poor penetration will just wound game.

ESC BLACK EAGLE

This Onedia bow continues the company's traditional look with limbs that break at a junction. The Engineered Structural Composite limbs can withstand temperatures up to 550 degrees Fahrenheit. This bow is camouflaged with Skyline Excel and has a wooden grip. This bow is up to 46 inches long and weighs 4½ pounds.

BOW SPECIFICATIONS
AMO Draw Length: 26 to 34 inches
Draw Weights: 35-55, 50-70, and 60-80 pounds
Bow Speed: NA
Axle-to Axle: NA, up to 46 inches long
SRP: **$649.99**

HAWK

An Oneida-style bow with a wooden grip and brace height up to 6⅛ inches. It is similar in design to all Oneida bows and has a sturdy aluminum riser and weighs 3.8 pounds. This bow is camouflaged with Mossy Oak Break Up.

BOW SPECIFICATIONS
AMO Draw Length: 22 to 26 inches
Draw Weights: 25 to 45 pounds
Bow Speed: NA
Axle-to Axle: NA, but its 40 inches tip-to-tip
SRP: $499.99

ESC BLACK EAGLE **HAWK**

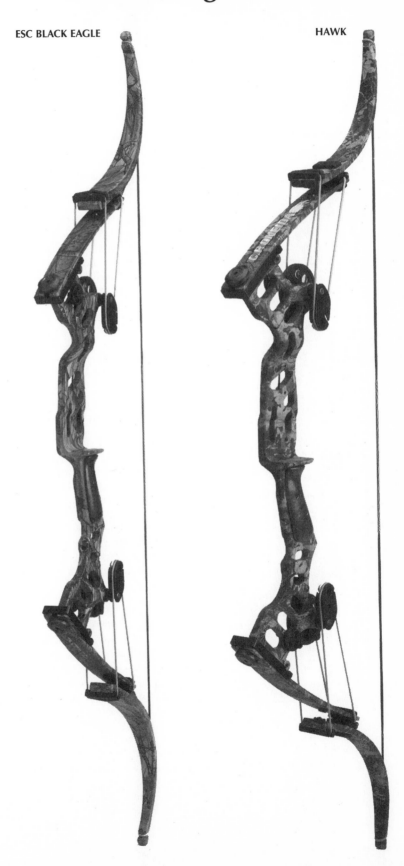

COMPOUND BOWS

Parker Compound Bows Compound Bows

HUNTER-MAG OUTFITTER COMBO

CHALLENGER

This smaller version of the popular Parker Ultra-Lite bows is designed for the shorter draw lengths of ladies and young archers. The Challenger has the same features as the Ultra-Lite series including an aluminum riser, walnut grip, and Power-Tuff composite limbs. This bow has a machined aluminum mini one-cam, cable guard and Superflauge finish.

BOW SPECIFICATIONS: CHALLENGER
AMO Draw Length: 23-, 24-, 25-, 26- and 27-inch with extra draw modules available.
Draw Weights: 30#, 40# and 50# with 10# adjustment down from set weight. 80 % let-off standard with 65% let-off optional.
Bow Speed: NA
Axle-to Axle: 32½-inches
SRP: **$319.95**

FEATHER-MAG II

The Feather-Mag uses a traditional deflex riser to provide a dependable and carefree compound bow. Most other features are same as the Ultra-Lite Pro. The Parker logo appears under the handle.

BOW SPECIFICATIONS: FEATHER-MAG II
AMO Draw Length: 26-, 27, 28-, 29-, 30-, 31-, 32- and 33-inch with extra draw modules available.
Draw Weights: 50#, 60# and 70# with 10# adjustment down from set weight. 80 % let-off standard with 65% let-off optional.
Bow Speed: 232 fps AMO; 298 fps IBO
Axle-to Axle: 37 inches
SRP: **$469.95**

FORCE-MULTIPLIER II

This bow has a unique third idler wheel located below the grip and attached to the bottom of the machined aluminum riser. The wheel absorbs torque to promote smooth arrow shots. This bow is available in left- and right-hand versions. The Force-Multiplier has Power Tuff composite limbs, a Force One-Cam, cable guard and a walnut wood grip. This bow has a 6-inch brace height, weighs 3.6 pounds and is covered in Superflauge.

BOW SPECIFICATIONS: FORCE-MULTIPLIER II
AMO Draw Length: 25-, 26-, 27, 28-, 29- and 30-inch with extra draw modules available.
Draw Weights: 50#, 60# and 70# with 10# adjustment down from set weight. 80 % let-off standard with 65% let-off optional.
Bow Speed: 250 fps AMO; 325 fps IBO
Axle-to Axle: 35 inches
SRP: **$599.95**
Tournament Model **$669.95**

HUNTER-MAG

This one-cam compound bow is similar to the Stealth-Hunter but has a solid machined aluminum riser and black, shock-free Kraton handle. Parker's Hunter-Mag weighs 3.6 pounds and has a 7-inch brace height.

The Hunter-Mag bow is also available in a factory set-up combo with a shipping box that is suitable for use as a permanent bow case. Combo features include: a Parker quiver, four Beman carbon arrows, a fiber-optic sight, a caliper release, Quik-Tune 800 rest, pep sight, string silencers and a braided sling. The combo bows are only available in 28-, 29- and 30-inch draw lengths and as 50-60# and 60-70# draw weights. These items have been specifically chosen to enhance the performance of and customer satisfaction with this bow.

BOW SPECIFICATIONS: HUNTER-MAG
AMO Draw Length: 25-, 26-, 27-, 28-, 29-, 30-, 31- and 32-inch with extra draw modules available.
Draw Weights: 50#, 60# and 70# with 10# adjustment down from set weight. 80 % let-off standard with 65% let-off optional.
Bow Speed: 239 fps AMO; 305 fps IBO
Axle-to Axle: 37 inches
SRP: **$319.95**
Hunter–Mag Outfitter Combo
. . . . **$429.95**

Parker Compound Bows Compound Bows

JUNIOR-MAG

The Junior-Mag is a scaled-down version of Parker's larger bows with a solid aluminum riser and with a 6-inch brace height, curved composite limbs and mini-cams. This model also has a walnut grip and Superflauge camo finish. This is a great consideration for a youth bow or a lady's first hunting bow when set at 40#.

BOW SPECIFICATIONS: JUNIOR-MAG

AMO Draw Length: 19-, 20-, 21-, 22-, 23- and 24-inch with extra draw modules available.

Draw Weights: 20#, 30# and 40# with 10# adjustment down from set weight. 80% let-off standard with 65% let-off optional.

Bow Speed: NA

Axle-to Axle: 31½-inches

SRP: **$229.95**

STEALTH-HUNTER

This Parker compound bow was introduced in 2002 and has a sleek machined 6061 aluminum riser and unique camouflaged, shock-absorbing Kraton grip. This bow is available for left- and right-hand shooters. The Stealth-Hunter features the Super One-Cam, hand built Power-Tuff composite limbs and a Superflauge finish.

The Stealth-Hunter is also available in a factory set-up combination that includes: a Parker quiver, four Beman arrows, fiber optic sight, caliper release, Quik-Tune 1000 arrow rest, peep sight, string silencer and braided string. The unique shipping box can serve as a permanent carrying case. This factory prepared bow kit is only available in 28-, 29- and 30-inch draw lengths and as 50-60# and 60-70# draw weights.

BOW SPECIFICATIONS: STEALTH-HUNTER

AMO Draw Length: 25-, 26-, 27, 28-, 29-, 30-, 31- and 32-inch with extra draw modules available.

Draw Weights: 50#, 60# and 70# with 10# adjustment down from set weight. 80 % let-off standard with 65% let-off optional.

Bow Speed: 239 fps AMO; 305 fps IBO

Axle-to Axle: 37 inches

SRP: **$439.95**

Stealth-Hunter Outfitter and case **$549.95**

JUNIOR-MAG

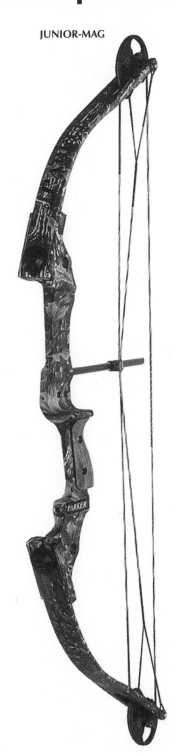

STEALTH-HUNTER OUTFITTER

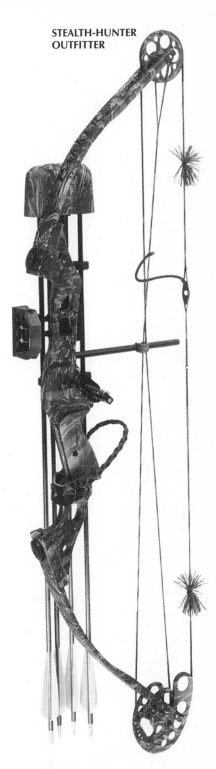

Parker Compound Bows Compound Bows

ULTRA-LITE 35

ULTRA-LITE 31

ULTRA-LITE 35

This compound bow is similar to the Ultra-Lite 31 in design with a longer axle-to-axle length and weight of 3.1 pounds. The bow is designed to accommodate archers with a longer draw length and is available in Superflauge camouflage.

BOW SPECIFICATIONS: ULTRA-LITE 35
AMO Draw Length: 25-, 26-, 27, 28-, 29-, 30-, 31- and 32-inch with extra draw modules available.
Draw Weights: 50#, 60# and 70# with 10# adjustment down from set weight. 80 % let-off is standard with 65% let-off optional.
Bow Speed: 243 fps AMO; 300 fps IBO
Axle-to Axle: 35 inches
SRP: **$569.95**

ULTRA-LITE PRO

This Parker compound bow is a continuation of the Ultra-Lite series with similar features as the 31 and 35 model. The Pro model is designed for longer draw lengths, tall archers, finger shooters and for anyone who likes a longer bow. The bow weighs 3.6 pounds and is available in Superflauge camouflage. Parker's Ultra-Lite Pro is available in left- and right-hand versions and has a larger $7\frac{1}{2}$-inch brace height.

BOW SPECIFICATIONS: ULTRA-LITE PRO
AMO Draw Length: 25-, 26-, 27, 28-, 29-, 30-, 31- and 32-inch with extra draw modules available.
Draw Weights: 50#, 60# and 70# with 10# adjustment down from set weight. 80 % let-off standard with 65% let-off optional.
Bow Speed: 240 fps AMO; 306 fps IBO
Axle-to Axle: 38 inches
SRP: **$579.95**

ULTRA-LITE 31

This bow is available in left- and right-hand configurations with a machined 6061 aluminum riser that offers a 7-inch brace height. Features include: power-tuff composite limbs, a super-One cam, carbon composite cable guard, walnut grip and a Superflauge camouflage finish. This bow weighs only 2.9 pounds and is available in a competition model.

BOW SPECIFICATIONS: ULTRA-LITE 31
AMO Draw Length: 23-, 24-, 25-, 26-, 27, 28-, 29- and 30-inch with extra draw modules available.
Draw Weights: 50#, 60# and 70# with 10# adjustment down from set weight. 80 % let-off is standard with 65% letoff optional.
Bow Speed: 240 fps AMO; 310 fps IBO
Axle-to Axle: 31 inches
SRP: **$569.95**
Tournament Model **$639.95**

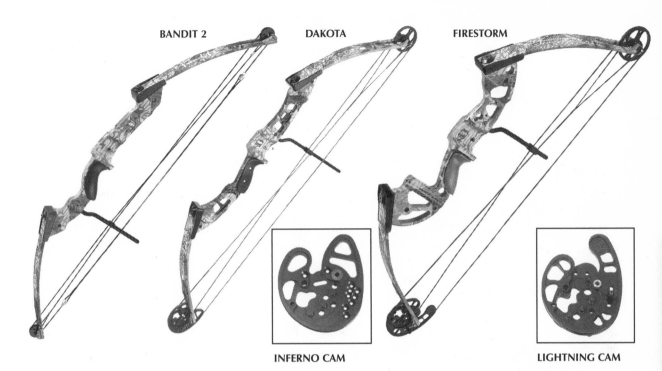

BANDIT 2   **DAKOTA**   **FIRESTORM**

INFERNO CAM   **LIGHTNING CAM**

COMPOUND BOWS

BANDIT 2

Here's another PSE youth bow that's made to successfully introduce small framed hunters and arrow enthusiasts to the thrills of archery. The Bandit is only available with a camouflage finish. Other construction features include: a molded wrap-around one-piece grip, solid riser and limbs and a reliable two-wheel cable system.

BOW SPECIFICATIONS: BANDIT 2
AMO Draw Length: 18-, 21-, 23- and 24-inch
Draw Weights: 20# in 18-inch draw, 30# and 40# in other draw lengths with 60% let-off
Bow Speed: IBO fps = 215
Axle-to Axle: 33 inches
Weight in hand: 2 lbs., 6 oz.
SRP:.....................$249
Tournament Model $269

DAKOTA

The Dakota compound bow is designed for finger shooters who need longer axle-to-axle length bows to permit smooth finger releases and avoid string pinch. Dakota offers a slightly deflexed riser, PSE's Magnaglass limbs and three wheel options. Hunting versions are available in Brush camouflage and competition models are also available. A molded wrap-around grip ensures better control and shooter hand comfort.

SPECIFICATIONS: DAKOTA
AMO Draw Length: 27 to 31 inches in 1-inch increments.
Draw Weights (lbs.): 60 and 70 with 75% let-off
Bow Speed: IBO fps = 300
Axle-to Axle: 39 inches
Weight: 4 lbs., 3oz.
SRP:.....................$369

SPECIFICATIONS: DAKOTA SYNERGY
AMO Draw Length: 28 to 30 inches in 1-inch increments.
Draw Weights (lbs.): 60 and 70 with 65% let-off
Bow Speed: IBO fps = 300
Axle-to Axle: 41 inches
Weight: 4 lbs., 3ozs.
SRP:.....................$339
   (add $15 for left-hand model)

SPECIFICATIONS: DAKOTA SYNERGY PRO 65
AMO Draw Length: 28- to 30-inch in 1-inch increments.
Draw Weights: 60# and 70# with 65% let-off
Bow Speed: IBO fps = 300
Axle-to Axle: 41 inches
Weight in hand: 4 lbs., 3ozs.
SRP:.....................$369
   (add $15 for left-hand model)

SPECIFICATIONS: DAKOTA SYNERGY PRO 75
AMO Draw Length: 28- to 31-inch in 1-inch increments.
Draw Weights: 60# and 70# with 75% let-off
Bow Speed: IBO fps = 297
Axle-to Axle: 41 inches
Weight in hand: 4 lbs., 3 ozs.
SRP:.....................$369
   (add $15 for left-hand models)

FIRESTORM LC

PSE's Firestorm was first introduced in 2001 and features an extremely short axle-to-axle length that works well for maneuvering and shooting in blinds and treestands. The bow has an 8-inch brace height and uses the company's Lightning Cam system to move arrows. The unique riser has a wrap-around solid wood grip and cable guard. Available only in Brush camo finish.

BOW SPECIFICATIONS: FIRESTORM LIGHTNING CAM
AMO Draw Length: 27- to 30-inch in 1-inch increments.
Draw Weights: 50#, 60# and 70# with 80% let-off but the bow adjusts to a 65% let-off
Bow Speed: IBO fps = 300
Axle-to Axle: 30 inches
Weight in hand: 3 lbs., 10 oz.
SRP: $669.99

PSE Compound Bows

FIRESTORM LITE

MACH II

VECTOR 5 CAM

FIRESTORM LITE

A compound bow that uses PSE's Lightning-3 One-Cam with solid limbs to improve the draw cycle. This bow's ultra-lightweight machined aluminum riser has an 8-inch brace height and aggressive design. The metal components and limbs have a lifetime warranty. Other features include a TRM wooden grip, cable guard and a totally redesigned model that's different from previous versions of this bow. It weighs 3.2 pounds.

BOW SPECIFICATIONS
AMO Draw Length: 26 to 30 inches
Draw Weights: 50, 60 or 70 pounds with 80% let-off, 65% optional
Bow Speed: 300 fps
Axle-to Axle: 30 inches
SRP: $579.99

MACH II

The Mach II is available in two models: the Vector 5 and the Stinger Cam version. The Mach II with the Vector 5 cam system is the tournament archery version.

PSE's Mach II Stinger is available in Brush camo. This bow uses the modular Stinger Cam and has the NC Vibration Dampening System.
BOW SPECIFICATIONS:
MACH II STINGER CAM
AMO Draw Length: 25- to 29-inch in 1-inch increments.
Draw Weights: 50#, 60# and 70# with 75% let-off.
Bow Speed: IBO fps = 292
Axle-to Axle: 39 inches
Weight in hand: 4 lbs., 3 oz.
SRP: $1089.99
Tournament Models $1169.99

MONARCH

The Monarch, with PSE's Ultimate One Cam system, is a hunting model that's coated with a Brush Camo finish. This bow has a distinct solid black riser with a shoot-through center brace. Other bow features include: carbon solid limbs, arrow rest and cable guard with slide.
BOW SPECIFICATIONS:
MONARCH ULTIMATE ONE CAM
AMO Draw Length: 26- to 31-inch in 1-inch increments.
Draw Weights: 60# and 70# with 80% let-off (65% let-off optional)
Bow Speed: IBO fps = 310
Axle-to Axle: 39 inches
Weight in hand: 4 lbs., 5 oz.
SRP: $1169.99
Pro Vectors. $1269.99

PSE Compound Bows

NITRO

NITRO ULTIMATE ONE CAM

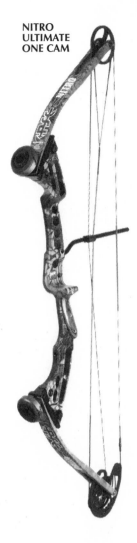

ULTIMATE ONE CAM

NITRO

This PSE compound bow is available with Maxi-Plus Twin cams or Centerfire One-Cams. Other features include Trimline pivoting limb pockets, the Phase III grip system, integrated cam-lock cable guard, and the NV vibration dampening system. The bow's brace height is approximately 6 inches and this model is coated with PSE brush camo. This bow is also available in three competition colors for additional costs.

BOW SPECIFICATIONS

AMO Draw Length: from 25 to 31 inches, varies by cam selection
Draw Weights: 60 or 70 pounds
Bow Speed: 315 fps One-Cam, 308 fps Twin cam
Axle-to Axle: 36 inches
SRP: **$669.99**

NITRO ULTIMATE ONE CAM

The bow's stout design incorporates a longer reflex handle and shorter limbs are mounted solidly in compact pivoting pockets. Other construction features include: NV System vibration control discs mounted on the front of the limb pockets, machined aluminum riser, a solid cable guard, Teflon coated cam and solid limbs. The Nitro is available in PSE's Autumn Brush camouflage or three vivid Color-Tech colors.

The Nitro Ultimate One Cam bow uses the Phase-3 grip system. You can use panels installed on each side of the riser, a full grip that wraps around the riser, or only the riser that has been radiused to permit hand-only shooting.

BOW SPECIFICATIONS:
NITRO ULTIMATE ONE CAM
AMO Draw Length: 25- to 30-inch in 1-inch increments.
Draw Weights: 60# and 70# with 80% let-off (65% let-off optional)
Bow Speed: IBO fps= 314
Axle-to Axle: 36 inches
Weight in hand: 3 lbs., 10 oz.
SRP: **$799.99**
Tournament Models **$889.99**

PRIMOS STL

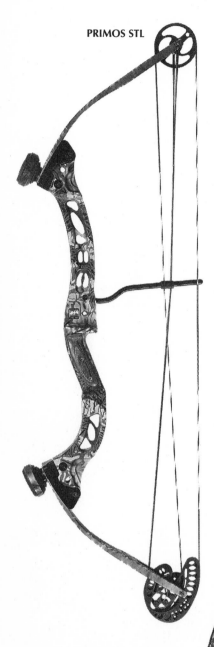

NOVA

The Nova is available with three cams: Arson, Vector Pro and Vector 5. Other features include integrated cam-lock cable guard, molded wrap around grips and solid carbon limbs. Note that the lower draw weights are available only in the shorter draw lengths in the Vector Pro model and that draw lengths are 24, 26, 28, 29 and 30 inches.

BOW SPECIFICATIONS: NOVA ARSON CAM
AMO Draw Length: 27- to 31-inch in 1-inch increments.
Draw Weights: 60# and 70# with 70% let-off
Bow Speed: IBO fps = 295
Axle-to Axle: 36½ inches
Weight in hand: 3 lbs., 12 oz.
SRP:.....................$269
Tournament Model $299
    (add $15 for LH models)

BOW SPECIFICATIONS: NOVA VECTOR PRO
AMO Draw Length: 24- to 30-inch in 1-inch increments.
Draw Weights: 30#, 40#, 50#, 60# and 70# with 75% let-off
Bow Speed: IBO fps = 280
Axle-to Axle: 38 inches
Weight in hand: 3 lbs., 9 oz.
SRP:.....................$249
Tournament Model $289
    (add $15 for LH models)

BOW SPECIFICATIONS: NOVA VECTOR 5
AMO Draw Length: 26- to 30-inch in 1-inch increments.
Draw Weights: 50# (26-inch draw length only), 60# and 70# with 65% let-off
Bow Speed: IBO fps = 275
Axle-to Axle: 39 inches
Weight in hand: 3 lbs., 9 oz.
SRP:.....................$249
    (add $15 for LH models)

PRIMOS STL

A PSE bow designed with input by hunting pro Will Primos, the Primos STL is designed for hunting and is coated with PSE Brush camo. Features are Phase III grips, a 7¾-inch brace height, integrated cam-lock cable guard and Centerfire one-cam system. This bow is also available in blue and red tournament colors. This bow weighs 3.95 pounds and has the NV vibration dampening system.

BOW SPECIFICATIONS
AMO Draw Length: 26 to 31 inches
Draw Weights: 60 and 70 pounds with 85% or 65% let-off
Bow Speed: 305 fps
Axle-to Axle: 38 inches
SRP: $629.99

QUANTAM ULTIMATE ONE CAM

This high-tech bow incorporates sleek lines and a trimline design to improve performance. This compound bow has a distinct multi-port vent system on the riser's upper and lower sections, plus solid limbs and cam. The Quantum Ultimate One Cam can use the Phase-3 grip system and is available in Brush camo. The Quantam's riser provides a 7½-inch brace height and the NV vibration dampening system can be installed.

BOW SPECIFICATIONS:
QUANTAM ULTIMATE ONE CAM
AMO Draw Length: 27- to 32-inch in 1-inch increments.
Draw Weights: 60# and 70# with 80% let-off (65% let-off optional)
Bow Speed: IBO fps = 305
Axle-to Axle: 39 inches
Weight in hand: 3 lbs., 10 oz.
SRP: $799.99
Tournament Model $899.99

ARSON CAM

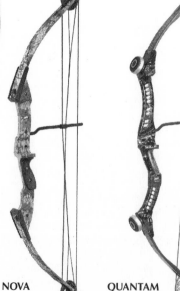

NOVA   **QUANTAM**

SUPRA

SPYDER

PSE's Spyder is designed for short-draw archers and can be adjusted across more than 5 inches of draw length. Other features for this compound bow include: a lightweight machined aluminum riser, integrated cam-lock cable guard, molded TRM grip and the Stinger cam system. This bow has a 6¾-inch brace height. The Spyder's shorter draw lengths and lighter draw weight combinations make this a great youth and lady's bow. The bow is available in Brush camo and blue colors.

The IBO speed for this bow was determined by shooting a 27-inch draw length.

BOW SPECIFICATIONS:
SPYDER STINGER CAM
AMO Draw Length: 23- to 27-inch in 1-inch increments.
Draw Weights: 40#, 50# and 60# with 75% let-off
Bow Speed: IBO fps = 275
Axle-to Axle: 35 inches
Weight in hand: 3 lbs., 5 oz.
SRP: $339
Tournament Model $369
   (add $15 for LH models)

SPYDER S4

A youth bow that's full of adult features best describes this compound bow. The Spyder S4 has a deflexed riser, molded composite wrap-around grip and cable guard. It utilizes solid limbs and is available in camouflage.
BOW SPECIFICATIONS: SPYDER S4
AMO Draw Length: 19- or 23-inch only.
Draw Weights: 20# in 19-inch draw, 30# and 40# in 23-inch draw with 65% let-off
Bow Speed: IBO fps = 240
Axle-to Axle: 32 inches
Weight in hand: 2 lbs., 6 oz.
SRP: $179.99

SUPRA

PSE's Supra is a competition bow with recurve Magnaglass limbs, machined limb pockets, chrome wheels, a cable guard and molded grip. The new lightweight machined riser significantly reduces felt vibration. This bow is offered in blue, red and good vibrations graphics. Two cam options are offered: Stinger or Synergy Pro-65 cams.

BOW SPECIFICATIONS
AMO Draw Length: 25 to 30 dependent upon cam selection
Draw Weights: 40, 50 or 60 pounds with 75% or 65% let-off based on cam selection
Bow Speed: 280 fps Stinger, 298 fps Pro-65 cam
Axle-to Axle: 39½ inches
SRP: . . . . **Starting at $529.99**

TEAM FITZGERALD NOVA STAGE 3

This package bow is endorsed by famed bowhunting advocates Dan Fitzgerald and Guy Fitzgerald and built by PSE. The bow package includes a two-prong arrow rest, fiber optic sight with clear pin guard, and one-piece arrow quiver. Other features include: a solid riser, wrap-around grip, cable guard and solid limbs. This bow is available only in PSE brush camouflage and with two-wheel technology. Other hunting related Fitzgerald products are available if you desire to increase the shooter's thrill and enthusiasm level. Just add arrows and start hunting!
BOW SPECIFICATIONS: TEAM FITZGERALD NOVA STAGE 3
AMO Draw Length: 24-, 27- and 29-inch.
Draw Weights: 40# (24-inch), 55# (27-inch) and 65# (29-inch) with 65% let-off
Bow Speed: IBO fps = 265
Axle-to Axle: 38 inches
Weight in hand: 3 lbs., 9 oz.
SRP: $239.99
   (add $15 for LH models)

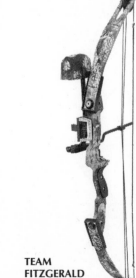

STINGER CAM

SPYDER

TEAM FITZGERALD NOVA STAGE 3

COMPOUND BOWS

PSE Compound Bows

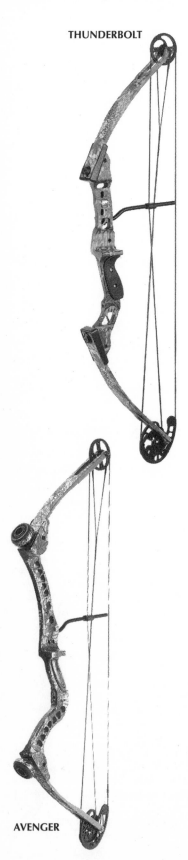

THUNDERBOLT

AVENGER

THUNDERBOLT

This lightweight bow is available with three wheel options: Maxis HL, Lightning Cam and Stinger Cam systems. The Maxis cam provides traditional twin-cam technology with high let-off. The adjustable Stinger cam features a pivoting module for easy draw length adjustment. The Lightning cam delivers fast arrow speeds and flat trajectory. This bow uses MagnaGlass limbs and has a molded one-piece wrap around grip and cable guard. The Maxis model is available in Brush camo finish only and the Lightning cam and Stinger cam models are available in blue.

BOW SPECIFICATIONS: THUNDERBOLT LIGHTNING CAM

AMO Draw Length: 27- to 31-inch in 1-inch increments.
Draw Weights: 50#, 60# and 70# with 80% let-off but the bow adjusts to 65% let-off
Bow Speed: IBO fps = 300
Axle-to Axle: 36 inches
Weight in hand: 3 lbs., 9 oz.
SRP: $419.99
Tournament Model $499

BOW SPECIFICATIONS: THUNDERBOLT MAXIS HIGH LET-OFF

AMO Draw Length: 26- to 30-inch in 1-inch increments.
Draw Weights: 50# (available in 26-inch draw length only), 60# and 70# with 75% let-off
Bow Speed: IBO fps = 300
Axle-to Axle: 38 inches
Weight in hand: 3 lbs., 9 oz.
SRP:. $419
    (Add $15 for LH version)

BOW SPECIFICATIONS: THUNDERBOLT STINGER CAM

AMO Draw Length: 23- to 27-inch in 1-inch increments.
Draw Weights: 40#, 50# and 60# with 75% let-off
Bow Speed: IBO fps = 278
Axle-to Axle: 37½-inches
Weight in hand: 3 lbs., 9 oz.
SRP:. $419
Tournament Model $499

PSE PRO SERIES

The following PSE bows are part of the company's Pro Series and feature upgraded grips, upgraded strings and performance enhancing components in most models. These bows are developed with the advanced archer in mind.

AVENGER

With a unibody construction providing a machined one-piece riser and limb pockets combination, the Avenger provides un-compromised limb alignment. Other construction features include: PSE's NV System for vibration reduction, Phase-3 grip system and a Color-Tech Autumn Brush camouflage finish. PSE takes great pride and care in the finish of their bows and the new Color-Tech system seems to show this attention to detail. The Avenger's Phase -3 grip system permits the changing of panels or to a full grip or to no grip with the use of the bare radiused grip if desired—a true custom feel and hand fit. The bow's Ultimate One-Cam can be converted to a 65% let-off, has easily changed modular draw stop adjustments, a built in draw stop and is Teflon coated. This bow is available in RH only.

BOW SPECIFICATIONS: AVENGER ULTIMATE ONE-CAM

AMO Draw Length: 26- to 31-inch in 1-inch increments.
Draw Weights: 60# and 70# with 80% let-off (65% let-off optional)
Bow Speed: IBO fps = 305
Axle-to Axle: 37 inches
Weight in hand: 3 lbs., 15 oz.
SRP: $799.99

BEAST **DIAMONDBACK II** **ENFORCER**

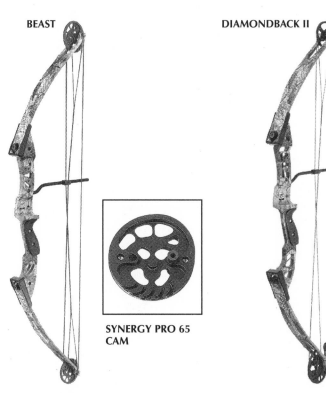

SYNERGY PRO 65 CAM

BEAST

The Beast was unleashed with a new machined aluminum riser in 2002 and offers three cam options: Inferno, Synergy Pro 65 and Synergy Pro 75. This bow is geared toward performance minded archers or hunters who also seek value. Other features include: an upper cable guard, 7–inch brace height, limb pockets securing solid limbs and a molded grip. The 40# and 50# draw weights are only available in the 26-inch draw length model. The Beast is also available only in PSE's Brush camouflage. LH models are available for an additional $15.

BOW SPECIFICATIONS: BEAST INFERNO CAM
AMO Draw Length: 27- to 31-inch in 1-inch increments.
Draw Weights: 60# and 70# with 75% let-off
Bow Speed: IBO fps = 290
Axle-to Axle: 36½-inches
Weight in hand: 3 lbs., 10 oz.
SRP: **$369.99**

BOW SPECIFICATIONS: BEAST SYNERGY PRO 65
AMO Draw Length: 26- to 30-inch in 1-inch increments.
Draw Weights: 40#, 50#, 60# and 70# with 65% let-off

Bow Speed: IBO fps = 295
Axle-to Axle: 39 inches
Weight in hand: 3 lbs., 8 oz.
SRP: **$249.99**

BOW SPECIFICATIONS: BEAST SYNERGY PRO 75
AMO Draw Length: 26- to 30-inch in 1-inch increments.
Draw Weights: 40#, 50#, 60# and 70# with 75% let-off
Bow Speed: IBO fps = 290
Axle-to Axle: 39 inches
Weight in hand: 3 lbs., 8 oz.
SRP: **$249.99**

DIAMONDBACK II

This camouflaged compound hunting bow is the result of unequalled quality meeting incredible value. Features of the Diamondback II include: solid limbs, PSE's Lightning cam, a solid molded grip and an upper cable guard.

BOW SPECIFICATIONS: DIAMONDBACK II
AMO Draw Length: 27- to 31-inch in 1-inch increments.
Draw Weights: 60# and 70#; 80% let-off, adjusts to 65% let-off
Bow Speed: IBO fps = 305
Axle-to Axle: 36½-inches
Weight in hand: 3 lbs., 9 oz.

SRP: **$419.99**
(additional $15 for LH models)

ENFORCER

The unique unibody machined riser and partially reflexed riser with angled grip give this bow a space age appearance and advanced performance capabilities. The Enforcer offers sleek lines, lightweight construction and vibration-free performance. Other features include: PSE's Ultimate One-Cam system with 6 changeable modules, NV vibration reduction, Autumn Brush camouflage finish, and Phase-3 grip system. This hunting oriented compound bow also has a one-piece upper cable guard and solid limbs.

BOW SPECIFICATIONS: ENFORCER ULTIMATE ONE-CAM
AMO Draw Length: 26- to 31-inch in 1-inch increments.
Draw Weights: 60# and 70# with 80% let-off (65% let-off optional)
Bow Speed: IBO fps = 300
Axle-to Axle: 34 inches
Weight in hand: 4 lbs., 2 oz.
SRP: **$799.99**
(add $15 for LH models)

COMPOUND BOWS

PSE Compound Bows

MACH 10

OUTLAW

STINGRAY

MAXIS HL CAM

MACH 10

This Pro Series compound bow uses PSE's Ultimate One-Cam system and NV vibration dampening system. Other features include: a Micro-Adjust two-prong rest, upper cable guard, Phase 3 grip system and PSE's Pivoting Limb Pockets. It's also available in PSE's Autumn brush only in the Maxis HL model. This bow is available in right-hand models only.

BOW SPECIFICATIONS: MACH 10 ULTIMATE ONE-CAM

AMO Draw Length: 26- to 31-inch in 1-inch increments.
Draw Weights: 60# and 70# with 80% let-off (65% let-off optional)
Bow Speed: IBO fps = 311
Axle-to Axle: 38 inches
Weight in hand: 4 lbs., 8 oz.
SRP: **$999.99**
Tournament Model **$1059.99**

BOW SPECIFICATIONS: MACH 10 MAXIS HL
AMO Draw Length: 27- to 30-inch in 1-inch increments.
Draw Weights: 60# and 70# with 75% let-off
Bow Speed: IBO fps = 307

Axle-to Axle: 39 inches
Weight in hand: 4 lbs., 8 oz.
SRP: **$999.99**

OUTLAW

The Outlaw was designed with one purpose: Getting youth interested and involved in archery. Outlaw's features include: a mildly deflexed riser, PSE's 535 Magnaglass limbs, and the adjustable Synergy 4-cam system. Other features include: a lower cable guard, molded one-piece composite grip and an Autumn Brush camouflage finish. This bow is lightweight and offered at a low draw weight so that almost any youngster could pick it up and immediately have fun for a long period of time without tiring.

BOW SPECIFICATIONS: OUTLAW

AMO Draw Length: 20-inch
Draw Weights: 25# with 70% let-off
Bow Speed: IBO fps = 210
Axle-to Axle: 32½-inches
Weight in hand: 2 lbs., 4 oz.
SRP: **$199.99**

STINGRAY

The Stingray is a compact, lightweight bow—approximately 3 pounds!—that's highly maneuverable and easy to carry while in the field and hunting. This bow features a PSE Lightning cam system, narrow profile TRM grip and laid-back limb angle. Other features include: an upper cable guard, solid one-piece wooden grip and solid limbs securely anchored in sturdy limb pockets. This bow is available with the Autumn Brush finish.

BOW SPECIFICATIONS: STINGRAY LIGHTNING CAM

AMO Draw Length: 26- to 30-inches in 1-inch increments.
Draw Weights: 60# and 70# with 80% let-off and it adjusts to 65% let-off
Bow Speed: IBO fps = 305
Axle-to Axle: 32 inches
Weight in hand: 3 lbs., 2 oz.
SRP: **$619.99**
    (additional $15 for LH models)

TEAM PRIMOS

This hunting oriented compound bow is endorsed by professional critter caller and call manufacturer Will Primos of Mississippi. Construction features include: a longer length, more than 40-inches overall, and a high brace height —7½-inches—that combine to create a fast bow that shoots with unbelievable forgiveness. Other features include: the NC vibration suppression system, Ultimate One-Cam with changeable parts, solid wood one-piece grip, solid limbs and an upper cable guard. The team Primos compound bow is available in PSE Autumn Brush camouflaged finish only. This is a good choice for any hunter with a long draw length and who wants a combination of speed and performance in a lightweight bow.

BOW SPECIFICATIONS: TEAM PRIMOS ULTIMATE ONE-CAM

AMO Draw Length: 27- to 32-inch in 1-inch increments.
Draw Weights: 60# and 70# with 80% let-off (65% let-off optional)
Bow Speed: IBO fps = 308
Axle-to Axle: 38 inches
Weight in hand: 3 lbs., 12 oz.
SRP: **$699.99**
   (additional $15 for LH models)

XCELLERATOR

Exhaustive hours of attention to detail and painstaking design considerations have been invested into the Xcellerator. This bow has an all new pivoting limb pocket for unequalled adjustability and excellent limb alignment. Other design features include: a moderately reflexed short riser, Ultimate One-Cam eccentric, Phase-3 grip system and an upper cable guard. The Xcellerator has a large 7¾-inch brace height and solid limbs. This is a hunting bow that proudly wears the Autumn Brush finish with PSE's Color-Tech contrast enhancement and increased durability.

BOW SPECIFICATIONS: XCELLERATOR ULTIMATE ONE-CAM

AMO Draw Length: 25- to 30-inch in 1-inch increments.
Draw Weights: 60# and 70# with 80% let-off (65% let-off optional)
Bow Speed: IBO fps = 302
Axle-to Axle: 32½-inches
Weight in hand: 4 lbs., 3 oz.
SRP: **$749**
   (add $15 for LH models)

TEAM PRIMOS   **XCELLERATOR**

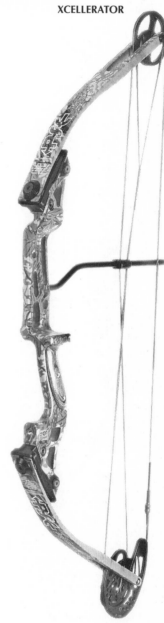

"You don't catch things with a bow and arrow. You kill them."
—Actor Kurt Russell responding to Newsweek reporter Nicki Gostin's query,
"Have you caught anything with a bow and arrow?"

COMPOUND BOWS

Reflex Compound Bows

BIGHORN

BUCKSKIN

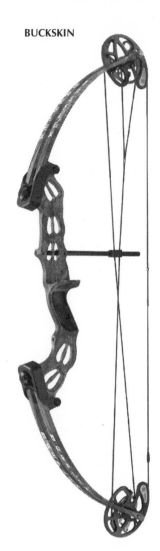

CARIBOU

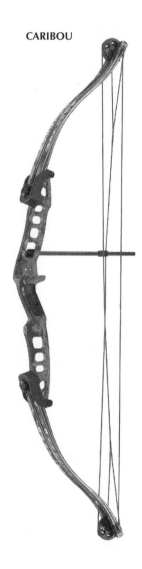

BIGHORN

This hunting-oriented compound bow is coated with a durable camouflage finish that will help it blend in at many hunting sites. The Bighorn features a dual-cam system with solid limbs. Other specifications include: a 7⅝-inch brace height, cable guard with roller and black molded grip.

BOW SPECIFICATIONS: BIGHORN
AMO Draw Length: 25- to 28½-inch or 28½- to 32-inch
Draw Weights: 40# to 50#, 50# to 60#, or 60# to 70#, with 75% let-off
Bow Speed: NA
Axle-to Axle: 40 inches
SRP: Starting at $220

BUCKSKIN

This bow is similar to the Timber Wolf but has a tamer riser with cut outs of deer tracks along the aluminum riser. This bow is camouflaged and has a 7½-inch brace height.

BOW SPECIFICATIONS
AMO Draw Length: 27 to 30 inches
Draw Weights: 50-60 and 60-70 pounds
Bow Speed: 306 fps IBO
Axle-to Axle: 34 inches
SRP:. $369

CARIBOU

This Reflex compound bow has a 9-inch brace height—one of the industry's biggest—and features an aluminum riser, split limbs and round wheel cams. This bow also has a molded grip, cable guard and unique limb pockets with a lip.

BOW SPECIFICATIONS: CARIBOU
AMO Draw Length: 28- to 31-inch adjustable
Draw Weights: 50# to 60#, or 60# to 70# with 65% let-off
Bow Speed: NA
Axle-to Axle: 45⅝-inches
SRP: . . . . . varies by dealer and state

DENALI

FALCON

PROWLER

COMPOUND BOWS

DENALI

This compound bow continues Reflex's hunting line. It's very similar in components and design to the Tundra and Falcon models with split limbs, an aluminum riser and single-cam system. The Denali's shorter length increases its maneuverability in hunting situations. This bow has an 8½-inch brace height and is camouflaged.

BOW SPECIFICATIONS: DENALI
AMO Draw Length: 27½- to 30½-inch adjustable
Draw Weights: 50# to 60#, or 60# to 70# with 60% to 75% adjustable let-off
Bow Speed: NA
Axle-to Axle: 34 inches
SRP: Starting at **$450**

FALCON

This Reflex model has a similar design and components of the Tundra. The cable guard has a roller bearing and the limb pockets are black and contrast against the bow's camo coating.

BOW SPECIFICATIONS: FALCON
AMO Draw Length: 27½- to 30½-inch adjustable
Draw Weights: 50# to 60#, or 60# to 70# with 60% to 75% adjustable let-off
Bow Speed: NA
Axle-to Axle: 36 inches
SRP: Starting at **$437**

PROWLER

The Prowler is an affordable compound bow that offers single-cam technology to archery enthusiasts. Its features include: split limbs, a weighted single cam and idler wheel system to propel arrows, and an under-the-grip cable guard. This bow's magnesium riser—with a 7¼-inch brace height—is thicker than most Reflex models and has a unique camo finish.

BOW SPECIFICATIONS: PROWLER
AMO Draw Length: 27½- to 30½-inch adjustable
Draw Weights: 50# to 60#, or 60# to 70# with 60% to 75% adjustable let-off
Bow Speed: NA
Axle-to Axle: 38 inches
SRP: Starting at **$270**

Reflex Compound Bows

TETON

TIMBER WOLF

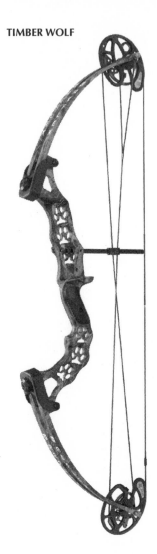

TUNDRA

TETON

This model is similar in design and components to Reflex's Prowler—including magnesium riser—but with dual cam technology. It's available with a camouflage finish and has a 6¾-inch brace height.

BOW SPECIFICATIONS: TETON

AMO Draw Length: 27- to 30-inch adjustable

Draw Weights: 50# to 60#, or 60# to 70#, with 75% let-off

Bow Speed: NA

Axle-to Axle: 38 inches

SRP: Staring at $210

TIMBER WOLF

This new Renegade compound bow has split limbs and a 6-inch brace height, molded rubber grip, cable guard with slide and unique riser with cut outs that resemble wolf tracks. The bow is camouflaged.

BOW SPECIFICATIONS

AMO Draw Length: 27 to 30 inches

Draw Weights: 50-60 and 60-70 pounds

Bow Speed: 315 fps IBO

Axle-to Axle: 36 inches

SRP:. $419

TUNDRA

The Tundra comes with a camouflage finish and long aluminum riser. This bow also has split limbs nestled into limb pockets, a single-cam design that includes a weighted cam and idler wheel, plus a molded grip and cable guard. The Tundra has a 7⅜-inch brace height.

BOW SPECIFICATIONS: TUNDRA

AMO Draw Length: 27½- to 30½-inch adjustable

Draw Weights: 50# to 60#, or 60# to 70# with 60% to 75% adjustable let-off

Bow Speed: NA

Axle-to Axle: 38 inches

SRP: Starting at $437

ALPHA-1

FISHMASTER EZ-1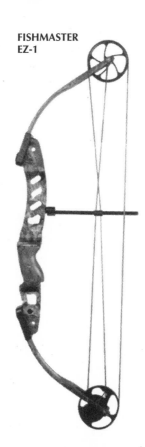

KOMBOW

LS-II 1 CAM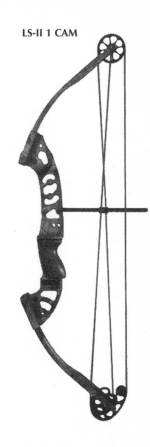

ALPHA-1

Renegade's Alpha-1 expands this Wisconsin bowyer's line. This compound bow has a short axle-to-axle length and large 8-inch brace height. It uses the radical flamethrower cams—cams that resemble small saw blades. Two models are available and both have PTS limbs, Mossy Oak camouflage and weigh 3.6 pounds. A one or two-piece grips is optional. One model offers 75% let-off and the other model delivers 65 or 80% let-off.

BOW SPECIFICATIONS
AMO Draw Length: 25-31 or 26-29-inches
Draw Weights: 45-60, 55-70,65-80
Bow Speed: 302 fps
Axle-to Axle: 31½ inches
SRP:.....................**$549**

FISHMASTER EZ-1 SOLO WHEEL

Don't let the name of this bowfishing oriented bow fool you, this bow is designed for hunting also. Features include a machined aluminum deflex riser, one-piece wood grip, PTS limbs anchored in a limb pocket, upper cable guard, and accommodating large

7⅞ brace height. Renegades' Fishmaster bow is coated in Mossy Oak Break-Up and utilizes the company's EZ-1 solo wheel system.

BOW SPECIFICATIONS:
FISHMASTER EZ-1 SOLO WHEEL
AMO Draw Length: 27- to 30-inch
Draw Weights: 50# with 75% let-off
Bow Speed: IBO fps = NA
Axle-to Axle: 33½-inches
Weight in hand: 3.4 lbs.
SRP:.....................**$439**

KOMBOW

The Kombow is designed by Renegade to serve the needs of finger and release shooters. It has a machined aluminum deflex riser that provides more than 8 inches of brace height. Other features include a comfortable wood grip, cable guard, PTS solid limbs and mossy Oak Break-Up finish.

The EZ-1 Solo Wheel Kombow model has a 37-inch axle-to-axle length, 28- to 31-inch draw length and 75% let-off.

BOW SPECIFICATIONS: KOMBOW 1 CAM
AMO Draw Length: 27- to 33-inch

Draw Weights: 60# or 70# with 80% or 65% let-off
Bow Speed: IBO fps = NA
Axle-to Axle: 36 inches
Weight in hand: 3.2 lbs.
SRP:.....................**$439**

LS-II 1 CAM

Renegade's LS-II is designed to help introduce youth, ladies and small-framed archers to bowhunting and to the sport of archery in an affordable manner. While this lightweight bow is smaller scaled, it incorporates many features found on full-sized bows like a wooden grip, cable guard, 1 Cam system and machined aluminum reflex riser. The bow also has PTS solid limbs and is coated with Realtree Hardwoods camouflage.

BOW SPECIFICATIONS: LS II 1 CAM
AMO Draw Length: 23- to 27-inch
Draw Weights: 30#, 40# and 50# with 65% let-off
Bow Speed: IBO fps = NA
Axle-to Axle: 32 inches
Weight in hand: 3 lbs.
SRP:.....................**$329**

Renegade Compound Bows

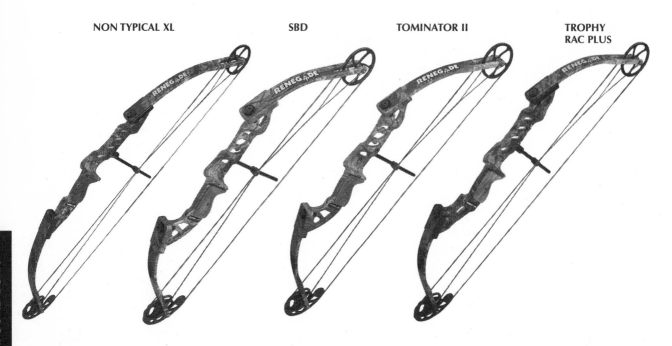

NON TYPICAL XL   SBD   TOMINATOR II   TROPHY RAC PLUS

NON TYPICAL XL

The Non Typical is one of the longest compound bows on the market today—41-inch axle-to-axle length— and is sure to attract the attention of finger shooters. The bow is available in the 1 Cam or EZ-1 Solo wheel systems and has a machined aluminum deflexed riser, wooden one-piece grip and solid limbs. Both models have large 9-inch plus brace heights. Renegade's Non Typical bow is coated in Mossy Oak Break-Up camouflage and uses a 104-inch string.

The EZ-1 Solo Wheel model offers 30- to 33-inch draw lengths and 75% let-off.

BOW SPECIFICATIONS:
NON TYPICAL XL 1 CAM
AMO Draw Length: 29- to 36-inch
Draw Weights: 60 or 70 pounds; 80% or 65% let-off
Bow Speed: IBO fps = NA
Axle-to Axle: 41 inches
Weight in hand: 4 lbs.
SRP:. **$459**

SBD

This new Renegade bow was introduced in 2002 and weighs in at 3 pounds. It has a short axle-to-axle length, one-piece wood grip, PTS solid limbs, upper cable guard, machined aluminum reflex riser and is coated in Realtree Hardwoods camouflage. This bow is only available with Renegade's 1 Cam system.

BOW SPECIFICATIONS: SBD 1 CAM
AMO Draw Length: 24- to 30-inch
Draw Weights: 60# or 70# with 80% or 65% let-off
Bow Speed: IBO fps = NA
Axle-to Axle: 31 inches
Weight in hand: 3 lbs.
SRP:. **$439**

TOMINATOR II

The Tominator is Renegade's newest compound bow model and was redesigned for its re-release in 2002. This lightweight hunting bow—only 3.2 pounds—is dipped in Realtree Hardwoods and designed for treestand hunting. It is available in a 1-Cam and EZ-1 solo wheel version. Both models offer a one-piece wood grip, PTS solid limbs, machined aluminum reflex riser and approximately 7-inch brace height. All models are available in 60# or 70# draw weights and have an upper cable guard with slide.

The Tominator II EZ-1 Solo Wheel model has a 90½-inch string, 33½-inch axel-to-axle length and 27- to 30-inch draw length.

BOW SPECIFICATIONS:
TOMINATOR II 1-CAM
AMO Draw Length: 24- to 31-inch

Draw Weights: 60# or 70# with 80% or 65% let-off
Bow Speed: IBO fps = NA
Axle-to Axle: 34 inches
Weight in hand: 3.2 lbs.
SRP:. **$439**

TROPHY RAC PLUS

This dependable, smooth shooting bow features a machined aluminum reflex riser dipped in Mossy Oak Break-Up camouflage. The Trophy Rac Plus is available with a 1-cam and EZ –1 Solo wheel system. Both models have one-piece wood grips and PTS solid limbs. Other features include a solid one-piece wood grip and upper cable guard with slide.

The EZ-1 Solo wheel model is similar to the 1 Cam version and has a 97⅝-inch cable, 6¾-inch brace height and 27- to 30-inch draw length with 75% let-off.

BOW SPECIFICATIONS:
TROPHY RAC PLUS 1-CAM
AMO Draw Length: 25- to 31-inch.
Draw Weights: 60# or 70# with 80% or 65% let-off
Bow Speed: IBO fps = NA
Axle-to Axle: 35¾-inches
Weight in hand: 3.8 lbs.
SRP:. **$439**

COMPOUND BOWS

Revolution Archery Compound Bows

SUPER SWIFT

This bow continues the Swift series traditions and features custom set draw weights and draw lengths, plus various axle lengths and numerous colors for the finish. Custom finishes for this bow include Mossy Oak camouflage. The bow has similar components to Revolution's Triumph bow model.

BOW SPECIFICATIONS: SUPER SWIFT
AMO Draw Length: From 25- to 30½-inch per customer request.
Draw Weights: From 30# to 65# with 65% let-off
Bow Speed: 319 fps IBO
Axle-to Axle: 36 and 37 inches
SRP: **$675**

TRIUMPH

This bow is designed for archers wanting a longer axle-to-axle length. Design features of the Triumph include CNC machined limbs with three layers of fiberglass laminations and a machined aluminum riser. Other features can be selected by the buyer to include brace heights ranging from 6½- to 6⅞-inches and a custom draw length from 28 to 32 inches. The cams are machined and rotate on needle bearings. This bow arrives with a Mossy Oak finish.

BOW SPECIFICATIONS: TRIUMPH
AMO Draw Length: From 28- to 32-inch per customer request.
Draw Weights: From 38# to 65# with 65% let-off
Bow Speed: 312 fps IBO
Axle-to Axle: 39 and 40 inches
SRP: **$695**

ULTRA SWIFT

This compound bow is designed for the shorter draw archer who desires speed and accuracy at lower pounds draw weight. The compact design makes this a good choice for women and kids. Features include fiberglass laminated limbs, machined riser and cams and finish colors like previous models. Brace heights for this bow range from 5¾- to 6⅜-inches.

BOW SPECIFICATIONS: ULTRA SWIFT
AMO Draw Length: From 23- to 28½-inch per customer request.
Draw Weights: From 28# to 65# with 65% let-off
Bow Speed: 312 fps IBO
Axle-to Axle: 32 and 34 inches
SRP: **$650**

SUPER SWIFT

COMPOUND BOWS

"There is no excellence in archery without great labor."
—Maurice Thompson, The Witchery of Archery, 1879

Stacey Archery Sales Compound Bows

MITEY MITE YOUTH

MITEY MITE ADULT

MITEY MITE

Stacey Archery Sales actively pursues the youth and small framed archer market with its Mitey Mite bows. Both models feature CNC machined aluminum risers, a Mossy Oak Break-Up camouflage finish, a split two piece grip and steel insert bushings for installation of a cable guard and stabilizer. Other features include a lockdown cable guard, Power Glass split limbs and a choice of speed cams or five-step wheels. Steel pivoting centers for the limb pockets ensure 3-point limb alignment and a removable shelf guard is added for safety. Gold or black hardware and limb pockets are available to help add flash and a true custom appearance to the bow to suit any shooter's artistic tastes.

These bows weight approximately 2.8 pounds.

The adult Mitey Mites are available as a package that includes the bow, a quiver, a dozen Easton arrows and a release aid. The youth model includes a stabilizer instead of a quiver.

BOW SPECIFICATIONS: MITEY MITE ADULT
AMO Draw Length: From 24- to 30-inch adjustable with modules.
Draw Weights: 20-30#, 30-40#, 40-50# and 50-60# with 65% let-off for speed cams, 65- to 70% let-off possible with wheels and draw length adjustments.
Bow Speed: NA
Axle-to Axle: 34 inches
SRP: $299.95
    package. $419.95

BOW SPECIFICATIONS: MITEY MITE YOUTH
AMO Draw Length: From 22- to 27-inch
Draw Weights: From 20-30#, 30-40# and 40-50# with 65% let-off for baby speed cams, 65% to 70% let-off possible with wheels and draw length adjustments
Bow Speed: NA
Axle-to Axle: 32½-inches
SRP: $259.95
    package. $369.95

SAWTOOTH

TARGHEE

TOM THUMB

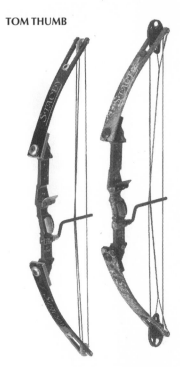

SAWTOOTH

This compound has a machined aluminum riser and limb pockets sculpted from 6061-T6 aluminum. The pivoting limb pockets utilize steel pivoting centers to ensure three-point alignment. The bow's add-on accessories—cable guard, plunger button and stabilizer—can be mounted in the installed steel insert bushings. Other features include a 5½-inch center shot window, choice of two wood grips, graphite glass limbs and your choice of high speed cams or a weighted single cam. The Sawtooth is available in Mossy Oak Break-Up. This bow model is available in a manufacturer's package that includes a quiver, one dozen Easton arrows and a Stacey release aid.

BOW SPECIFICATIONS: SAWTOOTH
AMO Draw Length: From 23- to 31-inch
Draw Weights: From 40# to 80# with 65% let-off for speed cams and optional 80% with the single cam system.
Bow Speed: NA
Axle-to Axle: 35 and 37 inches
SRP: **$529.95**
    package. **$679.95**

TARGHEE

This compound bow is built with models for hunting and the 3-D tournament trail. Customers can custom build a bow with a choice of three limb lengths (15, 16 and 17 inches), three types of wheels and cams, five riser colors and two styles of wooden grips. With this many options you can have the company build your dream bow. The Targhee has the same design features as the Sawtooth plus 60% let-off wheels. Limb choices include 17-inch laminated carbon graphite recurve limbs or Power Tuff Griplite glass limbs. The Targhee weighs 4.2 pounds. This bow is also sold in a package that includes a quiver, overdraw, and release.

BOW SPECIFICATIONS: TARGHEE
AMO Draw Length: From 24- to 34-inch
Draw Weights: From 40# to 80# with 65% let-off for speed cams, 60% with wheels and 65% with single cam.
Bow Speed: NA
Axle-to Axle: 37, 39, 41 and 42 inches
SRP: **$449.95**
    package. **$529.95**

TOM THUMB II

With draw lengths as short as 16 inches and draw weights as low as 10 pounds, this creative feature packed bow will help young archers of any skill level and frame size find something to get excited about. Stacey Archery uses machined aluminum risers and wheels, machined limb pockets and power glass limbs to build the Tom Thumb compound bow. Other features include a split wood grip, five-inch adjustable wheels, removable shelf guard, lockdown cable guard and Fast Flite string and cables. Risers are available in Mossy Oak camouflage.

The company offers an up-grade policy with each bow. For a small fee the bow can be outfitted with the next larger wheel size and string to increase the draw length and weight. This bow is sold as a package with bow, rest, glove and half-dozen Easton arrows with points installed. There is a lightly higher cost for one dozen arrows with package.

BOW SPECIFICATIONS:
YOUTH TOM THUMB II
AMO Draw Length: From 16- to 25-inch, adjustable to many lengths with wheels, baby cams and modules.
Draw Weights: From 10- to 40# in 10# increments with 65% to 70% let-off possible
Bow Speed: NA
Axle-to Axle: 30 inches
SRP: **$179.95**
    package. **$199.95**
    (slightly higher cost with one-dozen arrows option)

Wing Archery Compound Bows

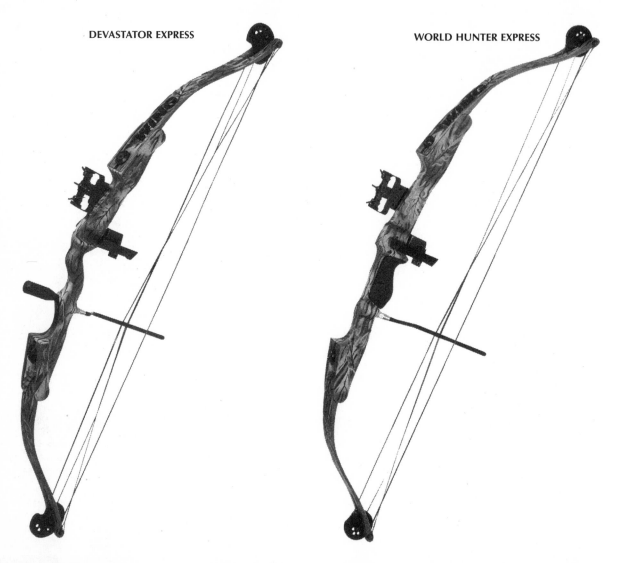

DEVASTATOR EXPRESS

WORLD HUNTER EXPRESS

COMPOUND BOWS

DEVASTATOR EXPRESS

An excellent bow for hunting or 3-D shooting, the Devastator Express features a magnesium riser with a thin-waisted grip. The cut-away arrow rest accepts most overdraws easily. Limbs are constructed of multi-layered glass laminate in a recurve design. All eccentrics are single-grooved, in-line design. This bow is available with a Super Flight Energy wheel or Kidney Kam. The Devastator Express is camouflaged in the company's unique Trailcover design. All bows are backed by a 3-year limited warranty and are available in right-hand models only.

BOW SPECIFICATIONS: DEVASTATOR EXPRESS
AMO Draw Length: 26- to 32-inch in 1-inch increments
Draw Weights: up to 80 pounds with 65% let-off
Bow Speed: NA
Axle-to Axle: 41 inches
Weight in hand: 4.4 lbs.
SRP: $339.95

WORLD HUNTER EXPRESS

This model is similar to the company's Devastator Express bow with a thicker riser and molded comfort grip. This bow is also camouflaged in Wing's Trailcover camouflage pattern and has a cable guard. The World Hunter Express uses either the Pass-Thru Power Kidney Kams or Super Flight Energy Wheels to propel arrows and control the string movement. The cables are fast flight split yoke design.

BOW SPECIFICATIONS:
WORLD HUNTER EXPRESS
AMO Draw Length: 26- to 32-inch in 1-inch increments
Draw Weights: up to 80 pounds with 65% let-off
Bow Speed: NA
Axle-to Axle: 42 inches
Weight in hand: 4.4 lbs.
SRP: $359.95

RECURVE BOWS

Black Widow Custom Bows Recurve Bows

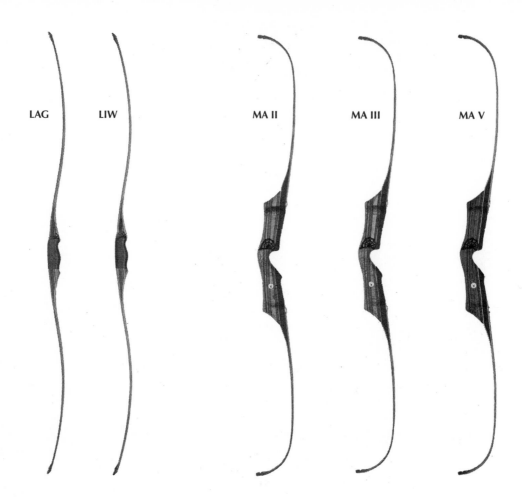

LAG   LIW   MA II   MA III   MA V

LAG AND LIW

These longbows are available in one-piece and take-down models. Black Widow's LAGs and LIWs utilize DynaFlex limbs, DynaFlight 97 strings, deflex designed risers and Shur-Grip rubber handles that can be removed. Features of these bows include: 7-inch brace height, clear marine finish, radiused shelf, and reinforced limb core and tip overlay. A Navajo bow sleeve is included, plus a hardcase for the one-piece models. Draw lengths range from 24 to 34 inches.

The LAG (Long Autumn Gray) model has an Autumn Oak brown outer laminate over Graybark gray wood at the grip. The LIW features Ironwood in the riser.

SRP: LAG one-piece **$740**
    take-down **$860**

LIW one-piece **$830**
    take-down **$950**

MA II, MA III AND MA V

Black Widow's MA limbs have been redesigned and dynamically balanced in recent manufacturing runs. A longer deflex handle with long sight window permits use of sights. This take-down bow has a radiused shelf, marine epoxy finish and solid brass bushings. Dual-Pin take-down ensures perfect limb alignment. The limbs fit into reinforced areas on the face of the riser toward the shooter. Draw length options range from 58 to 64 inches. Black Widow's MA II bows are Graybark color, MA III bows are Autumn Oak and the MA V is dark brown Ironwood.

SRP: II/III series begins **$830**

V series **$940**
Handle (riser) II/III series **$373**
    V series **$423**
Limbs II/III series **$457**
    V series **$517**

SA II, SA III AND SA V

SA model bows are similar in construction and components to Black Widow's MA series but with a 2-inch shorter handle to create a more maneuverable bow. This option is handy when hunting from treestands or ground blinds.

SRP: II/III series begins **$830**
    V series **$940**
Handle (riser) II/III series **$373**
    V series **$423**
Limbs II/III series **$457**
    V series **$517**

RECURVE BOWS

Black Widow Custom Bows Recurve Bows

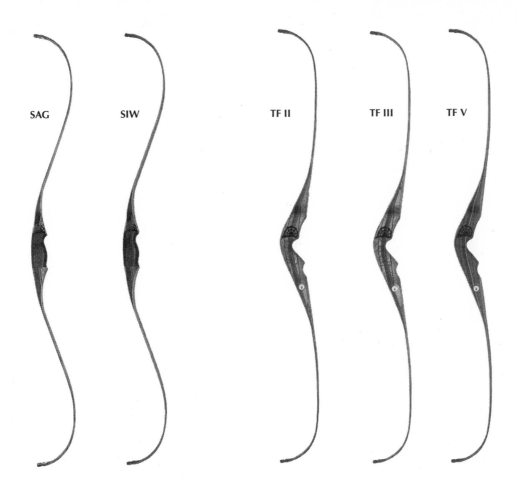

SAG   SIW   TF II   TF III   TF V

SAG AND SIW

These Black Widow short bows are based on a 1940s look—combining nostalgia and tradition—and are very maneuverable. This bow is available in a standard one-piece recurve design and as a take-down model with a unique locking device concealed under the leather grip. Features for the SAG and SIW series include: DynaFlex limbs, deflex riser, clear marine epoxy finish and Flemish-twist DynaFLIGHT 97 string. These bows come with all of the previously mentioned accessories. SAG models are available in Autumn Gray and Autumn Oak, SIG models are offered in the darker brown Ironwood. A custom grip can be designed for an additional $70.

SRP: SAG one-piece $740
take-down $860

SIW one-piece $830
   take-down $950

SENECA CONVERTIBLE TAKE-DOWN RECURVE

This youth bow is distributed by Black Widow and features black 46-inch solid fiberglass limbs. A unique feature is that this recurve can be easily converted from a left- to right-hand model by removing either of the two modules in the Ultra-Fiber black handle. The bow features: a Dacron bowstring, string silencers, knocking point, tip protector, and lock-on arrow rest. The complete kit includes an arm guard, finger tab, two fiber-glass arrows and a comprehensive instruction book. The draw weight is 20# at 24 inches draw length.

SRP: $51.00

TF II, TF III AND TF V

This Black Widow series of one-piece recurves uses TF limbs that are faced with transparent Bo-Tuff fiberglass. The deflex riser is pre-stressed and rein-forced with multiple layers of Bo-Tuff fiberglass. This bow's sight window is cut ⅛-inch past center and the inserted brass bushings will accept side-mount quivers, sights or stabilizer. These bows arrive with a bow stringer, Spyder string silencers, tip protector, Spider Webb shelf protector, nocking points, video and owner's manual. They are available in the same colors as the previously listed bows.

SRP: II/III series begins $830
V series $940

Bowhunting Traditions Recurve Bows

TAKE-DOWN
LONGBOW

BOWHUNTING TRADITIONS TAKE-DOWN LONGBOW

This unique longbow can be easily taken down for storage or transportation. It is similar in design and options to Bowhunting Tradition's Take-Down Recuve model and in 62-inches long. A Fast Flight Flemish string is included and custom woods, different lengths and other special features can be included in the construction of this longbow. Both right- and left-hand models are offered. Each bow is custom built one at a time.

BOW SPECIFICATIONS: BOWHUNTING TRADITIONS TAKE-DOWN LONGBOW
Draw Weight: varies
Length: 62-inch or other lengths are available
SRP: . . . . varies by selections

BOWHUNTING TRADITIONS TAKE-DOWN RECURVE

This 60-inch recurve bow by Bowhunting Traditions is offered in a right- or left-hand model and the grips can be low, medium or high. Handle risers are available in golden brown, rosewood or black laminated wood. Limbs are constructed of red elm with clear fiberglass laminates. All recurves have a special wedge built into the limb tip and the tips can be covered with antler tip, horn or mycarta. Buyer has the choice of wrench type bolts or hand-turned take-down knobs for the limb anchoring system.

BOW SPECIFICATIONS: BOWHUNTING TRADITIONS TAKE-DOWN RECURVE
Draw Weight: varies
Length: 60-inch and other lengths are available
SRP: . . . . varies by selections

TAKE-DOWN
RECURVE

Ethical bowhunters learn how to make lethal shots through vital organs by studying the anatomy of the intended target animal. Having a mental picture of the location of heart, lungs and other organs inside the animal enables the hunter to determine the most effective shot from a treestand, on level ground or whether the animal is quartering away or broadside.

RECURVE BOWS

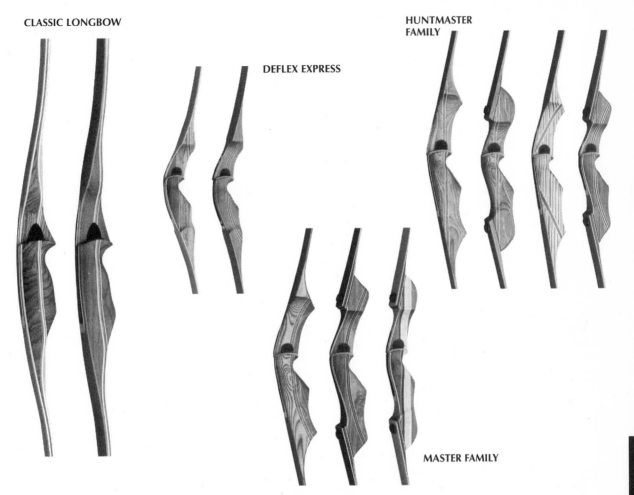

CLASSIC LONGBOW

DEFLEX EXPRESS

HUNTMASTER FAMILY

MASTER FAMILY

BRUIN CLASSIC LONGBOW

The buyer chooses the riser woods and limb cores to start the construction process for this bow and the overlays and tips will match those selections. This longbow is offered in 58- and 60-inch lengths. Bruin is one of a few companies that continues to make longbows.

SRP: Starting at $575

BRUIN DEFLEX EXPRESS

This traditional one-piece bow by Bruin provides a choice of riser woods, limb cores and the accent stripe through the riser. Other choices include overlays, limb wedges and tips that match or accent the color of the wood selections. This recurve is available in 58-, 60- and 62-inch lengths.

SRP: Starting at $795

BRUIN HUNTMASTER FAMILY

This series of recurves includes the Woodsmaster, Woodsmaster SE, and Huntmaster. These bows can be ordered as a traditional one-piece or in a take-down design. Length options include: 56-, 58- and 60-inch models.

SRP: from . . . . $465 to $695
   set of extra limbs for the
      T/D models up to $350

BRUIN MASTER FAMILY

This family of bows includes the Master, Master SE, and Master Express. These recurves have stylish laminated wood risers. Master and Master SE bows have slightly larger hand grips. Bruin's take-down models are offered in 56-, 58-, 60- and 62-inch lengths. Traditional one-piece bows are offered in 60- and 62-inch lengths.

SRP: Master SE, starting at $550
Master, starting at $750
Master Express, starting at $825
   The use of optional items and
   premium woods increases costs.

Custom Shooting Systems Recurve Bows

RT RECURVE

This recurve uses a T-6061 machined aluminum riser—in the System or Contender style—to propel arrows. Other features include the soft-touch grip (walnut wood is optional), Gordon thermal composite limbs and a built-in arrow shelf. The RT Recurve is offered in Mossy Oak Break-Up for hunting and black, blue and burgundy for competition.

BOW SPECIFICATIONS: RT RECURVE
Draw Weight: 40#, 50#, and 60#.
Length: 60 or 66 inches
SRP:. . . . . **varies by selection**

Fedora's Archery Shop Recurve Bows

HUNTER 60-INCH ONE-PIECE

This bow has been in production for more than 40 years and has a strong following of users. It is designed for draw lengths up to 30 inches without stack, and is a fast, quiet and smooth shooter. Features of the Hunter 60-Inch One-Piece include a custom grip and selection of the finish by the buyer.

BOW SPECIFICATIONS:
HUNTER 60-INCH ONE-PIECE
Draw Weight: varies
Length: 60-inch
SRP: Starting at **$425**

STALKER 52-INCH

This bow is designed to shoot where you're looking without any stack to compensate for adjustments. It is a great model to select for hunting. Features of Fedora's Stalker 52-Inch include a custom grip fitted to the shooter and a Fedora thumb rest. This bow works well for short draw archers. The buyer can select the finish.

BOW SPECIFICATIONS: STALKER 52-INCH
Draw Weight: varies and ranges up to 75#
Length: 52-inch
SRP: Starting at **$425**

XCELLERATOR-HYBRID DEFLEX-REFLEX BOW

This longbow will change your mind about using longbows for hunting and shooting! The Xcellerator-Hybrid Deflex-Reflex bow is offered in 58-, 60-, 62-, 64-, and 66-inch lengths and as a right- or left-hand model. The AMO speed exceeds 200 fps. The draw length for this bow ranges from 25- to 32 inches. You can select a dull, satin or hand-rubbed finish to add to the personal touch of your bow.

BOW SPECIFICATIONS: XCELLERATOR-HYBRID DEFLEX-REFLEX BOW
Draw Weight: varies
Length: 58-, 60-, 62-, 64, and 66-inch
SRP: Starting at **$425**

Fred Bear Recurve Bows

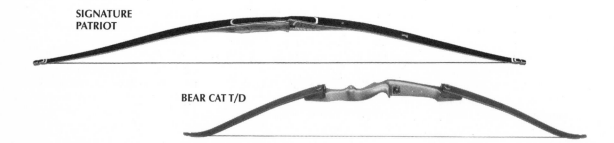

SIGNATURE PATRIOT

BEAR CAT T/D

BEAR CAT T/D

Technology and value take front stage on the Bear Cat T/D bow. The magnesium riser accepts the easy to bolt on fiberglass reinforced epoxy limbs. The Bear Cat uses a Dacron string and is drilled and tapped to accept any AMO standard accessories.

BOW SPECIFICATIONS: BEAR CAT T/D (MODEL 2293)
Draw Weight: RH only at 25#, 35# or 45#

Length: 60-inch
SRP:. **$149**

BYRON FERGUSON SIGNATURE PATRIOT

The Patriot blends longbow speed with a reflex/deflex design in a package that weighs less than 1.5 pounds. Each bow has Byron Ferguson's signature, a leather grip and FastFlight string. The rest shelf is crowned and radiused for smooth arrow take-off.

BOW SPECIFICATIONS: BYRON FERGUSON SIGNATURE PATRIOT (MODEL 2036)
Draw Weight: RH or LH models in 45#, 50#, 55#, 60# or 65#.
Length: 64-inch
SRP:. . . . . **varies**

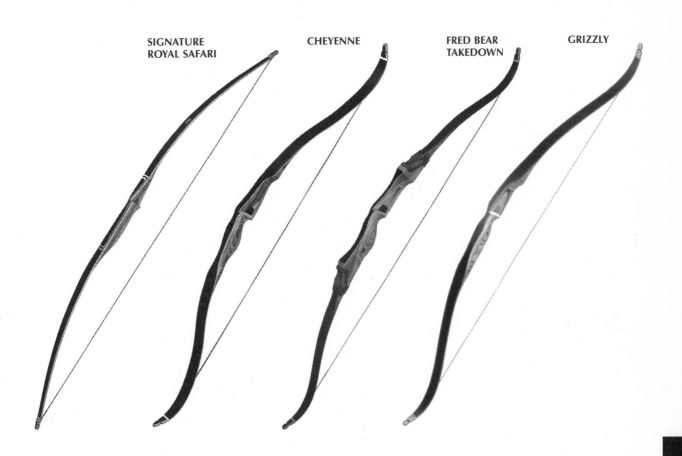

SIGNATURE ROYAL SAFARI   CHEYENNE   FRED BEAR TAKEDOWN   GRIZZLY

BYRON FERGUSON SIGNATURE ROYAL SAFARI

This longbow is designed to famed archer Byron Ferguson's specifications and built on a core of laminated hard rock maple. The bow's face and back are laminated with black fiberglass. The riser is constructed of brown and black hard rock maple with a decorative face. Other features include a leather grip and Fast-Flight string. This would be a top contender as a longbow that's designed for hunting.

BOW SPECIFICATIONS: BYRON FERGUSON SIGNATURE ROYAL SAFARI (MODEL 2038)
Draw Weight: RH or LH models in 45#, 50#, 55#, 60#, 65# or 70#.
Length: 66-inch
SRP: . . . . **varies**

CHEYENNE

This 55-inch recurve is constructed of select maple laminates and fiberglass laminate limbs. It incorporates a Radiused grip and FastFlight string. It

weighs less than 1.5 pounds and is recommended for hunting whitetails and elk. Left- and right-hand versions are available in this flagship product for the Fred Bear Elite Series.

BOW SPECIFICATIONS: CHEYENNE (MODEL 2032)
Draw Weight: 45#, 50#, 55# or 60# models available.
Length: 55 inches
SRP: **$449**

FRED BEAR TAKEDOWN

This bow is Fred Bear's masterpiece and is an excellent choice for the traveling hunter who visits remote regions. The TakeDown features a patented limb attachment system, crowned shelf with bear hair arrow rest and fiberglass reinforced tips. Two handle lengths—56-inch A-handle and 60-inch B-handle versions—are available.

BOW SPECIFICATIONS: FRED BEAR TAKEDOWN (MODELS 2075 (A) AND 2074 (B))

Draw Weight: 45#, 50#, 55#, 60# and 65# with left- and right-hand models available.
Length: 56-inch (A) or 60-inch (B)
SRP: **$999**

GRIZZLY

This recurve bow is considered the working man's bow. Fred Bear designed this bow to be tough, yet economical. Construction components include black fiberglass surfacing over laminated hardwoods and a final coat of non-reflective satin gloss. This bow comes with a Dacron string. The bow can be shot off the bear hair rest or from a rest attached to the maple sight window.

BOW SPECIFICATIONS: GRIZZLY (MODEL 2086)
Draw Weight: RH or LH models in 45#, 50# or 55#. Additional RH model at 60#.
Length: 58-inch
SRP: **$299**

RECURVE BOWS

Fred Bear Recurve Bows

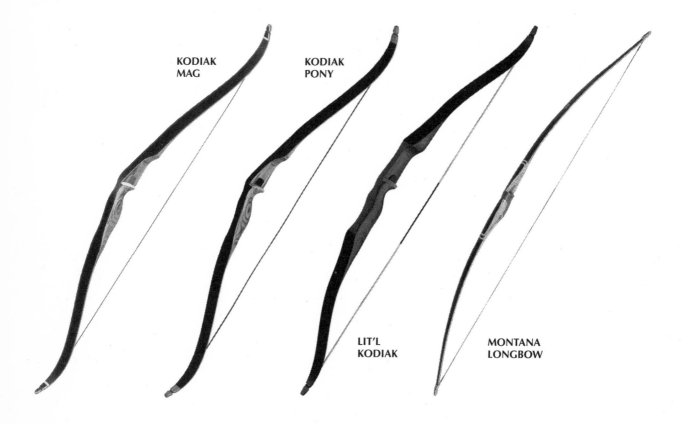

KODIAK MAG   KODIAK PONY

LIT'L KODIAK   MONTANA LONGBOW

RECURVE BOWS

KODIAK CUB

This Bear bow was designed to help the next generation enter into archery with a smooth transition. Handcrafted from North Country Hardwoods, the short-draw Kodiak Cub is hand sanded and hand surfaced and finished in satin. Other features include a Dacron string and stylish inlaid brass Fred Bear medallion.

BOW SPECIFICATIONS: KODIAK CUB (MODEL 2088)
Draw Weight: RH or LH models in 10#, 20# or 30# (at 24-inch AMO).
Length: 48-inch
SRP:.....................$179

KODIAK MAG

This Bear recurve bow is 52 inches long and features black fiberglass over select hardwood laminates. Other features include an inlaid Fred Bear brass medallion and rich satin finish. The medallion adds a true touch of prestige to this bow!

BOW SPECIFICATIONS: KODIAK MAG (MODEL 2030)
Draw Weight: 45#, 50#, 55#, 60#

and 65# right-hand models available. 55# and 65# left-hand models are available.
Length: 52 inches
SRP:.....................$399

KODIAK PONY

The Bear Kodiak Pony is a serious intermediate-level bow with a classic look and feel. The features of this bow include brown maple riser and matching wood tips that contrast against black glass. Other features include a crowned shelf, bear hair arrow rest and Dacron string.

BOW SPECIFICATIONS: KODIAK PONY (MODEL 2042)
Draw Weight: RH only models in 25#, 35# or 45# (at 25-inch AMO draw).
Length: 52-inch
SRP:.....................$299

LIT'L KODIAK

This is a scaled down recurve bow version that's designed to introduce small kids to archery. Features of the Lil' Kodiak include black glass limbs, lightweight maple laminate riser and

an arrow shelf with bear hair rest and leather side plate. A distinctive brass Fred Bear medallion is inlaid in the handle.

BOW SPECIFICATIONS: LIT'L KODIAK (MODEL 2094)
Draw Weight: RH only at 5# to 8# and 14-inch draw length.
Length: 30-inch
SRP:.....................$100

MONTANA LONGBOW

This bow is a fine example of ancient bowyer's craftsmanship combined with modern materials. Features include maple laminates and black glass overlays with an arrow shelf that's crowned and cut to center. Other features include a standard leather grip, reinforced tips and FastFlight string.

BOW SPECIFICATIONS: MONTANA LONGBOW (MODEL 2040)
Draw Weight: 45#, 50#, 55#, 60# right-hand models. LH at 50# or 55#
Length: 64-inch
SRP:.....................$299

SUPER KODIAK

Fred Bear Recurve Bows

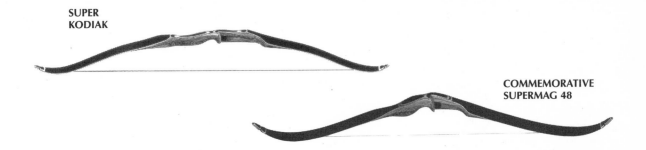

SUPER KODIAK

COMMEMORATIVE SUPERMAG 48

Fred Bear successfully hunted with this bow model on four continents. It is constructed with matched gray and brown laminates, black glass limbs and reinforced tips. The Super Kodiak includes a FastFlight string when purchased. The arrow shelf is crowned, cut past center and lined with bear hair.

The Commemorative Super Kodiak has a maple and rosewood riser, black and white glass laminates and scrimshawed medallion and compass inlays. Other features include an arrow shelf with leather side plate and Bear Hair rest and padded Fred Bear bow case. This bow looks like a true piece of art, but you could hunt with it in the fields and forests! It's a 1999 limited edition with limited supply. Available in RH or

LH models at 50# or 55#. The Model 2010's SRP is $675.

BOW SPECIFICATIONS: SUPER KODIAK (MODEL 2020)
Draw Weight: 45#, 50#, 55#, 60# and 65# right-hand models available. 50#, 55# and 65# left-hand models are available.
Length: 60 inches
SRP:. **$449**

SUPERMAG 48

This 48-inch recurve bow is built by Bear Archery and has eye-catching black and white tips that accept the FastFlight string. Other construction components include a black hard rock maple riser with black fiberglass limbs. The crowned arrow shelf has a

leather side plate and bear hair rest.

Commemorative SuperMag 48 has rosewood and black-over-white fiberglass laminates. Other features include an inlaid scrimshawed medallion and compass in the riser, FastFlight string and padded Fred Bear bow case. 2001 limited edition with limited supply. RH or LH at 50# or 55#. Model 2014/ SRP: $675.

BOW SPECIFICATIONS: SUPERMAG 48 (MODEL 2034)
Draw Weight: RH or LH models at 45#, 50#, 55#, or 65#.
Length: 48-inch
SRP:. **$329**

Golden Eagle Recurve Bows

LIT'L BRAVE

BRAVE RANGER

This discovery level recurve features a composite molded grip/riser with Robin Hood Green limbs. It has a distinctive Ranger logo that will be popular with any young shooter!
SRP:. **$29**

LIT'L BRAVE

This starter level recurve bow helps teach youngsters the basics of archery in an exciting format. Features include composite limbs and riser, black finish and integral grip. This bow is available in right-hand models only.

BOW SPECIFICATIONS: LIT'L BRAVE
AMO Draw Length/Weight: 13# at 16-inch draw; 28# at 24-inch draw
Length: 45 inches
Weight in hand: 1 lbs., 9 oz.
SRP:. **$39**

Great Plains Traditional Bow Co. Recurve Bows

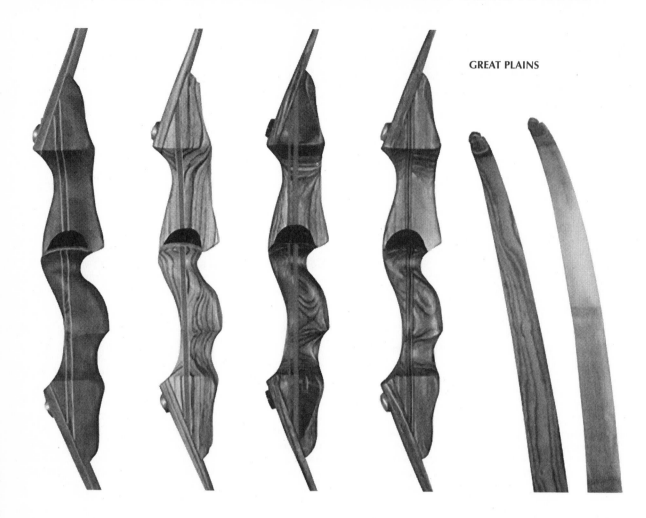

GREAT PLAINS

GREAT PLAINSMAN LONGBOWS
SRP:
Cedar and Elm $480
   add $90 for T/D with elm cores
Gray Limb $505
   add $65 for T/D with elm cores
Osagian $505
   add $65 for T/D model
Rio Bravo $505
   add $65 for T/D model
Cazador-Yew Wood $535
   add $50 for T/D model
Tulip and Osage $550
   add $60 for T/D model
Bamboo $550
   add $60 for T/D model

YOUTH RECURVE BOW BY GREAT PLAINS
SRP: $185

TAKE-DOWN TARGET BOW BY GREAT PLAINS
SRP: $710

ONE-PIECE RECURVES
SRP:
Red River (gray or brown) $510
   add $40 for B-model
Wolf Creek $510
   add $40 for B-model
Palo Duro $510
   add $40 for B-model
Rio Bravo $510
   add $40 for B-model
Cazador $525
   add $40 for B-model
Bamboo $540
   add $50 for B-model
Kiowa $390
   available in standard model only

TAKE-DOWN RECURVES
SRP:
Red River (gray or brown) $560
   add $50 for B-model
Wolf Creek $560
   add $50 for B-model
Rio Bravo $560
   add $50 for B-model
Palo Duro $560
   add $50 for B-model
Estacado (B-model only) $610
Cazador $575
   add $50 for B-model
Bamboo $600
   add $50 for B-model

BRUSH BOW

COMBO HUNTER

BRUSH BOW

This Horne's 28-ounce one-piece long-bow has limbs with a built-in reflex-deflex design for maximizing stored energy and reducing hand shock. The Brush Bow's riser has a 3-inch radiused sight window and radiused shelf covered with synthetic hair. The grip can be customized as medium or low. The Brush Bows are finished with matte or gloss finish, leather strike plate and hand-made Fast-Flight string. This custom bow is available in 60-, 62- or 64-inch lengths.

SRP: . . . . varies by wood and option selections

COMBO HUNTER

This is Horne's newest bow and combines superior craftsmanship with unmatched performance. This longbow riser has a 3-inch radiused sight window designed to be used with a take-down longbow or recurve limbs. With multiple limbs you can develop a personal bow for a wide assortment of hunting conditions and target shooting events.

The Combo Hunter is available in 60- and 62-inch recurve lengths and 62-, 64- and 66-inch lengths with the longbow limbs. This bow can be easily packed for travel.

SRP: Riser, starting at $225
Limbs in basic woods $275
There is an additional cost for premium woods.

Silence is golden when bowhunting. One way to quiet a noisy arrow rest is by applying moleskin to the launcher. Oiling the cams with vegetable oil will help keep them silent.

RECURVE BOWS

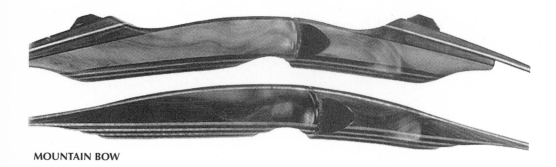

MOUNTAIN BOW

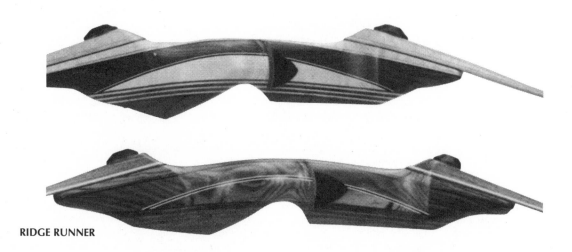

RIDGE RUNNER

MOUNTAIN BOW

Developed in the 1950s, this bow style has a medium or low grip that's wrapped ingoat skin or sinew. You can have a take down model built with 56-, 58-, 60- or 62-inch length with a 3½-inch radiused sight window. A one-piece Mountain bow is available in 60-inch length. Mountain bows have hardwood overlays and fadeout limb tips that can be matched to the bow's handle colors.

**SRP: Risers in basic wood,
begins at $150
Limbs in basic wood $275
Premium woods cost more and take-down bows cost more.
Call for pricing based on multiple options.**

RIDGE RUNNER

This classic take-down recurve is available with a 15- or 17-inch hardwood riser. The handle is built with multiple glass and hardwood overlays. The Ridge Runner is offered in 56-, 58-, 60- and 62-inch lengths. The handle can be contoured as a low, medium or high wrist grip. This bow can be crafted from your choice of woods and with fade-out limb tips.

**SRP: Ridge Runner risers,
start at $325
Solid-one-piece model riser,
starts at $200
Limbs in basic woods $275**

TRADITIONALIST

Available in 62-, 64-, 66- or 68-inch lengths, this Horne's longbow has a reflex-deflex design that forms a D-ring when strung. The contoured grip has a leather wrap to provide comfort.

**SRP: Riser start at $150
Limbs in basic woods $275**

BULLSEYE 54

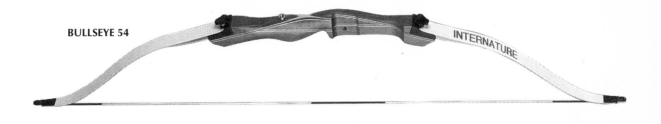

BULLSEYE 62

BULLSEYE 66

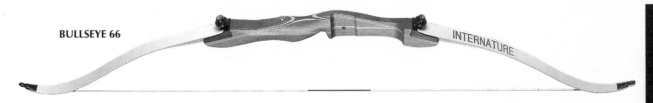

BULLSEYE

The Bullseye series of recurve bows are available in youth and recreation models. The youth bows are available in 48- (the Warrior) and 54-inch lengths with weights ranging from 15 to 38 pounds. Right- and left-hand models are also available. These bows feature laminated wood risers, limb pockets and threaded brass accessory receivers. All bows feature fiberglass limbs and stylish black reinforced tips.

These bows are commonly used in youth camps, schools and scouting programs.

Adult Bullseye series bows are 62- and 66-inches long and are designed and built the same as the youth models. The longer length models achieve the upper 30, 33 and 38 pound draw weight ranges. All bows have components (limbs and risers) that can be purchased separately for upgrades and repairs. SRPs for the

risers range from $42 to $66 and from $48 to $66 for the limbs.

BOW SPECIFICATIONS: BULLSEYE
Draw Weight: 15# to 38#.
Length: From 48 to 66 inches
SRPs: 48-inch Warrior:. $79.95
54-inch Bullseye:. $99.95
62-inch Bullseye:. $99.95
66-inch Bullseye:. $118.00

interNature Recurve Bows

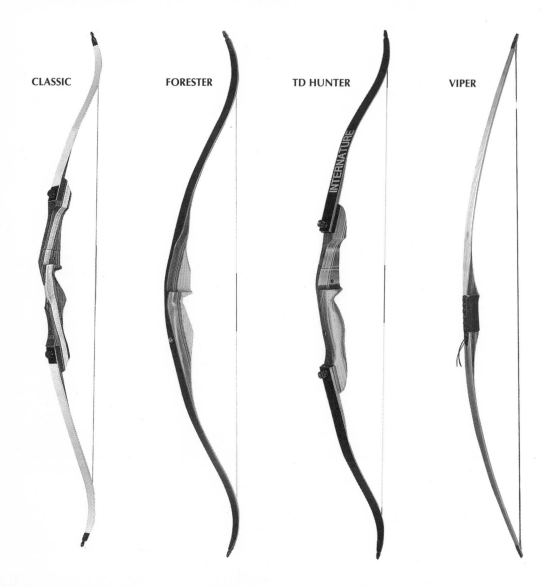

CLASSIC   FORESTER   TD HUNTER   VIPER

CLASSIC

This 66-inch recurve has a two-color laminated wood riser with carved grip surface and white fiberglass limbs. It is recommended for recreational shooting or targets plinking. The Classic is available in left- and right-hand models.

BOW SPECIFICATIONS: CLASSIC
Draw Weight: 20#, 25#, 30# and 35#.
Length: 66 inches
SRP:. $155

FORESTER

This more traditional one-piece multi-laminate bow has dark and contrasting light wood layers. A threaded brass bushing will accept a stabilizer or other accessories. This recurve would be a good choice by hunters.

BOW SPECIFICATIONS: FORESTER
Draw Weight: 30#, 40#, 45#, 50#, 55# and 60#.
Length: 58 inches
SRP:. $195

TD HUNTER

This take down recurve by interNature is made for the traveling hunter and those seeking a compact bow for storage. Features include multi-laminated wood riser with a red laminate layer running through the middle of the riser. Each limb is black and constructed of laminates.

The TD Hunter is offered in right- and left-hand models.

BOW SPECIFICATIONS: TD HUNTER

Draw Weight: 40#, 45#, 50#, 55# and 60#.
Length: 58 inches
SRP:. $150

VIPER

This classically styled long bow has a leather grip wrapped around multiple wood laminated layers and reinforced limb tips. A unique construction process ensures that no two bows look alike. The Viper can be obtained in left- and right-hand models.

BOW SPECIFICATIONS: VIPER
Draw Weight: 30#, 40#, 45#, 50#, 55# and 60#.
Length: 68 inches
SRP:. $195

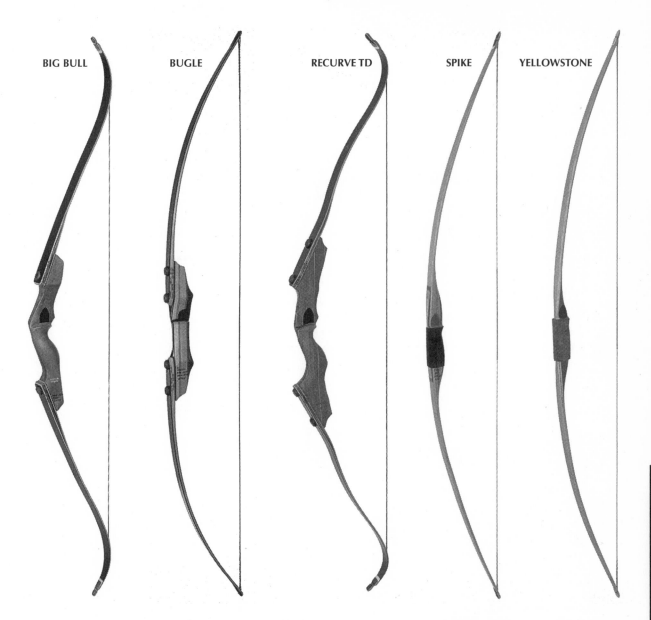

BIG BULL   BUGLE   RECURVE TD   SPIKE   YELLOWSTONE

WAPITI BIG BULL SERIES
RECURVES
SRP:. $495

WAPITI IMPERIAL SERIES
RECURVES
SRP:. $695

WAPITI ROYAL SERIES RECURVES
SRP:. $595
    take-down series is the same price

WAPITI LONGBOWS
WAPITI BUGLE
SRP:. $525
    extra limbs. $350

WAPITI QUIVERS
7- and 4-arrow capacity. $49.95
    with a bow purchase $34.50

WAPITI SPIKE
SRP: one piece $495
    take-down $555

WAPITI YELLOWSTONE
SRP: one-piece $450
    take-down $510

RECURVE BOWS

Mahaska Custom Bows Recurve Bows

MAHASKA RECURVE

MAHASKA FLATBOW

This flatbow has shorter and wider limbs for smoothness and speed. The Flatbow can be built in any wood and handle shape desired and is available in 62-inch length.

SRP: Starting at **$360**

MAHASKA LONGBOW

Available in 62-, 64-, 66- and 68-inch lengths, these longbows have a deflex-reflex design with a straight traditional style. Other features include a semi-pistol grip and a slightly dished locator.

SRP: Starting at **$360**

MAHASKA TRADITIONAL RECURVE

This one-piece recurve is designed to shoot off the shelf, a desire of many instinctive archers. Bow lengths range from 58 to 60 inches.

SRP: Starting at **$380**

Bowhunter education courses are excellent programs for both beginning and experienced archers. Taking this course can save you years of trial and error in the field. The courses are taught by qualified instructors who will share their knowledge and help you become an effective bowhunter. Contact your local archery club, pro shop or bowhunting association to learn where and when a course will be available in your area.

RECURVE BOWS

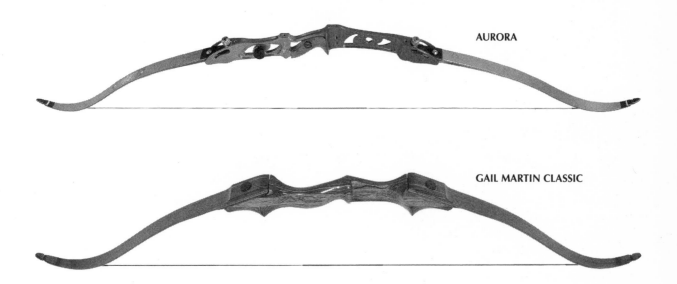

AURORA

GAIL MARTIN CLASSIC

AURORA

The technologically advanced Aurora target recurve bow by Martin Archery has an ergonomically designed riser that incorporates V.E.C. technology to eliminate riser vibration after arrow release. The riser uses a standard limb mounting system to use most any after-market target limb. The riser has a unique open design with appealing sculpted openings. The Aurora is available in Pro Red, Pro Blue, or Purple and in right- or left-hand models.

The Martin Design Team draws upon over 50 years of traditional bow making experience. This experience has been instrumental in the development of the Aurora Limb system. These limbs use the standard detent system and may be used on most any Olympic-style recurve handle with the detent system. The new Aurora limbs use proprietary core materials and lamination designed to maximize stability and torsion resistance. This limb system, designed by Aurora R&D team member Mike Gerard, allows the shooter to independently adjust limb weight and limb center. The bolt has an independent cam action that permits shifting the center of the limb and

adjusting the bow for individual needs. Once that adjustment is made, the weight can be changed without affecting the limb's center. The riser and limbs are sold separately for this target bow.

BOW SPECIFICATIONS: AURORA
AMO Draw Length/Weight: 30# to 50# at 28-inch draw
Length: Varies
Weight in hand: 3 lbs., 7 ozs.
SRP: $1,100

DREAM CATCHER

This one-piece 60-inch recurve by Martin has red elm laminations on the face that are backed with clear fiberglass. The bow's two-tone hardwood riser is sculpted from African hardwood and has accent strips. Other features include a Dacron string, bowstringer and traditional shelf rest. Sight and stabilizer bushings can be installed upon request. This bow is available in right- and left-hand versions and was introduced in 1997.
SPECIFICATIONS: DREAM CATCHER
Draw Weight: from 30# to 70# at 28-inch draw length in 5# increments.
Length: 60 inches
SRP: $450.00

GAIL MARTIN CLASSIC

The 60-inch Gail Martin Classic Take-Down, a bow displaying beauty and craftsmanship that reflects fifty years of pure archery enjoyment, graciously echoes the gratification and fulfillment that pioneer Gail Martin—the founder of Martin Archery—understands through traditional archery. The bow's smooth flowing lines are carefully sculpted by experienced hands and are showcased in a hand-applied glossy finish. Contrasting shades of color—gray and light brown—created by laminations of Bubinga and Maple create an eye-catching riser. Hand-laid laminations of Red Elm form limbs that gently accept the contours of the riser, tapering away to tips reinforced with layers of fiberglass and Bubinga wood. Hand-carved string-grooves gently cradle a hand-spliced Flemish bowstring. Everything about the Gail Martin Classic reflects a chance to own a piece of archery history.
SPECIFICATIONS: GAIL MARTIN CLASSIC
Draw Weights from 30# to 70#
Length: 60 inches
SRP: $632.99

RECURVE BOWS

Martin Archery Recurve Bows

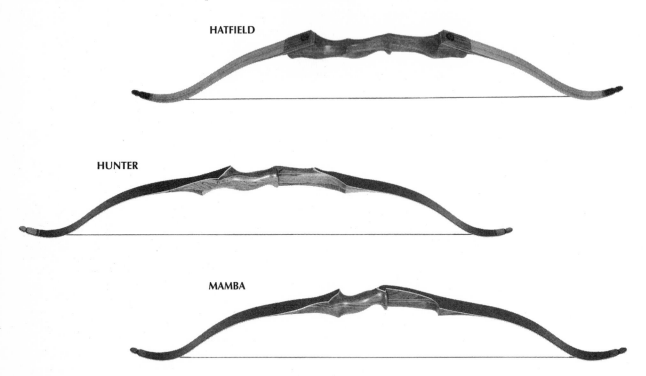

HATFIELD

HUNTER

MAMBA

RECURVE BOWS

HATFIELD

The 62-inch Hatfield take-down recurve bow by Martin Archery uses beautiful African hardwood laminations in the riser. Limbs are fashioned by hand from laminations of red elm and include reinforced tips that allow the choice of any bowstring material. This bow has an attractive brown riser with contrasting lighter limbs tipped with dark tips. Each Hatfield bow includes a traditional arrow rest, a bowstringer and a bowstring. The installation of sight and stabilizer bushings can be completed upon special request.

SPECIFICATIONS: HATFIELD
Draw Weight: from 30# to 70#
Length: 62 inches
SRP:.....................$479

HAWK

Starting with its unfinished form, the 66-inch Hawk longbow lets the buyer decide the shaping of the grip, the decoration and the finish. The Hawk is also a very economical way to get started in traditional archery. Made of yellow birch and hickory, the bow's durability is enhanced with the addition of a fiberglass laminate. Other features include a 6½- to 7¼-inch brace height and a mass weight of 1

pound, one ounce. A bowstring is included.

SPECIFICATIONS: HAWK
Draw Weight: from 30# to 60#
Length: 66 inches
SRP: $168.42

HI-SPEED

This 58-inch take-down recurve by Martin Archery weighs 2 pounds 7 ounces and is for the archer who wants a short, quick bow that's great for traveling. The gently contoured Hi-Speed riser is sculpted from laminated maple for both beauty and strength and has an approximately 8-inch brace height. Limbs are hand laid laminations of red elm and clear glass and feature reinforced tips. The whole bow is immersed in a deep glossy finish. (Available in Semi-Gloss finish by special request.) The Hi-Speed comes complete with a traditional arrow rest, a bowstringer and a bowstring. The installation of sight and quiver bushings are available upon special request.

SPECIFICATIONS: HI-SPEED
Draw Weight: from 30# to 70#
Length: 58 inches
SRP: $437.99

HUNTER

This Martin manufactured one-piece recurve has 62-inch limbs with maple laminations and black fiberglass backing. The hardwood riser has distinct accent stripes running up through it. Other features include a string, and traditional shelf rest. The bow comes with a bowstringer and standard stabilizer insert. This bow is available in LH and RH models.

SPECIFICATIONS: HUNTER
Draw Weight: numerous available at 28-inch draw length
Length: 62 inches
SRP: $350.00

MAMBA

This one-piece recurve bow is crafted by Martin with 58-inch limbs with maple laminations and backed by black fiberglass. Other features of the Mamba include a hardwood riser, standard stabilizer insert, Dacron bowstring and traditional shelf rest. Bow is shipped with a bowstringer. The Mamba is available in left- and right-hand models.

SPECIFICATIONS: MAMBA
Draw Weight: from 35# to 70# at 28-inch draw length and 5# increments
Length: 58 inches
SRP: $350.00

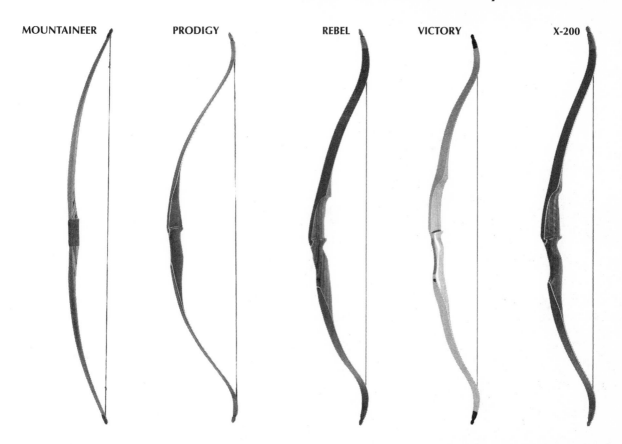

MOUNTAINEER   PRODIGY   REBEL   VICTORY   X-200

MOUNTAINEER

The 68-inch Mountaineer uses Zebra wood laminations and limbs with a reflex design to eliminate hand shock and stack. The grip section is enhanced with an attractive leather wrap. This bow weighs 1 pound, 5 ounces.

SPECIFICATIONS: MOUNTAINEER
Draw Weight: from 30# to 70#
Length: 68 inches
SRP: $350.00

PRODIGY

This Martin bow is for young archers who are serious about archery. The Prodigy is a scaled-down version of the company's adult bows and features a riser hand-crafted from African hard-woods and limbs of laminated maple. The bow has a contrsting red riser against dark limbs. The same hand-craftsmanship that goes into every Martin bow is used in the making of this 48-inch model. At only 10 oz., the Prodigy allows the young archer hours of enjoyable shooting without fatigue. Each Prodigy comes with a traditional rest and Dacron bowstring.

SPECIFICATIONS: PRODIGY
Draw Weight: from 10# to 25# at 24-inch draw
Length: 48 inches
SRP: $119.95

REBEL

While its design makes it look like a beginner or youth bow, or treestand hunting bow, the 52-inch Rebel recurve also excels at bowfishing. Durability and compact size are key elements required when the bowfishing action heats up. The Rebel by Martin is built to satisfy the most demanding bow fisherman, in the most demanding situations. Construction includes Shedua wood and fiberglass backings. A stabilizer or bowfishing reel adapter and sight mount bushing are each installed as standard equipment.

SPECIFICATIONS: REBEL
Draw Weight: from 20# to 50#
Length: 52 inches
SRP: $254.39

VICTORY

The 66-inch Victory's natural white color is derived from the use of hand-crafted hard maple. Its limbs have outer laminates of white glass and include reinforced tips that allow the use of any string material. A tradi-tional arrow rest and a bowstringer are included with each Victory. Sight and stabilizer bushings are also installed as standard equipment.

SPECIFICATIONS: VICTORY
Draw Weight: from 20# to 50#
Length: 66 inches
SRP: $249.39

X-200

The X-200 packs value into a solid starter's recurve. Features include 60-inch maple laminated limbs and a brown Shedua hardwood riser. This bow is shipped with a Dacron bow-string and plastic Dura-Flip elevated arrow rest. The X-200 is available in LH and RH models.

SPECIFICATIONS: X-200
Draw Weight: from 35# to 45# in 5# increments at 28-inch draw length.
Length: 60 inches
SRP:. $225

RECURVE BOWS

Monarch Bows LLC Recurve Bows

LONGBOW

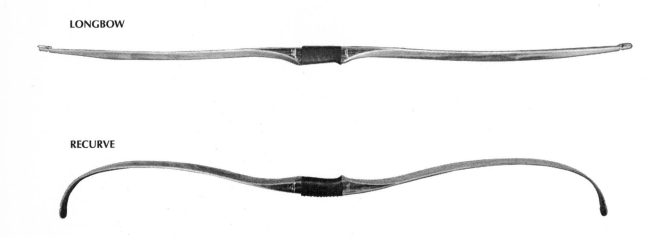

RECURVE

THIS DARBY, MONTANA, company has been producing bows since 1986. Buyer can create a custom bow by choosing: riser wood, limb wood, length, weight at draw length, size of riser to match hand, color of elk leather grip and personalized lettering. Features include elk horn tip, laced leather handle, tapered wood laminations, fiberglass reinforcement and satin finish. Most bows are available

in 58-, 60-, and 62-inch lengths. The Spike Recurve is available in 56- and 58-inch length. Available wood choices include: tulipwood, red elm, Pacific yew, bocote, and featherwood. The Royal Flatbow and Royal Recurve bows joined the product line in 1996. The unique Royal Recurve has 1950's styling with a longbow like handle, wide limbs, riser wood tip overlays and sweeping limb curves. Most

models are shipped with a string and polar fleece bow sock. Call (800) 793-3224 for ordering details.
SRP:
Imperial Longbow $590
Raghorn Longbow $398
Royal Flatbow $425
Royal Longbow. $510
Royal Recurve $525
Spike Recurve $495

Moosejaw Bows Recurve Bows

LONGBOW

MASTER BOWYER Gary Sentman pours more than 15 years of bow building experience into each handmade Moosejaw longbow. Each bow has a bamboo limb core, hand laminated African Bubinga wood and liner riser and Fast-Flite string. Available lengths include: 62, 64, 66 and 68 inches; 62, 64 and 66 inches

for the standard model with one-piece hardwood riser. Limb tips are laminated. A protective 72-inch bow sock is available for and additional $12 with purchase of a bow. This bow is backed by a 100% satisfaction guarantee for one year from date of purchase. Call (541) 592-6954 for full details.
SRP: Starting at $565

RAZORBACK BOW
The Razorback is similar to the Moosejaw longbow in 66- and 68-inch lengths with right- and left-hand pulls and with Ash or Bubinga wood risers.
SRP: Starting at $342

RECURVE BOWS

Palmer Bow Company Recurve Bows

LEGEND

THIS SANIBAL, TEXAS, based bowyer produces bows one at a time with keen attention to balance, beauty, performance, fit and finish. Palmer bows are offered in any draw length from 24 to 34 inches and in draw weights ranging form 20 to 70 pounds. Available bow lengths range from 58 to 64 inches.

Riser styles offered range from the two-toned Legend to the Gray Bark gray and Classicwhich has a blend of light and dark woods. The Dead Leaf is a rich brown. Standard risers are constructed of laminated hardrock maple and legends are produced from Texas Ebony hardwood. Palmer bow limbs are available in standard 4-layer,

custom carbon 5-layer, and double carbon 7-layer laminates. All bows can be ordered with a choice of laminated limbs, with or without carbon fiber and finished in Dead Leaf, Gray Bark and Texas Ebony finishes. Limbs are attached to the risers with two bolts at each limb base.

Palmer also offers a bow quiver and a soft case. Call (830) 988-2568 for bow manufacturing details and pricing info.

SRP:
Dead Leaf Brown and
  Tree Bark Gray $495
Bows with single carbon
  limb layer $595

Bows with double carbon
  limb layers . . . . $695.
Classic designed double carbon . . . .
  . . . . $725
Legend designed double carbon . . . .
  . . . . $795

SRP: Limbs with carbon,
  from . . . . $270 to $470
  Palmer's Classic and Legend limbs
  are the most expensive.

SRP: Recurve quivers that hold
  4 or 7 arrows $39.95

Predator Custom Recurves Recurve Bows

CLASSIC CUSTOM TAKE-DOWN
This recurve is offered in a 60-inch length only and has a riser carved from sturdy bubinga wood and impregnated maple. The limbs are black glass or clear glass crafted over red elm wood. Other features include a Flemish weave string and contoured pistol grip. Draw weights vary.
SPECIFICATIONS:
CLASSIC CUSTOM TAKE-DOWN
Length: 60 inches
SRP: $579.99

HUNTER RECURVE
This model features black glass limbs connected to a solid one-piece maple riser that's colored gray to blend in with the forest. The bow is 60 inches long and has a Flemish string. Draw weights vary per bow.
SPECIFICATIONS: HUNTER RECURVE
Length: 60 inches
SRP: $429.99

YOUTH 3-PIECE TAKE-DOWN
This youth oriented recurve displays the same colors as Predator's Hunter model with black glass limbs and a maple riser that's shaded gray. The Youth 3-Piece Take-Down is available in 48- and 52-inch lengths. The bow takes down via a bolt and beasel washer with stem system for packing, traveling and easy storage when not in use.
SPECIFICATIONS:
YOUTH 3-PIECE TAKE-DOWN
Length: 48 or 52 inches
SRP: $179.99

PSE Recurve Bows

INTREPID

SIERRA

PSE HERITAGE LINE:

INTREPID
Integrated adjustable limb pockets on the Intrepid help the user achieve optimal bow riser and limb alignment. This bow features a strong, lightweight design and innovative limb mounting system. The Intrepid has a precision machined one-piece riser and stainless steel limb bolts. Available riser colors include: polished red, polished blue and polished black. Note that the limbs are sold separately.

BOW SPECIFICATIONS: INTREPID
Draw Weight: NA
Length: 25 inches, and can vary based on a total length determined by limbs selected.
SRP: **$479.99**
 (LH models are available)

SIERRA
An economically priced machined aluminum riser in a one-piece design makes PSE's Sierra a popular riser. The riser is 23 inches long, has a comfortable wood grip installed and is available in satin blue or red. The limbs for this bow are sold separately.

BOW SPECIFICATIONS: SIERRA
Draw Weight: NA
Length: 23 inches, total length determined by limbs selected.
SRP: **$274.99**
 (LH models are available)

PSE LIMBS
For the risers sold above, PSE offers their Competition and Pro Elite limbs. The Competition limbs are constructed of high quality hard rock maple wood and glass laminates. These limbs are shaped and crafted to precise tolerances for straightness and consistency. They are economically priced and available in 68-inch, 30-40# and above in additional 2lb. increments.

The Pro Elite limbs are carbon laminated layers and designed by Kyung Rae Park. They utilize the International Limb Fitting System and are available in 66-inch lengths with 30-42# draw weight. Also available as 68-inch with 30-42# draw and 70-inch limbs for a 32-40# draw in 2lb. increments.
SRP: The prices of the limbs vary widely based on models, length and poundage selected. Visit your local pro shop—or visit www.pse-archery.com– to determine availability and price.

RECURVE BOWS

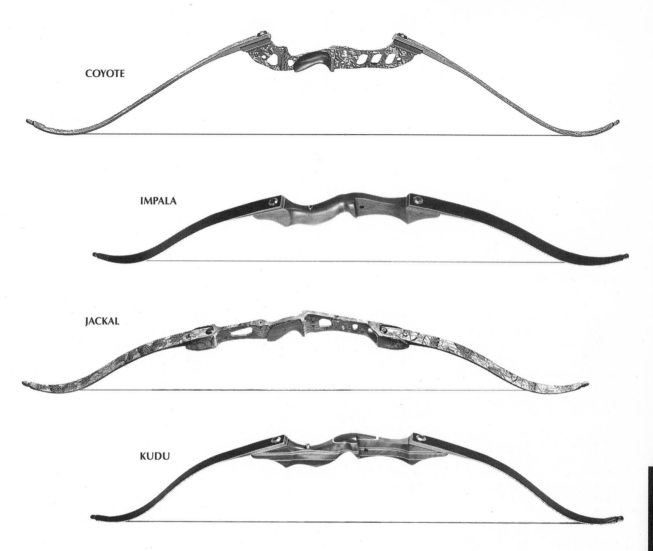

COYOTE

IMPALA

JACKAL

KUDU

COYOTE

The PSE Coyote represents value in a high-tech recurve. Features of this bow include a precision machined aluminum riser with a black wrap-around molded grip. This 60-inch bow is available in PSE's Brush camouflage finish and accepts PSE two-piece quivers.

BOW SPECIFICATIONS: COYOTE
Draw Weight: 35#, 40#, 45#, 50# and 55#.
Length: 60 inches
SRP: **$269.99**
   (LH models are available)

IMPALA

This PSE bow is perfect for the starting archer and features a new stylish handle. Other construction details include: a hardwood riser with detailed finish, bolt on laminated limbs and threaded receptors for accessories.

BOW SPECIFICATIONS: IMPALA
Draw Weight: 35#, 40#, 45# and 50#.
Length: 60 inches
SRP: **$189.99**
   (LH models are available)

JACKAL

The Jackal is a blend of high-tech Olympic style bows and traditional hunting recurves. It features a machined aluminum riser with wooden grip installed plus top-notch wood laminate limbs. The riser will accept a stabilizer and arrow rest. The Jackal is available in PSE's Brush camo.

BOW SPECIFICATIONS: JACKAL
Draw Weight: 40#, 45#, 50#, 55# and 60#

Length: 64 inches
SRP: **$439.99**
   (LH models are available)

KUDU

This takedown recurve is the latest in PSE's line up. It features eye-catching multi-layered laminates and solid brass accessory inserts which are the very best in quality, style and strength. The wide weight ranges offered with this model will accommodate bowfishermen and hunters.

BOW SPECIFICATIONS: KUDU
Draw Weight: 35#, 40#, 45#, 50#, 55# and 60#.
Length: 58 inches
SRP: **$299.99**
   (LH models are available)

Renegade Archery Company Recurve Bows

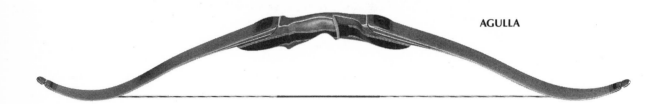

AGULLA

AGULLA AND AGULLA ULTRA

This competition bow offers a choice of machined Ultra riser or cast/forged Agulla riser. The Ultra riser features adjustable limb pockets and a riser with open design and points to accommodate accessories. Both bows feature weight and tiller adjustments. Available Agulla riser colors include: Sky blue, two tone blue, red, silver, and black. This recurve is sold as a separate riser and limbs and the riser will accept limbs from numerous manufacturers to suit the shooter's preference.

BOW SPECIFICATIONS: AGULLA AND AGULLA ULTRA
Draw Weight: 26#, 28#, 30#, 32#, 34#, 36#, 38#, 40#, 42# and 44#.

Length: 66 and 68 inches
SRP: Agulla riser $250
Agulla Ultra riser $499.95
Agulla Ultra Carbon limbs . . $399.95

HAWKEYE

This recurve has an unusual one-of-a-kind shaped laminated riser with unique rear limb mounting system that increases bow speed and accuracy. Black limbs with brown reinforced tips contrast against light wood riser. The Hawkeye is offered in LH and RH models by Samick.

BOW SPECIFICATIONS: HAWKEYE
Draw Weight: 40#, 45#, 50#, 55# and 60#.
Length: 62 inches

SRP: $399.95
(riser and limbs also sold separately)

JAZZ

This youth bow has innovative high-tech carbon glass limbs with a scaled outer finish. Other features include a blue painted metal Cupid riser and a slotted sight with one pin. Left- and right-hand models are available.

BOW SPECIFICATIONS: JAZZ
Draw Weight: 15# and 20#
Length: 46 inches
SRP: $89.95

Practicing on life-size targets in lifelike situations can improve your accuracy.
If you hunt from a treestand, practice shooting at 3-D targets from a stand set at the
appropriate height. If you stalk, practice shooting in awkward positions
such as kneeling or crouching to shoot under a limb.

RECURVE BOWS

Samick Recurve Bows

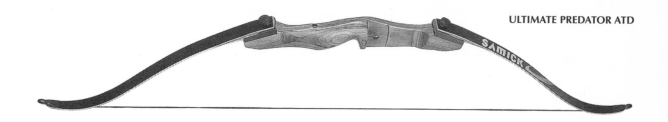

LAVITA

This bow was created to inspire young Olympic oriented archers. Its features include a precision forged and machined riser, positive limb mounting pin, long window, clicker mount hole, and a contoured grip with rubber side inlays. The Lavita uses multi-laminated wood limbs and an inside the riser shock-dump system to provide a smooth and consistent arrow release. A threaded brass bushing accepts accessories and the white limbs have distinct black tips. Available riser colors include: blue, red, and black.

BOW SPECIFICATIONS: LAVITA
Draw Weight: 18#, 20#, 22#, 24#, 26#, 28#, 30#, 32#, 34#, 36# and 38#.
Length: 64 and 66 inches
SRP: riser $90
limbs $105
(sold separately)

LEGEND

A one-piece longbow that has a traditional look and feel. The Legend offers a sleek design of laminate woods and one-of-a-kind true custom built. This bow is available in LH and RH versions.

BOW SPECIFICATIONS: LEGEND
Draw Weight: 40#, 45#, 50#, 55# and 60#
Length: 69 inches
SRP:. $215

PREDATOR

This lightweight hunting recurve is sculpted from hard rock maple. Black laminate limbs fit into limb pockets that are a great contrast with light brown riser. The riser has a threaded bushing to accept accessories. The Predator is available in LH and RH models.

BOW SPECIFICATIONS: PREDATOR
Draw Weight: 40#, 45#, 50#, 55# and 60#.
Length: 58 inches
SRP:. $195
   (Note: the riser and limbs are also sold separately)

PROGRESS I

This competition oriented recurve features rear lock-down limb screws to ensure perfect alignment of the multi-laminated ultra glass wood limbs with the magnesium painted risers. The available bow colors include two-tone blue, red/silver and black/silver. Other features include white limbs with the distinct logo and black reinforced limb tips.

BOW SPECIFICATIONS: PROGRESS I
Draw Weight: 20# to 40# in two pound increments.
Length: 66 inches
SRP:. $195

SPIRIT II

This hunting recurve has a new style rounded and shaped riser that is hand-crafted from rosewood and walnut. No limb pockets are used since the limbs are aligned with a hidden dual pin system. Black laminate limbs with a white Samick logo in contrast with rich colored wood riser. LH and RH versions are available.

BOW SPECIFICATIONS: SPIRIT II
Draw Weight: 40#, 45#, 50#, 55# and 60#.
Length: 60 inches
SRP:. $225
   (riser and limbs also sold separately)

ULTIMATE PREDATOR ATD

This recurve has a 6061 machined aluminum riser, wooden one-piece grip, and laminate limbs with a hard maple core inside Bow Tuff laminates. A phenolic tip overlay ensures years of durable service. This unique bow has Mossy Oak Break-Up camouflage and offers a three-year warranty.

BOW SPECIFICATIONS:
ULTIMATE PREDATOR ATD
Draw Weight: 45# - 70#
Length: 62-inch
SRP:. $449

WOODSMAN

Each Woodsman model is hand made and has a laminated riser with brown wood grain limbs. Look closely and you'll see a black stripe passing through the wood riser! These bows are prepared in LH and RH layouts by Samick.

BOW SPECIFICATIONS: WOODSMAN
Draw Weight: 45#, 50#, 55# and 60#
Length: 62 inches
SRP:. $450
   (riser and limbs also sold separately)

Wing Archery Products Recurve Bows

PRESENTATION I

PRESENTATION II

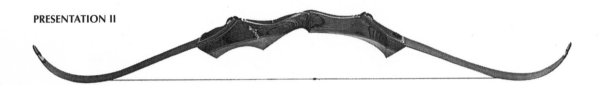

PRESENTATION I

This Wing take-down hunter has been designed with an emphasis on strength and durability as well as grace and performance. Riser is constructed of Wingwood laminates and limbs feature laminates and maple with dark glass. The bow also has a brass stabilizer receiver and quiver bushings. The Presentation I features a crown and radius rest for sweet shooting. These bows have been manufactured since 1951 and are backed by a 2-year limited warranty.

BOW SPECIFICATIONS: PRESENTATION I
Draw Weight: 40# to 70#.
Length: 62 and 64 inches
SRP:. **$369**

PRESENTATION II

Similar to the Presentation I, the Presentation II incorporates a myrtle-wood face and decorative padauk caps. The wood laminate riser provides up to 9 1/2- inches of brace height. Red elm wood is used in the construction of the limbs. This bow is available in right-hand models only.

BOW SPECIFICATIONS: PRESENTATION II
Draw Weight: 40# to 70#.
Length: 62 inches
SRP:. **$695**

Bowhunters need to be scent-free to avoid spooking target animals. Spray clothing, boots, your bow, arrows, backpack, even your rattling horns with an odor neutralizer. Wear scent-free clothing, including a hood that covers your mouth.

RECURVE BOWS

CROSSBOWS

CROSSBOWS

Barnett Crossbows

QUAD 300

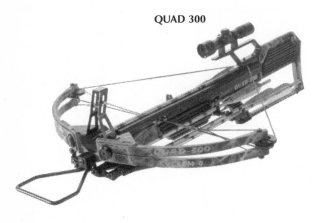

COMMANDO II

RC-150

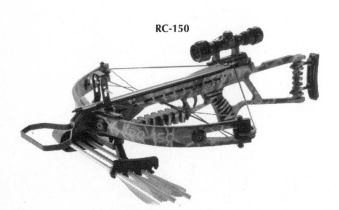

COMMANDO II
RECURVE

BARNETT QUAD 300

The crossbow uses quad limb technology teamed with cam technology to achieve high arrow speeds and peak performance. It has a synthetic harness system and 15¼-inch power stroke. This crossbow has a dark camouflaged stock, multiple rubber grip pads and a foot stirrup. The Quad 300 will accommodate a scope.

This bow is also offered in a kit that includes: bow, arrows, quiver, and 4X32 scope.

SPECIFICATIONS:
Draw Weight: 150 lbs.
Max Speed: 335 fps
SRP: Starting at **$245**
Kit **$300**

COMMANDO II

This crossbow combines a rear pivoting stock, sturdy locking arms and precision extruded cocking hooks with self-aligning roller guides to increase accuracy. The installed Rhino trigger mechanism features a short, smooth, ultra-light trigger pull. This crossbow has a 10½-inch power stroke with solid limbs and e-wheels. It is recommended for hunting at up to 60 yards. One prominent feature of the Commando II is the protruding under-the-arm hook on the lower rear of the open-style stock.

The Commando II Recurve has similar stock and design as the standard Commando II but it has solid recurve limbs. This bow has a 10-inch power stroke, 150-pound draw weight and is recommended at up to 40 yards.

SPECIFICATIONS:
Draw Weight: 150 lbs.
Max Speed: 260 fps
SRP: Compound mode starting . . . **$400**
Recurve model **$278**

RC-150

This Barnett crossbow is light—5½ pounds!—and compact. The bow has graphite composite limbs, aluminum flight track and machined alloy cams. It has a unique multi-ribbed forearm and rear bracket and open designed stock. The RC-150 is camouflaged in green and tan and has a 9½-inch power stroke. A metal foot stirrup helps control the bow while cocking. It will accommodate a scope and other accessories.

A recurve model by Barnett—the RX-150—has a similar stock and uses recurve limbs. It is a full-sized crossbow with an SRP of $105.

SPECIFICATIONS:
Draw Weight: 150 lbs.
Max Speed: 260 fps
SRP: Starting at **$165**
bow, quiver and four arrows . **$178**

Barnett Crossbows

REVOLUTION

RHINO QUAD

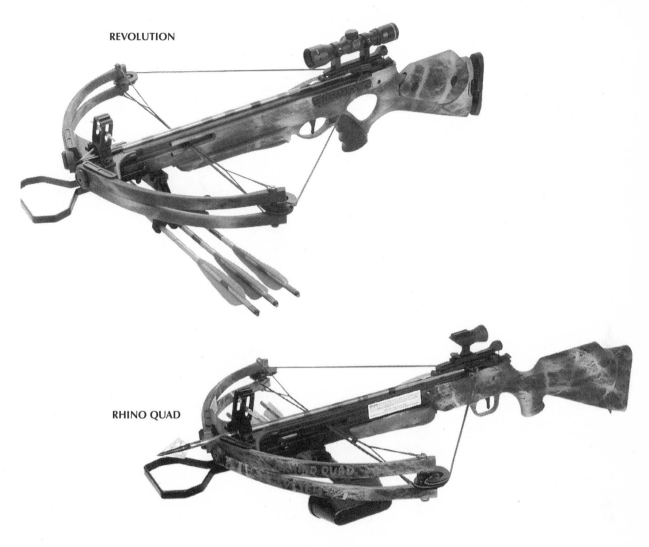

REVOLUTION

The Revolution uses Veloci-Speed cams and 4-limb technology to move arrows. Users can adjust the stock's cheek piece and rear stock plate to ensure proper eye alignment with the sights or a scope when installed. The front of the bow can be easily removed for transportation and storage. This bow has a nonskid black rubber pistol grip. It will accommodate a scope.

This bow is offered in a kit that includes: bow, quiver, arrows and a 4X32 scope.

SPECIFICATIONS:
Draw Weight: 133 lbs.
Max Speed: 340 fps
**SRP: Starting at $289
with a quiver and arrows . . . $314
Bow kit $359**

RHINO QUAD

The Rhino Quad has an ultra-light trigger pull, scope adjustment dial and an analog range gauge to help increase shooter accuracy. Other features include: a Monte Carlo stock, patented lever-action breakdown mechanism, locking sight pins, ambidextrous safety, adjustable fore grip and a Veloci-Speed Synthetic String. This crossbow has a 13-inch power stroke and will accommodate numerous accessories.

SPECIFICATIONS:
Draw Weight: 150 lbs.
Max Speed: 310 fps
**SRP: Starting at $247
with a quiver and four arrows
. . . . $275**

CROSSBOWS

Barnett Crossbows

WILDCAT III

RHINO SPORT MAGNUM

RHINO SPORT MAGNUM

This bow has a solid stock and uses 4-limb technology with Veloci-Speed cams to launch arrows. This unit has a lever-action take-down lever to make transportation and storage a breeze. The Rhino Sport Magnum has an adjustable foregrip, metal foot stirrup and is camouflaged.

SPECIFICATIONS:
Draw Weight: 150 lbs.
Max Speed: 260 fps
SRP: bow and a quiver stocked w/four arrows, starting at . . . $285

WILDCAT III

This crossbow has recurve limbs attached to a solid Monte Carlo ambidextrous stock. The entire unit is black and will accommodate multiple accessories. A stirrup assists with control while cocking. This bow is recommended at hunting ranges up to 40 yards.

SPECIFICATIONS:
Draw Weight: 150 lbs.
Max Speed: 235 fps
SRP: Starting at $123

Ben Pearson Archery Crossbows

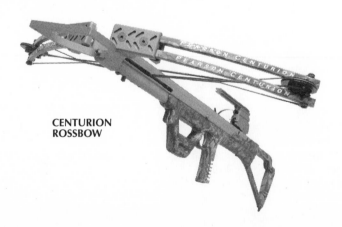

CENTURION ROSSBOW

CENTURION CROSSBOW

This high performance hunting bow has a Teflon impregnated aluminum barrel assembly and Superflage camouflaged stock with an open shoulder mount. Other features include a dry fire inhibitor, peep sight and pins, a Weaver-style scope mount base and built in fittings for a cocking device that is sold separately.

BOW SPECIFICATIONS
Draw Weight: 165 pounds
Bow Speed: 330 fps
SRP:. $729

MAXPOINT 305

MAXPOINT

This Buckmaster crossbow utilizes the exclusive MaxWing cam to deliver no let-off. The result—more stored energy. The Maxpoint features a four-limb design, machined aluminum riser and cocking stirrup. This crossbow is available with Realtree Hardwoods camo finish. The optional set model includes: sights, quiver and four bolts.

SPECIFICATIONS:
Draw Weight: 175 lbs.
Bow Speed: 340 fps
SRP:. $399
   set $549

MAXPOINT 305

This powerful crossbow delivers performance at an economical level. Features of this Buckmaster crossbow include: four Realtree Hardwoods camouflaged limbs, black aluminum riser and stock, and a grip that permits easy use by left- or right-hand shooters. The optional set includes: 1X30 Red Dot crossbow scope with cover and mount, plus four-arrow quiver, four bolts and field points.

SPECIFICATIONS:
Draw Weight: 150 lbs.
Bow Speed: 306 fps
SRP:. $349
   set $499

"... an hour's earnest practice each day for a month will make one begin to feel like a bowman, and three months of such work will make him a fair shot at thirty or forty yards."
—Maurice Thompson,
The Witchery of Archery, 1879

Excaliber Crossbows

EXOCET

POINT BLANC

EXOMAG

VIXEN

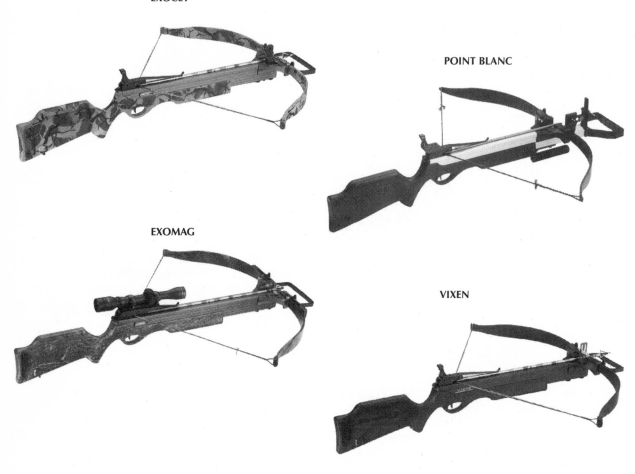

EXOCET
This Excaliber crossbow has a solid, one-piece stock and forearm that's offered with a Realtree Hardwoods or four-color camouflage finish. This crossbow has an ambidextrous manual safety, Magtip limbs and quick detach sling studs. The Exocet has a fiber optic sight and is drilled and tapped to receive a scope base.
SPECIFICATIONS:
Draw Weight: 175 lbs.
Max Speed: 300 fps
SRP: four-color camo $465
Realtree Hardwoods camo $515

EXOMAG
This recurve crossbow has a Realtree Hardwoods finish to help you blend in with your surroundings. Other features include: Magtip limbs and a Dissipator bar to reduce sound and recoil. The

Exomag also has detachable sling swivels and a fiber optic sight.
SPECIFICATIONS:
Draw Weight: 200 lbs.
Max Speed: 330 fps
SRP:. $560

POINT BLANC
This recurve crossbow is noticeable with its black stock and gold rail. The Point Blanc has a forward mounted stirrup, tuned trigger, and is drilled and tapped for a scope mount. The Deluxe version includes a stabilizer, sight level, forward mounted target sight and elevated rear aperture.
SPECIFICATIONS:
Draw Weight: 90 lbs.
Max Speed: NA
SRP: standard $360
deluxe model $450

VIXEN
This no-frills crossbow has solid recurve limbs and a solid-one-piece stock—and all covered in basic black. The Vixen weighs 6 pounds, has an ambidextrous manual safety and peep sights. It is drilled and tapped to accommodate a scope mount base.
SPECIFICATIONS:
Draw Weight: NA
Max Speed: 275 fps
SRP:. $390

CROSSBOWS

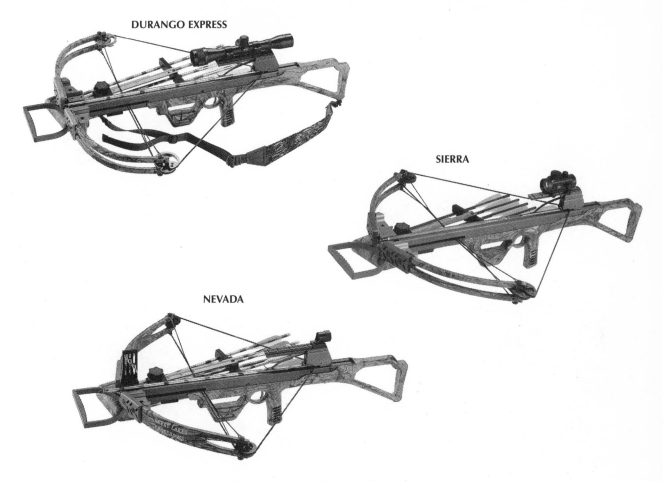

Great Lakes Crossbows Crossbows

DURANGO EXPRESS

SIERRA

NEVADA

DURANGO EXPRESS

The Durango has a powerful 17-inch power stroke and round energy wheels attached to pre-curved limbs with "0" deflex for a longer, more efficient power stroke. It is similar in design and features to the other Great Lakes models and also has a Weaver-style scope mount base. The stock and limbs are coated in Skyline's Excel camouflage.

SPECIFICATIONS:
Draw Weight: 165 lbs.
Max Speed: Up to 305 fps
SRP: **$649.99**

NEVADA AND NEVADA II

This crossbow features a one-piece solid limb design that helps produce pin point accuracy. It has a 13½-inch power stroke, precision machined arrow track, hard anodized Teflon coated barrel and a machined aluminum front riser. Its synthetic "Power Yoke" cables feature split anchor attachments on each limb to balance the limb torque. The Nevada has a patented dry-fire prevention mechanism and a center-balanced rifle-style safety for right- or left-handed shooters. Other features include: a universal Weaver-style scope mount and adjustable arrow hold down tension. The limbs are camouflaged.

The Nevada II is similar in design and features to the Nevada, and has stronger limbs and a fully camouflaged stock that's covered with Skyline's Excel camo.

SPECIFICATIONS:
Draw Weight: 150 lbs. for Nevada, 165 for Nevada II

Max Speed: 265 fps for Nevada, 277 for Nevada II
SRP: Nevada **$549.99**
Nevada II **669.99**

SIERRA

This Great Lakes crossbow has composite laminated quad limbs with alloy energy wheels along with a 15-inch power stroke. Other features for this crossbow include: machined arrow track, an anodized and Teflon impregnated barrel and a machined aluminum front riser. The Sierra has a patented trigger and dry fire prevention device. The safety operates similar to that found on most rifles.

SPECIFICATIONS:
Draw Weight: 150 lbs. and 165 lbs.
Max Speed: 275 fps for the 150# model, 294 for the 165# model
SRP: Starting at **$599.99**

CROSSBOWS

Horton Manufacturing Crossbows

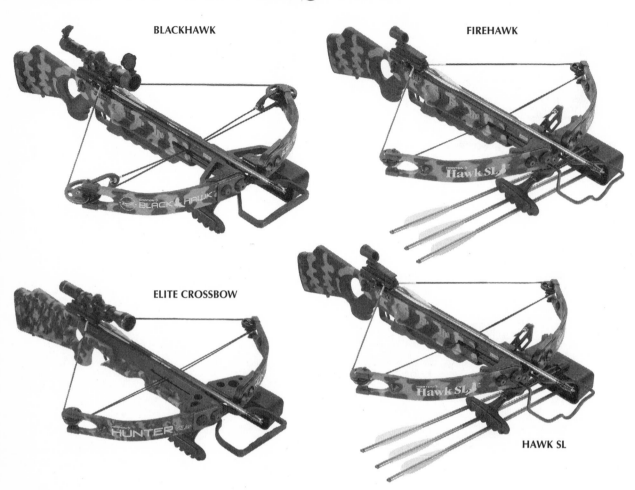

BLACKHAWK

FIREHAWK

ELITE CROSSBOW

HAWK SL

BLACKHAWK

This crossbow has similar features as the Firehawk and is camouflaged in Horton's Hawk camo—a unique dark and light contrast that helps you blend in under any hunting condition. The choice to forgo a franchised camouflage pattern makes this crossbow a more economical selection consideration. The Blackhawk also has an adjustable stock length and laminated limbs.

SPECIFICATIONS:
Draw Weight: 200 lbs.
Max Speed: 310 fps
SRP:. $500
    package $650

ELITE CROSSBOW

This 2003 introduction by Horton has external axle limb tips to eliminate drilled axle holes and reducing noise while strengthening the limb tips. The Hunter Elite features wide-body limbs, high output speed wheels, a composite thumbhole stock and Am-Busch camouflage. The arrow travels on a machined micorflite barrel. This crossbow weighs 8 pounds and has a 175-pound pull weight.

SRP:. $450

FIREHAWK

This crossbow uses Horton's Toughboy wide-body DP2 solid laminated limbs to move arrows at up to 320 fps. The limbs are attached to a solid stock that can be adjusted to the desired length. Other features include: machined aluminum reflex riser, SpeedMax power wheels, peep/pin sight, steel trigger and trajectory compensator. The limbs are tipped with Horton's Dura-Tip integrated yoke system. The stock is coated in Mossy Oak camouflage and has a scope base installed.

SPECIFICATIONS:
Draw Weight: 200 lbs.
Max Speed: 320 fps
SRP:. $600
    package $750

HAWK SL

This Horton crossbow has a rugged and durable solid stock with a thumbhole and the Hawk camouflage pattern as a finish. The stock can be adjusted with ¾-inch stock plates that are sold separately. Other features for this bow include: diecast riser, wide-body solid limbs, machined aluminum round wheels, a peep/pin sight and a dial-adjustable trajectory compensator.

SPECIFICATIONS:
Draw Weight: 150 lbs.
Max Speed: 270 fps
SRP:. $320
    package $350

CROSSBOWS

Horton Manufacturing Crossbows

HUNTER XS

STEEL FORCE

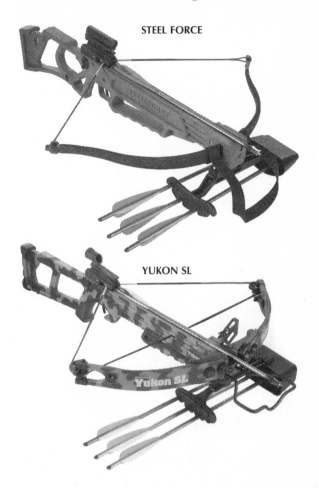

LEGEND II

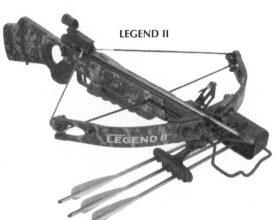

YUKON SL

HUNTER XS

This Horton crossbow features a solid composite stock with a thumbhole cut in and Mossy Oak Break-Up camo finish. Other features include: cable mufflers, machined aluminum reflex riser, SpeedMax power wheels, peep and pin sight and a steel trigger. The cable mufflers are a unique feature that is easily noticed. This crossbow also has: a stirrup, machined barrel, dial-a-range trajectory compensator and Weaver-Style scope base installed. The Hunter XS has one of the biggest draw weights in the industry—200 pounds—and moves bolts at 320 fps. This crossbow is offered in a package that includes a scope.

SPECIFICATIONS:
Draw Weight: 200 lbs.
Max Speed: 320 fps
SRP:. $600
    package. $750

LEGEND SL

This unit has ICAD steel cables, solid

Toughboy wide-body limbs with steel external axle limb tips and a stirrup. The Legend SL's composite stock has a thumbhole cut into the stock behind the grip and is coated with Am-Busch 3-D camouflage. Accessories for this crossbow must be purchased separately.

SPECIFICATIONS:
Draw Weight: 175 lbs.
Max Speed: 300 fps
SRP:. $400

LEGEND II

This crossbow has Toughboy wide limbs, high output wheels a Dial-A-Range trajectory compensator and peep-pin sights. The stock length is adjustable and the arrow launcher is based on steel cables. This crossbow has a 175-pound pull and a stirrup to assist with cocking.
SRP:. $400

STEEL FORCE

This recurve crossbow has limbs made of tempered steel. It also has

a composite barrel in the stock with a thumbhole also cut in behind the grip. Other features include a red dot sight and quiver with four target arrows and points. It is available in two weight ranges.

SPECIFICATIONS:
Draw Weight: 150 or 80 lbs.
Max Speed: 240 fps for 150 lbs., and 175 fps for the 80 lbs.
SRP: bows and accessory package
  . . . .$200

YUKON SL

This crossbow features solid glass limbs, an ICAD cable system, round wheels and magnesium riser. The composite stock has a thumbhole and open-designed butt section. The Yukon SL is coated in Horton's brown camouflage finish.

SPECIFICATIONS:
Draw Weight: 150 lbs.
Max Speed: 260 fps
SRP:. $300
    package. $340

CROSSBOWS

PSE Crossbows

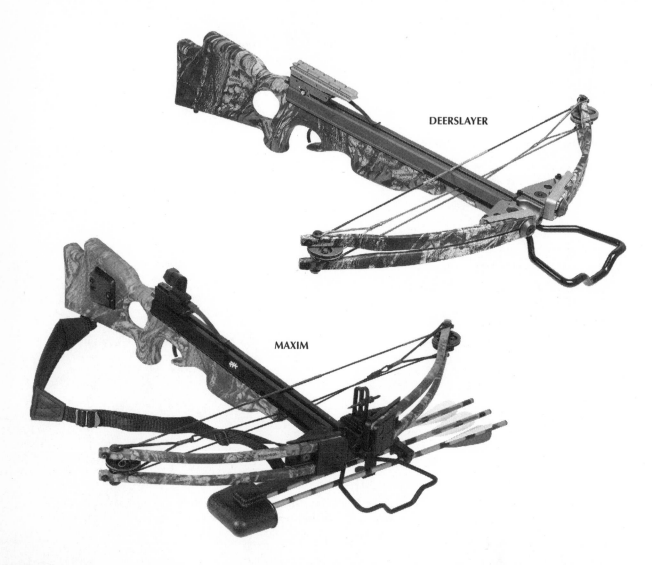

DEERSLAYER

MAXIM

DEERSLAYER
The Deerslayer has a power-touch trigger with an anti dry-fire mechanism. Other features for this crossbow include: a solid thumbhole stock with sling swivel studs installed, quad limb system with adjustable limb pockets and wheels, Acra-Angle barrel with patented Vibra-Crush and an aluminum barrel with PSE's Hard-Coat finish. The stirrup is custom coated and a scope mount base is included.
SPECIFICATIONS:
Draw Weight: 175 lbs.
Max Speed: NA
SRP: . . . . varies

MAXIM
The Maxim features TL-4 Quad limb system with steel cable and synthetic string and the Acra-Angle barrel with patented Vibra-Cush™ bow to barrel mounting system. The Econo trigger has an anti-dry-fire mechanism. Includes rear peep sight and front sight with pin and thumb-hole stock with sling swivel studs.
SPECIFICATIONS:
Draw Wieght: 165 lbs
Max Speed: NA
SRP: . . . . varies

PEREGRINE
This PSE crossbow is coated with the company's Brush camo finish and has an aluminum riser and machined aluminum wheels at the end of its solid limbs. It also has integrated cables and a Dacron string system. The solid stock is fitted with a Microflight aluminum barrel. A scope can be mounted on this crossbow.
SPECIFICATIONS:
Draw Weight: 175 lbs.
Max Speed: NA
SRP: . . . . varies

XB-270 PRO
This crossbow has a unique Oak Leaf camo finish on its stock and solid limbs. It is similar in design to PSE's Peregrine and has a rear peep sight and front pin sight system. It also has Dial-A-Range trajectory compensator and a machined trigger.
SPECIFICATIONS:
Draw Weight: 150 lbs.
Max Speed: 270
SRP: . . . . varies

BOW ACCESSORIES

Bow Accessories Cases and Slings

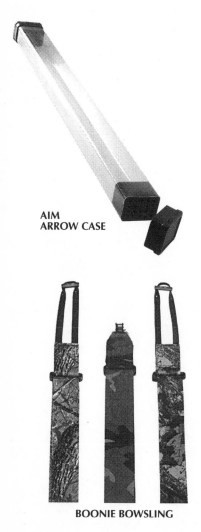

**AIM
ARROW CASE**

BOONIE BOWSLING

**LOOP LOCK
BOW SLING**

**MEGA BOW
SLING**

C.W. ERICKSON'S BOWSLING

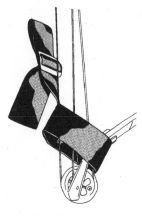

**C.W. ERICKSON'S
CWIK DRAW BOW HOLSTER**

AIM
Arrow Case
AIM's heavy-duty clear plastic arrow case holds up to a dozen arrows and protects your arrows from damage while in storage or transit.
SRP: **$15.95**

BOONIE PACKER
Boonie Bowsling
An over-the-shoulder sling that keeps your bow up front and ready when the sling is worn properly. The bow can also be carried over the shoulder and behind the back. The Boonie sling is 2-inch nylon webbing with a loop in each end. The sling is fully adjustable and available in Realtree Hardwoods, Woodland and Mossy Oak Break-Up.
SRP: **$21.99**

COBRA
Loop Lock Bow Sling
This sling has a metal bracket that fits over the bow's stabilizer hole and riser edge. It's drilled and tapped to accept a stabilizer. A $\frac{1}{2}$-inch wide strap wraps over your hand and wrist. Available in black and camouflage.
SRP: **$4.25**

Mega Bow Sling
The cord loop fits over your hand and wrist and it has a dual lock. The metal bracket fits over the bow's stabilizer hole and the extension is drilled and tapped to receive a standard stabilizer stud.
SRP: **$2.75**

C.W. ERICKSON'S MFG.
Bowsling
An over-the-shoulder strap that keeps your bow securely at your side. The webbing is 2-inches wide and permits easy-on and easy-off.
SRP: **$7.79**

Cwik Draw Bow Holster
This holster attaches to your belt and keeps your bow at your side while relieving arm strain. Can be sued while walking and standing. Accepts long, recurve and compound bows and the item is adjustable.
SRP: **$7.79**

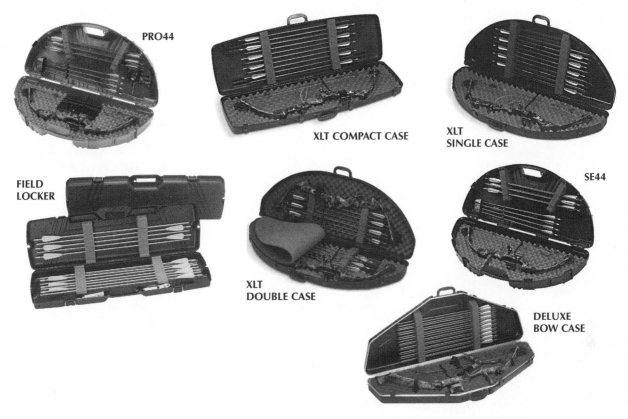

PRO44

XLT COMPACT CASE

XLT SINGLE CASE

FIELD LOCKER

SE44

XLT DOUBLE CASE

DELUXE BOW CASE

DOSKOSPORT
Deluxe Bow Case
Similar to the deluxe double bow (Bowguard) case, but it is designed to hold one bow and many arrows. Thick foam egg crate padding protects the bow.
SRP: . . . . **$79 to $89**

Field Locker Arrow Case
A hardside case by Doskosport that's designed to securely hold nearly two dozen arrows. The case latches closed and can be locked with three pad locks. Arrows are held in place by foam blocks. A must have for serious archers who travel with expensive carbon arrows.
SRP: . . . . **$14 to $19**

Pro44
Hardside bow case – features include durable steel hinge pins, large and wide angled feet for stability, two inches of extra thickness permits safe storage of the bow. A post inside permits you to attach a quiver with arrows in a secure position away for the bow. An accessory box holds broadheads and other items securely.

Tie-down straps hold the bow in place, and extra straps can hold arm guards, release aids, etc. Extra arrows can be securely stored in two rigid foam slotted blocks. The extra wide handle and four wide snap-over latches are recessed for easy carrying and loading. ATV tabs help tie this case to a four-wheeler's rack and it has two points for padlocks. This case is 44 inches long, 20 inches high and 9 inches thick outside dimensions when closed.
SRP: . . . . **$49-99 to $59.99**

SE44
SRP: (without the accessory box)
. . . . **$29.99 to $39.99**

XLT Compact Bow Case
Designed for smaller bows, such as those used by women and young archers. The case has 4 inches of inner locking foam to protect bows and hold them into place. Foam blocks hold up to 10 arrows. Latches are key lockable. This case's exterior is 47½-inches long by 15-inches tall.
SRP: . . . . **$49 to $59**

XLT Double Bow Case
The XLT Double Bow Case by Doskosport holds two full sized bows, arrows, and accessories. It features key lockable latches, slotted foam arrow retainer blocks and protective convoluted (egg crate) foam padding. The black case is 50 inches long and 18½ inches tall.
SRP: . . . . **$79 to $89**

XLT Single Bow Case
SRP: . . . . **$59 to $69**

JIM FLETCHER
ARCHERY AIDS
Bow Wrist Strap
This strap keeps your bow attached to your wrist and is adjustable. It connects to the bow behind your stabilizer. It's machine washable.
SRP: **$4.25**

Fleece Bow Wrist Strap
A soft and quite wrist strap that keeps your bow secure to your hand. These wrist straps help you relax your hand and be a better shot.
SRP: **$8.35**

Bow Accessories Cases and Slings

ARROW BOX

COMPOUND BOW CASE

BOWMASTER CROSSBOW

BOWMASTER

DOUBLE EDGE BOW GEAR BAG

SEALTECTOR

BOWTECTOR DELUXE

ARCHER

KOLPIN
Archer
A basic no-thrills compound bow case made from heavy weave polyester and with a Rhino Hide tip. This Kolpin case is camouflaged with Mossy Oak Break Up and has a strap handle and full length zipper. Available styles include long and short and with or without an exterior pocket.
SRP: . . . . **$27.99 to $32.99**

Arrow Box
This box is specially designed to fit in all Kolpin bow cases arrow pockets. It will safely and securely hold up to a dozen arrows with broadheads attached. Other features are a Hinged top and flip lock front and an embossed wildlife scene. Color: Green.
SRP: **$11.99**

Bowmaster
Reinforced with weatherproof shell
SRP: starting at **$44.99**

Bowtector
Exterior Rhino reinforced rib section, weatherproof. Models include a deluxe with exterior arrow case pocket, standard case and double bow case.
SRP: starting at **$64.99**

Bowmaster Crossbow
The exterior of this case is reinforced with Rhino Hide in high wear areas. Closed cell foam liner and camouflaged Mossy Oak exterior. Padded wrap around handles make transportation easy on the hands. A sturdy zipper holds the contents inside and a metal ring helps hang the bag for storage.
SRP: **$74.99**

Double Edge Bow Gear Bag
A soft-side case designed to hold two compound bows and lots of gear. The case is water repellent, has a center divide padded close cell foam partition and provide five exterior pockets for gear storage. A shoulder strap helps with transportation. Color: Brown.
SRP: **$126.99**

Sealtector Bow Case
Designed to strap onto the rack of any ATV. The case is waterproof with electrically welded seams and has a rugged 600 Denier exterior shell. Additional features include: padded wrap around grip handle, inside pockets for arrows and accessories, web-reinforced attachment straps, and a stretchable cargo net to hold down gear. Available in Mossy Oak camouflage.
SRP: **$179.99**

NORTH AMERICAN ARCHERY GROUP
Compound Bow Case
A soft-side canvas shelled bow case with brown trim, loop handles and arrow box storage pocket on the side. Zippered closure and soft padding.
SRP: 44 inch **$44.99**
SRP: 39-inch **$39.99**

Bow Accessories Cases and Slings

YOUTH BOW CASE

RECURVE BOW CASE

LONGBOW CASE

ARCHER'S ACCESSORY BOX

ARCHERY BOX

BOW-MAX

BOW-MAX ARROW CASE

PROTECTOR SERIES BOW CASE

Recurve Bow Case

A stylish canvas case with zippered closure and brown nylon trim and loop handles. Includes ID tag holder.
SRP: $45.99

Long Bow Case
SRP: $45.99

T/D Compound Bow Case

A compact canvas shelled case with two exterior pockets that's designed to hold the Bear Take-Down compound bow.
SRP: $59.99

Youth Bow Case

An adult-like version designed to hold the Brave youth bow. Features include a canvas shell with zippered closure and two loop handles. Length: 37 inches. Color: Green.
SRP: $19.99

PLANO MOLDING COMPANY
Archer's Accessory Box

A storage box designed to hold broadheads and touchy expandable broadheads also. A lift out tray is a good place to store nocks, field points and small items.
SRP: $6.99

Archery Box

A small multi-compartment storage box by Plano with a clear plastic lid and carrying handle to help you organize your must-have archery gear. Great for fieldor bench use. Has two lift out trays and foam area to securely hold broadheads.
SRP: $9.99

Bow-Max

A case with a two-part hip roof designed to cradle bows. A pivoting rubber bow retainer secures the bow in place and leaves room for the accessory box. A Sur-Lok arrow storage system retains arrows and covers the

broadheads and points. It is lockable and airline approved. The case is 46 inches long and 19½-inches tall.
SRP: $99.99

Bow-Max Arrow Case

A strong case designed to securely cradle expensive arrows. Holds up to 18 arrows and has a Pillarlock locking system. Sur-Lok system grips and retains arrows in place. This black case has a molded in comfort handle and is 36 inches long.
SRP: $19.99

Protector Series Bow Case

A case with a compact design and thick wall patented PillarLock construction. Velcro straps hold bow in place and Sur-Lok grips arrows and secures them in place. The 49-inch long case is lockable and airline approved. It's available in black and camouflaged colors.
SRP: black $27.99
camouflage $34.99

Bow Accessories Cases and Slings

BOW ACCESSORIES

DELUXE
BOW BAG

COMPOUND BOW ROLLER BAG

COMPACT ARCHERY CASE

DELUXE DOUBLE
RECURVE CASE

DOUBLE
TAKE-DOWN
RECURVE BAG

SIMMONS SYSTEM ARCHERY
The BushMaster Quiver

A unique round tubular quiver that is carried over the shoulder by a strap. The case exterior is camouflaged by Mossy Oak and the precision cut foam inserts inside the tube hold arrows in place to ensure stealth quietness while hunting. Tree sizes are available and can hold arrows ranging from 30½ to 34½ inches long.

SRP:. **$55**

Compact Archery Case

A case that's designed to hold a break-down recurve bow and two sets of limbs. This case has a sturdy HDPE shell, weather resistant O-ring seal and solid die cast zinc locks. Foam pre-cut strips will securely hold up to 18 arrows. A plastic toolbox is included and this also fits inside the case. The case is 36-inches long. Color: Black.

SRP: **$169**

Compound Bow Roller Bag

This roomy soft side bag will hold any SKB bow case plus an arrow box. It has oversized zippers, a strong 600 Denier exterior shell and wheels to keep the bag off the ground and provide easy airport movement. Color: Brown.

SRP: **$149.99**

Deluxe Bow Bag

A soft-side SKB case that holds one compound bow. D-rings inside can be used with bungee cords to hold smaller bows securely. Other features include a see-through mesh pocket to hold accessories, top quality leather trim and handles, arrow box storage section, full length pockets, and full padding to protect the bow and all contents. This case is large enough to hold a bow with a quiver and arrows attached. Color: Brown or green.

SRP: **$99.99**

Deluxe Double Recurve Case

Holds two takedown recurve risers, two sets of limbs, arrows, sights and a storage box. Color: Black.

SRP:. **$189**

Double Take-Down Recurve Bag

This soft-side SKB bow case has leather reinforced pockets to hold risers and limbs safe and secure. Large exterior pockets can hold accessories and an arrow storage box. Other features include full padding to protect the contents, sturdy leather grip handles, oversized self-repairing nylon zippers and a 600 Denier exterior shell. Colors: Green or Brown.

SRP: **$99.99**

ROTO BOW CASE

SMALL SINGLE COMPOUND BOW CASE

SMALL DOUBLE BOW CASE

INTERIOR

EXTERIOR

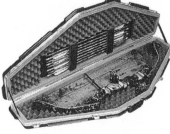

SINGLE BOW CASE

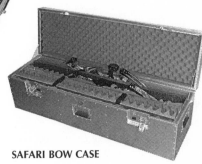

SAFARI BOW CASE

SKB

Roto Bow Case
A hard-shell case that will hold a compound bow with the quiver attached. Most stabilizers and hunting sights can also remain on the bow. This case opens from the end and an interior panel slides out to accept and hold the bow and accessories. The exterior shell is constructed of sturdy, rotational molded HDPE and strong structural ridges give support and protection to the bow inside. Additional features include: several interior cargo straps, two zippered interior storage pockets, and storage for up to 6 arrows, plus those in the quiver. The handle is molded in and the case is lockable and airline approved.
SRP: **$189.99**

Single Bow Case
A hard-side case that will hold one compound bow and up to 18 arrows. The interior is fully padded and the metal edge has a weather resistant O-ring seals to keep out dirt and moisture. Bumpers protect the case's hardware and it's lockable with solid die cast zinc locks. Color: Black
SRP: **$169**
Double Bow Case
   SRP: (Item 2SKB-6002) **$199**

Small Double Bow Case
Similar in design and style to the SKB small compound bow case but is designed to hold two smaller compound bows plus arrows. Thick egg-crate style foam separates the bows. A hard, swinging handle helps with transportation and two locks keep the contents secure. Color: Black.
SRP: **$189**
Small Single Compound Bow Case
SRP: **$179**

STRONG CASE
Strong Safari Bow Case
His heavy-duty metal case has sturdy one-piece construction of 14 gauge steel. A full-length piano hinge secures the top and recessed hardware makes moving easy. The foam interior liner is adjustable. Removable wheels help with airport moving. This case has a limited lifetime warranty and custom-built sizes are available.
SRP: Starting at **$225**

BOW ACCESSORIES

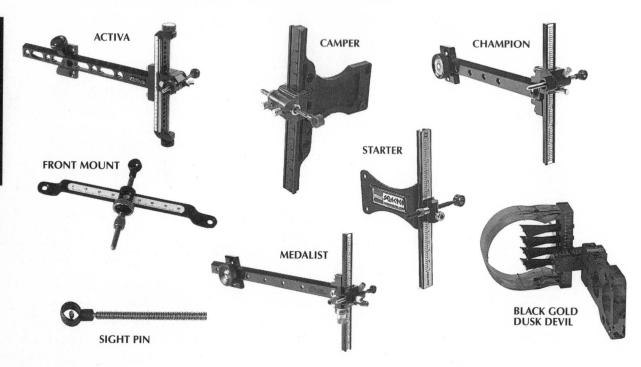

ACTIVA

CAMPER

CHAMPION

STARTER

FRONT MOUNT

MEDALIST

BLACK GOLD
DUSK DEVIL

SIGHT PIN

AIM
Activa Sight
This sight has ultra fine click adjustability with .002 increments. Parts are machined aluminum and level adjustments and 4-way sight pin. Other features include quick detach mounting bar, 9-inch extension bar and calibrated sight tape. Designed with 10/32 threads.
SRP: $199.95

Camper Sight
This sight's polymer and nylon construction means lightweight and durable construction. The Camper features a micro smooth windage adjustment, major elevation adjustment, embossed yardage bar and ring pin sight with a dot.
SRP: $17.00

Champion Sight
AIM's Champion sight has a streamline design and strong machined aluminum parts. Features include micro windage adjustment, quick detach 9-inch extension bar, calibrated sight tape and a free ring-pin sight.
SRP: $42.95

Front Mount Sight
This sight is designed by AIM for use on bows without any side-mount sight bushings.
SRP: $7.95

Medalist Sight
This competition sight is available in $8/32$ threads for recurves and $10/32$ for compound bows. It features a strong aluminum 9-inch extension bar, quick detach mounting bar and fine-elevation adjustment with a worm gear. The compound model has a level adjustment and the unit includes a free ring pin sight.
    SRP: (compound model) $110
    SRP: (recurve model) $59.95

Starter Sight
AIM's Starter Sight is designed for the beginning archer and offers durability and affordability. Features a deluxe ring sight and calibrated yardage tape.
    SRP: $10.95

Super Sight
A perfect sight for an intermediate archer. The Super Sight is constructed of polymer and nylon. Features include: smooth micro windage adjustments, a quick detach mounting base, major elevation adjustment, embossed yardage bar and a free ring sight.
SRP: $17.95

BLACK GOLD
Dusk Devil
This sight is bright because the fibers don't bend; they are located in line along a fin in the middle of the sight, in a straight away design. Other features of the Dusk Devil include direct mount bracket machined from 6061, T6 aluminum, horizontal and vertical gang adjustment and a black or Multi-Match camouflage finish. The sight is secured into place with a precision-machined dovetail bracket and over-sized bolts. Dusk Devil comes in three pin colors—red, green and yellow—and two pin sizes. The pins are easy to add or switch. Calibrations are clearly marked on the brackets. The pin guard has three quick-alignment dots to help you secure the target faster and align your sights.
SRP: black $79.25
camouflage $87.10
Dusk Devil w/ smaller
Micro Dot pins black $83.95
camouflaged $94.25
4-pin models. . . . . add $6.25
Standard sight replacement pins
SRP: . . . . ea. $8.35
Micro Dot pins
SRP: . . . . ea. $9.25

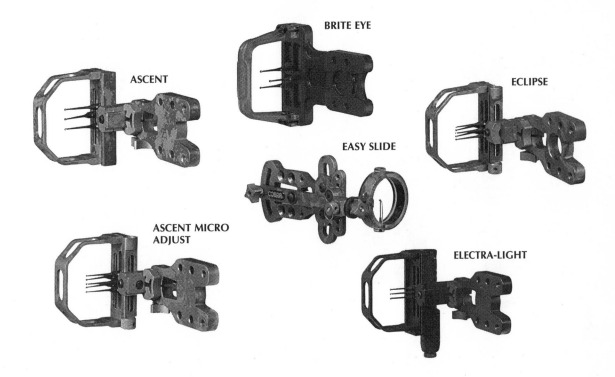

ASCENT

BRITE EYE

ECLIPSE

EASY SLIDE

ASCENT MICRO ADJUST

ELECTRA-LIGHT

COBRA
Ascent Sight
The Ascent by Cobra incorporates dual angle pin tracks for zero pin gap spacing. The metal and fiber-optic pins are protected by a metal guard that's vented with slots. The design of this sight includes the Posi-Stop adjustment system, dovetail slide, and sturdy metal base for attachment and positioning on the bow. Available in black and Mystik camouflage. Replacement pins and fibers are available.
SRP: black $33.99
camouflage $38.99

Ascent Micro Adjust
A bowhunting sight by Cobra with dual angled tracks to keep the pins in a single vertical sight plane. Features all metal constructions, five Micro TKO pins, easy adjustment, Posi-Stop module and a metal base with pre-drilled and tapped holes. The Ascent Micro has a vented square-edged metal sight guard and is available in black and Mystik camouflage.
SRP: black $43.99
camouflage $48.99

Mini Ascent Sight
SRP: black $36.53
camouflage $41.60

Brite Eye Sight
This Cobra sight uses three Brite Eye fiber optic and metal pins with double-lock hardware for separate windage and elevation adjustments. It has a solid non-glare smoked sight guard and a black one-piece base.
SRP: $10.66

Easy Slide Sight
A sight similar in design and construction to the Electra-Slide sight without the illumination system. This Cobra sight is easy to quickly adjust when mounted.
SRP: black $40.99
camouflage $45.99

Eclipse Sight
Similar in design and construction to the Mini Eclipse Sight but with a more squared and slightly larger sight pin guard when compared to the rounder Mini Eclipse sight guard. This sight is also all metal construc-

tion. Incorporates dovetailed slides and quick turn knobs.
SRP: black $54.56
camouflage $59.63

Mini Eclipse Sight
SRP: black $56.59
Mystik camo $61.66

Electra-Light Sight
This Cobra sight is new in 2003 and has a white LED light module built into the sight pin bracket and positioned to shine on the three ELT pins that are included. No stray light shines on the bracket; all light is focused on the pins. Other features include machined dovetail elevation and windage adjustments, Posi-Stop module and sturdy base for attachment to the bow with pre-drilled and tapped holes.
SRP: black $45.99
camouflage $50.99

Bow Accessories Sights and Peep Systems

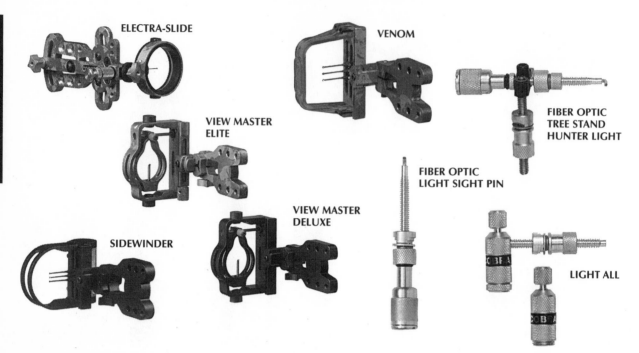

ELECTRA-SLIDE

VENOM

FIBER OPTIC TREE STAND HUNTER LIGHT

VIEW MASTER ELITE

FIBER OPTIC LIGHT SIGHT PIN

VIEW MASTER DELUXE

SIDEWINDER

LIGHT ALL

Electra-Slide Sight

This camouflaged bowhunting sight has a slide apparatus so that the shooter can adjust elevation quickly after turning a knob. A large round sight window contains a single metal fiber-optic pin. A red light—housed in the windage adjustment—illuminates the pin at dawn and dusk. The pin can only be illuminated from the side position. Accessories include: E Star replacement pins, Micro E Star replacement pins, replacement fibers and a spare battery for the light.

SRP: black. $50.99
  Mystik camouflage. $55.99

Sidewinder Sight

This all-metal sight features fiber optic pins with more than 2-feet of light gathering fiber optic cord to ensure brighter sight pins with .030-inch diameter. The Posi-Stop module permits quick detachment with a turn of the knob. It comes with three sight pins and a unique cylinder with the fiber optic cord coiled inside. A mounting bracket and pin guard are included on this black sight.

SRP: black. $44.99
  Mystik camouflage. $49.99

Venom Sight

Similar in design and all-metal construction to the Mini Venom but with a larger, rectangular sight pin guard and longer elevation bracket. Three TKO or Micro TKO pins are included.

SRP: black. $19.99
  camouflage $23.99

Mini Venom Sight

SRP: black. $21.30
  camouflage $25.36

View Master Elite Sight

A camouflaged bowhunting sight with a teardrop shaped pendulum suspended on ball bearings. A single all-metal STK fiber-optic pin is in the bottom of the teardrop. This sight is micro adjustable and has dovetailed bases and quick detach system. Vibration elimination buttons are mounted on the top and bottom of the sight guard.

SRP: black. $49.99
  Mystik camouflage. $54.99

View Master Deluxe Sight

SRP: black. $39.99
  Mystik camouflage. $44.99

COBRA ACCESSORIES FOR SIGHTS

These accessories are available for Cobra sights:

Light: All red. $7.36
Fiber Optic light sight pin
  (red) $8.11

Starlight Pin:
  (green or red). $2.75
Bright Eye Double locking pins:
  (red, green and yellow) $3.99
Up/Down position Micro STK pins:
  (green and yellow). $2.99
Lighted sight battery
  per 2 pack: $2.99
Micro E-Star pins:
  (green, red and yellow) $2.99
E-Star pins, standard:
  (green, red and yellow) $2.99
Ultra TKO replacement fibers:
  (assorted 3/pack) $3.99
ELT pins:
  (red, green and yellow) $4.57

Fiber Optic Light Sight Pin

This Cobra pin has a positive locking system and a battery operated illuminated .040-inch diameter red fiber optic tip that illuminates brightly at dawn and dusk when turned on. Battery can be easily replaced.

SRP: $8.11

Fiber Optic Tree Stand Hunter Light

SRP: $14.20

Light All

SRP: with stem $7.36
SRP: without stem $6.45

Bow Accessories Sights and Peep Systems

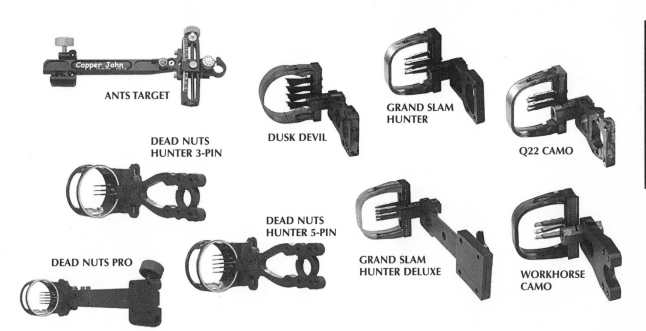

ANTS TARGET

DEAD NUTS HUNTER 3-PIN

DUSK DEVIL

GRAND SLAM HUNTER

Q22 CAMO

DEAD NUTS PRO

DEAD NUTS HUNTER 5-PIN

GRAND SLAM HUNTER DELUXE

WORKHORSE CAMO

COPPER JOHN
Copper John ANTS Target Sight
This top-grade target sight has a quick adjust mounting bracket with a large finger-operated knob, a solid extension arm and double-sided quick adjust pin bracket. The pin bracket exterior frame features Sprung Relief Technology. A Third Axis knob assists with precision tuning options.
SRP: $249.95

Dead Nuts Hunter Sights
These sighs were introduced in 1999 and feature all metal construction, a round pin guard with an orange highlight ring surrounding it, and an open-style mounting bracket to reduce weight. Sights are offered with three or five pins and have a level installed inside the lower sight window circle. Available in Mossy Oak camouflage for approximately $20 more per unit.
SRP: three pin $59.95
   five pin $69.95

Dead Nuts Pro Series
These pins are designed for competition archery and have smaller precision sight pin tips—down to 29- and 19 thousandths. The vertical gang adjustment and level setting feature are part of the same mechanism on this sight. The Pro II and Pro III models have a solid extension arm form the mounting

bracket to the sight bracket.
SRP: Pro standard $79.95
   Pro II $89.95
   Pro III. 99.95

MONTANA BLACK GOLD
Dusk Devil
The fibers are located in line along a fin in the middle of the sight in a straight-away design. Other features include direct mount bracket machined from 6061 T6 aluminum, horizontal and vertical gang adjustment and a black or Multi-Match camouflage finish. The sight is secured by a precision-machined dovetail bracket. Dusk Devil comes in three pin colors—red, green and yellow—and two pin sizes. Calibrations are clearly marked on the brackets. The pin guard has three quick-alignment dots to help you secure the target faster and align your sights.
SRP: black. $79.25
   camouflage $87.10

Grand Slam Hunter
The economical version with calibrations marked and guard surrounding the pins.
SRP: standard $62.50
   camouflage $71.25

Grand Slam Hunter Deluxe
SRP: standard $83.65
   with Micro pins. $89.20

Q22
This Black Gold bow sight is specifically designed to fit a Mathews bow. It is a direct mount and has 4standard or 4 Micro dot pins, plus calibrated brackets.
SRP: standard $39.00
   black. $42.00
   camouflaged $69.10
   black sight with Micro dots $74.15

Workhorse
This new economical bow sight has three pins and a direct base mount.
SRP: black. $39.95
   camouflaged $44.25

Bow Accessories Sights and Peep Systems

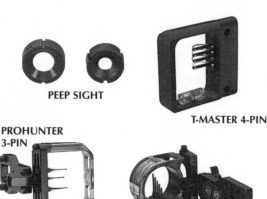

PEEP SIGHT

PROHUNTER 3-PIN

T-MASTER 4-PIN

FEATHERWEIGHT PENDULUM

PENDULUM MAX

TROPHY RIDGE

PROLITE 3-PIN

QC RANGER

FIBER MAX SUPERIOR

NORTH AMERICAN ARCHERY GROUP
Peep Sight
Round disc sight with beveled center. These peeps are available in medium, large and X-large sizes.
SRP: **$2.49**

ProHunter 3-Pin Fiber Optic
This 3-pin fiber optic sight has a machined aluminum body, smoke pin guard and level. The metal fiber optic pins can be adjusted vertical individually and vertical and horizontal as a gang.
SRP: **$39.49**

ProLite 3-Pin Fiber Optic Lighted Sight
A machined aluminum sight with a light built into the pin guard. Color: Black.
SRP: **$45.99**

T-Master 4-Pin Fiber Optic
A machined aluminum sight system with four pins and a level in the base of the pin guard. Color: Black.
SRP: **$64.99**

Trophy Ridge 5-Pin Fiber Optic
This sight incorporates a SIMS

vibration dampener, Microtech and Camlock pin levers and Nitor light system. Available in Hardwoods High-Definition and Mossy Oak Break-Up camouflage. (Item 6085-065 is Custom Hardwoods model at same SRP)
SRP: **$99.99**

SAVAGE SYSTEMS
Featherweight Pendulum
This sight has twin riser mount holes so you can choose the best position. The Pendulum pin is house din a clear bracket. This sight is available in black or camouflaged.
SRP: with NightHawk Tritium pin,
. . . . **$49.95 to $79.95**
Add $10 to $15 more for camouflaged sights

Fiber Max Superior
These fixed position standard designed bow sights by Savage Systems have sturdy mounting brackets and a calibrated sight window bracket. This si... has keyless adjustment thanks to ... nut on top. Your choice of three ... pin set ups with the sight. The ... easily converted from left to ...nd use.
... hree pin **$36.95**
...e pin **$47.95**

Nighthawk Tritium pin **$62.95**
Pendulum Max
This sight has a solid mounting bracket, and the swinging pins are housed inside a polycarbonate window. Numerous pin choices are available. The Smoke Featherweight sight is similar and has a smoke clear housing around the swinging pendulum sight.
SRP: . . . . **$64.95 to $89.95**

Pendulum Super Max
The single pin sight swings on a pendulum inside the sight window and is on line to nearly 30 yards distance from your tree stand. The Nighthawk pin uses a tritium light source to enhance the fiber optics.
SRP: Nighthawk pin **$94.95**
FiberGlo pin **$69.95**

QC Ranger
This Savage System sight is fully adjustable and adjusts to the bows speed out to 70 yards. It has laser engraved yardage markings, accepts pendulum sights and comes with fiber optic or Nighthawk sight pins. The lever swings across an arch at the back of the sight to rapidly adjust to the determined yardage. The pin moves freely inside a pendulum.
SRP: **$134.95**

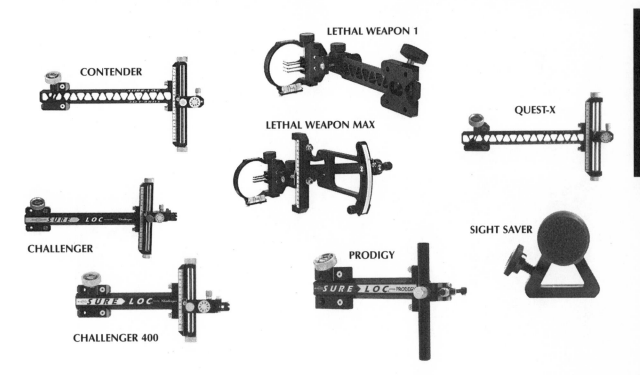

CONTENDER

LETHAL WEAPON 1

LETHAL WEAPON MAX

QUEST-X

CHALLENGER

SIGHT SAVER

CHALLENGER 400

PRODIGY

SURE-LOC
Challenger
This package include either a 400 or 550 frame in black only, choice of 6-, 9- or 12-inch extension, mounting block and hardware, offset bracket, armored 3d axis, scope rod holder, durable carrying case. Available in left and right models (must specify.)
SRP: **$177.99**

Contender
Contender is similar to the Quest-X and is offered in black only. The Contender and the Quest-X are for recurve bow use only and not to be used with a scope.
SRP: **$181.99**

EZ-Adjust Eagle Eye
This sight has a bracket like the Fiber Max and uses a smaller sight window and less pins.
SRP: **$31.95**

Lethal Weapon 1
A hunting bow sight with .0015-inch windage and elevation adjustments. A bubble can be placed on either side to check level. The windage block gives a full 1½-inch mass adjustment. Four steel pins with fiber optic in .019 and .029 sizes. Quiver mount is an accessory.
SRP: **$178.95**

Lethal Weapon 2M
SRP: **$155.95**

Lethal Weapon Max
This Sure-Loc hunting bow sight has 2 and 3 axes leveling capabilities and solid 2½-vertical slide action. Uses a lock to secure sight into position and the sight has three pins and numerous micro adjustment options.
SRP: **$229.99**

Prodigy Sight
This new target sight by Sure-Loc provides the novice target archer with a dependable starter sight. The features include elevation and windage adjustments, positive elevation locking knob and it's totally reversible from right- to left-handed. This sight is made for all bows—compound and recurves—up to 44 pounds pull. Includes a 550-size frame, 6-inch extension, mounting block and sight aperture. Available in black only.
SRP: **$89.99**

Quest-X
A target sight with no-lock vertical and horizontal tracking. Features a lightweight 5½-inch frame with 9-inch extension anodized in bright silver, black or the new Glory pattern. This sight package includes a 5.5-inch sight, a 9-inch extension and a recurve style 8/32 aperture holder with Beiter washer package. This sight also has a carrying case. Specify right or left model when ordering.
SRP: **$304.99**

Sight Saver
Designed to use the popular Simms Vibration Knobs, this mini triangle can be mounted on a sight bar to reduce damaging vibration. Does not interfere with the sight's operation or use when mounted properly.
SRP: **$24.99**

Bow Accessories Sights and Peep Systems

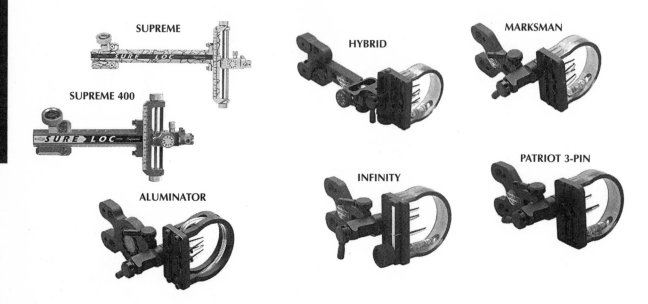

Supreme

Designed for compound bows with no-lock design and accurate tracking system. It is micro adjustable in repeatable increments up to .002-inch. Package includes either a 400 or 550 frame in silver, black or the new Glory pattern, choice of 6-, 9- or 12-inch extension, offset bracket, armored 3rd axis, scope holder, and carrying case. Must order as a right or left model.

SRP: $294.99

Supreme 400

This hunting sight has black knobs, a 6-inch extension, quiver mount and fixed pin attachment. The sights have black anodized sturdy metal surfaces. Buyer can choose from 5 brass pins or 3 fiber optic pins in this size or razor size. Package includes a 4-inch frame, 3- or 6-inch extension, mounting block, black offset bracket, quiver mount, choice of sight pins and a durable carrying case.

SRP: $294.99

Sure-Loc Challenger 400

SRP: $177.99

TOXONICS
Aluminator

Sight features all machined construction from 6061-T6 aircraft aluminum and superior light gathering capabilities with three feet of fiber optics strand housed in a durable Teflon coating. Two rows of sight pins are angled to meet perfectly in the middle of the sight. All models—three are available—feature the Aluminator sight system and quick knobs that permit finger operation.

SRP: $89.98
Model M-CT3 . . . . $104.98
Model M-CT2 . . . . $99.98

Hybrid Sight Series

This bow sight series by Toxonics have a phosphorous insert in the tinted pin guard to make pin detection easier at dawn and dusk. Add $10 extra and you purchase the camouflaged models for your hunting bow.

Hybrid III
  SRP: $39.99
Hybrid IV
  SRP: $59.99
Hybrid V
  SRP: $109.99

Infinity Sights

This sight has two fixed pins and a third adjustable pin that can be moved up and down with a quick turn of the dial. The third pin will adjust to infinite yardage settings and a yardage indicator shows distance marks around the dial. Other features include an easy adjust knobs, smoke clear sight guard and a level in the base of the sight window platform.

SRP: M-FT1 . . . . $79.98
Model M-FT3 . . . . $89.98
M-FT2 . . . . $89.98

Marksman 4-Pin

The Marksman is equipped with four long necked steel fiber optic sight pins backed by .040 fibers. The twin rows are angled to create a perfect pin alignment within the GLO-RING pin housing. Three Toxonics Marksman sight models are available, and an optional Photon light retails for $24.95.

Model M-DT1 . . . . $49.98.
Model M-DT2 . . . . $59.98

Patriot 3-Pin

SRP: $28.88

Bow Accessories Sights and Peep Systems

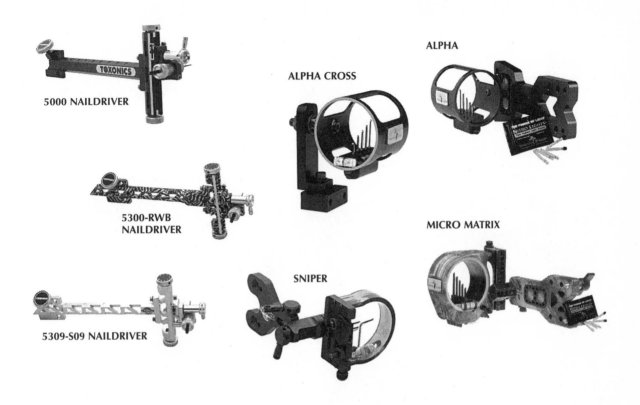

5000 NAILDRIVER

5300-RWB NAILDRIVER

5309-S09 NAILDRIVER

ALPHA CROSS

ALPHA

MICRO MATRIX

SNIPER

Naildriver Series

Sights for the tournament archers. The Naildriver series has a 10-click knob for compute generated sight tape compatibility. These sights are hand machined with a patented locking mechanism. Depress the knob for rapid movements, and twist the knob to lock the sight block and lead screw securely into position.

5000 Original Heavy Duty Naildriver
    SRP: $249.99
5309-S09 Silver Naildriver
    SRP: $299.99
5300-RWB Naildriver
    SRP: $359.99

Sniper Sights

Toxonics' Sniper sights operate with a pendulum and three-pin fiber optic system. The top pin swings and is great for tree stand bowhunting situa-tions. This sight is equipped with a level, tinted pin guard, GLO-RINGS, laser engraved yardage and windage scales. Sight must be adjusted with a hex wrench.
SRP: M-ET1 . . . . $79.89
M-ET2 . . . . $89.98

TROPHY RIDGE
Alpha

Base is for mounting on a bow's riser. This sight has vertical pins, a more open tubular sight window and is available with three or five pin design.
SRP: . . . . $74.99 to $79.99

Alpha Cross (crossbow)
SRP: . . . . $49.99 to $57.99

Micro Matrix

The prominent features of this sight include: a great field of view through the round sight window that rimmed by a reflective sight ring; clearly marked calibration markings on the sight bar and extension for adjust-ments; finger operated quick release on the mounting bracket and a level in the sight window. The pins are steel with fiber optic points. This sight is available in three and five-pin designs, with .029 and .019 size pin heads, and in right- or left-hand models. You can add Power plus lens to create magnification of the view and pins. You can install Nitro lights for low light situations. These sights are available in Mossy Oak and Realtree camouflage.
SRP: . . . . $117 to $125

Matrix (Steel pins and round sight ring)
SRP: . . . . $109 to $119

Bow Accessories Sights and Peep Systems

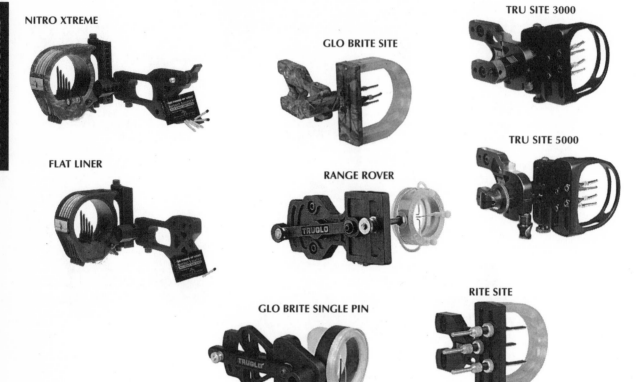

NITRO XTREME

FLAT LINER

GLO BRITE SITE

RANGE ROVER

GLO BRITE SINGLE PIN

TRU SITE 3000

TRU SITE 5000

RITE SITE

Nitro Xtreme
Covered in Realtree X-tra Grey, this sight is offered with three or five pins and a bubble in the bottom of the round sight window. A five-pack of Nitro lights are included and these miniature light sticks last up to 12 hours. The vertical pins in the sight have fiber optic tips and the fiber optic coils wrap around the round sight window.
SRP: . . . . $79 to $89

Flat Liner (w/out camo or level)
SRP: . . . . $44.99 to $49.99

TRUGLO
Glo Brite Site
The sight pins have coils of fiber optic cable wrapped around their base and are protected by a smoke colored polycarbonate pin guard. The mounting bracket holds the sight bracket with a dove-tailed grip. Two slots permit precision pin adjustments. A newer model

of this sight is available with a battery-operated light installed in the pin guard for approximately $25 more.
SRP: three-pin $32.99
    Five-pin camouflaged. $47.99

Glo Brite Single Pin
This sight has a single pin protruding up for the bottom of a light-gathering ring. The tritium coating in the pin keeps the tip glowing when light conditions drop below those collected but the 24 inches of fiber optic cable. This sight is easily adjusted and black in color.
SRP: $89.99

Range Rovers
This series of sights by TRUGLO has a finger-touch adjustment option and you can adjust the pins and sight for precise distances. The large aperture ring is 1½-inches diameter and the sight is also offered with a single pin within a rectangular pin guard.
SRP: $85.99
    single pin $64.99

Rite Site
A basic and solid bow sight by TRUGLO with three brass-based blade pins that have a rib of fiber optics along the spine. Available in black and camouflage.
SRP: black. $32.99
    camouflaged $37.99

Tru Site 5000
Constructed of machined metal, this sight offers precise micro-adjustable windage and elevation adjustments. Four pins are included and can be adjusted inside two slots on the pin bracket.
SRP: $72.99
    with tritium sight pins $92.99

Tru Site 3000 (Without micro-adjust)
SRP: $62.99
    with a tritium pin $82.99

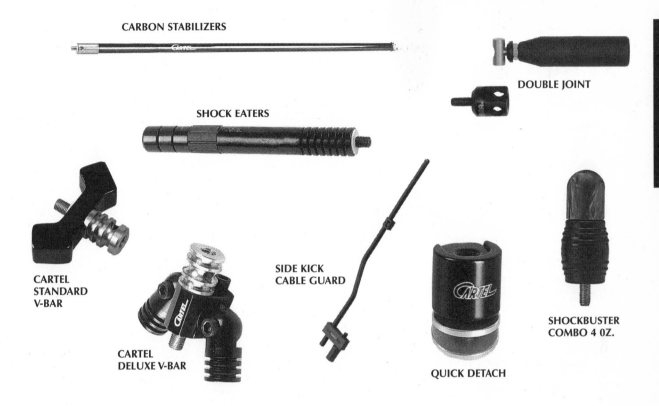

CARBON STABILIZERS

SHOCK EATERS

DOUBLE JOINT

CARTEL
STANDARD
V-BAR

CARTEL
DELUXE V-BAR

SIDE KICK
CABLE GUARD

QUICK DETACH

SHOCKBUSTER
COMBO 4 OZ.

CARTEL
Aluminum/Carbon Stabilizers
SRP: 1-inch diameter, 26-, 28-
and 30-inch length $79.95
same as 06213 in 10- and
12-inch length $45.00

Carbon and Carbon Aluminum Stabilizers
SRP: $49.95
  ½-inch diameter model . . . $64.95
  10- and 12-inch. $29.95
  ½-inch diameter model . . . $49.95

Hydraulic Carbon/Aluminum Stabilizers
SRP: 1-inch diameter, 26-, 28-
and 30-inch length
  black. $89.95
  camo $99.95
7-, 10- and 12-inch length
  black. $49.95
  camo . . . . $ 55.00

Deluxe V-Bar
This unit attaches to your bow's
threaded bushing and permits the
installation of two stabilizers at once.
Can be set at any angle.

SRP:. $65
  standard V-Bar. $24.95

Shock Eaters
This series of stabilizers has a flexible
rubber ring near the tip to reduce bow
recoil and shock. These stabilizers have
vibration dispersal rings, three stack-
able end weights and hardened $\frac{5}{16}$-inch
threads for connection with bow's
threaded bushing. Available sizes
include: 2-, 4-, 7-, 10-, and 12-inch.
SRP: . . . . $12.95 to $34.95

Stabilizer Quick Detach
A new item for Cartel in 2001.
This unit permits archer to remove
stabilizers and extenders from bow
or V-bars with quick and easy quarter
turn. Unique design keeps stabilizer
tight through shooting sessions.
SRP. $17.95

COBRA
Double Joint
Use this item to disconnect and remove
a stabilizer for storage or transportation.
Simply turn the disconnect and remove
the brass connector, or turn the brass
connector to swing the stabilizer out of

the way like a knuckle. Stabilizers can
be moved up to 90 degrees.
SRP: $6.60
  camouflage double joint . . . $8.11

Shockbuster
Designed to be placed between accessories and bow, this mini shock
threads into AMO-ATA standard
threaded holes and then accepts
threaded studs.
SRP: $8.11

Shockbuster Stabilizer Combo
(4-, 6- and 8-ounce sizes placed on
the front or back of the bow)
SRP: 4 ounce. $17.99
  6 ounce. $18.99
  8 ounce. $19.99

Side Kick Cable Guard and Threaded Cable Guard
One guard attaches to the bow's front
or rear stabilizer hole and is adjustable
from 10 to 13 inches long. The other
model screws directly into the bow's
handle and has a non-glare finish.
SRP: adjustable $9.39
  standard threaded $6.19

Bow Accessories Stabilizers

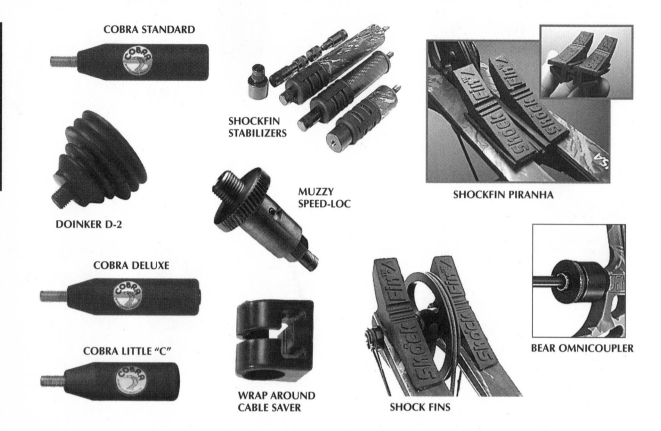

COBRA STANDARD

SHOCKFIN STABILIZERS

DOINKER D-2

MUZZY SPEED-LOC

SHOCKFIN PIRANHA

COBRA DELUXE

COBRA LITTLE "C"

WRAP AROUND CABLE SAVER

SHOCK FINS

BEAR OMNICOUPLER

Standard Stabilizer
This 12-ounce stabilizer has a durable non-glare matte finish over steel alloy construction.
SRP: $3.81

Deluxe Stabilizer (12-ounce, drilled and tapped receiver hole in the front for standard AMO/ ATA threaded stud.)
SRP: $4.99

Little "C" Stabilizer (8-ounce steel alloy, matte black finish.)
SRP: $3.70

Wrap Around Cable Saver
This cable guard slide wraps securely around the cable guard and reduces cable wear while it quiets the bow during release and draw.
SRP: $1.19

DOINKER
Doinker D-2
A lightweight mini stabilizer that weighs 2.3 ounces and has shock absorbing ribs. It can be used solo or attached on the tip or as a base for other stabilizers. Made of rubber.
SRP: $15.99

5-Inch Doinker
SRP: $36.95
Original Doinkers (4- or 7-inch, black or camouflage)
SRP: $41.95
Standard Doinkers (Fit between bow and other stabilizers)
SRP:. $16

GLOBAL RESOURCES
Shock Fins
These vibration and noise reduction fins are mounted on the tip of the bow limbs. They can be installed inside or outside on a bow limb with adhesive strips that are included.
SRP: 4 fins $18

Shockfin Piranha
These vibration reduction fins are joined by a flexible base that can be inserted in between split limbs on a quad limb bow.
SRP: per pair $26.96

Shockfin Stabilizers
These lightweight stabilizes are made of carbon and use inverted piston weight technology.
SRP: $34.99

MUZZY
Muzzy Speed-Loc
This adapter makes changing a stabilizer a snap. It can also be used to add a string tracker or to quickly break down your bow for easy storage and transportation. Made by the Muzzy broadhead company. (Item 400 and 400-Black)
SRP: $19.92

NORTH AMERICAN ARCHERY GROUP
Bear OmniCoupler
Used to quickly attach and remove any standard threaded stabilizer from any bow for transportation and storage
SRP: $29.99

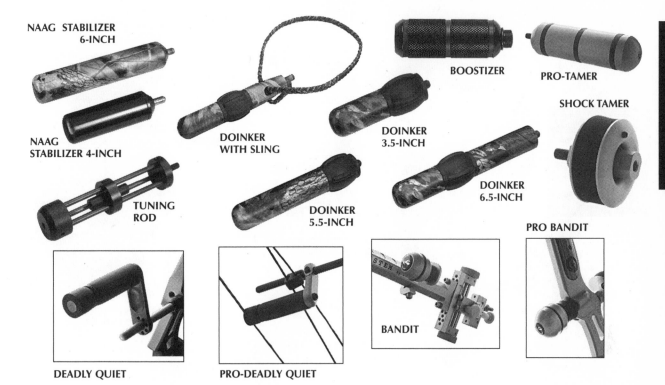

NAAG STABILIZER 6-INCH

NAAG STABILIZER 4-INCH

DOINKER WITH SLING

BOOSTIZER

PRO-TAMER

SHOCK TAMER

DOINKER 3.5-INCH

TUNING ROD

DOINKER 5.5-INCH

DOINKER 6.5-INCH

PRO BANDIT

BANDIT

DEADLY QUIET

PRO-DEADLY QUIET

Doinker 3.5-Inch

This 3.5-inch stabilizers fits into a bow's standard threaded receptacle. Available in Mossy Oak Break-Up, Custom Hardwoods, and Realtree Hardwoods and Hardwoods High Definition camouflage patterns. Features a rubberized spacer/bushing at the rear.
Weight: 3.6 ounces
SRP: **$29.99**

Doinker 5.5-Inch

Weight: 6 ounces
SRP: **$34.99**

Doinker 6.5-Inch

Weight: 7.2 ounces
SRP: **$38.99**

Doinker with Sling

Weight: 8.4 ounces
SRP: **$39.99**

Stabilizer 6-Inch

This camouflaged tube-type stabilizer is one solid piece and is distributed by the North American Archery Group. It's available in Mossy Oak Break-Up and Realtree Hardwoods High Definition camo. Also available in black.
Weight: 5.3 ounces
SRP: black. **$9.49**
camouflaged **$13.99**

Stabilizer 4-Inch

SRP: **$7.49**

Tuning Rod

An innovative design with end caps connected by three rods with a balance weight suspended between caps.
Weight: 6.4 ounces
SRP: **$34.99**

SAUNDERS ARCHERY EQUIPMENT COMPANY
Bandit

A mini cap stabilizer and shock absorber that can be used solo or added to a stabilizer. With a dovetail bracket you can add this unit to a sight extension bar. This is an innovative unit you must see and try to believe.
SRP: **$24.95**
bracket attachment **$9.95**

Pro Bandit (Two micro caps encased in visco-elastic polymer)
SRP: **$38.95**

Boostizer

A micro stabilizer than can enhance the performance of other units or used alone. It has three patented internal

absorbers. This unit is available in black only.
SRP: **$28.95**

Deadly Quiet and Pro-Deadly Quiet

This system from Saunders Archery quiets the bow's string when the string reaches it. The units mount on a cable guard and the string stops when it reaches the rear of the Deadly quiet. This unit mounts on a standard 3/8-inch cable guard rod.
SRP: Deadly Quiet. **$19.95**
pro model **$34.95**

Shock Tamer

This stabilizer has an internal chamber that's a death trap for shock and vibration. An adjustment plate neutralizes stabilizer sag and energy is converted to heat via a patented visco elastic polymer. Available in black, titanium gray and chameleon camouflage. A stand off unit can be installed on the bow to act as a base.
SRP: **$98.95**
stand off base **$10.95**

Pro-Tamer (Two cylinders on floating delivery rod)
SRP: **54.95**

Bow Accessories Stabilizers

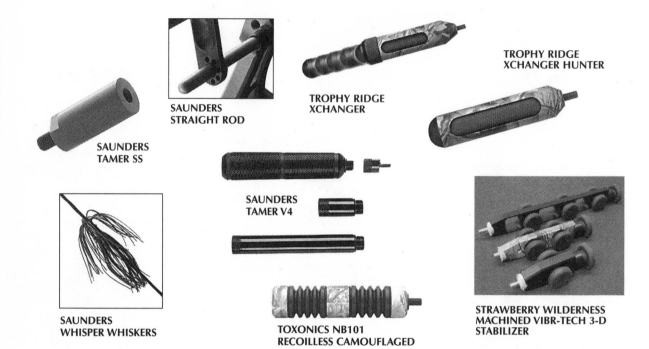

SAUNDERS TAMER SS

SAUNDERS STRAIGHT ROD

TROPHY RIDGE XCHANGER

TROPHY RIDGE XCHANGER HUNTER

SAUNDERS TAMER V4

SAUNDERS WHISPER WHISKERS

TOXONICS NB101 RECOILLESS CAMOUFLAGED

STRAWBERRY WILDERNESS MACHINED VIBR-TECH 3-D STABILIZER

Tamer SS (Mini version of the Pro-Tamer, 6.4 ounces)
SRP: $42.95

Straight Rod
A short aluminum rod that's ideal for mounting a deadly quiet unit from the rear port when front mounting interferes with sights.
SRP: $8.95

Torque Tamer and Tamer V4
These dynamic stabilizers use three internal shock chambers to kill shock and vibration. The tamer is not sensitive to cold, cannot leak and has no metal-to-metal moving parts. The torque tamer is 6.5 inches long and weighs 9 ounces. The Tamer V4 can be made into: a 5-inch unit weighing 9.5 ounces; a 6.25 inch unit weighing 10.4 ounces; a 9.25 inch unit weighing 12.2 ounces or a 10.5 inch system weighing 13.1 ounces.
SRP: Torque Tamer $28.95
SRP: Tamer V4 . . . . $45.95

Whisper Whiskers
The durable and waterproof rubber whiskers can be tied to the bow's string to provide quietness. Available in assorted colors or black.
SRP: $2.45

STRAWBERRY WILDERNESS ARCHERY PRODUCTS
Machined Vibr-Tech 3-D Stabilizer
An odd looking bow stabilizer that uses a series of four Sims Limb Savers to stop noise and vibration. The body of this unit is machined from 6061 T-6 aluminum and three cut outs reduce the weight. Available colors include red, purple, blue and black. The stabilizer is 12 inches long and weighs 9.9 ounces.
SRP: $89.95

Machined Vibr-Tech Stabilizer
Similar to the 3-D stabilizer (above) but the base is solid and five Sims Limb Savers are mounted on the camouflaged base. This unit is 7 inches long and weighs 9.5 ounces.
SRP: $63

TOXONICS
Recoilless Stabilizers
These Toxonics stabilizers work to offset the recoil of the release as well as dampen the vibration of the bow throughout the shot cycle. The stabilizers do not use hydraulics or oil, but do use an open cell foam piston and center shaft. Silicon rubber boots help with the dampening process. Several

models are available:
NB-100 Recoiless
black. $29.99
NB101 Recoilless
camouflaged $36.99
NB-105 Extender
SRP: $14.99

TROPHY RIDGE
Xchanger
This new stabilizer uses Sorbodome and can be changed in length to fine tune your bow. The unit is lightweight, effective, 100% fluid free and can be telescoped from 6½- to 10½-inches long. It has a camouflaged exterior.
SRP: black. $64.99
camouflaged $69.99

Xchanger Hunter
Similar to the Xchanger but it does not lengthen. This stabilizer weighs 3 ounces and has open celled Sorbodome foam.
SRP: black. $44.99
camouflaged $49.99

Bow Accessories Stabilizers

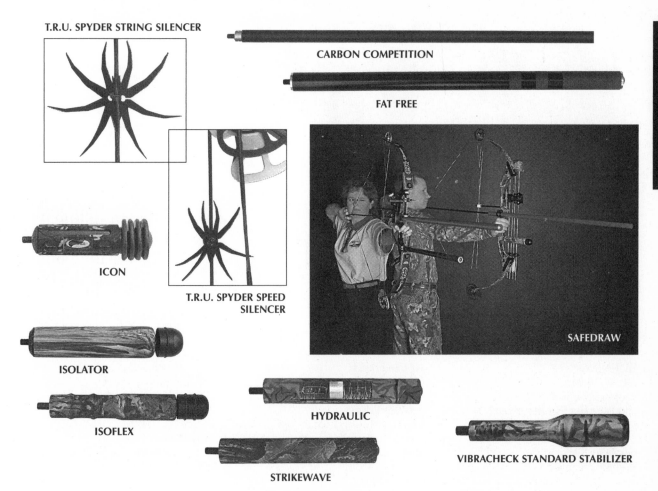

T.R.U. SPYDER STRING SILENCER

CARBON COMPETITION

FAT FREE

ICON

T.R.U. SPYDER SPEED SILENCER

SAFEDRAW

ISOLATOR

ISOFLEX

HYDRAULIC

STRIKEWAVE

VIBRACHECK STANDARD STABILIZER

T.R.U. BALL STABILIZERS
T.R.U. Ball Spyder Silencers
Made from durable Hypalon, these spider shaped silencers help gain bow speed and silence string twangs. The speed silencer attaches with a ball system and the string silencer attaches with serving thread.

SRP: String silencer per four . . $7.99
     Speed silencer per four . . . $14.99

VIBRACHECK
Carbon Competition Stabilizers
These are designed for serious competitors. Available lengths include: 8, 20, 24, 28 and 34 inches long. Weights range from 2 to 6 ounces.
SRP: $124.95

Fat Free Stabilizers (3-D tournament, 18, 26 and 38 inches. 7, 8 and 9 ounces)
SRP: $125

Hydraulic and Strikewave.
The Hydraulic is 6.5 inches long, weighs 8 ounces and has an inner spring and weight. The Strikewave is the same length, weighs 6 ounces and has gel inside.
SRP: $29.95

Icon
A small unit that's 7 inches long and weighs 7 ounces. It has a nippled tip and uses VibraSORB gel inside an aluminum sleeve.
SRP: $39.95

Isolator
This unit is rubber coated and has a machined aluminum body. The inside is filled with VibaSORB gel and a 2-ounce activating weight.
SRP: $54.95
Isoflex. $44.95

Safedraw
This training aid by Virbacheck permits you to draw and fire your bow without an arrow. It is excellent for target panic therapy and can be used in a bow shop when customers are trying a bow. It mounts on a bow's rest and attaches to the bowstring. The shooter can use a bow exactly like it was being released at the target range.
SRP:. $130

Standard Stabilizer
This unit is 5 inches long, weighs 5 ounces and is machined from solid aluminum stock.
SRP: $18.95

3-D Pro
These 10-inch long stabilizers by Vibracheck are either spring loaded or have Vibrasorb gel.
SRP:. $69

Bow Accessories Strings

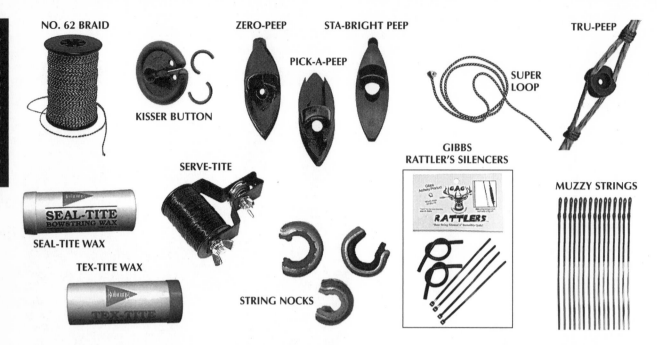

NO. 62 BRAID
KISSER BUTTON
ZERO-PEEP
PICK-A-PEEP
STA-BRIGHT PEEP
TRU-PEEP
SUPER LOOP
SERVE-TITE
SEAL-TITE WAX
TEX-TITE WAX
STRING NOCKS
GIBBS RATTLER'S SILENCERS
MUZZY STRINGS

BOHNING
No. 62 Braid
This material is durable Spectra and Polyester blended together. The polyester grips the bowstring and the Spectra rides on the outside for durability. Great for finishing bow strings. Available in .018-, .021- and .025-inch diameters.
SRP: $22.34

Kisser Button
This lightweight kisser button is easy to install and use.
SRP: $1.97

Seal-Tite Wax
Designed for high tensile bowstrings, this wax and silicone lubricates and holds strands together. 1 ounce tube.
SRP: $2.39

Serve-Tite String Server
You can adjust the tension and create smooth thread flow with this device. Mono and nylon serving models are available. Thread is also offered to fit each unit.
SRP: $18.66
mono thread, per spool $4.99
nylon thread, per spool $5.25

String Nocks
Available in target (blue), cam (red) and Hunter (black) models to fit string

sizes and needs.
SRP: per 6 . . . . $2.87

Tex-Tite Wax
A natural base wax for all bow strings. It is not sticky when cool. 1 oz. tube.
SRP: $2.22

Zero Peep
This standard peep is oval in shape, fits in the string and aligns with a tube and clip that are provided.
SRP: $6.99

Pick-A-Peep (Multiple adjustments)
SRP: $7.99

Sta-Bright Peep (Extra-large hole for low light conditions)
SRP: $6.99

GIBBS ARCHERY GEAR
Rattler's Bow String Silencers
These rubber tubes are woven and tied onto a bow string to reduce vibration and humming. Makes a unique rattlesnake rattler pattern when applied per directions.
SRP: $4.99

Super Loop
These loops can be affixed to a bowstring and used with a release aid to prevent string and serving wear.

Multiple colors are available.
SRP: per pair $4.99

JIM FLETCHER ARCHERY AIDS
Bow Wax
This specially formulated bow wax keeps strings moist while keeping water out. It extends the life of your bowstring.
SRP: $3.20

Tru-Peep Sights
These peeps fit into the string and are used to sight pins. The aluminum peeps are lightweight and provide a shaded hole at the draw. Available sizes include: hunter $\frac{1}{8}$-inch, Large $\frac{1}{16}$-inch, small $\frac{3}{16}$-inch and micro $\frac{1}{32}$-inch hole. A new Super Hunter model has a $\frac{3}{16}$-inch hole.
SRP: $3.50

MUZZY
Muzzy Strings
Numerous styles and colors are available. Additional charges are incurred for 450-plus braided centers, one color and two-color strings.
SRP: standard Dacron compound
bowstrings $9.95
traditional recurve and
longbows strings 9.95
Fast-Flite standard strings. . . . $51.95
Yoke System cables $27.95

BOW ACCESSORIES

C.W. ERICKSON'S CHRONOGRAPH STAND

C.W. ERICKSON'S OUTDOOR CHRONOGRAPH STAND

C.W. ERICKSON'S PAPER TUNING RACK

GOLDEN KEY-FUTURA QUIET ENHANCING KIT

C.W. ERICKSON'S EQUALIZER BOW PRESS

C.W. ERICKSON'S WORKBENCH BOW VISE

C.W. Erickson's Mfg. Chronograph Stand

This adjustable stand and base are lightweight and will securely and steadily hold a chronograph. Height adjustment is from 32- to 60-inches tall.

SRP: $54.99

Equalizer Double-Action Pull Lever Bow Press

This press is fully adjustable to hold any bow. It's quick, simple to operate and safe. Two rubber rollers protect the bow's limbs. Weighs 23 pounds.

SRP: $144.89

Outdoor Chronograph Stand

This stand spikes into the ground to hold a chronograph securely in place. Height adjustment is from 32- to 60-inches tall.

SRP: $42.99

Paper Tuning Rack

This rack hold paper steady while the shooter releases arrows and checks flight alignment. Provides a 20x18-inch shooting face and uses 18-inch freezer paper. Instructions and one
roll of paper are included.

SRP: $99.96

Workbench Fully-Adjustable Bow Vise

Vise is secured to the edge of a workbench and grasps the limbs of any style bow. Can rotate the bow up to 360-degrees and will hold all bows, including crossbows.

SRP: $46.99

Golden Key-Futura Bow Quiet Enhancing Kit

This complete kit include all the items you need to silence a bow's rest, accessories and shelf. Includes adhesive felt, shrink tubes, eliminator buttons and string silencers.

SRP:. $20

Bow Accessories Tuning Aids and Tools

COMPLETE TUNING KIT

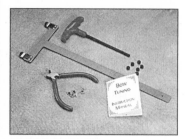

BASIC TUNING KIT

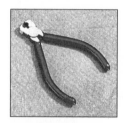

NOK SET PLIERS

QUICK NOK SHOOTING LOOP

DIGITAL GRAIN SCALE

HANSON BOW SCALE

SIMS LIMB SAVERS

METAL BOW SQUARE

Complete Tuning Kit
This bow kit includes a pocket tuning guide and instructional video to tell you how it's done, then a Tru-Center gauge, metal bow square and Nok-Set pliers will help you do it. Noks are included.
SRP:. $60

Basic Tuning Kit (Lacking the Tru-Center gauge)
SRP:. $18

DGS Digital Grain Scale
Precision weigh tips, broadheads and arrows to assist with proper selection and tuning. This electronic scale is a must for creating precision arrows. It will handle laods up to 750 grains. Has an Led digital displayand includes two precion weights for checking and calibrating. Can operate on a 9-Volt battery or AC adapter.
SRP:. $285

Hanson Bow Scale
These quality scales are used to determine a bow's draw weight and other needs. One scale ranges to 100 pounds and the other model will accommodate and record up to 300 pounds accurately.
SRP: 100-pound $78
300-pound. $85

MatchPoint Tuning Kit
Chuck Adams designed this bow and arrow tuning kit. It's features include a step-by-step tuning guide, three matchpoints, tackle box arrow rollers, tuning matchstrips, tuning marker and storage box. Matchpoint weights can be configured to duplicate and broadhead blade design and weight.
SRP: $24.99

Metal Bow Square
A one-piece solid square used for correctly setting nocks. Blue.
SRP:. $8

Nok Set Pliers
These are must have pliers for setting and removing nocks on a bowstring. The pliers are constructed of quality steel and have comfort grip handle wraps.
SRP:. $8

Quick Nok Shooting Loop
Eliminate string torque and serving wear with this easy to install nylon cord. It's strong and works well with all models of release aids. It's available in two diameters: 1¹⁄₆- and ¹⁄₈-inch.
SRP:. $9

Sims Limb Savers
These mushroom shaped rubber buttons attach to a bows limbs and reduce shock, vibration and noise. Can be installed on split or solid limbs (must select proper model). These units are lightweight and will not interfere with strings or cables.
SRP: solid. $15

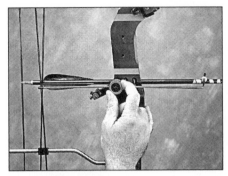

TRU-CENTER GAUGE

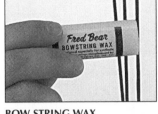

BOW STRING WAX

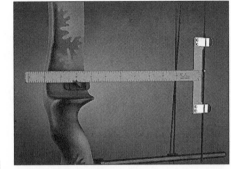

NAAG BOW SQUARE

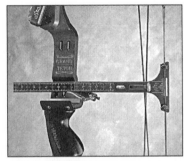

TAKE-DOWN BOW SQUARE

T-WRENCH

SWINGARM CABLE GUARD

NOCKING POINT PLIERS

Take-Down Bow Square
This square folds for easy and compact storage, plus it has levels to help determine proper string and sight alignment.
SRP:. $14

Tru-Center Gauge
Use this thin wire gauge to determine your bow's center shot. This model is improved and straddles the rest's mounting bolt.
SRP:. $15

T-Wrench
This is the same wrench used by the pro shops. It's a 3/16-inch hex wrench solidly attached to a large molded handle. It is easy to use to adjust a bow's draw weight.
SRP:. $7

NORTH AMERICAN ARCHERY GROUP Bow String Wax
String wax helps increase life of your bow's string and reduce fraying and water absorption that can affect accuracy and arrow flight.
SRP: $3.49

Bow Square
Check and adjust your nock's alignment against the arrow rest placement as you tune your bow. Color: blue.
SRP: $6.49

Nocking Point Pliers
The green rubber-coated grips on these pliers help assure a firm grip and precision nock alignment.
SRP: $5.49

Recurve Bow Stringer
Protect your recurve's tips and safely install the string with this system.
SRP: $11.99

Upper Mount SwingArm Cable Guard
This cable guard has a micro-adjust system and will mount on most bows.
SRP: $39.99

PROCHRONO (photo on p.260)
ProChrono Digital Chronograph
Features an expanded shooting area that's nearly two times the size of comparably priced models. Measures velocities from 56 to 9,999 feet per second and runs on a single .9-volt battery. Shoot in all weather since this chronograph operates in temperatures as low as 32° and as high as 100° Fahrenheit. Allows you to review 50 shots with power-down memory (review at home), high and low velocity settings, standard deviation, number of shots, average velocity, deletes current velocity and even has a printer interface so you can hook it to a printer to get a hard copy of the data. Shows metric or fps scales and features durable plastic diffusers. Measures just 16 x 3¼ inches. Mounting hole thread measures ¼ x 20 inches.
SRP: $99.99

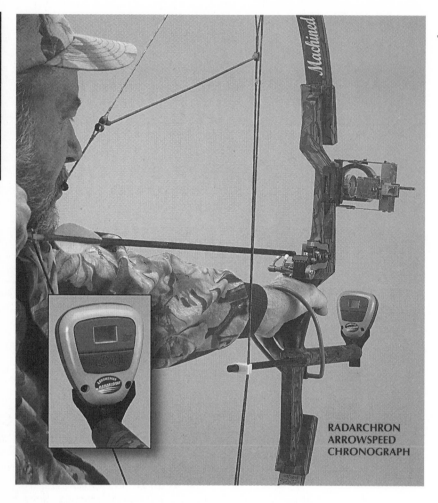

RADARCHRON
ARROWSPEED
CHRONOGRAPH

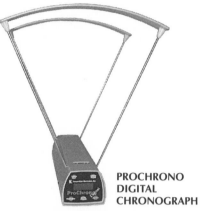

PROCHRONO
DIGITAL
CHRONOGRAPH

ARCHERY SHOOTING CHRONY F-1
& BETA-CHRONY

R.S. ARCHERY
ArrowSpeed Chronograph

This chronograph is used by many pro shops when archers want to fine tune or enhance the performance of their bows. It's a small Doppler radar that measures the speed of the arrow as it is shot from the bow. The unit can be attached to the end of a stabilizer or to an extension rod that is provided.
SRP: **$142.55**

Bow Leveling Tuning System

This vise is used by the pros to hold bows in an upright position while offering the flexibility to hold the bow horizontally or vertically. A level tuning kit snaps to the string to check for horizontal and vertical positioning. Multiple accessories are offered. Call 800-444-9619 for details.
SRP: **$89.95**

SHOOTING CHRONY INC.
Archery Shooting Chrony F-1
& Beta-Chrony

Check velocities ranging from 30 fps to 7,000 fps with any Chrony Model and within 0.5 percent accuracy with any projectile: arrow, bullet, pellet, etc. LCD read-outs stay on the screen until next shot is fired. The Beta Chrony features a 60-shot memory (divided into six strings of 10 shots each); each string gives you Hi, Lo and Average velocity, ES and SD; it has a permanent memory for at-home data retrieval. All Chronys have steel housing for strength and less expansion/contraction deviation than plastic housings. Weight 2.5 lbs
Shooting F-1 Chronograph
SRP: **$79.99**

Shooting Beta Chronograph
SRP: **$109.99**

Shooting Chrony Beta Master
SRP: **$139.99**

SPORTS SENSORS, INC.
Radarchron Arrowspeed
Chronograph

Using microwave Doppler radar, the RADARchron is accurate within +/- 2percentfrom 150 to 450 feet-per-second. LCD display toggles between hundredths and tenths of fps units. A threaded adapter attaches to the end of most stabilizers. The included extension rod can be used in place of stabilizer and connected directly to bow, and it can be carried anywhere, thanks to an ultra-compact size. Compatible with both aluminum and graphite/carbon arrows. Operates on a 3-volt lithium battery (included).
SRP: **$99.95**

ARROWS

AIM Arrows

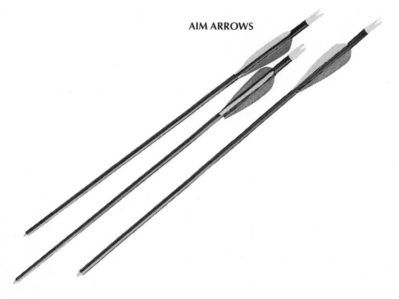

AIM ARROWS

AIM ARROWS
These fiberglass target arrows are distributed by AIM and are perfect for kids, camps and schools. Fletched with vanes and available in 26-, 28- and 30-inch lengths.
SRP: per _ gross box $175

Beman Arrows

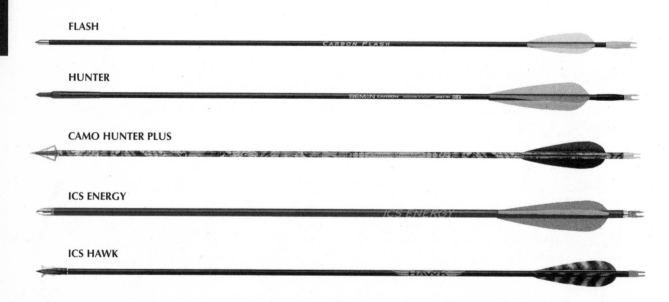

FLASH

HUNTER

CAMO HUNTER PLUS

ICS ENERGY

ICS HAWK

CARBON FLASH
Similar to Carbon Hunter with outside diameters of $^{13}/_{64}$ and $^{14}/_{64}$.
SRP: $40.32

CARBON HUNTER
Made of pultruded carbon fibers and designed for hunters and target shooters. Outside diameter sizes are $^{15}/_{64}$ and $^{16}/_{64}$.
SRP: $65.35

CARBON METAL MATRIX
These carbon shafts are available in 460, 400, 340 and 300 sizes and have plus/minus .003-inch straightness. The shafts have an aluminum core and carbon fiber outer layers.
SRP: $137.25

ICS CAMO HUNTER PLUS
Similar to the ICS Trebark shafts but coated in Mossy Oak Break Up.
SRP: per dozen $89.71

ICS ENERGY
Super priced arrow for recreational use. Sizes include: 1000, 900, 780, 690, 600, 520, 460, 410 and 360.
SRP: $70.25

ICS HAWK
Affordable priced and excellent for 3-D shooting describes the Hawk. Super nocks are installed along with RPS point inserts.
SRP: $66.85

ARROWS

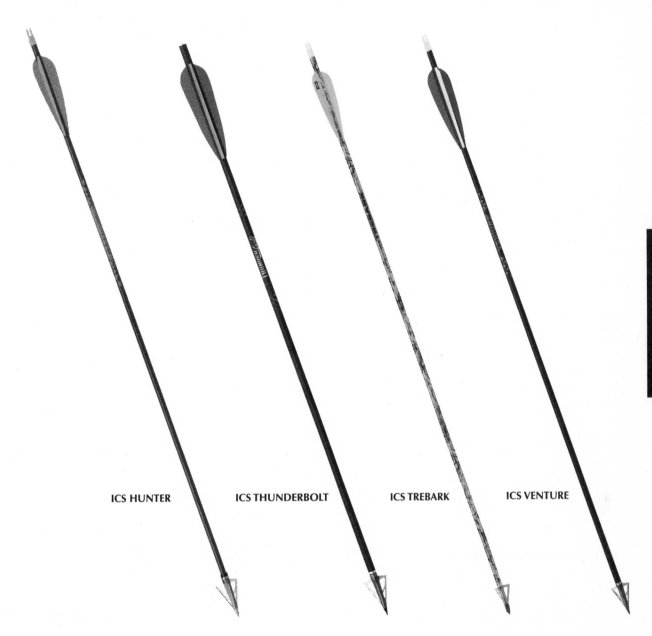

ICS HUNTER · ICS THUNDERBOLT · ICS TREBARK · ICS VENTURE

ICS HUNTER

These arrows feature a multi-layer design and plus/minus 1.5-inch straightness. The shafts have a partial graphic green camo pattern.
SRP: per dozen $73.92

ICS THUNDERBOLT

Designed for crossbow use with a $^{22}/_{64}$ths outside diameter and offered in 20- and 22-inch lengths.
SRP: 20-inch length $48.10
22-inch length $48.50

ICS TREBARK

Beman's ICS Trebark shafts are an addition to their camouflaged hunting shaft selection. The camouflage coating on these shafts offer the ultimate in concealment with a PhotoFusion finish that's protected with Beman's Infinity Performance System (IPS). Shaft options include: 500-size shafts that weigh 7.9 grains per inch, 400-size at 9.1 gpi, 340-size at 10 gpi and 300-size at 10.1 gpi. The shafts are constructed with longitudinal unidi-

rectional carbon fiber layers over high strength composite fibers for better mass. The IPS coating also provides a more consistent spine and heavier weight for the shaft. Inserts and Super Nocks are included.
SRP: per dozen $76.18

ICS VENTURE

These Beman shafts represent value and multi-carbon layering. Sizes include 500, 400, 340 and 300.
SRP: $59.47

Blackhawk Archery Arrows

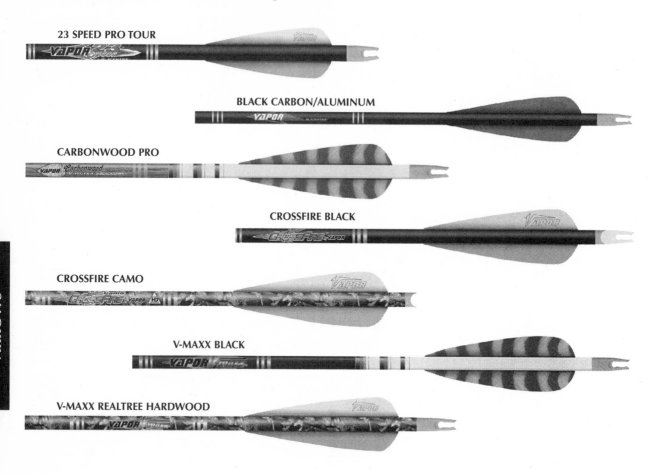

23 SPEED PRO TOUR

BLACK CARBON/ALUMINUM

CARBONWOOD PRO

CROSSFIRE BLACK

CROSSFIRE CAMO

V-MAXX BLACK

V-MAXX REALTREE HARDWOOD

23 SPEED PRO TOUR ARROWS

These top quality sahfts are selected
for tournament archers who demand
precision arrows with exact tolerances
and weights.

SRP: shafts only, per dozen . $119.95
with vanes, per dozen $124.95
with shafts per half-dozen . . . $62.95

BLACK CARBON/ ALUMINUM SHAFTS

These Blackhawk arrows have carbon
layers wrapped over an aluminum core.
SRP: shafts, per dozen $99.95
with vanes, per dozen $104.95
six pack with vanes $64.95

CAMO PRO SERIES

Blackhawk's more economical carbon
arrows with less exact tolerances.
These arrows shoot and fly with precision. Offered in Timber HD,
Hardwoods Green and X-Tra gray.
SRP: shafts, per dozen $79.95
with vanes, per dozen $84.95
with vanes, half-dozen $59.95

CARBONWOOD PRO SERIES

V-Maxx Carbonwood series shafts with
a wood-grain finish and flashy crest
are offered for those who want arrows
with a traditional look.
SRP: Carbonwoods six-pack
with vanes. $59.95
Carbonwood Pro shafts or arrows,
per dozen $84.95

CROSSFIRE CROSSBOW ARROWS

These shafts are designed for high performance crossbows and utilize 120-
gram unidirectional carbon material
along with the EXP 120 manufacturing
process for parallel seams. The shafts
are offered in one spine—the 30.06
series—and are rated for use with
95- to 200-pound crossbows. Crossfire
shafts yield a plus/minus .004 straightness and a larger outside diameter of
22/64 or .344-inch.
SRP: standard black, per doz.. $64.95
Hardwoods HD green camo,
per dozen $69.95

V-MAXX 22/64 SERIES

Blackhawk's V-Maxx arrows are
specially designed for the hunter
who uses fixed-blade broadheads.
The V-Maxx series of shafts offers a
larger $2/64$ outside diameter that makes
them easier to remove from most foam
targets. The shafts have 10 grains-
per-inch weight and permit maximum
helical fletching and rest clearance
while providing forgiving tuning
capabilities.
SRP: Realtree's Hardwood HD green
or Standard black shafts,
per dozen . . . $99.95 and $104.95
six-pack $58.95

Browning Archery Arrows

BROWNING BULLETS

MICRO BROWNING BULLETS

BROWNING BULLETS

Carbon and fiberglass combination arrows are still in production and becoming available in a wider range. Browning's Bullet hunting arrows are now offered in 30/50—7.4 grains per inch—and 55/70—9.6 grains per inch models. These four-layer shafts utilize multi-directional, high-grade carbon fibers oriented at 90-degrees over a fiberglass unidirectional core. Each shaft is precision ground to a .005-inch straightness. The 30/50 shafts are

fletched with three 2½-inch Duravanes and the 55/70s have three 4-inch Duravanes. For those who like to build their own arrows, 30/50 and 55/70 shafts are now available for $72.95 per 12-pack without fletching. If you want to micro tune your arrows, Browning also offers weight tubes in 3 grains per inch and 2 grains per inch weights. These are available in a dozen per pack for approximately $15.
SRP: per six standard arrow . . $47.95

MICRO BROWNING BULLETS

Browning's Micro Bullets are designed for young archers, bows shooting lower poundages, and for shooters with shorter draw lengths. Large quantity arrow packs are offered for youth camps and situations where many arrows are needed.
SRP: per half-dozen $21.95
72 Micro Bullet arrow pack,
**   per arrow $2.69**

Carbon Express Arrows

CX CROSSBOLTS

CX CRESTED SHAFTS

CX CROSSBOLTS

These Carbon express arrows are designed for crossbows and offered in 20- and 22-inch lengths. Available with vanes or feathers.
SRP: with vanes, per dozen . . $37.50
with feathers, per dozen. $44

CX DIPPED AND CRESTED SHAFTS

Each shaft is dipped in scratch resistant white and hand crested. Standard weight sizes are available and crest color options include red, green and orange.
SRP: $113.25

CX HUNTERS

Similar to the CX shafts but camouflaged and coated with Carbon Express' durable BuffTuff. Weights include: 200, 300, and 400. All internal components are used in construction.
SRP: shafts, per dozen $188.50
**   with vanes, per dozen . . . $141.54**
72 bulk pack with vanes,
**   per arrow $11.55**

Carbon Express Arrows

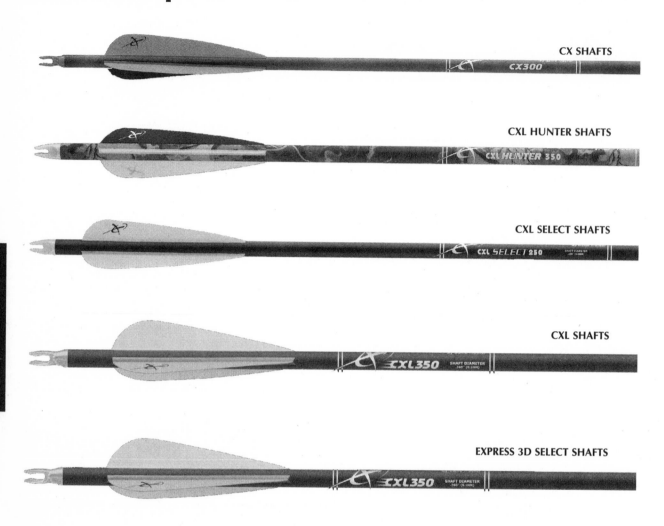

CX SHAFTS

CXL HUNTER SHAFTS

CXL SELECT SHAFTS

CXL SHAFTS

EXPRESS 3D SELECT SHAFTS

CX SHAFTS

These all-carbon shafts have internal components and are available in 100, 200, 300 and 400 weights and offer plus/minus .003-inch straightness. These are also available as fletched arrows wit feathers or vanes.

SRP: crested shafts, per doz. $133.25
   with vanes, per doz. $120.68
   with feathers, per doz. . . . $133.85
72 bulk pack, per arrow $9.90

CXL HUNTER SHAFTS

A large diameter shaft designed for speed, accuracy and maximum penetration. Coated with Buff Tuff and camouflaged. These are available as shafts only or fletched with vanes. Weights: 250 and 350. The 250 series features a ³/₆₄-inch diameter and weighs 11 grains per inch. The 350 series weighs 11.5 grains per inch. Both shafts are now available in Advantage. BuffTuff coating seals the arrow shaft's pores, increases its strength and makes the arrow quieter in flight. Weight tubes can also be easily installed in the CXL Hunters and are $10.50 per six for archers who want to fine-tune their arrows.

SRP: shafts. $126.60
   with vanes. $144.71

CXL SELECT SHAFTS

A group of hand selected shafts that meet the NAA equipment rules and have a maximum shaft diameter of 9.3mm.

SRP: per dozen $139.99

CXL SHAFTS

These Carbon Express shafts are available in 150, 250 and 350 weights and have plus/minus .006-inch straightness.

SRP: $104.94

EXPRESS 3D SELECT SHAFTS

The 3-D Select series—weights include 100, 200, 300 and 400— are handmatched per package for weight and straightness to ensure consistency. Each shaft is plus/minus 1 grain per package.

SRP: per dozen $116.50

Carbon Express Arrows

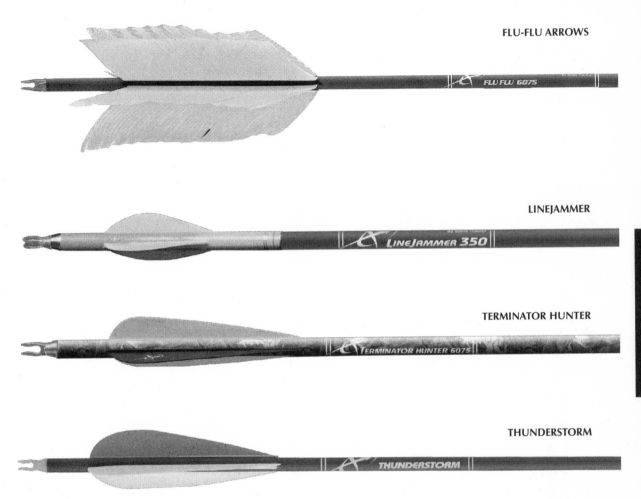

FLU-FLU ARROWS

LINEJAMMER

TERMINATOR HUNTER

THUNDERSTORM

FLU-FLU ARROWS
Great for hunting small game, these arrows feature six 4¼-inch full feathers for the ultimate arrows delivering great speed for short distances. A must have item for any serious archer. Available in 45-60 and 60-75 sizes.
SRP: 18 bulk pack, per arrow. . $9.37

LINEJAMMER
These Carbon Express arrows and shafts are created with archery competitors in mind. They are offered in 350 size and have a large exterior diameter. Available in Black BuffTuff only.
SRP: per dozen $139.99

TERMINATOR HUNTER SERIES
The Hunter series is similar to Terminator shafts and camouflaged with River Bottom camouflage.
SRP: shafts, per dozen $80.28
with vanes installed,
per dozen $101.09
72 bulk pack, per arrow $8.26

TERMINATOR SHAFTS
Economical priced shafts constructed of wrapped carbon composites. Available in a wide assortment of weights and shafts with plus/minus .006-inch straightness. The Hunter series is camouflaged with River Bottom camouflage.
SRP: shafts, per dozen $61.76
with vanes, per dozen $79.76
72 bulk pack, per arrow $6.46
Select shafts and arrows are also available at a slightly higher price.

THUNDERSTORM AND THUNDER EXPRESS
Youth arrows and products designed by Carbon Express for intermediate shooters. These feature carbon construction and a tunable press-fit nock. Spined for draw weights from 30 to 50 pounds.
SRP: Thunderstorm
shafts, per dozen $55
with vanes, per dozen $70
six arrow pack $37

SRP: Thunder Express shafts,
per dozen $71
72 bulk pack – great for camps –
per arrow $2.15

Carbon Tech Arrows

HIPPO

RHINO

WHITETAIL

HIPPO
Similar to Rhino with a large exterior diameter and five or six wraps of carbon for strength and durability. Sizes 23/525 and 23/400.
SRP: per dozen **$126.99**

RHINO
The Rhino series has plus/minus .0015 tolerances and weigh 9.5 gpi in the 35/60 size, 10 gpi in 45/70 and 11.5 gpi in 55/80 diameter shafts. Sizes 23/525 and 23/400.
SRP: per dozen **$126.99**

WHITETAIL
The Whitetail XP provides extreme performance with a plus/minus .0015 straightness tolerance and 7.9 grains per inch (gpi) for the 40/65 shafts and 9.5 gpi for the 65/80 diameter sizes. The Whitetail Hunter series has the same weights and diameters but .005 straightness. The Whitetail shafts have up to six wraps of carbon that incorporate a precision multi-directional carbon layer design
SRP: per dozen **$94.99**

ARROWS

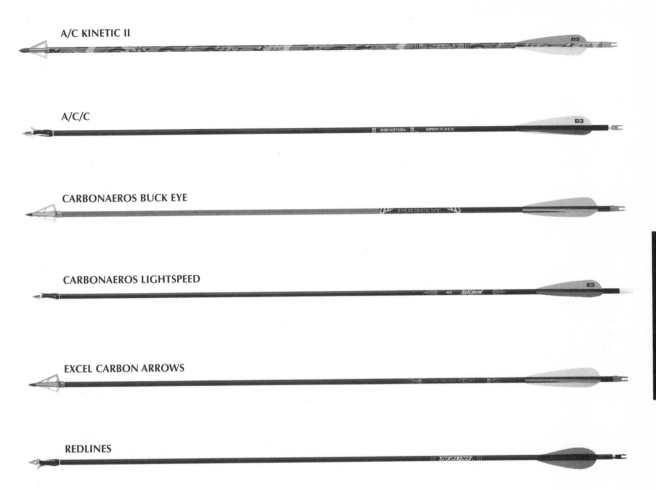

A/C KINETIC II

A/C/C

CARBONAEROS BUCK EYE

CARBONAEROS LIGHTSPEED

EXCEL CARBON ARROWS

REDLINES

A/C KINETIC II AND A/C/C- ALUMINUM CARBON

A rolling process ensures a proper carbon and aluminum bond with these shafts. Each has a plus/minus .003-inch straightness and the Kinetic has a heavier aluminum wall, plus Photofusion camouflage. Prices reflect per dozen with vanes.

SRP: A/C Kinetic $172.10
A/C/C $163.44

CARBONAEROS BUCK EYE

These shafts are Easton's newest offerings and they utilize the company's Infinity Performance System (IPS) coating which adds weight where it's needed—at the point-end of the shaft. This results in more kinetic energy and improved balance. The tree green colored IPS coating also protects the shaft against wear and makes it quieter to draw and release. The Buck Eye shafts include RPS inserts and factory installed Super Nocks and are offered in four popular sizes: 300, 340, 400 and 500.

SRP: per dozen $156.75

CARBONAEROS LIGHTSPEED

For bowhunters who shoot 3-D as a sideline or as warm-up practice in preparation for the hunting season, Easton's CarbonAeros Lightspeed are new this year and have a polished matte finish and utilize multi-layered wrapped construction. Easton (801-539-1400) will provide a free brochure with all the details.

SRP: per dozen $70.25

EXCEL CARBON ARROWS

These all carbon arrows are offered in 340, 400 and 500 sizes. They feature multi-layered wrapped construction.

SRP: $64.52

REDLINES

This all carbon shaft uses Easton's C2 manufacturing process and meets strict weight and straightness standards. Redlines have a plus/minus 1.5-inch straightness and use the UNI nock system. These arrows are available in 9 sizes.

SRP: with vanes, per doz . . . $102.48

Easton Arrows

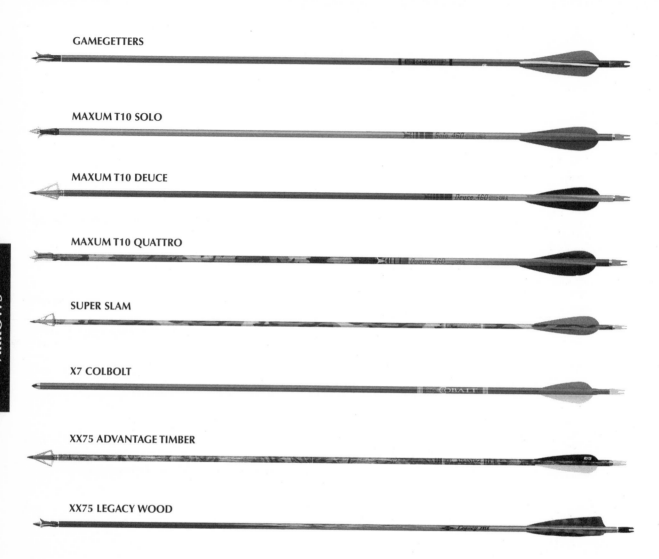

GAMEGETTERS

MAXUM T10 SOLO

MAXUM T10 DEUCE

MAXUM T10 QUATTRO

SUPER SLAM

X7 COLBOLT

XX75 ADVANTAGE TIMBER

XX75 LEGACY WOOD

ALUMINUM SERIES BY EASTON

GAMEGETTERS
Similar to the XX75s and available in eight sizes. A very popular economical arrow. RPS inserts are included. Gamegetter Camo Hunters and Gamegetter IIs are similar and comparable in price. These aluminum shafts must be cut to length and have inserts installed.
SRP: 3-color camo $57.79
**   olive green $48.72**

MAXUM T10-ALUMINUM
A new aluminum shaft that's offered in three styles: Solo bronze, deuce two tone crested look and Quattro with PermaGraphic camo. These arrows are economically priced and designed with bowhunters in mind. Inserts are included and Super UNI bushing and Super Nocks are installed.
SRP: Solo $59.80
**   Quattro $66.69**

SUPER SLAM
An aluminum arrow constructed with 7178-T9 aluminum alloy with a plus/minus .0015-inch straightness tolerance. Super UNI bushings and nocks are installed. RPS inserts are included for installation after the shafts are cut to length. Available in 15 sizes! Super slam Select shafts are hand picked and cost slightly more.
SRP: $83.33

X7 COBALT
You'll recognize this target arrow by its flashy blue Cobalt color. Swage technology is used in the construction of this 7178-T9 aluminum arrow. Available in 11 sizes from 191114 to 2512. Great for 3-D shooting also.
SRP: $91.89

XX75
A very popular Easton aluminum shaft known for performance and value. These provide a plus/minus .002-inch straightness and have factory installed UNI Bushings and Super Nocks. Available in bronze and Advantage and Mossy Oak camouflage. A XX75 Legacy with wood grain pattern and feather fletching is offered for slightly less cost.
SRP: per dozen $81.32
slightly cheaper in solid color

Gold Tip Arrows

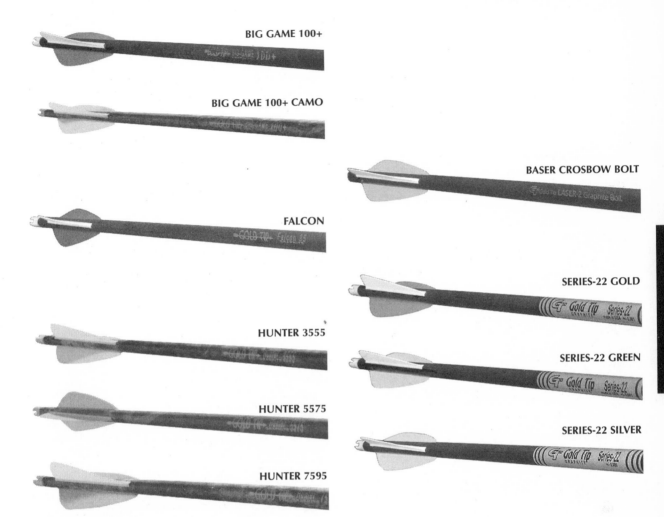

BIG GAME 100+

BIG GAME 100+ CAMO

BASER CROSBOW BOLT

FALCON

SERIES-22 GOLD

HUNTER 3555

SERIES-22 GREEN

HUNTER 5575

SERIES-22 SILVER

HUNTER 7595

BIG GAME 100+

Big Game 100+ shafts combine a +/-0.003-inch straightness tolerance with unmatched strength and an ultra-smooth finish. These shafts are spined for approximately 75 to 100 pounds of draw weight. Additional layers of graphite provide added weight and strength to meet the minimum arrow weights imposed by some states and countries. Shafts are available with vanes or feathers and with Realtree Hardwoods camouflage.
SRP: . . . . $76.93 to $93.73
Add $14 for camouflaged arrows and shafts

FALCON

Gold Tip's youth series provides the ultimate in durability and strength. These shafts were tested at Boy Scouts of America archery ranges.
**SRP: shafts, per dozen $36.33
shafts with vanes,
per dozen $37.33**

HUNTER

For hunters who avoid switching to graphite and carbon shafts because of the expense, Gold Tip introduces the economical Hunter shafts. Available in 3555, 5575 and 7595 as bare shafts or with feathers or vanes. Also available in Realtree Hardwoods camouflage finish.
**SRP: Standard shafts, per dozen,
. . . . $51.35 to $68.33**
Add approximately $18 per dozen more for camouflaged models.

LASER CROSSBOW BOLTS

These bolts are designed to provide unsurpassed durability and kinetic energy for maximum penetration. These bolts are available in 20- and 22-inch lengths and with or without vanes.
SRP: per dozen . . . $51.73 to $62.93

SERIES-22

These competition shafts offer one of the largest diameters allowed in IBO competition. Shafts are available in one spine size (.325) and three grades: +/-0.006-inch Silver Label, +/-0.003-inch Green Label and +/-0.001-inch Gold Label.
SRP:. . . . . $69.93 to $121.73
Silver series is least expensive and Gold series is most expensive.

Gold Tip Arrows

TARGET 3D 3555

TARGET 3D 5575

TARGET 3D 7595

XT3555

XT5575

XT7595

TARGET 3-D

These shafts are Gold Tip's premier competition shafts. Each shaft is straight to within +/-0.001 inch and has a wide .390-inch diameter. Available in Gold or Green grades with Gold shafts in sizes 3555, 5575 and 7595.
SRP: per dozen . . $95.13 to $111.93
Add up to $14/dozen for X-Cutter series.

XT SERIES

This series is Gold Tip's best all-around hunting arrows. The shafts are precision crafted with five layers of strategically placed graphite to create a durable and consistent arrow shaft. These shafts have a straightness tolerance of +/-0.003 inch. Lock Nocks and inserts are standard. The Camo XT series is coated with Realtree Hardwoods and is available with 3555, 5575 and 7595 shafts and as unfletched shafts or with vanes or feathers.
SRP: per dozen . . $83.93 to $100.73

The standard XT series is available minus the camouflage finish. Same specifications as camo series and as raw shafts or with vanes or feathers. Feathers are more expensive than vanes.
SRP: per dozen . . . $65.73 to $82.53

North American Archery Group Arrows

BRAVE

BRAVE WARRIOR

BRAVE 24-INCH
Designed to be used with the Brave youth bow. Fiberglass shaft, plastic vanes and chromed field points. Three per pack.
Item 3800-003 . . . . SRP varies

BRAVE WARRIOR 28-INCH
Same as Brave arrows but 28 inches long.
SRP. . . . . varies

ARROWS

PSE Arrows

CARBON FORCE COMPETITION PRO

CARBON FORCE DOMINATOR

CARBON FORCE EXTREME

CARBON FORCE ARROWS
PSE Carbon Force arrows are available in three models: Competition Pro, Extreme and Dominator. The high-performance Competition Pro shafts have a guaranteed .001 straightness—one of the best in the industry—and will be offered as shafts only. The Dominator series will offer a .006-inch guaranteed straightness. This series is now coated in PSE's Fall Brush camouflage and the exterior coating is so durable that it's nearly impossible to scratch with a knife blade.
SRP: Competition Pro,
shafts only $99
Dominators with fletching,
per dozen $79.99

RADIAL CROSS WEAVE
Target shooters and 3-D enthusiasts will welcome PSE's new Radial Cross Weave ultra-high performance shafts. This woven—not rolled and ground—shaft technology could be the future standard in carbon shaft construction. The technology comes from the aerospace and fishing rod industries. Since there is also less waste during construction and no grinding will be performed on the finished product, this will translate into a great value and premium product for shooters because there's less manual labor involved and much improved straightness and strength per shaft produced. This shaft could debut as a hunting shaft as early as 2004. You'll notice its unusual construction process by a unique jagged, on-the-shaft pattern when viewed under bright lights. When the shaft is damaged—such as when you shoot a Robin Hood, which could occur more often—the shaft unwinds instead of breaking off and splintering. This could result in superior penetration through mass retention and less break offs in hunting applications.
SRP:

EASTON. ALUMINUM ARROW SHAFTS

SHAFT & COMPONENT SPECIFICATIONS

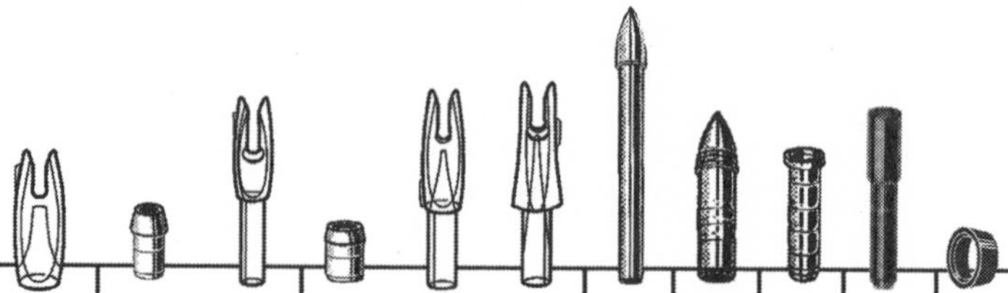

Shaft Size	Shaft Weight			Shaft Weight @ 29"	Spine @ 28" Span	Stock Shaft Length[5]		Conventional Nock Size[2]	UNI System[1]		Super UNI System[1]			NIBB Point	One-piece Bullet Point	RPS[4] Insert Alum.	RPS[4] Insert Carbon	Broad-head Adapter Ring[6]
	XX75[6]	XX78[7]	X7[15]			75[6]/78[7]	X7[15]		Bushing	"G" Nock[2]	Bushing	Super Nock	3D Super Nock					
	Grains per Inch			Grains	Deflection in inches	Inches	Inches	Inches	Grains	Grains	Grains[5]	Grains[5]	Grains[5]	Grains[5]		Grains	Grains	Grains
1214	5.93	—	—	172	2.501	26	—	—	—[13]	—	—	—	—	—	45	—	—	—
1413	5.94	—	—	172	2.036	26	—	7/32	—	—	—	—	—	—	35	—	—	—
1416	7.15	—	—	207	1.684	27	—	7/32	—	—	—	—	—	46	52	—	—	—
1512	—	—	5.84	169	1.553	—	27	—	5	7	—	—	—	49[3]	—	—	—	—
1514	—	—	6.83	198	1.379	—	26	—	5	7	—	—	—	61[3]	—	—	—	3[14]
1516	7.34	—	—	213	1.403	27½	—	1/4	—	—	—	—	—	48	54	—	—	3[14]
1612	—	—	6.27	182	1.298	—	28	—	6	7	—	—	—	55[3]	—	—	—	3[14]
1614	—	—	7.73	224	1.153	—	28	—	5	7	—	—	—	51	—	—	—	3[14]
1616	8.36	—	—	242	1.079	28½	—	1/4	—	—	—	—	—	56	63	—	—	3[14]
1712	—	—	6.70	194	1.099	—	28½	—	7	7	—	—	—	62[3]	—	—	—	—
1713	7.42	—	—	215	1.044	29	—	1/4	—	—	—	—	—	54	—	—	—	—
1714	—	—	8.07	234	0.963	—	29	—	7	7	—	—	—	56	—	—	—	—
1716	9.03	—	—	262	0.880	29	—	1/4[9]	—	—	—	—	—	60	68	10	—	—
1812	—	—	7.30	212	0.879	—	29½	—	9	7	—	—	—	67[3]	—	—	—	—
1813	7.86	—	—	228	0.874	30	—	1/4[9]	—	—	—	—	—	56	—	14	8	—
1814	—	—	8.57	249	0.799	—	29½	—	8	7	—	—	—	60	—	—	—	—
1816	9.27	—	—	269	0.756	30	—	1/4[9]	—	—	—	—	—	63	74	12	7	—
1912	—	—	7.60	220	0.778	—	30	—	9	7	—	—	—	70[3]	—	—	—	—
1913	8.34	—	—	242	0.733	31	—	9/32[9]	—	—	—	—	—	64	—	17	10	—
1914	—	—	9.28	269	0.658	—	30½	—	9	7	—	—	—	64	—	—	—	—
1916	10.05	—	—	291	0.623	31	—	9/32[9]	—	—	—	—	—	72	82	16	9	—
2012	—	—	8.00	232	0.680	—	31½	—	(10)[10]	7	5	13	12	83[3]	—	22	12	—
2013	9.01	—	—	261	0.610	32½	—	9/32[9]	—	—	5	13	12	68	—	21	12	—
2014	—	—	9.56	277	0.579	—	31½	—	(10)[10]	7	5	13	12	71	—	—	—	—
2016	10.56	—	—	306	0.531	32	—	9/32[9]	—	—	4	13	12	80	90	20	11	—
2018	12.28	—	—	356	0.464	32½	—	5/16[9]	—	—	4	13	12	89	—	19	10	—
2020	13.49	—	—	391	0.426	33	—	5/16	—	—	—	—	—	64	—	18	10	—
2112	—	—	8.42	244	0.590	—	31½	—	(10)[10]	7	7	13	12	88[3]	100	25	14	—
2113	9.30	—	—	270	0.540	32½	—	5/16	—	—	7	13	12	78[11]	100	25	14	—
2114	9.86	9.94	9.94	286	0.510	32½	32½	5/16[9]	(11)[10]	7	7	13	12	78	100	25	14	—
2115	10.75	—	—	312	0.461	33	—	5/16[9]	(11)[10]	7	7	13	12	83	100	25	14	—
2117	12.02	12.13	—	349	0.407	33	—	5/16[9]	—	—	7	13	12	97	100	25	14	—
2212	—	8.84	8.84	256	0.505	32½	32½	—	13[10]	7	9	13	12	102[3]	100	31	16	—
2213	9.83	9.92	9.92	285	0.460	33½	33½	5/16[9]	13[10]	7	9	13	12	88	100	30	16	—
2214	—	—	10.41	302	0.425	—	33	—	13[10]	7	9	13	12	103[3]	100	—	—	—
2215	10.67	10.77	—	309	0.420	33	—	5/16[9]	—	—	9	13	12	95	100	30	16	—
2216	12.02	12.13	—	349	0.376	33	—	5/16[9]	—	—	9	13	12	98	100	29	15	—
2219	13.77	13.89	—	399	0.337	34	—	11/32	—	—	8	13	12	107	—	26	14	—
2312	—	9.48	9.48	275	0.423	33	33	—	(15)[10]	7	11	13	12	99[3]	100	37	19	—
2314	10.67	10.76	10.76	309	0.390	33½	33½	11/32	(14)[10]	7	10	13	12	—	100	34	18	—
2315	11.67	11.77	—	338	0.342	34	—	11/32	—	—	11	13	12	—	100	37	19	—
2317	13.26	13.38	—	385	0.297	34	—	11/32	—	—	11	13	12	—	100	37	19	—
2412	—	9.65	9.65	280	0.400	34	34	11/32	(17)[10]	7	12	13	12	110	100	40	20	—
2413	10.40	10.50	10.50	302	0.365	34	34	11/32	(17)[10]	7	12	13	12	110	100	40	20	—
2419	14.55	—	—	422	0.268	34½	—	11/32	—	—	12	13	12	—	100	37	19	—
2512	—	10.28	10.28	298	0.321	34½	34½	—	(20)[10]	7	15	13	12	108[3]	100	52	25	—
2514	11.33	11.43	—	329	0.305	34½	—	11/32	(18)[10]	7	14	13	12	—	100	48	23	—
2613	—	11.49	11.49	333	0.265	—	34½	—	(22)[10]	7	17	13	12	—	150	58	27	—

— Indicates not available
1 UNI—Universal Nock Installation System
2 Nock size for standard swaged nock taper.
3 This NIBB point will provide approximately an 8% F.O.C. All other NIBB points are approximately 7% F.O.C. F.O.C. is Front-of-Center balance position on the arrow shaft.
4 RPS = Replaceable Point System with 8-32 AMO-Standard thread
5 Length is approximate stock shaft length for each size.
6 XX75 Mossy Oak Break-Up, Advantage Timber,Yukon, Camo Hunter, GameGetter, GameGetter II, Jazz, Platinum, Legacy.
7 XX78 Super Slam Select, Super Slam.
8 Jazz, Legacy, GameGetter and GameGetter II, are produced without reduced diameter taper and can also use the next largest conventional nock size.
9 Super UNI Bushing is factory-installed on these shafts. Parenthesis indicates smaller (A/C/E Nock) UNI Bushing size is available as an accessory. Except Super Slam Select.
10 2113 shafts use 2114 X7/XX75 NIBB points and 2114-2117 components.
11 NIBB point grain weights are ±0.5 grain. All other components are ±1 grain.
12 3D Super Nock also available; 12 grains.
13 Weight calculated for 29" length.
14 Shaft sizes 1716, 1813 and 1816 use A/C/C 3-60; sizes 1913 and 1916 use A/C/C 3-71 broadhead adapter rings.
15 X7 Eclipse and Cobalt.
16 1214 accepts "G" Nock directly: 7 grains.
Note: sizes 1416, 1516, 1616 and 1713 are not suitable for bowhunting.

EASTON SHAFT SELECTION

1. Determining Correct Hunting Arrow Length

Bows with cut-out window

The Correct Hunting Arrow Length for bows with a broadhead cut-out sight window (including bows with overdraws) is determined by drawing back an extra-long arrow and having someone mark the arrow one inch in front of where the arrow contacts the most forward portion of the arrow rest.

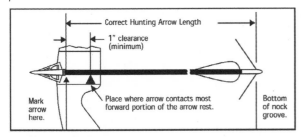

Bows without cut-out window

The Correct Hunting Arrow Length for bows without a cut-out sight window (which will not allow a fixed blade broadhead to be drawn past the front of the bow handle), mark an extra-long arrow one inch in front of the riser as shown below.

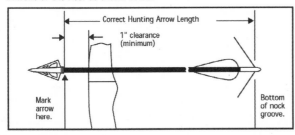

Bow Draw Length

Draw length is measured at full draw from the front of the bow to the bottom of the nock groove. Actual arrow length and draw length are only the same if the end of the arrow shaft is even with the front of the bow at full draw.

USING THE EASTON HUNTING SHAFT SIZE SELECTION CHARTS

1. Once you have determined your Correct Hunting Arrow Length and Calculated Peak Bow Weight, you are ready to select your correct shaft size:
   1.1 Compound bows. In the "Bow Weight" column (left-hand side of the CHART) select the column with the type cam on your bow. Then locate your Calculated Peak Bow Weight in that column.
   1.2 Recurve bows. In the "Bow Weight" column (right-hand side of the CHART) locate your Actual Peak Bow Weight at your draw length.
   1.3 Long bows. See Legacy chart below.

TUNING THE ARROW SHAFT

Our Hunting Shaft Size Selection Chart indicates that more than one shaft size may shoot well from your bow. You may decide to shoot a lighter shaft for speed, or a heavier shaft for greater durability and penetration. Also, large

2. Determining Actual Peak Bow Weight for Compound Bows

Compound bows must be measured at the peak bow weight as the bow is being drawn and not while letting the bow down.

The suggested shaft sizes in the charts on pages 26-27 were determined using a "Standard" Setup which includes:
- Use of a release aid.
- 75-100 grain arrow point weight.
- Compound bow with brace height greater than $6\frac{1}{2}$".

If your setup differs from the "Standard" Setup, use the Variables (following) to make adjustments to determine the Calculated Peak Bow Weight so the correct arrow size can be selected on the Chart on pages 26-27.

Variables to the "Standard" Setup for Compound Bows:
- Finger release - Add 5 lbs.
- Point weight over 100 grains – Add 3 lbs.
- Bows with brace heights less than $6\frac{1}{2}$" – Add 5 lbs.

Overdraw Compound Bows

If you are using an overdraw, make the calculations (if any) in the Variables section, and then modify the Calculated Peak Bow Weight of your bow using the chart below.

Bow Weight	Overdraw Amount				
	1"	2"	3"	4"	5"
For 60#-70# Actual/Calculated Peak Bow Weight, add to bow weight—	1#	3#	6#	9#	12#

3. Determining Actual Peak Bow Weight for Recurve Bows

Your local archery pro shop is the best place to determine the actual draw weight of your bow. Actual Peak Bow Weight for recurve bows should be measured at your draw length.

2. Move across that row horizontally to the column indicating your Correct Arrow Length. Note the letter in the box where your Calculated Peak Bow Weight row and Correct Hunting Arrow Length column intersect. The "Shaft Size" box below the CHART with the same letter contains your recommended shaft sizes. Select a shaft from the Chart depending on the shaft material and type of shooting you are doing.

variations in shooting style, bow efficiency, type of wheels or cams, and type of release may require special bow tuning or a shaft size change. Easton's "Arrow Tuning and Maintenance Guide" provides additional information on tuning.

Easton's "Arrow Tuning and Maintenance Guide" available online at www.eastonarchery.com or call Easton at 801-539-1400.

EASTON HUNTING SHAFT SIZE SELECTION CHART

COMPOUND BOW Calculated Peak Bow Weight - Lbs.		Correct Hunting Arrow Length											RECURVE BOW Bow Weight - Lbs. Finger Release 75-100 grain points
Medium Cam	Single or Hard Cam	22.5 / **23"** / 23.5	23.5 / **24"** / 24.5	24.5 / **25"** / 25.5	25.5 / **26"** / 26.5	26.5 / **27"** / 27.5	27.5 / **28"** / 28.5	28.5 / **29"** / 29.5	29.5 / **30"** / 30.5	30.5 / **31"** / 31.5	31.5 / **32"** / 32.5	32.5 / **33"** / 33.5	
37 to 41	32 to 36	A	B	B	C	C	D	E	F				32 to 36
42 to 46	37 to 41	A	B	B	C	C	D	E	F	G	H		37 to 41
47 to 51	42 to 46	B	B	C	C	D	E	F	G	H	I	J	42 to 46
52 to 56	47 to 51	B	C	C	D	E	F	G	H	I	J	J	47 to 51
57 to 61	52 to 56	C	C	D	E	F	G	H	I	J	J	K	52 to 56
62 to 66	57 to 61	C	D	E	F	G	H	I	J	J	K	L	57 to 61
67 to 72	62 to 66	D	E	F	G	H	I	J	J	K	L	L	62 to 66
73 to 78	67 to 72	E	F	G	H	I	J	J	K	L	L	L	67 to 72
79 to 84	73 to 78	F	G	H	I	J	J	K	L	L	L		73 to 78
85 to 90	79 to 84	G	H	I	J	J	K	L	L	L			79 to 84
91 to 96	85 to 90	H	I	J	J	K	L	L	L				85 to 90

Group A

Shaft Size/Spine	Shaft Model	Shaft Wt. Grs/Inch	Wt@29"
1813/875	75	7.86	228
1716/880	75	9.03	262
780	Rdln	6.30	183

Group B

Shaft Size/Spine	Shaft Model	Shaft Wt. Grs/Inch	Wt@29"
1913/730	75	8.34	242
1816/755	75	9.27	269
690	Rdln	6.27	182

Group C

Shaft Size/Spine	Shaft Model	Shaft Wt. Grs/Inch	Wt@29"
2013/610	75	9.01	261
1916/625	75	10.05	291
3L-18/620	A/C/C	7.47	217
600	Rdln	6.92	201

Group D

Shaft Size/Spine	Shaft Model	Shaft Wt. Grs/Inch	Wt@29"
2113/540	75	9.30	270
2016/530	75	10.56	306
3-18/560	A/C/C	7.82	227
500	CAeros, KII	CAWT	CAWT
520	Rdln	7.09	206

Group E

Shaft Size/Spine	Shaft Model	Shaft Wt. Grs/Inch	Wt@29"
2212/510	SS	8.84	256
2114/510	SS, 75, Max	9.86	286
2115/460	75	10.75	312
2018/465	75	12.28	356
3-28/500	A/C/C	8.11	235
500, 460	CAeros, KII	CAWT	CAWT
520	Rdln	7.09	206

Group F

Shaft Size/Spine	Shaft Model	Shaft Wt. Grs/Inch	Wt@29"
2212/510	SS	8.84	256
2213/460	SS, 75, Max	9.83	285
2115/460	75	10.75	312
2018/465	75	12.28	356
3-28/500	A/C/C	8.11	235
500, 460	CAeros, KII	CAWT	CAWT
520	Rdln	7.09	206

Group G

Shaft Size/Spine	Shaft Model	Shaft Wt. Grs/Inch	Wt@29"
2312/425	SS	9.48	275
2215/420	SS, 75, Max	10.67	309
2117/400	SS, 75, Max	12.02	349
2020/425	75	13.49	391
3-39/440	A/C/C	8.58	249
400	CAeros		
460	Rdln	7.32	212

Group H

Shaft Size/Spine	Shaft Model	Shaft Wt. Grs/Inch	Wt@29"
2215/420	SS, 75, Max	10.67	309
2314/390	SS, 75, Max	10.67	309
2117/400	SS, 75, Max	12.02	349
2216/375	SS, 75, Max	12.02	349
3-49/390	A/C/C	8.83	256
400	CAeros, KII	CAWT	CAWT
410	Rdln	7.60	220

Group I

Shaft Size/Spine	Shaft Model	Shaft Wt. Grs/Inch	Wt@29"
2413/365	SS, 75, Max	10.40	302
2314/390	SS, 75, Max	10.67	309
2315/340	SS, 75, Max	11.67	338
2216/375	SS, 75, Max	12.02	349
3-49/390	A/C/C	8.83	256
400	CAeros, KII	CAWT	CAWT
410	Rdln	7.60	220

Group J

Shaft Size/Spine	Shaft Model	Shaft Wt. Grs/Inch	Wt@29"
2512/320	SS	10.28	298
2413/365	SS, 75, Max	10.40	302
2315/340	SS, 75, Max	11.67	338
2219/335	SS, 75	13.77	399
3-60/340	A/C/C	9.45	274
340	CAeros, KII	CAWT	CAWT
360	Rdln	8.31	241

Group K

Shaft Size/Spine	Shaft Model	Shaft Wt. Grs/Inch	Wt@29"
2512/320	SS	10.28	298
2514/305	SS, 75	11.33	329
2317/295	SS, 75	13.26	385
3-71/300	A/C/C	9.92	288
300	CAeros, KII	CAWT	CAWT

Group L

Shaft Size/Spine	Shaft Model	Shaft Wt. Grs/Inch	Wt@29"
2514/305	SS, 75	11.33	329
2613/265	SS	11.49	333
2317/295	SS, 75	13.26	385
2419/265	75	14.55	422
3-71/300	A/C/C	9.92	288
300	CAeros, KII	CAWT	CAWT

CarbonAeros & Kinetic II (CAWT)

Shaft Size	Evolution Weight Grs/In	Evolution Weight Wt@29"	Buck Eye Weight Grs/In	Buck Eye Weight Wt@29"	Epic Weight Grs/In	Epic Weight Wt@29"	Excel Weight Grs/In	Excel Weight Wt@29"	Kinetic II Weight Grs/In	Kinetic II Weight Wt@29"
500	8.02	233	7.86	228	7.28	211	7.10	206		
460									9.40	273
400	9.12	264	9.00	261	8.41	244	8.12	235	10.20	296
340	10.01	290	9.90	287	9.31	270	8.80	255	11.00	319
300	10.14	294	10.03	291	9.45	274			11.60	336

Shaft Size/Spine – indicates suggested shaft size and spine. Shaft size and spine for carbon shafts are identical.

CAWT – Refer to CarbonAeros & Kinetic II box (left) for specific model and weight.

Color Designation for Aluminum Shafts – Within each box the aluminum arrow shafts are color-coded. Red shafts are the lightest and fastest. Green shafts are medium weight offering good speed and durability. Blue represents heavier weights for excellent durability and penetration. Black represents aluminum/carbon and carbon.

SS	XX78 Super Slam Select and Super Slam Shafts (7178-T9 alloy)
75	XX75: Yukon, Platinum, Legacy, Camo Hunter, GameGetter, GameGetter II (7075-T9 alloy)
Max	Maxum T10: Solo, Deuce, and Quattro
A/C/C	Aluminum/Carbon/Composite shafts
Rdln	Redline Carbon Composite Shafts
CAeros	Buck Eye, Evolution, Epic, Excel
KII	Kinetic II

Shaft Model	UltraLite A/C/C UltraLite A/C/E	UltraLite Aluminum SuperLite A/C/C	SuperLite Aluminum	Lite Aluminum	Standard Aluminum
SHAFT WEIGHT CATEGORY					
Models Used for Competition and Recreational Archery					
X10®	1000 750 600 450 900 700 550 410 830 650 500 *380				
A/C/E®	*1400 920 670 470 *1250 850 620 430 *1100 780 570 400 1000 720 520 370				
A/C Navigator	1000 810 610 480 880 710 540 430				
Vector	1050 770 580 920 700 530 840 640 480				
Carbon Redline®	100 690 460 900 600 410 780 520 360				
X7 Eclipse		1512 1812 2112 2412 1612 1912 2212 2512 1712 2012 2312	1514 1914 2214 1614 2014 2314 1714 2114 2413 1814 2213 2613		
X7® Cobalt™		2112 2412 2212 2312 2512	1914 2114 2314 2014 2213 2413		
XX75 Platinum™ Plus			1713 2013 2413 1813 2114 1913 2213	1416 1716 2016 1516 1816 2115 1616 1916 2315	
Jazz			1214 1813 2013 1413 1913	1416 1616 1816 1516 1716 1916	
Models Used for Competition, Recreational Archery and Bowhunting					
Carbon Epic™		500 400 340 300			
Carbon Excel™		500 400 340			
LightSpeed™		500 400 340			
HyperSpeed	2L-18 2-28 2-49 2-71 2-18 2-39 2-60				
A/C/C®		2-00 2L-04 3-04 3-39 3L-00 2-04 3L-18 3-49 3-00 3X-04 3-18 3-60 3L-04 3-28 3-71			
XX75 Legacy™				(1916) 45-50 (2216) 65-70 (2016) 50-55 (2315) 70-75	(2018) 55-60 (2219) 70-75 (2020) 60-65 (2117) 60-65
Models Used for Bowhunting					
Carbon Evolution™		500 400 340 300			
A/C Kinetic™ II		460 400 340 300			
Buck Eye™		500 400 340 300			
Maxum	510 (2114) 400 (2117)	460 (2213)	420 (2215) 375 (2216)	390 (2314) 340 (2315)	365 (2413)
XX78 Super Slam®		2212 2312 2512	2114 2314 2514 2213 2413 2613	2215 2315 2216	2117 2317 2219
XX78® Super Slam® Select		2212 2312 2512	2114 2213 2314 2413	2216 2315	2117
XX75 Mossy Oak® Break-Up™			2013 2213 2413 2114 2314 2514	2216 2315	2117
XX75® Advantage® Timber™			2013 2213 2413 2114 2314 2514	2216 2315	2117
XX75® Yukon™			2114 2213 2314 2413	2016 2216 2315	2117
XX75 Camo Hunter®			1913 2112 2213 2413 2013 2114 2314 2514	1816 2016 2215 2315 1916 2115 2216	2018 2117 2317 2219 2419
XX75 GameGetter® II				1716 1916 2115 2216 1816 2016 2215 2315	2018 2117 2219
XX75 GameGetter®				2016 2216	2018 2117 2219

* Special Order

ARROWS

Ace Broadheads and Arrow Points

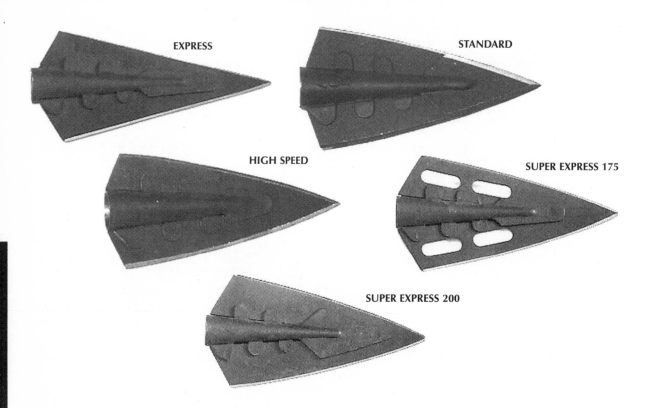

EXPRESS

STANDARD

HIGH SPEED

SUPER EXPRESS 175

SUPER EXPRESS 200

ACE EXPRESS
Similar to the Super Express in design and construction but slightly smaller to create a 165-grain weight broadhead.
SRP: per six-pack $19.95

ACE HEX BLUNTS
These small game and blunt practice points are made of carbon steel and have a hollow point. Both glue-on and Screw in points are available. The glue-on point weights are: 125, 145, 160, 175 and 200-grains. The screw in points are 100, 125, 145 and 160 grains.
SRP: per six-pack $8.95

ACE HIGH SPEED
Lightweight—100 grains weight—and designed for high speed bows and set ups. This head is $^{11}/_{16}$-inch wide and $^{27}/_{16}$-inch long. It is a one-piece solid construction. And designed to fit on wooden shafts but can be adapted to modern arrow use.
SRP: per six-pack $18.95

ACE STANDARD
This one-piece double-edged broadhead included high carbon steel that is spot welded and copper brazed, then heat-treated with a triple laminated tip. It uses the ACE Interlocking Ferrule. The company tests the broadheads by shooting them into concrete with no damage to the heads! These can be used on modern arrows with a ferrule adapter.
SPECIFICATIONS
Weights: 125-, 145- and 160-grain
Blades: Two
SRP: per six pack $18.95

ACE SUPER EXPRESS
This one-piece broadheads first debuted in the 1950s and has returned today to the delight of traditional archer everywhere. This broadhead has a similar design and construction of the others in the ACE line-up and included 4 bleeder holes. The 200-grain head is solid construction without the holes. These blades are $2^{13}/_{13}$-inch long and $1^{7}/_{16}$-inch wide.
SPECIFICATIONS
Weights: 175- and 200-grain
Blades: Two
SRP: per six pack $20.95

Barrie Archery Broadheads and Arrow Points

IRONHEAD

PREMIER

ASSASSIN

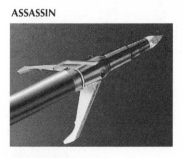

ROCKY'S AVANTAGE

TI100

TI125

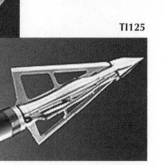

ARROWS

IRONHEAD 125 BY ROCKY MOUNTAIN

This broadhead has a one-piece steel ferrule, Barrie Knife-Point tip that cuts on impact, UNICUT body to align blades, self-centering stainless steel Blade Lock collar and 1⅛-inch cutting diameter.

SPECIFICATIONS
Weights: 125 grain
Blades: three with 1⅛-inch cutting diameter
Available: Three or six-pack
SRP: per three **$17.66**
per six-pack. **$32.90**
Blades. **$6.79**

ROCKY'S ADVANTAGE

These hard-hitting, bone crushing broadheads arrive per-assembled with surgically sharp blades and are pre-aligned. Features a Tri-Cut tip, .030 blades and Blade-Lock collars. Provides a 1⅛-inch cutting diameter.

SPECIFICATIONS
Weights: 100 grains
Blades: three
Available: three or six-pack.
SRP: per three **$17.82**
per six. **$33.95**

ROCKY MOUNTAIN PREMIER SERIES

These broadheads are designed for today's high speed bows and provide great flight and penetration. Features cut-on impact tips, strong .030 stainless steel blades, and Blade-Lock collars. The 75-grain cuts 1⅛-inch, the 100-grain cuts 1³/₁₆-inch diameter and the 125-grain cuts 1¼-inch diameters.

SPECIFICATIONS
Weights: 75-, 100- and 125-grain.
Blades: Three.
Available: Packs of three and six.
SRP: per three **$15.85**
per six. **$28.95**
Blades. **$6.79**

ROCKY MOUNTAIN TI 85, TI 100 AND TI 125

These three-blade broadheads are crafted from soliditanium and are ten time stringer than aluminum and weigh less than half the weight of steel broadheads. Features include a space-age one piece ferrule design, cut-on impact tip, UNICUT body and patented self-centering stainless steel Blade-Lock collar. The 85- and 100-grain heads cut 1⅛-inch holes, and the 125-grain cuts 1³/₁₆-inch diameter.

THIS TROPHY SERIES FEATURES A THREE-BLADE DESIGN

ASSASSIN

This Rocky Mountain expandable broadhead has three replaceable .030-inch thick razor sharp blades behind a cut-on-impact Power Point tip. Blades open to 1½-inch cutting diameter and rest on a stainless steel collar. Blades are retained with an O-ring during flight.

SPECIFICATIONS
Weights: 85- and 100-grains.
Blades: Three.
Available: Package of three.
SRP: 85 grain. **$22.20**
100-grain **$22.20**
extra blades. **$8.44**
O-rings **$2.68**

Barrie Archery Broadheads and Arrow Points

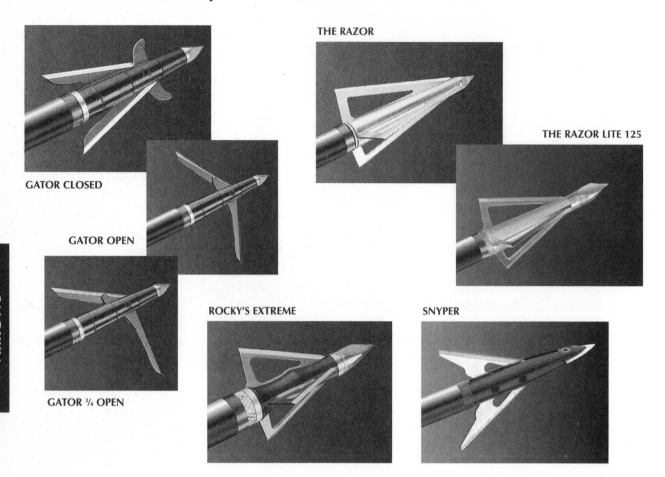

THE RAZOR

GATOR CLOSED

GATOR OPEN

THE RAZOR LITE 125

GATOR ¾ OPEN

ROCKY'S EXTREME

SNYPER

ARROWS

GATOR

This unique Rocky Mountain two-blade expandable broadhead has two .030-inch thick free-floating blades. On impact the blades expand to cut 2 inches point-to-point. No O-rings required and they use a cut-on-impact high carbon steel Power Point.

SPECIFICATIONS
Weights: 80- and 100-grain.
Blades: Two
Available: Package of three.
SRP: 100-grain. $19.20
    80-grain $19.42
six extra blades $6.39

ROCKY'S EXTREME

This three-blade expandable head uses a cut-on-impact Tri-Cut tip and flies like a field point. Blades are .030-inch thick and open to cut 1⅜-inch diameter. Comes pre-assembled with a rubber band retention system.

SPECIFICATIONS
Weights: 100-grain.
Blades: Three
Available: Three pack.
SRP: $22.54
extra washers, per dozen $1.28
nine blades $8.70

SNYPER

This new Rocky Mountain broadhead has a cam-action blade system and a traditional cut-on-impact tip. The two .035-inch thick blades expand to 1⅜-inch. The blades slide rearward upon impact and begin cutting.

SPECIFICATIONS
Weights: 100-grain
Blades: Two, plus cutting tip.
Available: Three pack.
SRP: $24.50
extra blades. $8.99

THE RAZOR
BY ROCKY MOUNTAIN

A broadhead with .020-inch thick stainless steel fixed blades that provide 1¼-inch cutting diameter.
Specifications
Weights: 125-grain
Blades: Three
Available: Three pack and six pack.
SRP: per three $15.85
per six. $28.95

THE RAZOR LITE

The Razor Lite is similar to the Razor with Tri-Cut tip and surgically sharpened blades.

SPECIFICATIONS
Weights: 100- and 125-grain.
Blades: Three
Available: Three and six packs.
SRP: per three $13.90
per half-dozen. $25.15
extra blades. $7.42

Barrie Archery Broadheads and Arrow Points

THE REVOLUTION - CLOSED

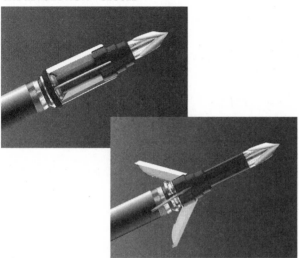

THE REVOLUTION - OPENED

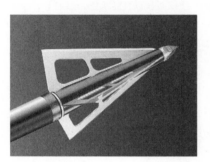

THE ULTRA

WARHEAD 100 FIXED

THE WARHEAD - CLOSED

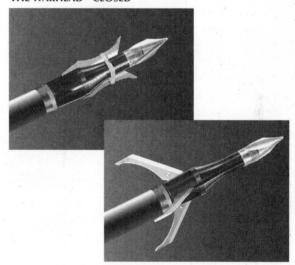

THE WARHEAD - OPENED

THE REVOLUTION BY ROCKY MOUNTAIN

The Revolution is an expandable broadhead with blades that fold back into the cutting position on impact. The broadhead comes assembled with a slide-on replacement blade cartridge and 100-grain weight. The blades expand to 1⅜-inch cutting diameter, begin cutting on impact, and are .030 thick. Titanium and aluminum bodies are available.

SPECIFICATIONS
Weights: 100-grain
Blades: Three
Available: Three pack.
SRP: standard ferrule $23.18
titanium ferrule $34.95

THE ULTRA

Utilizes double-vented reinforced blades and Rocky Mountain's heat-treated Power Point. This broadhead has .020-inch thick stainless steel blades and self-centering stainless steel collar. The Ultra's blades expand to cut 1½-inch diameter.

SPECIFICATIONS
Weights: 125
Blades: Three
Available: Three and six packs.
SRP: per three $14.32
per six $26.47
extra blades. $6.63

THE WARHEAD

This broadhead by Rocky Mountain also uses the slide on cartridge design and a pre-aligned Tri-Cut tip for increased penetration. Blades are .303-inch thick and expand to 13/8 ths cutting diameter.

SPECIFICATIONS
Weights: 100-grains.
Blades: Three
Available: Three pack.

SRP: $22.04
extra cartridges with enough blades
for three broadheads $8.75
extra rubber bands,
**   per dozen $2.00**

WARHEAD 100 FIXED

This broadhead by Rocky Mountain is a replaceable blade fixed version of their expandables, and uses a unique slide-on blade cartridge to change the blades. This head has a Tri-Cut tip and cuts 1⅜-inch diameter. It can be converted to an expandable broadhead by installing the expandable blade cartridge.

SPECIFICATIONS
Weights: 100-grain
Blades: Three blades.
Available: Three and six pack.
SRP: per three $18.99
per half dozen $35.95
extra blade cartridges $10.65

Crimson Talon Broadheads and Arrow Points

ARROWS

CRIMSON TALON

CRIMSON TALON

2XJ Enterprises of North East, Maryland, has unleashed a new broadhead with curved blades that spin the broadhead and arrow in flight. The V-Lock ferrule and locking system grips the blades to provide rock solid anchoring. The blade's tips sport patent-pending mini gut hooks that also help keep the wound from closing.

SPECIFICATIONS
Weights: 100 grain
Blades: Three.
Available: Three pack.
SRP: $23.50

G5 Broadheads and Arrow Points

B52

MONTEC

WARHEAD 100 FIXED

B52

This dark two-blade broadhead is sleek, powerful and provides excellent penetration. It has multi-tapered maul blades that are easy to sharpen and a reinforced tip. This head delivers a 1⅛-inch cutting diameter.

SPECIFICATIONS
Weights: 100 and 125 grain
Blades: Three.
Available: Three pack.
SRP: per three $24.99

B52 Sharpening Stone (Has preset angles to maintain the optimum angle while sharpening the B52 broadhead.)
SRP: $24.99

MONTEC

This new broadhead is one-piece from head to thread. It's crafted from solid stainless steel with three strong multi-tapered blades and a cut-on-impact nose. The blades angles permit easy sharpening. This head uses Monoflow air technology and cuts 1⅛-inch diameter ($1^{1}/_{16}$-inch diameter with the 100-grain Montec).

SPECIFICATIONS
Weights: 100, 125 and 140 grain
Blades: Three.
Available: Three pack.
SRP: per three $32.99

Montec Diamond Sharpening Stone (Help you quickly and easily resharpen the Montec broadheads.)
    4-inch w/carrying case . . . $27.99
    6-inch w/leather
       carrying case $35.99

PRESEASON MONTEC

Same as the standard Montec above, but with rounded edges. It is designed for practice and designed to create minimum wear on targets. A Lubricious coating resists rust and provides durability. These practice heads cut the same diameter as the standard Montec based on grain weight and are recommended instead of field points when hunting with Montec broadheads.

SPECIFICATIONS
Weights: 100 and 125 grain
Blades: Three.
Available: Three pack.
SRP: per three $28.99

Gold Tip Broadheads and Arrow Points

EZ PULL 85

GLUE IN X-CUTTER 80

EZ PULL 125

GLUE IN X-CUTTER 140

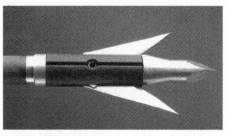

GLADIATOR 2 BLADE

GLADIATOR 4 BLADE

EZ PULL TARGET POINTS
A unique double taper makes retrieval from tight bales and foam targets effortless.

SPECIFICATIONS
Weights: Available grains include 85, 100 and 125.
SRP: per dozen **$6.93**
per 100 poiints **$41.93**

GLADIATOR
This expandable broadhead uses a patented friction bump system (no rubber bands) to ensure precision

flight and dynamic opening. The expandable blade diameter is 1½ inches. Features include two rotating and opening blades and a ground aluminum chisel point.

SPECIFICATIONS
Weights: Available in 85-, 100- and 125-weights.
Blades: Two rotating.
SRP: 85- and 100-grain heads. $15.33
125-grain broadhead **$16.73**
replacement blades **$8.33**
points **$1.33**

GLUE IN POINTS
These field and target points can be glued onto a shaft tip and used for archery practice and plinking situations.

SPECIFICATIONS
Weights: Available in 50-, 100-, 125- and 140-grain weights in .246, Series 22 and X-Cutter models.
SRP: per dozen **$11.13**

Grim Reaper Broadheads and Arrow Points

GRIM REAPER
Grim Reaper Broadheads has improved its Razortip. The new design uses Trocrazor tips with mini razor blades and the Locknotch blade retention sysem that holds the blades in flight without O-rings and rubber bands. The 440C stainless steel blades open smoothly and a high strength steel cup holds the blade ring in

place. You can also shoot this head as a broadhead by locking the blades open before shooting. Deliver 1⅜ ths cutting diameter.

SPECIFICATIONS
Weights: 85, 100 and 125 grain
Blades: Three.
Available: Three pack.
SRP: **$29.99**

GRIM REAPER - RAZORTIP

ARROWS • Broadheads and Arrow Points **283**

InnerLoc Broadhead Broadheads and Arrow Points

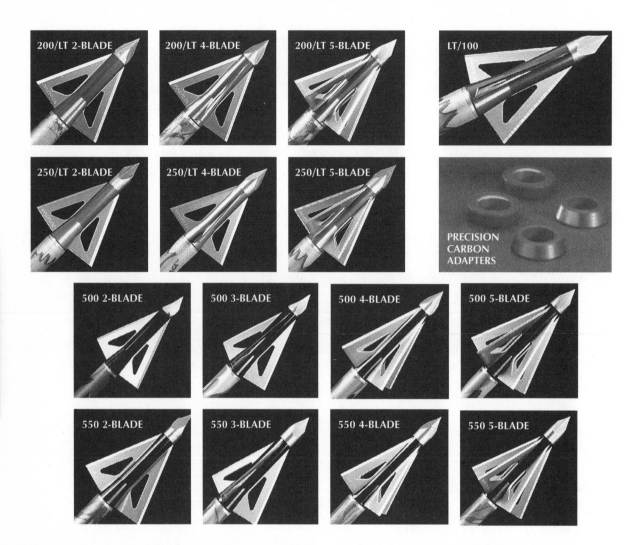

200/LT SERIES

This InnerLoc broadhead. These 85-to 150-grain broadheads are designed for lighter arrows providing flatter trajectory and higher speed.

SPECIFICATIONS
Weights: 85 grain 2-blade; 105 grain 4-blade and 115 grain 5-blade
Blades: 2, 4 and 5
SRP: per six. **$32.00**

250/LT SERIES

These broadheads weigh 250 grains and are offered in 2, 4 and 5 blade designs.

SPECIFICATIONS
Weights: 95 grain 2-blade; 105 grain 4-blade and 115 grain 5-blade

Blades: 2, 4 and 5
SRP: per six. **$35.00**

500 AND 550 SERIES

These heavyweight broadheads deliver cutting power and increase kinetic energy on target.

SPECIFICATIONS
Weights: 105 grain 2-blade and 115 grain 3-blade, 124 grain 4-blade and 135 grain 5 blade in the 500 series. In the 550 series 115 grain 2-blade, 125 grain 3-blade, 135 grain 4-blade and 145 grain 5 blade.
Blades: 2, 3, 4 and 5
SRP: per six . . . . . . **$35.00 to $40.00**

LT/100 GRAIN

Similar to the 200 LT but a three blade head weighing 100 grains.
SRP: per six. **$32.00**

PRECISION CARBON ADAPTERS

These rings fit between larger broadhead bases and the smaller diameter carbon arrow shafts to assist with arrow flight and removal from targets.
SRP: per six-pack. **$5.00**

#205 AND #206

This four-blade broadhead has an 1-inch cutting diameter and screws into an insert inside of the arrow shaft. The #206 model is offered in with a Realtree camouflage finish. Optional filler inserts can turn this broadhead into a two-blade for $4.71.

SPECIFICATIONS:
Weights: 90 grain/205; 125 grain/206
Blades: 4
Available: six pack for #205 and three per pack for #206.
SRP: **$33.57**
replacement blades **$15.14**
replacement tips **$9.07**

#207

A lightweight 75-grain three-blade broadhead with an 1-inch cutting diameter. It screws into an insert.
Specifications:
Weights: 75 grain.
Blades: 3
Available: six-card pack
SRP: **$33.57**
replacement blades **$15.14**
replacement tips **$9.07**

#209

This 100-grain four-blade broadhead is offered in Realtree camouflage and has a threaded ferrule.

SPECIFICATIONS:
Weights: 100 grain.
Blades: 4
Available: Six-pack card standard, three pack in camo
SRP: **$33.57**
per three in camo **$25.00**
replacement blades **$15.14**
replacement tips **$9.07**

#215

A 115-grain broadhead by Muzzy with four blades. It has a 1⅛th cutting diameter.

SPECIFICATIONS:
Weights: 115 grain.
Blades: 4
Available: six-pack card.
SRP: **$33.57**
replacement blades **$15.14**
replacement tips **$9.07**

#225

This 100-grain broadhead screws in and has a 1³⁄₁₆ths cutting diameter.

#205

#206

#207

#209

#215

#225

#235

#245

#255

#265

#285

SPECIFICATIONS:
Weights: 100 grain.
Blades: 4
Available: Six-pack card standard and three pack card in Realtree camo.
SRP: **$33.57**
per three in camo **$25.00**
replacement blades **$15.14**
replacement tips **$9.07**

#235

A 125-grain three-blade Muzzy broadhead with a threaded ferrule.
SPECIFICATIONS:
Weights: 100 grain.
Blades: 4
Available: Six-pack card standard, three pack in camouflage.
SRP: **$33.57**
per three in camo **$25.00**
replacement blades **$15.14**
replacement tips **$9.07**

#245

This 130-grain screw-in broadhead has four blades and is green.
SPECIFICATIONS:
Weights: 130 grain.
Blades: 4
Available: six-pack card.
SRP: **$33.57**
per three in camo **$25.00**
replacement blades **$15.14**

ARROWS

Muzzy Broadheads and Arrow Points

200 SERIES

300 SERIES - GLUE ON

300 SERIES - GLUE IN

GRASSHOPPER TIPS

ARROWS

#255

This 145-grain broadhead is recommended for big and dangerous game.

SPECIFICATIONS:
Weights: 145 grain.
Blades: 4
Available: six-pack card.
SRP: $33.57
per three in camo $25.00
replacement blades $15.14

#265

This Muzzy specialty broadhead weighs 120 grains and has two blades. It screws into an insert.

SPECIFICATIONS:
Weights: 120 grain.
Blades: 2
Available: six-pack card.
SRP: $33.57
per three in camo $25.00
replacement blades $15.14

#285

This Muzzy four-blade broadhead has a five-degree taper for wood or swedged aluminum shafts. It must be glued on and filler inserts are optional.

SPECIFICATIONS
Weights: 125 grain.
Blades: 4
Available: in a six-pack card
SRP: $33.57

per three in camo $25.00
replacement blades $15.14

GRASSHOPPER TIPS

These Muzzy spring-loaded blunt tips can be shot solo at stumps or added behind a Muzzy broadhead to create a low penetration turkey hunting broadhead.

SPECIFICATIONS
Weights: NA
Blades: three prongs
Available: Three pack standard blunt or as a combo 75-grain to fit behind a broadhead.
SRP: standard blunt $45.64
combo Grasshopper $6.57

MUZZY 200 SERIES

All 200 Series broadheads must be glued onto the carbon shaft and are sold fully assembled. Available sizes include 200-2200, 20-2300, 200-22400, 200-1564 and 200-1664. They will fit AFC 2200, AFC 2300, and AFC 2400 shafts respectively. The 1564 and 1664 models fit the corresponding Beman shafts with the same size numbers. These heads have a 1-inch cutting diameter.

SPECIFICATIONS:
Weights: 100 grain.
Blades: Four

Available: six per card pack
SRP: $33.57
replacement blades $15.14
replacement tips $9.07

MUZZY 300 SERIES

This broadhead fits AFC's 2100, 2200, 2300, and 2400 shafts, plus CAE and Carbon Tech 210, 220, 230 and 240 shafts. The 1564 and 1664 models fit Beman's ¹⁵⁄₆₄ and ¹⁶⁄₆₄ shafts. The 3390 models fit ACC 3.39 shafts and the 3490 models fit ACC 3.49 shafts. The 300-3600 broadhead will fit ACC 3.60 shafts and Beman ICS and GoldTip arrows. These heads have a 1⅜ths cutting diameter.

SPECIFICATIONS:
Weights: 100 grain.
Blades: Three
Available: six per pack
SRP: $33.57
replacement blades $15.14
replacement tips $9.07

MUZZY FIELD POINTS

These points are available in assorted weights and styles. The 100 grain glue-on field points can fit Beman, AFC and Carbon Tech shafts. Screw in points in 75-, 90-, 100-, 115-, 125-, 130- and 145-grain weights are available to help you practice in preparation for hunting with Muzzy broadheads that weigh the same.
SRP: All field points $00.20

MUZZY PERSONALIZED BROADHEADS

You can now have your name engraved on your favorite style of Muzzy broadheads. Personalized braodheads must be paid for in advance and there's a 15 character maximum. Call Muzzy at 770-387-9300 for more details or to place an order.

New Archery Products Broadheads and Arrow Points

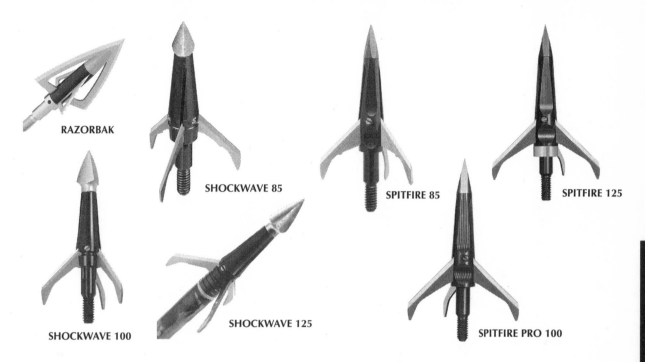

RAZORBAK

SHOCKWAVE 85

SHOCKWAVE 100

SHOCKWAVE 125

SPITFIRE 85

SPITFIRE 125

SPITFIRE PRO 100

ARROWS

RAZORBAK

The return of the popular Razorbak broadheads by NAP also means the unveiling of a new design. This new-era Razorbak has stainless steel blades set in a composite core. The main blades is .039-inch thick and the bleeder blades are .020-inch thick. The tip is designed to cut on impact.

SPECIFICATIONS

Weights: Available in 100- and 125-grains.
Blades: Four blades.
Available: Three broadheads per pack.
SRP: **$32.99**

SHOCKWAVE

These mechanical opening broadheads from New Archery Products have O-rings to hold the blades closed during flight and offer a more economical broadhead. Other features include a bone-crushing Tri-Vex point with super-sharp replaceable blades, and a strong durable ferrule. These broadheads are sold three per package and replacement blades and replacement retention rings are available separately.

SPECIFICATIONS

Weights: Available in 85-, 100- and 125-grains.
Blades: Three blade design.
Available: Three pack of broadheads and replacement blades
SRP: **$24.99**

replacement blade **$11.99**
retention rings, per 50 . . . . . . **$3.99**

SPITFIRE

The Spitfire mechanical broadheads by New Archery Products feature a 3-blade design with a patented snap-lock blade retention system. No O-rings or rubber bands are required to hold the .030-inch thick blades in place. These broadheads cut a 1½-inch diameter circle after opening.

SPECIFICATIONS

Weights: Available in 85-, 100- and 125-grains.
Blades: Three blade design per unit.
Available: Three pack of broadheads and replacement blades
SRP: **$31.99**
replacement blade **$16.99**
Practice blades insert into the ferrules but that do not open and cut can be obtained for $8.99

SPITFIRE GOBBLER GETTER

These mechanical opening broad-heads from NAP have the same Spitfire design and use a cone-shaped silver bullet point to provide knock-down power to the turkey.

SPECIFICATIONS

Weights: Available in 100- and 125-grains.
Blades: Three blade design per unit.
Available: Three pack of broadheads

and replacement blades
SRP: **$32.99**
replacement blade **$16.99**
Practice blades that do not open and cut can be obtained for $8.99

SPITFIRE PROSERIES

The Spitfire Pro Series is similar in design and cutting dimension to the standard Spitfire and incorporates a microgroove ferrule. Practice blades can also be used with this model.

SPECIFICATIONS

Weights: Available in 85-, 100- and 125-grains.
Blades: Three blade design per unit.
Available: Three pack of broadheads and replacement blades
SRP: **$34.99**
replacement blade **$16.99**
Practice blades that do not open and cut can be obtained for $8.99

New Archery Products Broadheads and Arrow Points

THUNDERHEAD 85   **THUNDERHEAD 100**   **THUNDERHEAD 125**   **THUNDERHEAD PRO 100**

THUNDERHEAD

Thunderheads feature a patented Slimline Ferrule and Trophy Tip. The .027-inch thick blades are constructed of Diamize stainless steel. This broadhead is a three-blade fixed design and the blades fit into slots and are held in place with a metal ring at the base that is backed with a rubber O-ring that helps in alignment and balancing. Replacement blades are offered separately and must be acquired to fit a specific broadhead weight model. The cutting dimensions for each style are: 1³/₈-inch for the 85 grain, and 1³/₁₆-inch for the 100- and 125-grain models.

SPECIFICATIONS
Weights: Available in 85-, 100- and 125-grains.
Blades: Three blade.
Available: Six pack of broadheads and replacement blades
SRP: **$33.99**
replacement blade **$16.99**

THUNDERHEAD FOR CARBON ARROWS

Bowhunters who shoot carbon arrows can now obtain the same Thunderheads for standard arrows with an adapter to help obtain proper shaft-to-head fit. Thunderheads UBARS—Universal Broadhead Adapter Rings—make it possible. The adapter is placed behind the O-ring on the broadhead.

SPECIFICATIONS
Weights: Available in 85-, 100- and 125-grains.
Blades: Three blade.
Available: Six pack of broadheads and replacement blades
SRP: **$35.99**
replacement blade **$16.99**
Note: The UBARS are also sold separately. A package of 6 rings has an SRP of $4.99.

THUNDERHEAD PRO SERIES

Thunderhead Pro Series broadheads feature the same blades as the standard series but have micro-grooved ferrules to increase penetration. This broadhead uses a nickel plated point that's 50% harder than stainless steel. The blades have an exclusive Diamize edge. Available UBAR adapters will make these broadheads compatible with trimmer carbon shafts.

SPECIFICATIONS
Weights: Available in 85-, 100- and 125-grains.
Blades: Three blade.
Available: Six pack of broadheads and replacement blades
SRP: **$38.99**

Note: The UBARS are also sold separately. These rings can be used with most popular sizes of carbon/aluminum arrows and with small aluminum shafts and with all popular broadheads. A package of 6 rings (Item 60-269) has an SRP of $4.99. Visit www.newarchery.com to order.

THUNDERHEAD REPLACEMENT PARTS

Owners of Thunderhead broadheads will want to acquire replacement O-rings and lock rings. These items are used to realign broadheads and to hold the blades in place at the base. The standard O-rings fit all models and the lock rings must be purchased to fit specific broadhead weights.

SPECIFICATIONS
Available: In a package of a dozen for the O-rings and six for the lock rings.
SRP: O-rings **$1.99**
lock rings **$1.99**

PDP Broadheads and Arrow Points

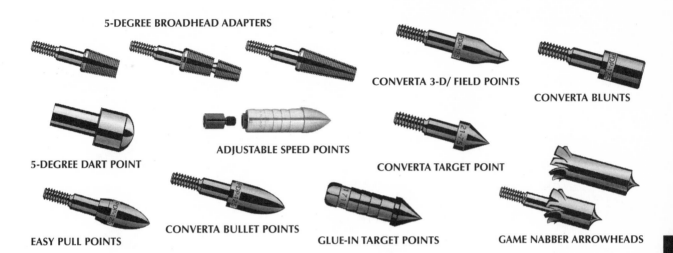

5-DEGREE BROADHEAD ADAPTERS

CONVERTA 3-D/ FIELD POINTS

CONVERTA BLUNTS

5-DEGREE DART POINT

ADJUSTABLE SPEED POINTS

CONVERTA TARGET POINT

EASY PULL POINTS

CONVERTA BULLET POINTS

GLUE-IN TARGET POINTS

GAME NABBER ARROWHEADS

ARROWS

5-DEGREE BROADHEAD ADAPTERS
These adaptors are used when installing traditional broadheads into shafts with inserts. Various sizes will fit numerous styles of broadheads. Call PDP at 620-331-0333 for more details.
SRP: Starting, per dozen $3.85

5-DEGREE DART POINT
This blunt pike point is used while shooting the interactive DART video archery screen. Weighs 125 grains.
SRP: per five $9.59

ADJUSTABLE STEEL SPEED POINTS
These points come in numerous weights, including 10, 30, 50 , 60, 70, and 100 grains, and will fit popular arrows such as Express/Vapor, Gold Tip, X-Cutter, LineJammer, CXL, and shafts sizes ranging from 2012, 2112, 2412, to 2613.
SRP: per dozen $2.34 $11.55
Note: A 5-grain set screw can help

increase weight and has an SRP of $2.34. A special Speed point tool can be used to install grain weights through the Uni-Bushing. The tool has an SRP of $13.34.

CONVERTA 3-D/ FIELD POINTS
Smoother contour increases target life, yet maintains a durable tip. Each point is stamped with size and weight for identification and accurate practice.
SRP: per dozen $2.20

CONVERTA BLUNTS
These blunts are designed for small game hunting and roving. Available in 100 and 125 grain weights.
SRP: per dozen $2.55

CONVERTA BULLET POINTS
A point with a sharp tip and precise body blend. More rounded than the I3-D points above.
SRP: per dozen $2.20

CONVERTA TARGET POINTS
Light weight and designed for flat trajectory, these target points are available in weights including 55, 65 and 75 grains.
SRP: per dozen $2.20

EASY PULL POINTS
An oversized and chamfered point to drastically enhance removal from foam targets.
SRP: per dozen $3.60

GAME NABBER ARROWHEADS
These semi-blunt points perform like a mini-broadhead and resist sticking to trees or sliding under grass while shooting small game, large birds and stumps.
SRP: per half-dozen $5.45

GLUE-IN TARGET POINTS
These target points are designed for field target and arrows without inserts.
SRP: per dozen $2.35

Razor Caps Broadheads and Arrow Points

RAZOR CAPS
The world's only three-blade, cut-on-contact broadhead with replaceable blades that unscrew from the ferrule. The three-blade blade unit is solid, one-piece construction of stainless steel. The blades can be resharpened. The long, lean design assists with perfect flight. The ferrules and blades are sold separately as replacement units and combined pieces can make

broadheads of your desired weight. Visit www.razorcaps.com to order.
SPECIFICATIONS
Weights: Available in 100-, 125-, 150-, 175- and 200-grain weights.
Blades: Three blade, one piece unit.
Available: Three pack of blades or ferrules.
SRP: blades $16.95
ferrules $7.95

RAZOR CAPS

Satellite Archery Broadheads and Arrow Points

BEAR RAZORHEAD

BEAR RAZORHEAD LITE

BUCK MASTER VECTOR

SPEARPOINT 125

SPEARPOINT 100

ARROWS

SUPER SLAM 2

SUPER SLAM 3

SUPER SLAM 4

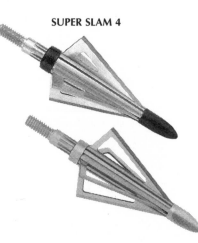

BEAR RAZORHEAD

This broadhead has been on the market since 1952 and produces 4-blade performance and results. Features a re-sharpenable two-edged .040-inch main stainless steel blade and positive-locking auxiliary blade. Able to withstand 300 pounds tensile load. Both models cut 1¹⁄₁₆th diameter on impact and feature a chisel tip point.

SPECIFICATIONS
Weights: (Lite) 110- and (Super) 145-grain.
Blades: Three stainless replaceable
Available: Three or six per pack.
SRP: Supers 3/pack **$12.99**
  6/pack **$19.99**
Lites 3/pack. **$14.99**
  6/pack **$23.99**

BUCKMASTER VECTOR

A three-blade broadhead with a hardened steel chisel point tip and .027-inch stainless replaceable blades. Produces a 1⅛-inch diameter cutting radius.

SPECIFICATIONS
Weights: Vector 75- or 100-grain.
Blades: Three stainless replaceable
Available: Three per pack.
SRP: **$14.99**

CHUCK ADAMS SPEAR POINT

Chuck Adams designed this 3-blade broadhead for superior performance based on low friction penetration. Has cutting edges from the tip to the blades. Cuts a 1⅛-inch diameter radius. The 125grain Spear Point has .15-grain replaceable stainless blades and a 20-grain point. The 100-grain model has.10-grain blades and a .15-grain tip.

SPECIFICATIONS
Weights: 100- or 125-grain.
Blades: Three stainless replaceable
Available: Three per pack.
SRP: **$24.99**

CHUCK ADAMS SUPER SLAM BROADHEAD SYSTEM

A revolutionary 12-slot aircraft aluminum ferrule lets the user assemble two-, three-, or four-blade configurations. Blades can be installed to align with any fletching configuration, including four fletch. The 90- to 110-grain system utilizes .027-inch stainless replaceable blades and the 110- to140-grain system uses dark, larger tips and dark security rings. Both systems cut 1⅛ diameter holes and have case hardened spear points.

SPECIFICATIONS
Weights: 90 to 110-grain; or 110- to 140-grain.
Blades: Three stainless replaceable
Available: Three per pack.
SRP: **$27.99**

Satellite Archery Broadheads and Arrow Points

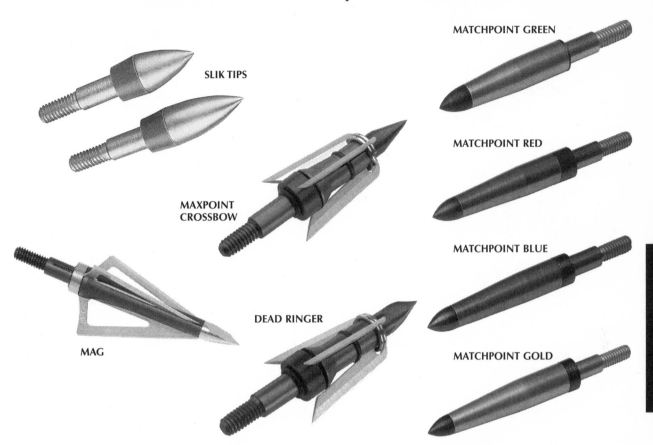

SLIK TIPS

MATCHPOINT GREEN

MATCHPOINT RED

MAXPOINT
CROSSBOW

MATCHPOINT BLUE

DEAD RINGER

MAG

MATCHPOINT GOLD

DEAD RINGER

This expandable 3-blade broadhead cuts 1⁵/₁₆-inch diameter upon impact. Blades are non-vented and positioned backward for flight. Hardened steel Trocar point assists with penetration. High-tech design assures low flight pattern. Dead Ringer 75-grain model cuts 1³/₁₆ inch hole and uses 027-inch replaceable stainless blades.

SPECIFICATIONS
Weights: 75- and 100-grain.
Blades: Three stainless replaceable
Available: Three per pack.
SRP: **$23.99**

MAG

This broadhead series features a hardened steel chisel point with a Quick-Silver Tip, three-blade design and light weight for maximum speed. The 100- and 12 grain heads use .027-inch stainless replaceable blades and the 75-grain head uses .020-inch stainless replaceable blades. The Mag 125 cuts 1³/₁₆ diameter and the other versions cut 1¹/₈ diameter holes.

SPECIFICATIONS
Weights: 75-, 100- and 125-grain.
Blades: Three stainless replaceable
Available: Three or six per pack.
SRP: 3/pack **$14.99**
    6/pack **$24.99**

MATCHPOINTS

This unique point duplicates any combination of blades and any range of weights to provide a precision practice point. Design by Chuck Adams, the head is adjustable to duplicate length, balance and weight distribution of any broadhead. This kit is used for tuning a bow for hunting. The assorted colors indicate various weights.

SPECIFICATIONS
Weights: Available in 75-, 90, 100- and 125-grain.
Blades: None
Available: One per pack.
SRP: kit **$8.49**

MAXPOINT CROSSBOW BROADHEAD SYSTEM

This expandable 3-blade broadhead has a conical tip and cuts 1⁵/₁₆-inch diameter hole upon impact and opening. Blade assembly slides back instead of opening outward and low profile assures consistent flight pattern and blade penetration. Comes with matched WeightPoint for arrow flight tuning. Uses .036 stainless resharpenable blades.

SPECIFICATIONS
Weights: 100-grain.
Blades: Three stainless replaceable
Available: Three per pack.
SRP: **$25.99**

SLIK TIPS

Target friendly field points that are 27.6% easier to remove describes these new tips. Tests found these tips could be removed with approximately 28.5 lbs. of force from foam targets. A self-lubricating Dupont Derine collar combined with an oversized nickel-plated point makes the easy extraction possible.

SRP: . . . . **per dozen $ 5.25**

Satellite Archery Broadheads and Arrow Points

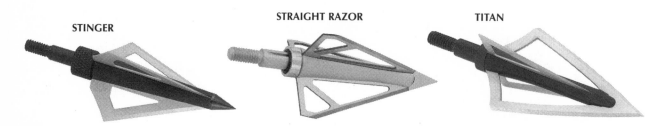

STINGER

STRAIGHT RAZOR

TITAN

ARROWS

STINGER

This 3-blade broadhead uses .016 replaceable stainless blades to deliver 1³/₁₆-inch cutting diameter. Features a conical point and black body.

SPECIFICATIONS
Weights: 100- or 125-grain.
Blades: Three stainless replaceable
Available: Three per pack.
SRP: $9.99

STRAIGHT RAZOR

The case-hardened steel pyramid tip on this broadhead aligns with the three blades and begins cutting upon impact. The Straight Razor uses three .027-inch replaceable stainless blades. The 100-grain broadhead cuts 1¹/₈ inches diameter and the 125-grain head cuts 1³/₈ diameter.

SPECIFICATIONS
Weights: 100- and 125-grain.
Blades: Three stainless replaceable
Available: Three per pack.
SRP: $23.99

TITAN

This broadhead is sharp to the point and begins cutting on contact. Produces high penetration with eight inches of cutting surface. Utilizes replaceable blades and a resharpenable .036-inch main blade. The replaceable blade on the Titan 125-grain head is .027 inch and .015 inch on the 100 grain head. Both broadheads cut a 1¹/₈ diameter hole.

SPECIFICATIONS
Weights: 100- and 125-grain.
Blades: Two stainless replaceable and one two-edge fixed blade.
Available: Three per pack.
SRP: $23.99

Saunders Archery Broadheads and Arrow Points

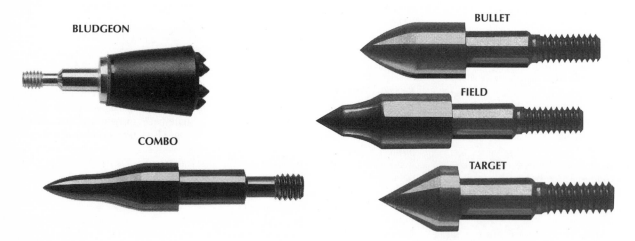

BLUDGEON

BULLET

FIELD

COMBO

TARGET

BLUDGEONS

Used for small game hunting, these can also stop arrows from sticking into logs or sliding under grass.
SRP: 4 pack $7.95
   Slip on models $5.95

COMBO POINTS

Great to 3-D shooting and leaves a smaller entry hole and creates less wear on targets. These are available in many sizes.
SRP: per dozen $4.95

FIELD, BULLET AND TARGET POINTS

The tried-and-true points that all archers have and use while practicing. These are available in numerous weights. Field points are long and pointed, bullet points are rounder and more blunt and target points are smaller.
SRP: per dozen $3.95

Saunders Archery Broadheads and Arrow Points

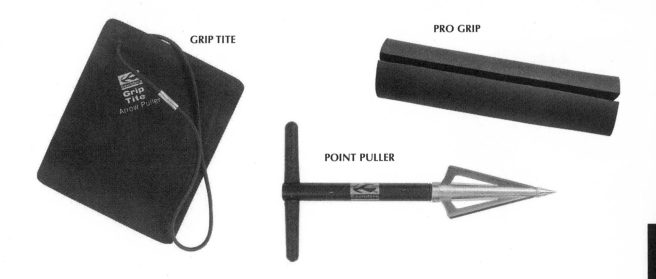

GRIP TITE

PRO GRIP

POINT PULLER

GRIP TITE ARROW PULLING PAD
A flexible super grip pad to make arrow removal easier.
SRP: **$3.95**

PRO GRIP
This soft-n-tough cylinder is big enough to easily grip when an arrow is placed in it's slot.
SRP: per two **$6.95**

POINT PULLER
Machined from carbon alloy steel and plated and then finished with foam handles, this puller will fit in your pocket but can help you remove broadheads and practice points with ease.
SRP: **$5.95**

Scorpion Broadheads and Arrow Points

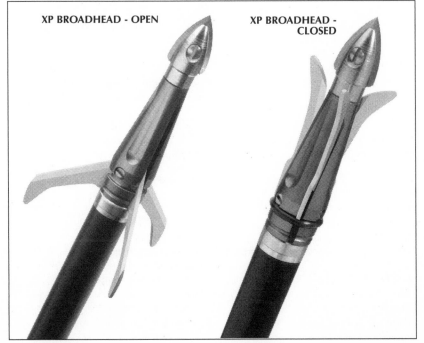

XP BROADHEAD - OPEN

XP BROADHEAD - CLOSED

XP Broadhead
Nap has released the Scorpion, a new mechanical broadhead with a super-penetrating, cut-on-contact tip. The replaceable tip has a low profile. The broadhead's extra strong aluminum ferrules have PowerGrooves for quick penetration. Three tough and sharp .030-inch thick knife grade stainless steel blades open to provide a 1½-inch cutting diameter. The ScorpionXP is offered in 100 grains.
SRP: . . . . **per three $22.99**

Simmons System Archery Broadheads and Arrow Points

LANDSHARK 125

LANDSHARK 160

LAND SHARK BROADHEADS

The flared-base, .042-inch thick blades in the 125 model are solid, and the 160-grain model .050-inch thick blades have small bleeder holes. Insert bleeder blades can be added to both models. The 160-grain broadhead cuts 1^{19}/$_{16}$-inch and the 125-grain model cuts 1^{3}/$_{16}$-inch wide.

SPECIFICATIONS
Weights: 125 and 160 grain
Blades: Two or four with bleeder
Available: Six pack
SRP: $25.00

Steel Force Broadheads and Arrow Points

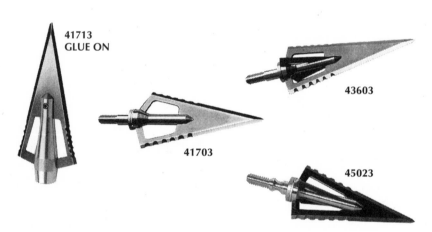

41023

41713 GLUE ON

41703

43603

41423

45023

STEEL FORCE STAINLESS STEEL SERIES:

41023/75 GRAIN
SPECIFICATIONS
Weights: 75 grain.
Blades: Two-edge single blade.
Available: Three pack.
SRP: $18.99

41413/125 GRAIN AND 41713/140 GRAIN
SPECIFICATIONS
Weights: 125- and 140-grain.
Blades: Two-edge single blade.
Available: Three pack
SRP: $21.99
Note: These blades are for gluing onto the arrow shaft and are not threaded

41423/100 GRAIN
SPECIFICATIONS
Weights: 100 grain.
Blades: Two-edge single blade cutting 1^{3}/$_{16}$-inch
Available: Three pack
SRP: $18.99

41703/125 GRAIN
SPECIFICATIONS
Weights: 125 grain.
Blades: Two-edge single blade.
Available: Three pack
SRP: $18.99

43603 LD/125 GRAIN
SPECIFICATIONS
Weights: 125 grain.
Blades: Four blade lock down design.
Available: Three pack

SRP: $19.99
Note: Requires special blade pliers to change the bleeder blade

45003/100 GRAIN
SPECIFICATIONS
Weights: 100 Grains
Blades: Four
Available: Three pack.
SRP: $21.99

45023/85 GRAIN
SPECIFICATIONS
Weights: 85 grain.
Blades: Four blade.
Available: Three pack
SRP: $21.99
Note: These are designed for fast shooting compound bows

ARROWS

Steel Force Broadheads and Arrow Points

45723

21703

75503

55723

25723

75703

25003

75003

71023

75723

45723/125 GRAIN
SPECIFICATIONS
Weights: 125 grain.
Blades: Four blade.
Available: Three pack
SRP $21.99

55723/150 GRAIN HELLFIRE
SPECIFICATIONS
Weights: 150 grain
Blades: Four blade, all are serrated and cryogenically treated.
Available: Three pack
SRP: $23.50

STEEL FORCE PREMIUM SERIES
The blades do not have serrated edges

25003/100 GRAIN AND 21003/100 GRAIN
SPECIFICATIONS
Weights: 100 grain
Blades: Four, and two in the 21003 model
Available: Three pack.
SRP: 25003 . . . . $19.99
21003 . . . . $17.99
Note: The blades do not have serrated edges on these broadheads.

21533/210 GRAIN
SPECIFICATIONS
Weights: 210 grain
Blades: Two fixed, solid one-piece construction, designed for dangerous game.

Available: Three pack.
SRP: $32.25
Note: Moly coating is standard.

21703/100 GRAIN
SPECIFICATIONS
Weights: 125 grains
Blades: Two blade design
Available: Three pack
SRP: $17.99

25723/125 GRAIN
SPECIFICATIONS
Weights: 125
Blades: Four blade design
Available: Three pack
SRP: $19.99
Note: This broadhead is the same as the Sabertooth 125 but without serrations.

71023/65 GRAIN
SPECIFICATIONS
Weights: 65 grains
Blades: Two blade with 1-inch cutting span
Available: Three pack
SRP: $31.75

75003/75 GRAIN
SPECIFICATIONS
Weights: 75 grain
Blades: Four
Available: Three pack.
SRP: $33.50

75503/85 GRAIN
SPECIFICATIONS
Weights: 85 grain
Blades: Four
Available: Three pack
SRP: $33.50

75703/100 GRAIN
SPECIFICATIONS
Weights: 100 grain
Blades: Four blade design
Available: Three pack
SRP: $33.50

75723/125 GRAIN HELLFIRE
SPECIFICATIONS
Weights: 125 grain
Blades: Four
Available: Three pack
SRP: $34.50
Note: This unique Steel Force blade is purple and gold

STEEL FORCE TITANIUM SABERTOOTH
Steel Force's Titanium Sabertooth broadheads feature serrated blades, titanium ferrules and cut-on-contact points. The large main blades are constructed of laser cut, grade 5 aerospace titanium.
SPECIFICATIONS
Weights: 65-125 grains
Blades: Four blade design
Available: Three pack
SRP: $33.50

Wasp Broadheads and Arrow Points

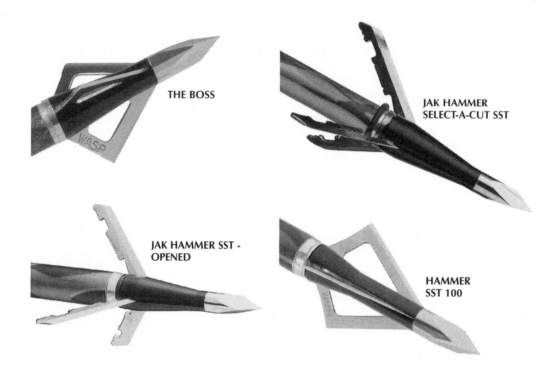

THE BOSS

JAK HAMMER
SELECT-A-CUT SST

JAK HAMMER SST -
OPENED

HAMMER
SST 100

THE BOSS

A broadhead designed for traveling more than 300 fps with .027-inch thick blades and a sharp SST tip delivers a large wound channel on the largest game animals. Cutting diameter for the BOSS is 1⅛-inches.

SPECIFICATIONS
Weights: 100 grain
Blades: Three
Available: Six pack
SRP: $29.99

JAK HAMMER
SELECT-A-CUT SST

WASP's latest innovation adds versatility to mechanical broadheads. You decide upon a 1½- or 1¼-inch cutting diameter by rotating the Select-A-Cut washer that's located between the blades and the arrow shaft. The washer has been machined at two different beveled edges to stop the blades at the preferred cutting diameter.

SPECIFICATIONS
Weights: 100 grain
Blades: Three
Available: Three pack
SRP: per three $25.99

JAK HAMMER SST
AND SST 11/4 CUT

This mechanical broadhead opens up to 1¾-inch with three cutting blades. An O-ring secures the blades while in flight. A Trocar tip aids with penetration. NOTE: A newer model, the JAK-Hammer SST 1¼-inch Cut is similar in design and cuts 1¼-inch diameter. A unique feature is that you can tie the blades in place for standard per-contact flight with Spider Wire fishing line or a lightweight wire and shoot the broadhead into foam targets without the blades opening. This is a great way to check your arrow flight prior to hunting.

SPECIFICATIONS
Weights: 100 and 125 grain
Blades: Three
Available: Three pack
SRP: both models $24.99

HAMMER SST

These WASP fixed blade broadheads have a Trocar heat-treated SMART tip that provides superior penetration. An extra long front foot on each blade helps lock the blades into the ferrules so that they stay put under the toughest conditions. Cutting diameters are 1⅛-inch for the 75 grain head and 1³⁄₁₆-inch for the other weights.

SPECIFICATIONS
Weights: 75, 85, 90, 100 and 125 grain
Blades: Three
Available: Six pack
SRP: $29.99

HI-TECH CAM LOK SST

This WASP broadhead is sleek, streamlined and devastatingly simple. The SMART tip aids with the three-point positive locking blade security system. One solid, double-wound high tensile steel ring exerts continuous even pressure to lock the blades into place. Cutting diameter is 1³⁄₁₆-inch.

SPECIFICATIONS
Weights: 100 and 125 grain
Blades: Three
Available: Six pack
SRP: $29.99

Zwickery Broadheads and Arrow Points

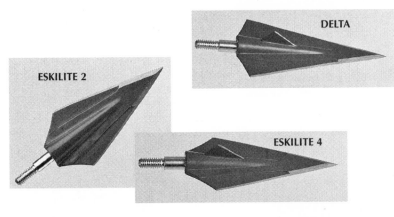

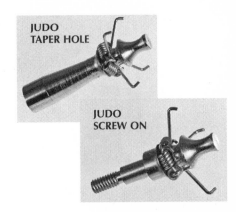

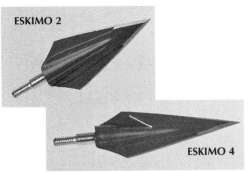

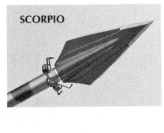

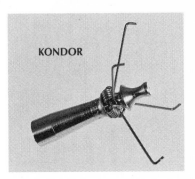

ZWICKEY BLACK DIAMOND

The Zwickey broadheads are available in numerous sizes. The heads use heat treated and tempered steel. All models—Eskimo, Eskilite, and Delta—have a rugged two-blade cut on impact points and two bleeder blades. These broadheads are very popular with traditional bowhunters and can be used with modern archery gear. Four and two edge versions are available.

ZWICKEY DELTA 2½-INCH BROADHEADS

SPECIFICATIONS
Weights: 135- and 170-grains.
Blades: 2 and 4-blade configurations
Available: 6- and 3-packs.
SRP: 2-edge 135-grain $19.50
4-edge 135-grain $21.50
170-grain 2-edge screw-on. . . $13.40
4-edge screw-on 4-edge
broadheads $14.80

ZWICKEY ESKILITE 2½-INCH BROADHEADS

SPECIFICATIONS
Weights: 110- and 135-grains.
Blades: 2 and 4 configurations
Available: 6 per pack in 110 grain, and 3 per pack in 135 grains.
SRP: 110-grain 2-blade $16.50
110-grain 4-blade $18.50
135-grain 2-blade screw-on . . $11.20
135-grain 4-blade screw-on . . $12.80

ZWICKEY ESKIMO 2½-INCH BROADHEADS

SPECIFICATIONS
Weights: 125- and 160-grain
Blades: 2 and 4 configuration
Available: Standard glue on and screw-on styles
SRP: per 6 standard 2- and 4-blade
125 grain $16.50
per 3-pack 2 edge
160-grain $11.20
per 4-edge 160-grain
screw-on. $12.80

ZWICKEY JUDOS

SPECIFICATIONS
Weights: 100-,125-, 135- and 120-grains
Blades: 4 prongs each
Available: 100- and 125-grain screw on for standard arrow inserts, 135- and 120-grani glue on with 5-degree taper hole
SRP: per two $6.00

ZWICKEY KONDOR

SPECIFICATIONS
Weights: 105- and 145-grains
Blades: 4 prongs
Available: screw on or 5-degere taper hole glue-on
SRP: each $4.00

ZWICKEY SCORPIO

SPECIFICATIONS
Weights: 20 grains each
Blades: 4 prongs
Available: five sizes to fit various arrow shafts: $20/64$, $21/64$, $22/64$, $23/64$, and $24/64$
SRP: per 2-pack $3.00

Arizona Rim Country Arrow Building Components

E-Z FLETCH

E-Z Fletch
The E-Z Fletch is a compact, lightweight, arrow-fletching unit that is easy to use, even in the field. It automatically adjusts to any size arrow shaft from 2013 to 2613 and It comes in straight, straight offset, right- or left-helical design. It will also do any style of three or four fletch with nothing extra to buy. The E-Z Fletch's new Carbon Arrow model will fletch the smallest carbon shaft up to a 2018 aluminum shaft. This new, patented design ensures precision alignment and includes interchangeable arms.
SRP: **$46.99**

Bohning Arrow Building Components

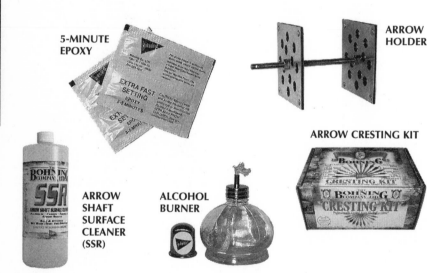

5-MINUTE EPOXY

ARROW SHAFT SURFACE CLEANER (SSR)

ALCOHOL BURNER

ARROW CRESTING KIT

ARROW HOLDER

UNIVERSAL ARROW PAD

STANDARD ARROW PAD

ARROW FLETCHING KIT

5-Minute Epoxy
Bonds points and inserts to all types of shafts. Available in easy-to-mix packets.
SRP: **$4.45**

Alcohol Burner
This glass burner with a wick is excellent for hot melt adhesive applications. It uses denatured alcohol.
SRP: **$11.61**
extra wicks **$1.00**

Arrow Cresting Kit
Use this complete package to crest aluminum, fiberglass or wooden arrows. A video takes you through the process step-by-step. Kit includes a standard crester, dip tube, Fletch-Lac thinner, six cresting colors, paint caddy, white lacquer, set of arrow hiolders, two camel hair brushes, shaft cleaner and the video.
SRP: **$135.22**

Arrow Fletching Kit
Bohning has done the shopping and assembling for you and created this kit that has everything you need to install nocks and inserts, plus attach fletchings. This kit includes an instructional video along with Fletch-Tite, Bond-Tite, Ferr-L-Tite, signature nocks, T nocks, 4- and 5-inch Fletch tite vanes, a Pro-Class fletching jig and shaft cleaner. Must specify right, left or straight clamps.
SRP: **$72.58**

Arrow Holders
Used to dip multiple shafts at once, these racks fit all types of arrow shafts.
SRP: per dozen **$30.61**

per two dozen. **$42.51**

Arrow Pads
Use with the box to keep arrows organized and uniformly separated. The universal fits large and small diameter shafts, the standard size fits mid-range diameter shafts. Available in 100 packs.
SRP: **$13.55**

Arrow Shaft Surface Cleaner (SSR)
This high-strength cleaner is designed for today's anodized process. It degreases and prepares aluminum and carbon shafts. Simple to use: add hot water to the powder and safely clean the shafts. Not intended for use on wood products.
SRP: pint. **$3.84**
up to gallon. **$16.21**

Bohning Arrow Building Components

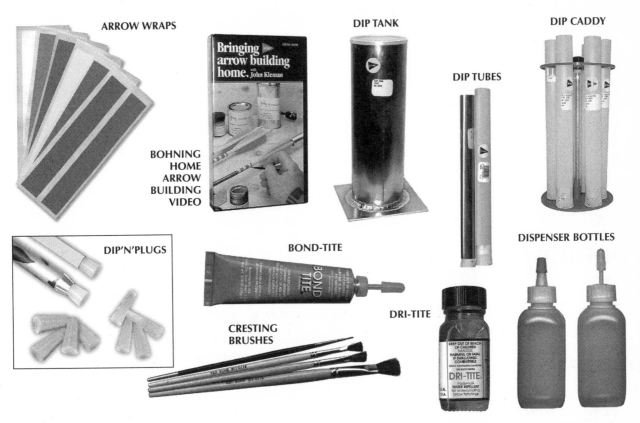

ARROW WRAPS

BOHNING HOME ARROW BUILDING VIDEO

DIP TANK

DIP CADDY

DIP TUBES

DIP'N'PLUGS

BOND-TITE

DRI-TITE

CRESTING BRUSHES

DISPENSER BOTTLES

BOHNING ARROW WRAPS

Bohning's arrow wraps are available in traditional wraps, specialty wraps that include a screaming eagle, and wild wraps that include several tiger stripe patterns. These graphics are easy to install with the use of a mouse pad. Arrow wrap colors include white, yellow, orange, red green and pink. Must specify carbon or aluminum shafts.
SRP: per dozen $16.15

BOND-TITE

Bonds feathers, vanes and nocks to CARBON shafts. A waterproof, solvent-based formula. Offered in tubes, ½ pint, pint, quart, and gallon quantities.
**SRP: ¾-ounce tube $2.67
to gallon $62.23**

BOHNING HOME ARROW BUILDING

A step by step video guide on how to prepare, dip and fletch arrows. A must for anyone wanting to learn the process.
SRP: $18.19

CLAMP RELEASE TAPE

This special tape can be applied to the edge of the clamp to prevent adhesion build up and provide a quick clean-up.
SRP: $1.19

CRESTING BRUSHES

These quality camel hair brushes can be sued to paint lines on arrow shafts. Available in thin, ⅛-, ¼-, and ½-inch widths.
SRP: fine brush . . . . . $3.55 to $6.77

DIP CADDY

This rack by Bohning is great for Crown Dips and holds six 1-inch tubes.
SRP: $9.10

DIP'N PLUGS

Plugs to seal the ends of carbon and Uni-Bushing style shafts to prevent cresting paint from entering the end of the shaft. Available per dozen or 100 pack.
**SRP: per dozen $3.60
per 100. . . . . $19.78**

DIP TANKS

A convenient way and system to dip arrow shafts for cresting. The aluminum tube has a welded flat base to ensure solid performance. Specify 4- or 6-inch diameter.
SRP: 36-inch tank. . $46.18 to $61.59

DIP TUBES

Single tubes for dipping an arrow shaft. Length options include 12-, 24-, 32- and 34-inches.
SRP: 32-inch tube . . $7.93 to $14.82

DISPENSER BOTTLES

A great way to store and apply solvents and adhesives. The nearly clear bottles reveal how much mixture remains inside.
**SRP: thinner $1.10
adhesive $2.43**

DRI-TITE

A waterproof dressing formulated for arrow feathers—and dry flies for fishing. It eliminates flattening and loss of body and it will not stiffen or add weight. The solution dries instantly and will not harm finishes. Available in a 1-ounce bottle and must be brushed onto the shaft
SRP: $4.58

Bohning Arrow Building Components

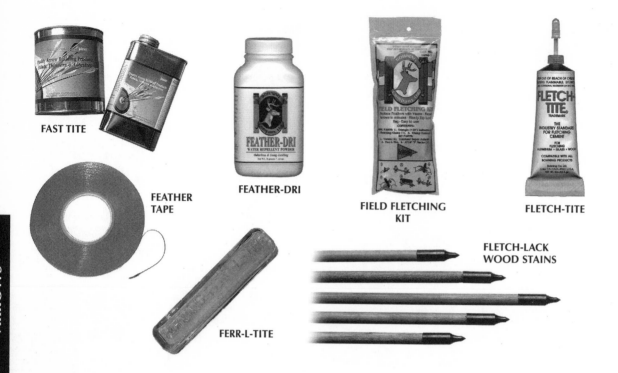

FAST TITE

FEATHER TAPE

FEATHER-DRI

FIELD FLETCHING KIT

FLETCH-TITE

FLETCH-LACK WOOD STAINS

FERR-L-TITE

FAST TITE
This water-repellent adhesion is used to quickly build arrows. Available in ½ pint, pint, quart and gallon sizes. Thinner is offered in pint, quart and gallon quantities.

SRP: ½ pint $7.13
gallon $62.23

FEATHER-DRI
A water repellant powder for feathers that is colorless and odorless and will not affect the fletch adhesion.

SRP: $6.42

FEATHER FLETCHING TAPE
This tape is easy to apply and creates a strong, reliable bond on contact. Can be used to fletch more than three dozen arrows.

SRP: roll $6.06

FERR-L-TITE
A stick of hot melt cement that's tough, elastic and waterproof. Can be used to adhere points and inserts to aluminum or wood shafts. Heat reversible. Specify stick or brick.

SRP: stick $2.22
pound brick. $19.44

FIELD FLETCHING KIT
Make arrow vane and feather repairs in the field with this simple and easy to use kit. Includes everything you need to field repair 12 arrows including, fletching tool, 36 five-inch vanes, instant gel, 1 stick of Ferr-L-Tite and a dozen nocks.

SRP: $3.85

FINISH AND SOLUTION CONTAINERS
Use these containers to store and separate various cresting solutions. Sizes range from ½ pint to gallon plastic. 1-ounce and quart size glass containers are also available.

SRP: ½ pint $1.56
up to gallon container $2.97

FLAT WHITE
A dull base-coat finish to begin the cresting process. Available in ½ pint, pint, quart, gallon and 5-gallon quantities.

SRP: pint $12.78
to gallon $68.22

FLETCH-LAC BLUE AND CLEAR
This solution produces sharper, brighter colors. Can be sued to

seal wooden shafts or as a dip for aluminum shafts. Do not thin.

SRP: ½ pint $6.54
to gallon $52.14

FLETCH-LACK WOOD STAINS
Use these stains to tint raw wood shafts and bring out the natural grain as you customize the appearance of your arrows. Stain colors include shadow gray, rich mahogany, autumn glow, olive haze and walnut hue. Available in ½ pint, pint, quart and gallon quantities.

SRP: pint $7.18
up to gallon. $57.37

FLETCH-TITE
A tube of glue that bonds feathers, vanes and nocks to aluminum, wood and fiberglass shafts. It's available in tubes or cans and in half-pint, pint, quart and gallon quantities.

SRP: ½ pint $6.06
to gallon $50.38

FLETCH TITE
A 2-ounce tube provides the same easy-application tip but a larger, economical size.

SRP: per 2-oz $5.31

Bohning Arrow Building Components

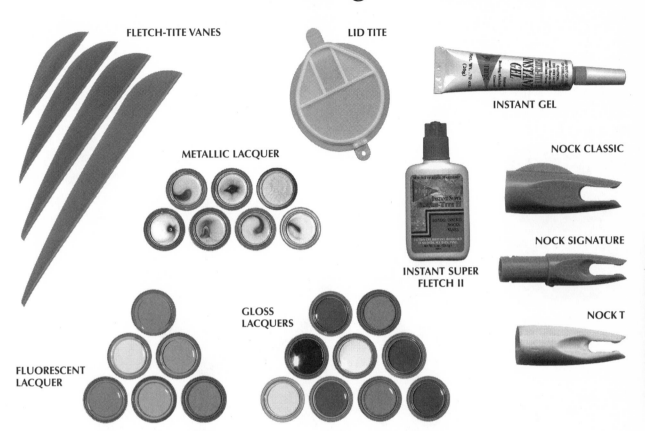

FLETCH-TITE VANES

LID TITE

INSTANT GEL

METALLIC LACQUER

NOCK CLASSIC

NOCK SIGNATURE

INSTANT SUPER FLETCH II

NOCK T

GLOSS LACQUERS

FLUORESCENT LACQUER

FLETCH-TITE VANES
The base of these vanes are chemically treated to promote excellent adhesion. Must specify color and size. These vanes are offered in 36 packs, 100 packs and 1,000 packs for the archer with lots of arrows and friends. Sizes include 2-, 3-, 4- and 5-inch lengths. Colors include red, green, yellow, white, black, hot pink, teal blue, purple, orange, olive drab, bark brown, gray, dark green and several fluorescent colors.
SRP: 36 (4 and 5-inch only) . . . $2.77
per dozen $6.77

FLUORESCENT LACQUER
Add brilliant colors to your crests with these Bohning lacquers. Stabilized for long wear and life. Note: Must use a white base-coat under these colors. Options include; signal green, blaze orange, saturn yellow, rocket red, chartreuse, and aurora pink. Available in quantities from 1-ounce to one gallon.
SRP: ½-pint $10.80
to gallon $98.46

GLOSS LACQUERS
Bright true colors for cresting shafts and creating custom arrows. Easy to apply. Colors include: green, orange, purple, white, red, blue, burgundy, black and yellow.
SRP: ½-pint $7.91
to gallon $68.22

INSTANT GEL
This quick-setting gel can be used to install and repair fletching.
SRP: three gram tube $2.48
20-gram tube $9.17

INSTANT SUPER FLETCH II
An instant bond for nocks and vanes to aluminum, carbon or wood shafts. An anti-blush additive minimizes frosting.
SRP: per ounce $11.32

LID TITE
These self-sealing lids make pouring and storage of paints, adhesions and solvents a snap.
Specify quart or gallon container size

METALLIC LACQUER
Great for pin stripes and dips. Easy to apply and dries to a brilliant sheen. Make your arrows stand out in the crowd. Available in multiple quantities and colors: gold, plum, silver, jade, blue, pearl and copper.
SRP: ½-pint $9.08
to gallon $88.27

NOCKS
Bohning offers Signature, T and Classic nocks with the built-on mini vane in many sizes to fit a wide selection of shafts. Color options include: fluorescent lime, fluorescent apricot, fluorescent rose, fluorescent ruby, black, white, kiwi, mandarin, plum, yellow, green, gray, orange and red. Color selection varies by type of nock selected and not all colors are offered in all nock styles. For more details, call Bohning at 800-253-0136 or visit www.bohning.com.
SRP: Signature nocks, per doz.. $4.48
     per 100. . . . . $18.18
T nocks, per 50 pack $4.30
Classic nocks, per 50 pack. . . . $4.30

Bohning Arrow Building Components

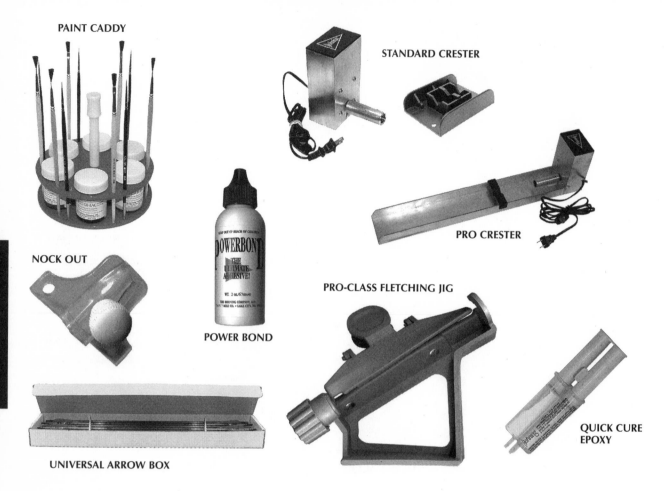

PAINT CADDY

STANDARD CRESTER

PRO CRESTER

NOCK OUT

POWER BOND

PRO-CLASS FLETCHING JIG

QUICK CURE EPOXY

UNIVERSAL ARROW BOX

ARROWS

NOCK OUT
A handy tool to assist with the removal or alignment of Signature nocks. This device will not damage the nocks.
SRP: $1.68

PAINT CADDY
A convenient and stable way to hold paints and brushes during the arrow cresting process.
SRP: $7.28

POWER BOND
The ultimate insert and point adhesion that works on all types of arrow shafts. This easy to use one-step adhesion works well on wrapped carbon applications and does not get brittle under any condition or temperature. Heat reversible. No mixing required and no mess to clean. Two drops cures in approximately 8 hours. One tube completes 300 to 400 hours.
SRP: per 2 oz. $11.39

PRO AND STANDARD CRESTER
This motor driven unit turns arrows up to 300 rpms and makes cresting easy and professional. A replacement chuck is available.
SRP: Standard $102.01
Pro $140.73

PRO-CLASS FLETCHING JIG
You can create a perfect fletch every time with this jig that uses a quick-set magnetic clamp adjustment. Vane and feather style options include straight, right or left helical. A crossbow bolt adapter costs $6.44.
SRP: $54. 23

QUICK CURE EPOXY
A double syringe with epoxy and cure that permanently bonds points or inserts to all types of shafts.
SRP: $9.92

SUPER COAT
A clear lacquer that cures to super hard finish. Use this as a one-coat sealer on wood shafts.
SRP: pint $7.18
up to gallon. $57.37

THINNERS
These solutions (Fletch-Tite and Fletch-Lac) can be used to thin paints and various cresting solutions. Offered in quantities ranging from pint to a quart.
SRP: pint $7.81
to gallon $34.36

UNIVERSAL ARROW BOX
The industry standard arrow box that fits 34- or 336-inch shafts. This box is great for storing a dozen arrows.
SRP: 50 pack $73.10

Carbon Express Arrow Building Components

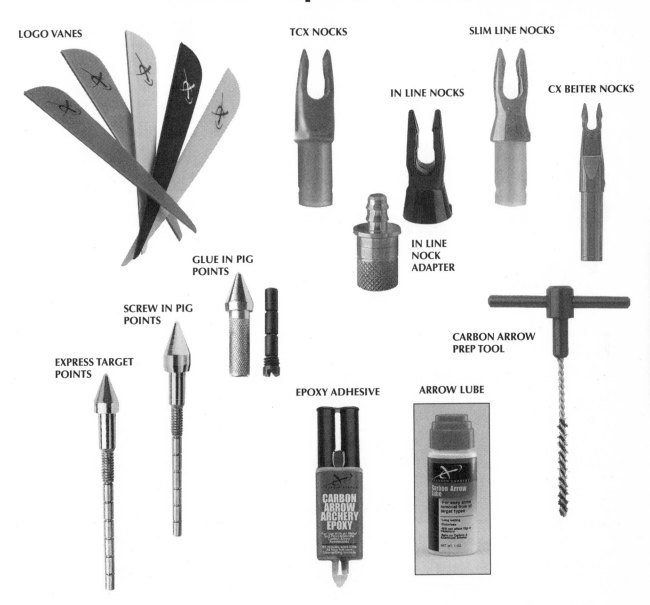

LOGO VANES

TCX NOCKS

SLIM LINE NOCKS

IN LINE NOCKS

CX BEITER NOCKS

IN LINE NOCK ADAPTER

GLUE IN PIG POINTS

SCREW IN PIG POINTS

CARBON ARROW PREP TOOL

EXPRESS TARGET POINTS

EPOXY ADHESIVE

ARROW LUBE

CARBON EXPRESS LOGO VANES
These colorful—yellow, orange, green, white and black—vanes are available in 4-inch lengths and 100 per pack. They have the distinct Carbon Epxress logo and can be used on all carbon shafts.
SRP: 100 pack **$18.92**

COMPONENTS
per 6 units unless stated otherwise:
TCX NOCKS
   SRP: **$5.40**
IN LINE NOCKS
   SRP: **$6.50**

SLIM LINE NOCKS
   SRP: **$4.50**
   100 nocks **$35.00**
CX BEITER NOCKS
   SRP: per dozen **$18.95**
IN LINE NOCK ADAPTERS (TYPE 1)
   SRP: per dozen **$6.50**
IN LINE NOCK ADAPTERS (TYPE 2)
   SRP: per dozen **$6.50**
SCREW IN PIG POINTS
   SRP: per 12 pack **$9.00**
GLUE IN PIG POINTS
   SRP: per dozen **$18.10**
EXPRESS TARGET POINTS
   SRP: **$21.70**

INSERTS
   SRP: per 12 pack **$5.34**
SHAFT WEIGHTS (2- OR 3-GRAINS PER IN.)
   SRP: **$10.50**

MISCELLANEOUS ARROW CONSTRUCTION SUPPLIES
EPOXY ADHESIVE
   SRP: **$12.58**
ARROW LUBE
   SRP: **$7.15**
CARBON ARROW PREP TOOL
   SRP: **$6.30**

Easton Arrow Building Components

ASSORTTED NOCKS

ADHESIVES

HOT MELT FOR INSERT INSTALLATION
SRP: 3.30
EPOXY (AAE)
SRP: 12.40
FAST SET FLETCHING ADHESIVE GEL
SRP: (3grams) $6.23

NOCKS

Offered in black, white, green, red
and yellow and in multiple styles and
sizes. You must select a style to fit
your arrow shaft.
SRP: per dozen $4.60
specialty target per dozen . $12.93

SHAFTS

More than 19 models are offered,
including carbon, carbon with
aluminum cores and aluminum.
Finishes range from black to camouflage and simulated wood grain.
SRP: aluminum target $32.76
carbon $142.48

TOOLS

SUPER NOCK TOOL
SRP: $15.62
G NOCK TOOL
SRP: $15.62

Easy-Eye Arrow Building Components

EZE-WRAPS

EZE-Eye offers more than 60 styles of
arrow wraps to help you make your
mark in style. The company's #401
Buck skull is a winner. Other arrow
wrap options from Eze-Eye include:
crests, fades, crest/fade combos, Elite
wraps and X-treme graphics. Eze-Eye
can also print custom wraps with
your name on the wrap. The company
makes a solid wrap that's highly
visible in chartreuse, red, hunter
orange, yellow and white.
SRP: per dozen . . . $10.00 to $12.00

SKULL GRAPHIC (DETAIL)

CREST

CREST/FADE
COMBO

ELITE

FADE

XTREME
TEAM USA

ARROWS

Flex-Fletch Arrow Building Components

FLEX-FLETCH PRODUCTS

This St. Paul, Minnesota, company makes more than a dozen target and hunting vanes. Colors and style vary widely and prices reflect current production and styles and lengths. Contact 651-426-4882 for pricing details.

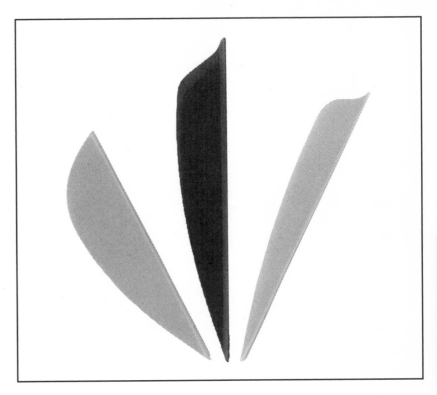

G-5 Arrow Building Components

ARROW SQUARING DEVICE (ASD)

The ASD is a tool that permits arrow builders and archers the ability to machine, clean and deburr the face of an insert or square the tip of the shaft for more accurate tip and broadhead alignment. This tool eliminates removing and re-gluing inserts and other steps to create an arrow that flies true. The ASD is offered in two models: one for aluminum shafts and one for carbon shafts. To operate, place the shaft in the groove and push the end of the shaft and face of the insert against the cutter and rotate the arrow shaft. Replacement cutters are available.

SRP: aluminum **$34.99**
carbon **$36.99**

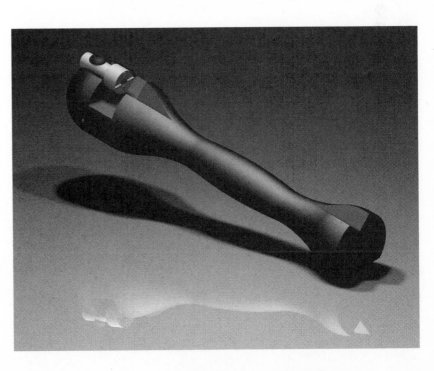

Gateway Feathers Arrow Building Components

GREEN CAMO MAGNUM

GREEN CAMO PARABOLIC

GREEN CAMO SHIELD

WHITE BARRED MAGNUM

WHITE BARRED PARABOLIC

WHITE BARRED SHIELD

ARROWS

GATEWAY FEATHERS This Douglas, Arizona company controls the quality and quantity of it feathers. Feathers are offered in 50 and 10 packs and 4 shapes, 9 sizes and 27 colors so every archer will find something to suit their taste. Sizes range from $1^7/_8$-inch to 12-inch full-length feathers. Visit www.gatewayfeathers.com for additional details.

Shapes include parabolic, shield cut, cut section, magnum and full length. Colors include white, red, chartreuse, desert brown, blue, gray, yellow, orange, pink, fluorescent yellow, black and green. Camouflaged feathers include tre brown, tre green, tre yellow, tre red, tre bark, tre purple, and tre orange. Barred feathers include white, red, green, brown, blue, yellow and orange. Must specify left or right feathers when ordering.

SRP: 4-inch parabolic, average
per 50 . . . . $16.50 - $18.99
4- or 5-inch feathers,
per 100 . . . . $30.00 to $35.00
Shield cut feathers, per 50 . . . $19.25
Full cut flu-flu-feathers,
per 50 . . . . $27.25

Fletching Size
A faster arrow can use a smaller fletch and remain stable. A slower arrow requires a larger fletch(which will make it even slower). Choose an optimum size that stabilizes the arrow over the longest distance you will have to shoot. Use the fletch size that maintains arrow speed long enough to reach the target but is as large as you can get away with for the most forgiving shot.

Golden Key-Futura Arrow Building Components

BITZENBURGER FLETCHER
You can fletch your own arrows with this time proven fletching jig. You have a choice of straight, right wing or left wing clamps, plus standard or TM style nock receivers.

SRP:. $102
Nock receivers $27

GRAYLING FLETCHER
A lighweight unit that puts on one fletch at a time with a special clamp.

SRP:. $44

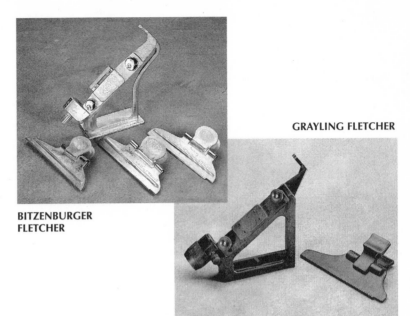

GRAYLING FLETCHER

BITZENBURGER FLETCHER

ARROWS

Gold Tip Arrow Building Components

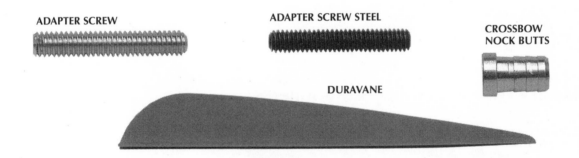

ADAPTER SCREW

ADAPTER SCREW STEEL

CROSSBOW NOCK BUTTS

DURAVANE

ADAPTER SCREWS
These adapter screws help secure weights and nocks to the nock end of shafts. These adapters are available in aluminum (10-grain) and steel (30-grain) models.

SRP: per dozen $2.09
per 120 . . . . $20.58

CROSSBOW NOCK BUTTS
These bolt inserts are available in three styles, including a 70-grain brass insert.

SRP: per dozen $2.73
brass, per dozen $4.13

DURAVANES
These durable field and range proven vanes are available in four lengths— 3-, 4-, 5- and 1.8 inch—to suit target archers and hunters. Available colors include: black, blue, brown, florescent green, florescent orange, florescent red, florescent yellow, gray, green, olive, orange, purple, red, white and yellow.

SRP: per 100 . . . . $6.93
1.8-inch vanes, per 100 . . . . . . $9.73
3-D models, per 50 . . . . $9.73

GATEWAY FEATHERS
For archers who want forgiving feathers and performance. Available in: white, red, chartreuse, desert brown, blue, yellow, orange, pink, florescent yellow, black, green, and dimensional patterned bark, green, brown, yellow, orange, red and purple. Only available in 4-inch right wing parabolic format.

SRP: per 100 . . . . . . $23.23 - $25.13

GOAT TUFF GLUE
Designed to help arrow vanes and feathers stick to shafts like a mountain goat does to a cliff. Available in assorted quantities.

SRP: 1oz, beginning at $5.25

Gold Tip Arrow Building Components

LOCK NOCK - SERIES 22

THREADED INSERT - SERIES 22

ADAPTER WEIGHT

NOCK ADAPTER ULTRA-LIGHT

THREADED INSERT - X-CUTTER

LOCK NOCKS

These patented lockable nocks securely positions the nock without glues, epoxies or adhesives. Adjustments can be made quickly by loosening a small allen screw in the notch of the nock. Nocks are available in .246 (15 grain) and 22 Series (23 grain) Lock Nocks. Color choices include black, green, orange, pink, blue, white and yellow.
SRP: per dozen **$5.53**
   per 100 . . . . **$34.95**

NOCK ADAPTERS

Available models include Ultra-Light, .246, .22 series and X-Cutter nock adapters. All are designed to match the performance of Gold Tip shafts.
SRP: per dozen . . . . . **$2.73 to $4.13**

THREADED INSERTS

Gold Tip's threaded inserts are designed to complete the company's carbon/graphite shafts. Models include .246, 22 Series and X-Cutter. *Weight:* 47 grains each.

SRP: per dozen **$2.73**
   per 120 . . . . **$26.53**
X-Cutters . . . . **per dozen $4.13**

WEIGHTS

Six sizes and styles of adapter weights help archers fine tune arrow flight. Available weight in grains includes: 10, 20 and 40.
SRP: per dozen **$2.09**
   per 120 . . . . **$20.58**

Muzzy Arrow Building Components

MUZZY BUTANE TORCH

MUZZY 10-MINUTE EPOXY

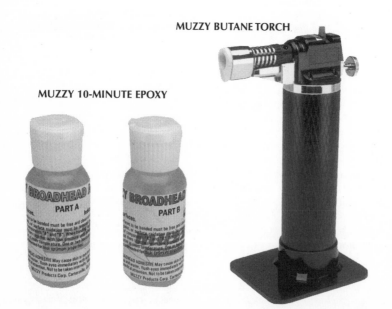

MUZZY 10-MINUTE EPOXY

A two-part epoxy that's great for emergency field repairs and is suitable for permanent repairs of inserts and adapter, plus for gluing on broadheads and fishpoints. The epoxy sets in 10 minutes.
SRP: **$6.87**

MUZZY BUTANE TORCH

This 5½-inch tall torch is great for building arrows and shafts repairs. It can be filled with standard drug store butane and will burn for 2 to 3 hours on one refill.
SRP: **$29.27**

ARROWS

NORTH AMERICAN ARCHERY GROUP (NAAG) in Gainesville, Florida, is also known for producing Bear, Golden Eagle, and Jennings bows.

ARROW NOCKS
High visible nock colors include red and orange. Available in sizes $5/16$ or $11/32$.
SRP: 12/pack. **$3.49**

FLETCHING GLUE
A tube or archery cement with applicator tip used to secure fletching to arrow shafts.
SRP: **$3.49**

QUICK DIP FOR ARROWS
Customize your arrows and also increase their visibility to increase recovery rate. Available in White, Fire, Fluorescent Yellow and Reflective White colors.
SRP: **$11.99**

FLETCHING GLUE

ARROW NOCKS

ARROWS

PDP (Precision Designed Products)
Arrow Building Components

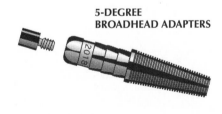

5-DEGREE BROADHEAD ADAPTERS

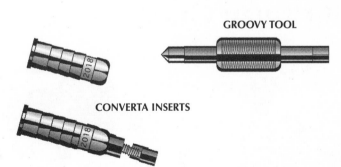

CONVERTA INSERTS

GROOVY TOOL

5-DEGREE BROADHEAD ADAPTERS
A new lightweight design makes this adapter by PDP the same weight as an insert. Simply remove the insert and glue in the adapter to maintain the identical weight. A broadhead is easily attached to tapered and threaded shaft.
SRP: per dozen **$6.75**

CONVERTA INSERTS
All PDP inserts are stamped for permanent identification. Many sizes exist to fit all popular aluminum and carbon shafts.
SRP: per dozen . . . . **$2.16 to $12.55**

GROOVY TOOL
This innovative tool from PDP forms microscopic grooves inside many sizes of arrow shafts to help secure the insert in place and helps the glue grip the shaft. Never have points pull out again.
SRP: **$27.90**

Saunders Archery Arrow Building Components

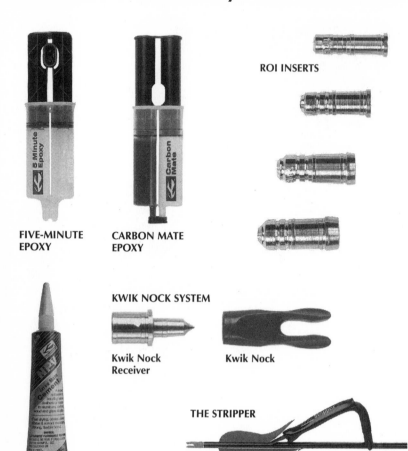

ROI INSERTS

FIVE-MINUTE EPOXY

CARBON MATE EPOXY

KWIK NOCK SYSTEM

Kwik Nock
Receiver

Kwik Nock

THE STRIPPER

NPV CEMENT

ADHESIVES

Saunders Archery has several types of adhesives:

NPV Cement	**$4.95**
Five-Minute Epoxy	**$7.95**
Carbon Mate Epoxy	**$8.95**
Hunt-Bond Hot Melt	**$2.95**

KWIK NOCK SYSTEM

These nocks have patented stepped alignment rings and can be purchased as a Uni-to Kwik nock adapter.

SRP: receivers	**$6.95**
nocks per dozen	**$4.95**

ROI INSERTS

Light-Speed inserts are 33% lighter than standard models. Heavy weigh versions provide more kinetic energy. Available in three styles with alignment rings.

SRP: per dozen	**$3.95**

THE STRIPPER

A tool to remove fletching and glue from an arrow shaft in one easy stroke.

SRP:	**$11.9**

Sportsman Graphics Arrow Building Components

WRAP/CREST/TRAIL MARKER SERIES

The wraps offered by Sportsman Graphics include standard crests, reflecto-wraps, and a series that depicts white-tailed bucks, bull elk, wild boar, deer tracks, wild turkeys and monster bucks.

SRP: Standard crests, per 6 . . .	**$6.50**
Reflecto-wraps, per 6	**$6.85**
Game animal series, per 6	**$5.65**

Steel Force Arrow Building Components

BEYOND BOND ACCELERATOR

BEYOND BOND GLUE

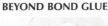

BEYOND BOND COMBO

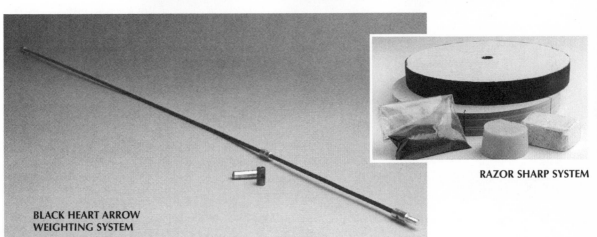

RAZOR SHARP SYSTEM

BLACK HEART ARROW
WEIGHTING SYSTEM

BEYOND BOND ACCELERATOR

This accelerator speeds up the required drying time when building arrows. Spray onto the shaft before placing vane or feather into position.
SRP: 2 oz. **$6.50**

BEYOND BOND COMBO

This package has a bottle of Steel Forces Beyond Bond Glue and a bottle of Beyond Bond Accelerator for applying vanes and feathers to arrow shafts.
SRP: **$10.50**

BEYOND BOND HI-TECH GLUE

This incredibly strong high-tech glue signifantly erduces arrow building time and dries in minutes. To work best, you put glue on the feather or vane edge and spray accelerator on the arrow shaft. This glue is available

in ½ ounce and 2-ounce sizes with a resealable applicator tip bottle.
SRP: ½-oz. **$4.95**
2 oz. **$12.95**

BLACK HEART ARROW WEIGHTING SYSTEM

These carbon rods insert inside .245-inch inside diameter carbon arrows to add weight as needed and recommended when hunting dangerous game with bow and arrows. The weight does not affect arrow spine and center weights can be moved to change front of center percentage. The Steel Force special kit includes: three 32-inch carbon rods (can be cut to desired length), four adapters and a specially threaded insert rod.
SRP: per kit **$28.50**

RAZOR SHARP SYSTEM

This Steel Force broadhead sharpening kit features a special silicone carbide abrasive grit 8-inch wheel and a slotted wheel with a white rouge for create a perfect polisher/stropper like a barber shop. The kit includes additional sharpening grit, white rouge, conditioning grease and two 1x8-inch wheels that can be attached to a home arbor bench grinder.
SRP: per kit **24.95**

Trueflight Arrow Building Components

BARRED ROUND BACK

BARED SHIELD BACK

FULL BARRED FEATHER

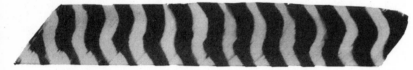

FULL FEATHER

ROUND BACK

SHIELD BACK

BARRED FEATHERS

These feathers have the distinct natural barrs in the feathers. Must specify left or right. Feathers. Color options include white, green barred, red barred, autumn brown barred, yellow-green barred, leaf green barred, orange barred, royal purple barred, chartreuse barred.

SRP: per 100 feathers
4-inch barred w/ rounded
   or shield back **$46.45**
5-inch barred w/rounded
   or shield back **$49.20**
Maxi-Fletch w/larger
   round back **$52.05**
Full length section so you
   can cut your own **$48.10**

FEATHERS

These solid colored pre-cut feathers are offered in: fluorescent white, pink, chartreuse, and scarlet red, sunshine yellow, blaze orange, kelly green, sky blue, shadow black, bronzed brown, autumn brown, leaf green, goose grey and royal purple. Must specify left or right feathers.

SRP: per 100 feathers
2½-inch round back. **$16.70**
3-inch round back **$18.95**
4-inch round back **$25.10**
5-inch round back **$30.25**
Maxi-Fletch larger feather . . . **$35.05**

A helical on the vanes will straighten out an arrow much faster than straight fletching, lessening effects of bad releases, bad nock travel or bad bow movements. The larger the fletching, the quicker the arrow will correct itself.

ARROWS

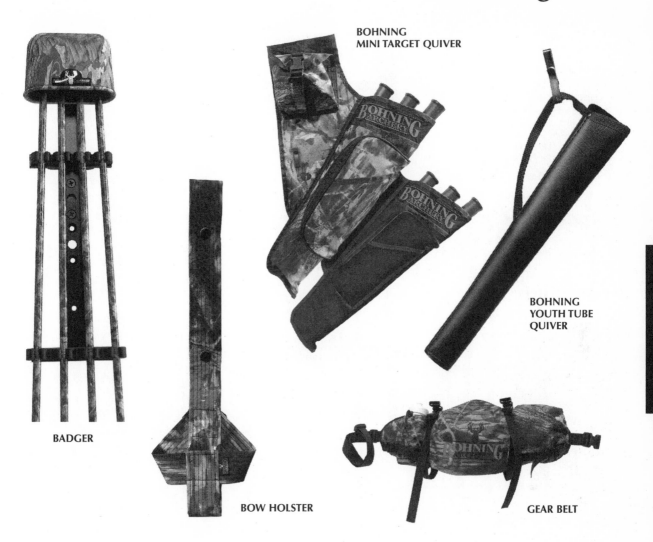

BOHNING
MINI TARGET QUIVER

BOHNING
YOUTH TUBE
QUIVER

ARROWS

BADGER

BOW HOLSTER

GEAR BELT

BADGER

Similar to the Guardian but only designed to hold 4 arrows.

SRP: black **$28.85**
camouflaged **$34.91**

BOW HOLSTER

An easy snap adjustment helps you position this bow holder at the right height for quick access. The larger pocket holds single-cam bows with ease. Your bow is always in place in any hunting or shooting situation. Camouflaged in Mossy Oak Break Up.

SRP: **$6.35**

BOWHUNTER'S GEAR BELT

This system will accept the Bohning target quiver. The belt has zippered pockets to hold essentials, quick disconnect shoulder straps to make carrying a load more comfortable and extra straps to lash gear on the outside. A fully adjustable padded belt has a quick-disconnect system. The quiver is sold separately.

SRP: **$28.30**

MINI TARGET QUIVER

A miniature adult version of the popular Bohning hip quiver. The quiver is 14-inches long with two arrow tubes. It's available in LH and RH and camouflaged.

SRP: **$17.92**

TARGET QUIVERS

These hip mounted quivers are made of durable and lightweight Cordura. These items are available in Mossy Oak and black and in LH and RH models. These quivers have three tubes and an external accessory pocket.

SRP: **$30.80**

YOUTH TUBE QUIVER

Designed to hold smaller youth arrows for beginning target shooters.

SRP: **$9.38**

Guardian Quivers

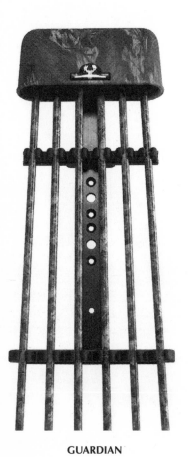

GUARDIAN

JACK-PINE 5

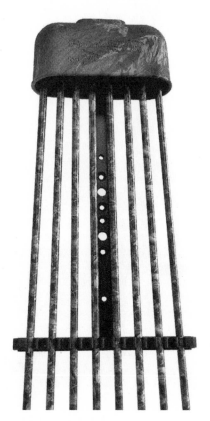

PINNACLE MAX

GUARDIAN

You can carry up to a half dozen aluminum or carbon arrows with this quiver. Mechanical broadheads can fit into the sound dampening hood liner. An aluminum stem secures the quiver sections together.
SRP: black. $29.54
camouflaged $36.20

Jack-Pine 5: 5-arrow quiver
SRP: black. $12.56
camouflaged $18.88
The Lynx: 4-arrow quiver
Hood liner $3.75
SRP: black. $16.96
camouflaged $22.62
Pinnacle Lite: 5-arrow quiver
SRP: black standard $23.62

camouflaged $28.32
Pinnacle Max: 8 arrow quiver
SRP: black. $25.54
camouflaged $30.14
Sentry: 3-arrow
SRP: black. $11.87
camouflaged $17.93

No matter what type of arrow shaft you shoot, carbon or aluminum, make sure you select arrows with the correct spine. An overspined or underspined arrow can result in poor arrow flight, making it difficult to shoot tight groups.

KWIKEE 3

KWIKEE COMBO QUIVER

KWIKEE KOMPOUND KWIVER

KWIKEE KWIVER

4-Arrow Kwikee Quiver for Recurves With hood to cover broadheads and an arrow gripping system that stays pliable in extreme temperatures. Ultra-Lock locking system for the attachment base and back-up knob to eliminate rattle and bracket noise. This set of gator-like jaws will grip the limbs of recurve and longbows. The grips fasten into place securely with perma-nently installed spring steel clips. Broadhead shield is included.

SRP: **$18.99**

Kwikee Combo Quiver
   SRP: $24.99
Kwikee Kompound
   SRP: $21.99
   camouflage and colors. . . . $18.99
Kwikee 3
   SRP: $19.99

Neet Quivers

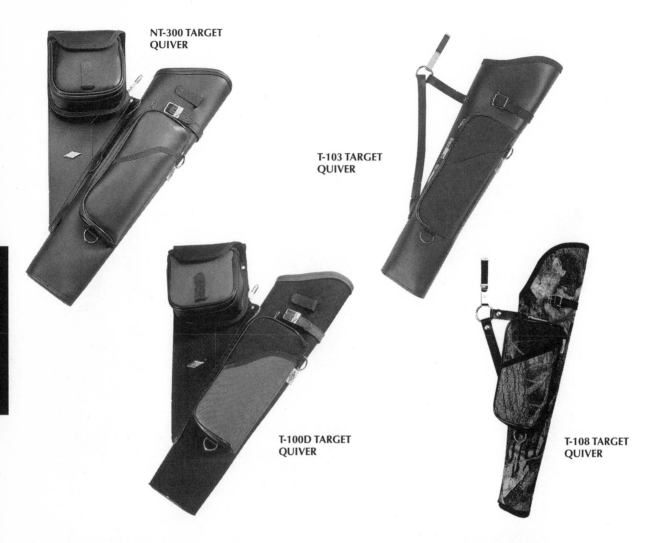

NT-300 TARGET
QUIVER

T-103 TARGET
QUIVER

T-100D TARGET
QUIVER

T-108 TARGET
QUIVER

LINED LEATHER BELT

Can be worn to held many of the Neet waist quivers. Sizes from 32 through 46 in even sizes and two-layer construction. Colors include black and burgundy.
SRP: **$44.15**

NT-300 TARGET QUIVER

A stylish hip quiver with four arrow tubes, a large flap pocket and two zipped pockets. Includes two accessory clips. Cordura panels are available on some models and 9 colors are offered, including Advantage Timber and Mossy Oak Break Up.
SRP: camouflaged **$49.35**
NT-2100 Target Quiver
   SRP: **$51.85**
NT-2300 Target Quiver
   SRP: **$70.52**

T-100 TARGET QUIVER

A waist quiver with a 19-inch body, three tubes and accessory clip and pencil tube.
Available in white and black vinyl and camouflaged Cordura models.
SRP: colors **$24.65**
   camouflaged **$30.25**
T-100D Target Quiver
   SRP: **$44.95**
      higher for camouflaged

T-103 TARGET QUIVER

This hip quiver attaches to your waist with a loop and harness. This quiver has a 19-inch body, three 1½-inch diameter arrow separator tubes, a large accessory pocket and single belt clip attachment. Available in black, white and camouflage.
SRP: **$19.95**
   camouflaged **$24.40**

T-104 TARGET QUIVER

   SRP: **$12.85**
      higher for camouflaged

T-108 TARGET QUIVER

This hunting oriented hip quiver has an 18-inch body, a zippered pocket, arrow divider strap and is offered in right- and left-hand models. It's available in Advantage, Mossy Oak and black.
SRP: **$15.85**
camouflaged **$17.45**

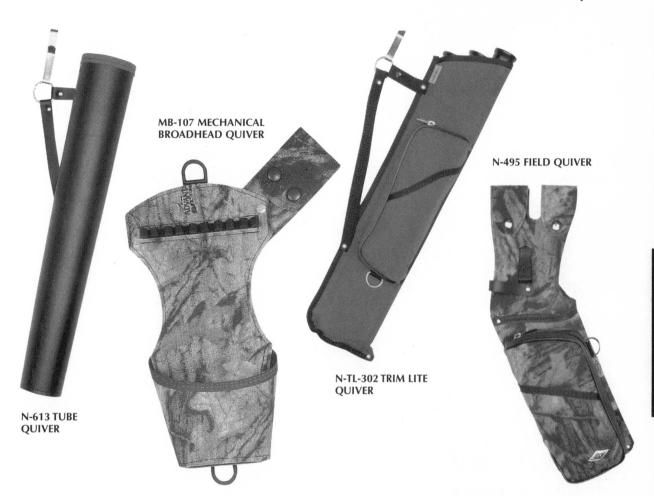

MB-107 MECHANICAL
BROADHEAD QUIVER

N-495 FIELD QUIVER

N-TL-302 TRIM LITE
QUIVER

N-613 TUBE
QUIVER

N-613 TUBE QUIVER
This hip quiver has a17-inch vinyl body, 3-inch opening and single belt attachment. It is black with optional trims in red, blue and gray smoke.
SRP: $6.75
N-615 Tube Quiver
SRP: $5.75

MB-107 MECHANICAL BROADHEAD QUIVER
This Neet Quiver has two molded arrow holders that will suspend four arrows. The swivel belt loop makes left to right-hand conversion simple. A firm center stave aids with arrow support. This quiver is camouflaged and comes with a web belt and adjustable web strap.
SRP: $34.95

N-495 FIELD QUIVER
A quiver with a trim body design, snap over belt loops and arrow divider strp. It has a large storage pocket.
SRP: $21.95

N-500 FIELD QUIVER
This Neet quiver is designed for filed use and keeps the arrows higher on your body and closer to reach. The quiver includes an accessory clip, large 8-inch zippered pocket and arrow divider. It's available in RH and LH, and in black, Advantage and Mossy Oak.
SRP: $21.95
  higher for camouflaged
N-491 Field Quiver
SRP: $18.45

TRIM LITE QUIVERS N-TL-301 TRIM LITE QUIVER
This hip quiver has two exterior pockets, is 19-inches deep and has three arrow separator tubes. It's available in RH and LH and in black, red, blue, Advantage and Mossy Oak Break Up.
SRP: $21.95
  higher for camouflaged
N-TL-302 Trim Lite Quiver
  SRP: $16.75
  camouflaged $18.45

N-TL-304 Trim Lite Quiver
  SRP: $11.55
N-TL-400 Trim Lite Quiver
  SRP: standard $46.85
  camouflaged $48.50
N-TL-401 Trim Lite Quiver
  SRP: $42.65
  camouflaged $45.25
N-TL-404 Trim Lite Quiver
  SRP: $16.25

NY-109 TARGET OR FIELD QUIVER
A quiver that's designed for young shooters with a 15-inch quiver body and snap over belt attachment system. It's available in RH and LH and black, camouflage and black with red, blue or gray smoke trim.
SRP: $22.65
  higher for camouflaged models

ARROWS

Arrow Accessories Quivers

ARROWS

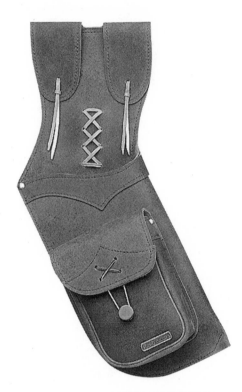

T-2595 FIELD QUIVER

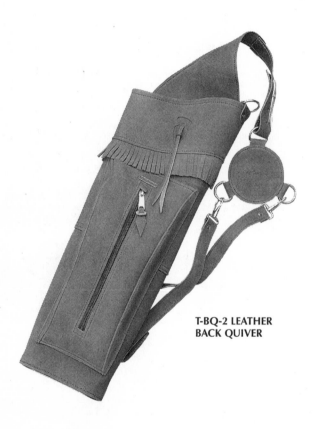

**T-BQ-2 LEATHER
BACK QUIVER**

T-108 TARGET QUIVER
This model is made for young archers and clips to your belt and has an exterior storage pocket. Available in assorted colors and camo patterns.
SRP: **$15.65**
   higher for camouflaged models

T-BQ-2 LEATHER BACK QUIVER
A traditional quiver constructed of leather. This quiver is 22-inches long, has a zippered accessory pocket and an arrow tube to separate arrows. It features and adjustable shoulder strap and brass plated buckles.
SRP: **$92.60**
T-BQ-3 Medium Back Quiver
   SRP: **$73.55**
T-BQ-20 Economy Back Quiver
   SRP: **$61.55**
T-BQ-30 Med Economy Back Quiver
   SRP: **$38.45**

T-2595 FIELD QUIVER
A waist-worn hip quiver that is short in design to keep arrows close to your body. It features brass rivets, hand lacing and straps to look authentic. It's offered in LH and RH models and in burgundy leather or honey brown suede leather.
SRP: **$44.75**

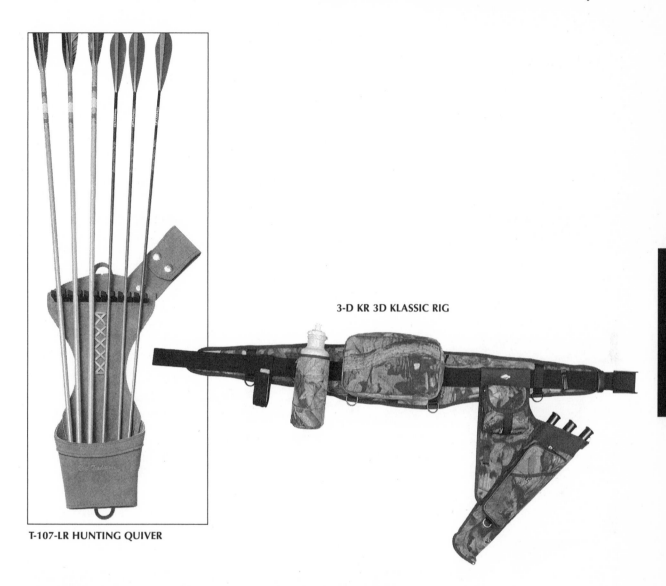

3-D KR 3D KLASSIC RIG

T-107-LR HUNTING QUIVER

ARROWS

T-107-LR HUNTING QUIVER

This Neet traditional style quiver has a swiveling belt loop to permit right- or left-hand use and a molded arrow holder securely holds six carbon or aluminum arrows. It has leather D-rings on the top and bottom to permit hanging it in a treestand.

SRP: **$49.25**

3-D KR 3D KLASSIC RIG

A system based on a foam padded support belt and the rig includes the quiver, a 2-inch wide accessory belt, fanny pack, water bottle and bow rest. Its available in LH and RH models and black, Navajo, and camouflage.

SRP: **$106.25**

3-D SR Standard Rig

 SRP: **$78.85**

Arrow Accessories Quivers

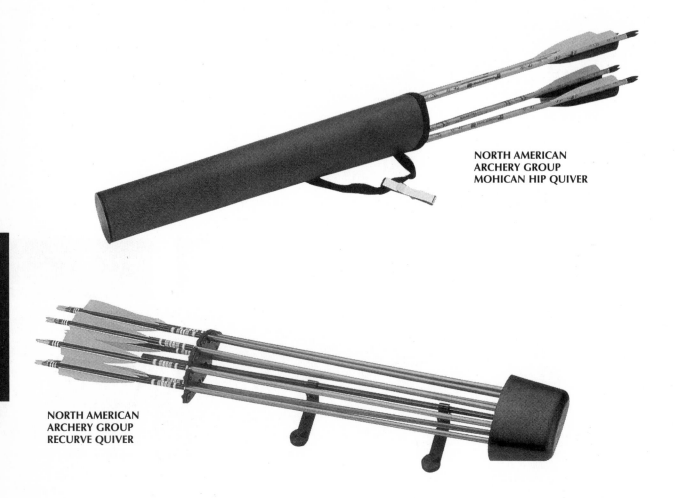

NORTH AMERICAN
ARCHERY GROUP
MOHICAN HIP QUIVER

NORTH AMERICAN
ARCHERY GROUP
RECURVE QUIVER

NORTH AMERICAN ARCHERY GROUP
Mohican Hip Quiver
Clips to your belt and brown simulated leather padded tube holds many full-length arrows.
SRP: **$6.49**

Recurve Quiver
A quiver designed to securely hold up to 6 arrows, and it attaches to a recurve bow. Offered in black only.
SRP: **$44.99**

If you use a detachable quiver, don't tune and sight-in your bow with the quiver attached, then remove the quiver to shoot. Likewise, you shouldn't sight-in and tune your bow with the quiver removed, then reattach the quiver when shooting. Such actions can cause erratic arrow flight. Always shoot the bow the same way it's been tuned.

RELEASE AIDS

Release Aids

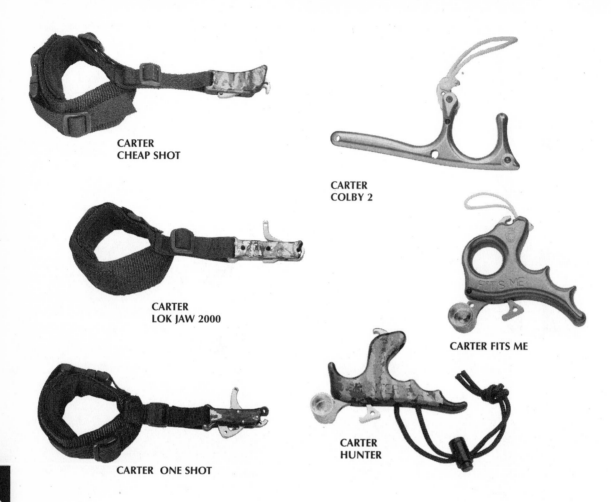

CARTER
CHEAP SHOT

CARTER
COLBY 2

CARTER
LOK JAW 2000

CARTER FITS ME

CARTER
ONE SHOT

CARTER
HUNTER

RELEASE AIDS

Release aids have far out-paced the use of fingers in the archery world. They provide several key benefits and yield much smoother releases when used properly. The styles and price ranges are nearly limitless today and more models are released, excuse the pun, each year.

A good bowhunting tip that hits home with many hunters: If you use a release aid, pack an extra one in your fanny pack or daypack, or at least have one in your vehicle. When you loose this item, it's nearly impossible to make a smooth release with fingers after relying on a release aid unless you have practiced extensively. Good bowhunting and shooting.

CARTER
Cheap Shot
This Carter hunting release aid has a wrist strap and an open (metal) jaw or closed (rope) jaw design. The closed jaw can shoot with the string, with a D-loop or with the attached rope. The wrist strap has multiple adjustments for a secure and comfortable fit.
SRP: black. **$58.99**
      camouflaged **$63.99**

Colby 2
This chrome release aid has a straight handle, and is offered in a hinged or spike version. Use it with the D-loop or rope.
SRP: **$104.99**

FitsMe
A Carter release that's designed to fit small to medium sized hands. It has a center hole and rope string catch.
SRP: **$153.99**

Hunter
This Carter release aid has a double sear, open jaw design and a d-loop hook. A lanyard secures the release to your wrist to prevent loss in the field.
SRP: **$153.99**

Lok Jaw 2000: (Index finger release – 3/8-inch jaw. Adjustable trigger, fall-away release, open or closed jaws, and either Velcro or a super buckle wrist strap)
SRP: narrow jaw **$68.99**
      Standard **$73.99**

One Shot: (Index finger release. Jaw lock and thumb safety)
SRP: black. **$93.99**
      camouflaged **$98.99**

Release Aids

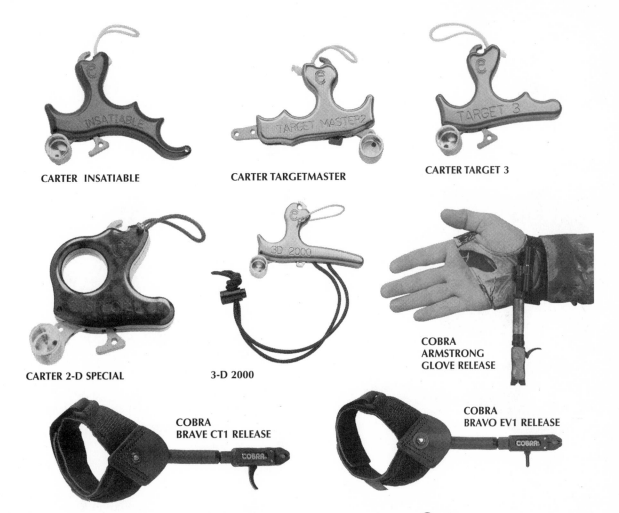

CARTER INSATIABLE

CARTER TARGETMASTER

CARTER TARGET 3

CARTER 2-D SPECIAL

3-D 2000

COBRA ARMSTRONG GLOVE RELEASE

COBRA BRAVE CT1 RELEASE

COBRA BRAVO EV1 RELEASE

Insatiable
This T-style hand-held release has finger grooves and smooth round edges. The arched handle helps place the elbow at a more natural position for better control while shooting.
SRP: **$153.99**

Target Master
This T-style release is hand held and has smooth handle, plus it can be shot with either the thumb or little finger with the simple adjustment of a set screw.
SRP: **$158.99**

Target 3
This Carter three-finger release allows you to drop your little finger off the release. A loop attaches to an enclosed jaw to hold the bow's string.
SRP: **$153.99**

3-D 2000
This release aid has a closed jaw to hold the loop and an open style, smooth handle to fit any hand. The wide separation between the index finger and middle finger creates a solid anchor. The release is supplied with a lanyard and is drilled and tapped for accessories.
SRP: **$153.99**

2-D Special
You'll remember this release aid when you see its odd design, but it is one of the most torque free aids on the market. It is available in $\frac{1}{2}$- or $\frac{5}{8}$-inch thickness and has a two-finger design.
SRP: **$153.99**

COBRA
Armstrong Glove Release
The swing-away module swivels 360 degrees and the over-the-thumb glove is leather lined and covered with a Saddle Cloth camouflaged exterior. The extension and head are camouflaged also. This release is available in right-hand only and in two sizes.
SRP: **$38.56**

Brave CT1 Release
(Curved gun-style trigger)
SRP: **$17.50**

Bravo EV1 Release
Has a padded loop lock strap and peg trigger on the side of the black anodized release head. This release has distinctive COBRA gold letters.
SRP: **$17.50**

Release Aids

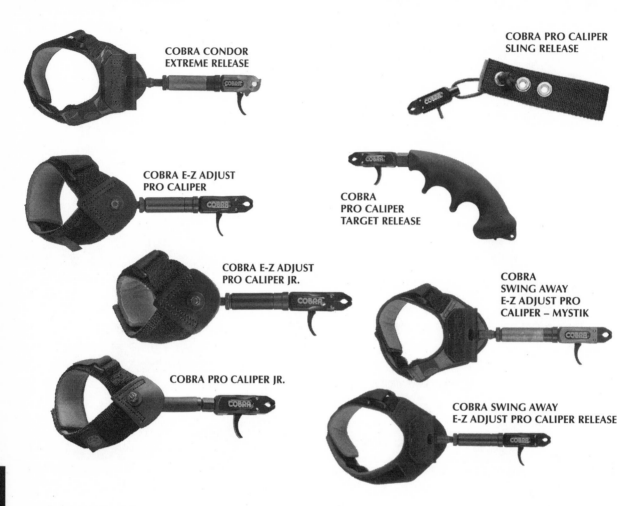

COBRA CONDOR
EXTREME RELEASE

COBRA PRO CALIPER
SLING RELEASE

COBRA E-Z ADJUST
PRO CALIPER

COBRA
PRO CALIPER
TARGET RELEASE

COBRA E-Z ADJUST
PRO CALIPER JR.

COBRA
SWING AWAY
E-Z ADJUST PRO
CALIPER – MYSTIK

COBRA PRO CALIPER JR.

COBRA SWING AWAY
E-Z ADJUST PRO CALIPER RELEASE

Condor Extreme Release

A release designed for loop bowstring shooters with an Extreme Wing on the release jaws that's easy to open with one finger. Self-loading internal springs allow you to close the release with one finger. A swing away module on the wrist strap rotates 360 degrees. The head is the E-Z adjust module that requires no tools and features a guns-style trigger. This release is available in black and Mystik.

SRP: black **$30.99**
    Camouflage **$34.99**

E-Z Adjust Pro Caliper

This release by Cobra requires no tools to adjust and has a padded loop wrist strap. The black anodized head has a gun-style trigger. A replacement wrist strap is available

SRP: **$23.50**

E-Z Adjust Pro Caliper Junior
  (Reduced length designed to fit women and youth)

SRP: **$21.99**

Pro Caliper Jr.

SRP: **$18.78**

New Generation Release

The New Generation is a swing-away model by Cobra with a release head that swivels 360 degrees. The module needs no tools for adjustment, and the black anodized release head has a gun-style trigger. The wrist collar is padded.

SRP: **$28.99**

Pro Caliper Sling Release

This is a basic release by Cobra with an adjustable sling strap that fits around the wrist. A string attaches the black anodized release head to the strap. A peg activates the precision machined center release jaws on the release head.

SRP: **$14.20**

Pro Caliper Target Release

This Cobra target release features an ergonomic grip with grooved finger slots while it rests inside a closed hand. It has a black anodized head and curved gun-style trigger.

SRP: **$21.82**

Swing Away E-Z adjust Pro Caliper–Mystik

A release that features an extension and release head in Mystik camouflage. Swing away base on the wrist strap that permits the extension and release to move out of the way while your are performing chores such as climbing to a treestand. The head rotates 360 degrees and has gun-style trigger.

SRP: **$30.99**

Swing Away E-Z Adjust Pro Caliper Release (Black only)

SRP: **$28.93**

Release Aids

GOLDEN KEY CASCADE #8

COPPER JOHN EAGLE SERIES HUNTING RELEASE

STAN

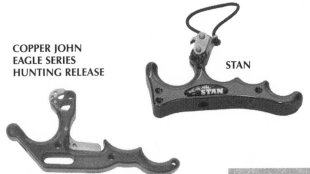

GOLDEN KEY ANSWER ANTI-PUNCH RELEASE

GOLDEN KEY CASCADE #10

GOLDEN KEY AUTO-X

GOLDEN KEY ER-300

COPPER JOHN
Eagle Series Hunting Release

This Copper John release has a wrist strap and trigger, plus an unique trigger clamp that settles around your index finger. It's offered with two, three and four-finger versions.

SRP: standard **$59.95**
    swept handle **$69.95**

STAN

These release aids are held between the fingers with a comfortable handle. Two, three and four finger models are available. Some models can be micro-adjusted. The original version has brass tip set screws and 440 stainless steel components. The newer models have thumb activation.

SRP: Original **$64.95**
    Micro adjust model **$135.00**

GOLDEN KEY-FUTURA
Answer Anti-Punch Release

The Answer can be adjusted into three shooting modes. Mode one prevents a quick punch release, mode 2 lets you deactivate the quick punch block and Mode 3 lets you shorten the trigger travel and by-pass the anti-punch option. This release has two jaws that are activated by a trigger and a lined leather wrist strap.

SRP: **$172.50**

Auto-X

An adjustable, precision made release by Golden Key-Futura that releases through back tension to prevent punching or the unit can be adapted to a thumb release. The release has a leather wrist strap.

SRP: **$90**

Cascade #8

A T-shaped release that is CNC machined with tight tolerances. The release occurs when the trigger is relaxed, instead of when pushed. The black handle is secured to the wrist by a comfortable strap.

SRP: **$186.30**

Cascade #10
SRP: **$201.25**

ER-300

An all metal release with a loop cord to capture the bowstring. The T-handle is attached to a wide, leather wrist strap.

SRP: **$40**

Release Aids

GOLDEN KEY HIDE AWAY CALIPER RELEASE

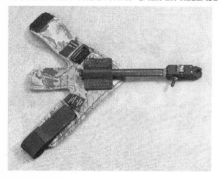

GOLDEN KEY SHARPSHOOTER

FLETCHUNTER

FLETCHER 3-D

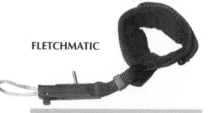

FLETCHHUNTER TF

FLETCHMATIC

GOLDEN KEY TOP GUN CALIPER RELEASE

FLETCHMATIC TR

Hide Away Caliper Release

A quality, smooth shooting release with a precision adjustable head designed to retract into the strap and free up your hands when the release is not needed. This double jawed release has a camouflaged wrist strap and black anodized head with GKF logo on it. A Hide Away release wrist strap kit can be used to turn any GKF Answer or Top Gun release into a Hide Away style release.
SRP:. $75

Sharpshooter

Metal double jawed head and trigger-like prong release activator. It is offered in numerous styles with a buckle or web strap, and with an advanced strap, camouflaged strap and smaller strap for youth and ladies.
SRP: standard. $28
  camouflaged $30
  youth style. $35

Top Gun Caliper Release

This release aid is constructed with CNC machined components and can be adjusted for trigger activation speed. A comfortable black nylon wrist strap fits all sizes. The REL-2600

Model has a hide-away strap and adjustable length from wrist to fingers.
SRP: $109.25

JIM FLETCHER ARCHERY AIDS
Fletcher 3-D

This release has a wide jaw with a smooth radius to eliminate string serving wear. The design is extremely accurate and forgiving in nature. The trigger is fully adjustable and the wrist strap keeps the unit in pale and ready to use. The self-locking head is anodized hunter green.
SRP:. $75

Fletchunter

This clip-on style release fastens directly to the bowstring and does not damage the serving thanks to smooth and rounded jaw edges. The over-center linkage system is fully adjustable from hair to heavy and comes in three models: The concho, the wrist strap and the swivel grip concho. The Fletchunter has a black anodized finish.
SRP: concho. $55
  wrist strap $60
  deluxe wrist strap. $70

Fletchhunter T-Models

Similar to the Fletchmatic models, these releases use a steel jaw to secure the string. A third style in this series is the two-finger handle that can be used a thumb or third finger release. These units are anodized in hunter black.
SRP:. $70

Fletchmatic (Release uses a rope ring to wrap around the string)
SRP: concho. $55
  wrist strap $60
  deluxe wrist strap. $70

Fletchmatic T-Models

The Fletcher T-Models secure the bow-string with a rope loop and are used primarily by indoor and target archery enthusiasts. The TR unit has a three-finger handle with a thumb activated trigger. The FF unit is three finger held with a fourth finger activation. Both units feature over center hardened steel rollers, comfortable machined handles and fully adjustable triggers. These units have a gold anodized finish.
SRP:. $70

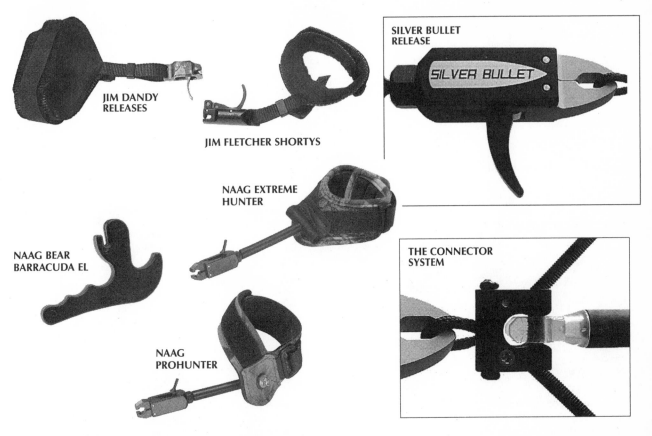

JIM DANDY RELEASES

JIM FLETCHER SHORTYS

SILVER BULLET RELEASE

NAAG EXTREME HUNTER

NAAG BEAR BARRACUDA EL

NAAG PROHUNTER

THE CONNECTOR SYSTEM

Jim Dandy Releases

This wrist strap secured release has a forward trigger near the tip of the jaws to help reduce draw length loss found in many releases. The Jim Dandy Release clips easily to a bowstring or loop and has an infinitely adjustable trigger pull and a small, compact release. It's available with a camouflaged anodized finish and has a smooth, double-roller trigger action.

SRP: $49.95

Shortys

These Fletcher releases feature the Fletchunter (jaw) and the Fletchmatic (rope loop) attachment systems. The shorty is designed to fit a wide array of hand sizes and is comfortably secured to the wrist with a wide strap. The release head is similar to the other Jim Fletcher Archery Aid models.

SRP:. $70

NORTH AMERICAN ARCHERY GROUP

Bear Barracuda EL

This economical hand-held, molded release has an adjustable trigger. This is an entry- level item.

SRP: $6.49

ProHunter Release

A wrist-strap release featuring a camouflaged Velcro strap, a 360-degree swivel head and adjustable trigger and dual jaws.

SRP: $19.99

Xtreme Hunter Release

This release features a 360-degree swivel head (like the Prohunter), adjustable trigger and enlarged wrist strap with comfort ribs. It has a camouflaged strap.

SRP: $24.99

PRO RELEASE

Silver Bullet Release

This release aid has been CNC machined for close tolerances from aircraft aluminum and steel. The precision calipers provide incredible performance and a perfect arrow release every time. The jaws open extra wide and the trigger is adjustable. This release will fit either right or left hands and is available with a pistol grip, concho style or Wrist strap.

SRP: wrist $68.95
      Concho. $62.95
      Pistol grip $74.49

The Connector System

A loop and base unit that attaches to a bowstring to make a consistent and convenient connection between the archer, release aid and bowstring. The connector works with either fixed-head or rotating head release aids. The Connector 1 model allows up to 180-degrees of rotation and the Connector 2 rotates 360-degrees. This item eliminates string and serving wear and maintains a perfect loop position behind the arrow every time.

SRP: Connector 1 . . . . $19.95
       Connector 2 . . . . $21.95

Release Aids

STACEY D-LOOP

T.R.U.
SWEET SPOT

STACEY HOOK, HOOK-O AND 3-D SUPREME

T.R.U.
CHAPPY BOSS

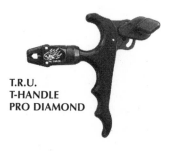

T.R.U.
T-HANDLE
PRO DIAMOND

STACEY ARCHERY SALES
D-Loop
Similar to Stacey's Two- and Four-Play models in style and appearance but it's designed to clip directly the bow string or rolled shut on and shot with a string loop. This model is shot only with the index finger pressure.

SRP: $79.95

Hook, Hook-O and 3-D Supreme
These Stacey creations deliver tight tolerances through CNC machining of an aluminum shell while the inner parts are machined from steel which is then case hardened and nickel plated. Each release has a travel adjustment and can be adjusted to hair-trigger lightness. All releases operate quietly and are available in: blue, silver, red, gold, purple and camouflage finishes. These releases fit over the fingers with rings. Adjustable barrel triggers give more flexibility in feel and angle of the trigger for the shooter. These will fit most popular brands of releases and provide up and down adjustment along with 360-degree rotation adjustment.

SRP: releases only $109.95

Two- and Four-Play
These hand-held release aids can be used as a forefinger or thumb release system and rope or clip-on The Four-

Play will shoot by: index pressure clip on, thumb relaxation clip-on, index finger pressure as a rope and thumb relaxation as a rope. Shooter can change system to determine best option. Other features include case-hardened inner parts, durable aluminum outer case, thumb safety and an angles string slot which lines up for a perfect release at full draw.

SRP: $79.95

T.R.U. BALL (TOMORROW'S RESOURCES UNLIMITED)

Chappy Boss
Features no load up, firm triggers and a travel adjustment screw. The Chappy Boss also features a sensitivity adjustment screw and three-piece adjustable trigger. This release has been proven in tournament victories everywhere and by hunters. The King George and Little Boss have thumb release options and are similar to the Chappy Boss. The Pinky Boss has pinky finger release capabilities only. All are available with standard caliper jaw, single- and double-ball jaws and talon rope head options. Available colors include black, blue and red.

SRP: . . . . $151.99 to $164.99

Hunting T-Handles
These releases are the hunting version of T.R.U. Ball's tournament proven hand-held releases. The Pro Diamond is ultra-quiet, has an adjustable trigger and can fasten to your bowstring while you wait in your treestand. It holds three patents for innovation and design features. The Thumb Pull model is has a loop for your thumb, the T-Handle Thumb Push utilizes a push lever to activate the release and the Pinky Pull has a lever that is operated by applied pressure by the shooter's pinky finger. All releases are available with the four common jaw options and in the three standard colors.

SRP: . . . . $64.99 to $98.99

Sweet Spot
This release has a string that wraps around your bow's string and locks into a small finger on the release's head. Four models are available: Ultra 4, 4 Spot, Ultra 3 and Ultra 2. The free-floating head permits you to shoot up and down hills without compromising string travel. The grips can be held with 4 to 2 fingers to ensure complete shooter comfort and control. Available colors for the Sweet Spots are black, red and blue.

SRP: $164.99

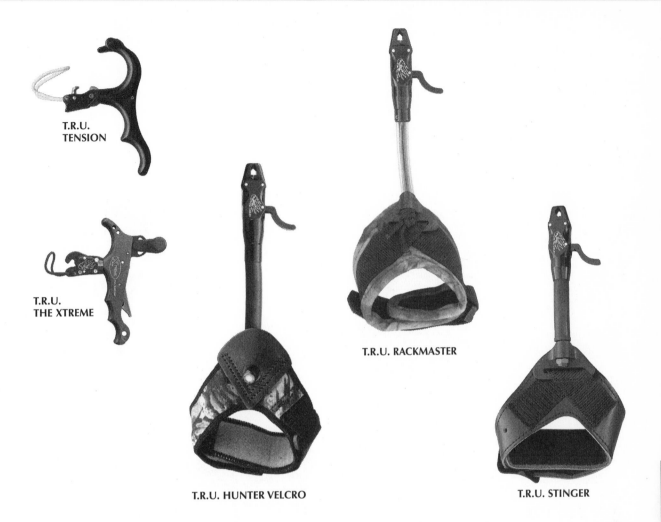

T.R.U.
TENSION

T.R.U.
THE XTREME

T.R.U. RACKMASTER

T.R.U. HUNTER VELCRO

T.R.U. STINGER

T.R.U. Tension
This is a T-type, in-the-fingers release that uses a wrap around double string to secure your bow's string. The release's head rotates on the same plane as the handle. Different configurations—four models available—provide secure feel and control for any shooter's demand. Available colors include black, blue and red.
SRP: $49.99

The XTreme
This hand-held release is available with a standard caliper jaw, single or double ball, and talon rope head release system. The Extreme provides $^7/_{16}$ more draw length and features open, comfortable finger grooves. Available colors include black, blue and red. The Little XTreme, Pinky

XTreme and King George XTreme are in the XTreme family line and offer smaller grips, thumb or pinky release options and caliper jaws, rope or ball jaws to grip the string.
SRP:. . . . . $151.99 to $164.99

Hunter Velcro
The standard caliper jaws or single- and double-ball jaw options with this release provide selection options to fit the tastes of any archer with T.R.U. Ball's Hunter series. The head rotates 360 degrees and attaches to the wrist strap with a rod. These releases are available with Velcro closures only and in several styles.
SRP: . . . . $50 to $65

Rackmaster
Torque-free rope connection from the wrist strap to the jaws. Versions include standard caliper jaws, single- and double-ball jaws and LoopMaster head. Black leather or camouflage cloth wrist straps are available.
SRP: . . . . $39.99 to $52.99

Stinger
Solid rod attaches jaws to the wrist strap, 360-degree swivel movement. Stinger Velcro has camouflaged wrist strap. Stinger Buckle incorporates buckle closure with black leather wrist strap. Both releases use standard T.R.U. Ball caliper jaws.
SRP: $32.99

Release Aids

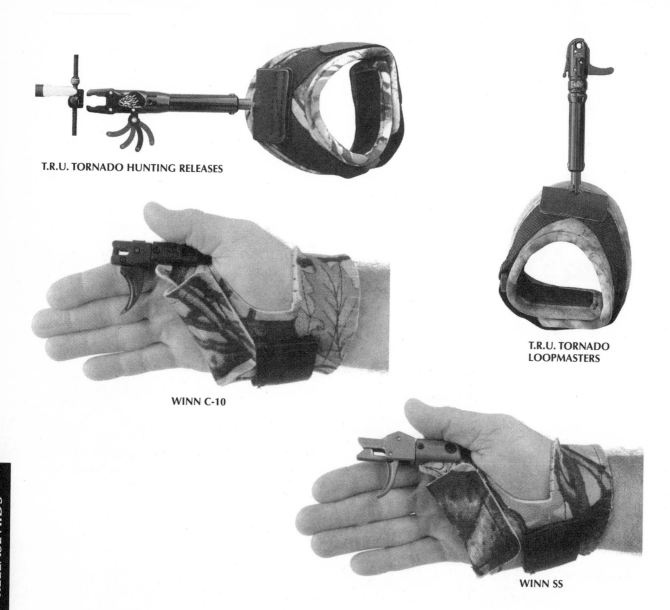

T.R.U. TORNADO HUNTING RELEASES

T.R.U. TORNADO LOOPMASTERS

WINN C-10

WINN SS

Tornado Hunting Releases
Rotating and swiveling heads, closed-cell wrist strap has a 4-way adjustable trigger (Deluxe) or no-travel trigger (Accu-Touch) Independently operated funnel shaped jaws
SRP:. . . . . $69.99 to $164.99

Tornado LoopMasters
360-degree rotating head. Wrist straps available in Velcro or buckle closures. Works with all jaw releases.
SRP: . . . . $64.99 to $81.99

WINN ARCHERY
C-10
The release head and the trigger are crafted from solid hardened steel. The trigger has adjustable pull and travel features. The glove is built with 8 ounces of leather and reinforced with a Cordura overlay to prevent stretching. This release is available in X-small youth sizes through X-large adult sizes with right- and left-hand models.
SRP: $55.50

C-12 (Relaxed trigger release. Uses the standard Winn replacement glove)
SRP: $55.50

SS
This release by Winn Archery uses the company's glove base and has a solid stainless steel "Free Flight" caliper mechanism with large, easy-loading jaws that are easy on the string's serving. The trigger is adjustable and does not use springs, the trigger must be held forward at the beginning of the draw. This release will use the stan-

ARROW RESTS

ARROW RESTS

Arrow Rests

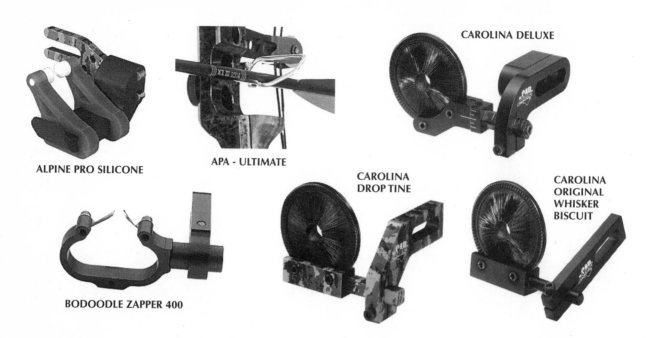

ALPINE PRO SILICONE

APA - ULTIMATE

CAROLINA DELUXE

CAROLINA DROP TINE

CAROLINA ORIGINAL WHISKER BISCUIT

BODOODLE ZAPPER 400

ALPINE ARCHERY
Pro Silicone Rest

The popular WhipserFlite arrow rest by Alpine Archery has been upgraded into their Pro Silicone fixed-position rest. The rest base and launcher support shelf are constructed of rugged extruded aluminum. The arrow rests on two white Teflon glides that are held in place by two flexible silicone triangular launchers. This rest is very simple to install and adjust. The Pro Silicone rest is also unlike any other in construction and design and can be adjusted without tools.

SRP:. $32

APA ULTIMATE
Ultimate Rest

In the solid rest category, APA Innovation's Ultimate rest is offered in a new lighter and more affordable model this year—the Ultra-Lite. The arrow rides on two stainless steel

lazer-engraved cradle arms as it passes under an overhead bracket. Left and right-hand versions are offered. These rests use machined 6061-T6 aircraft aluminum brackets and stainless steel screws.

SRP: $49.99
   Junior. $25.99
   Release rest. $65.99

BODOODLE RESTS
Zapper 400

This unusual rest permits you to shoot arrows weighing more than 400 grains without stressing the three prongs and causing erratic arrow flight. The rest is constructed of machined aluminum and has a top-loading feature. It can be easily converted from left to right-hand. It's available in black and camouflage.

SRP: black. $42.55
camouflaged $49.55

CAROLINA ARCHERY PRODUCTS
Deluxe

This rest has the biscuit and vertical adjustments, a lockdown screw and match marks outlined on the mounting arm and brackets.

SRP: $58.00

Drop Tine

The Drop Tine rest has the famous Whisker Biscuit but the mounting arm has is curved to position the rest lower. It's available in camouflage.

SRP: $46.00

Original Whisker Biscuit

The Original is similar to the new model but with a full circle. All models will hold carbon arrows, aluminum arrows and bowfishing arrows when the donut is changed. Left and right hand models are available. Color: Black.

SRP: $36.00

ARROW RESTS

Arrow Rests

CAROLINA WHISKER BISCUIT DELUXE QS

CAROLINA REPLACEMENT BISCUITS

CAROLINA WHISKER BISCUIT DROP TINE QS

CAVALIER BADGER

CAVALIER AVALANCHE EXTREME

CAVALIER STINGER

COBRA FRONTIERSMAN

CAVALIER PRONGHORNS

Whisker Biscuit

A small section removed at about the 2 o'clock position permits the quick insertion of an arrow without having to start the loading process from the tip of the shaft. Rests are only available to right-hand shooters.

Whisker Biscuit Drop-Tine QS (camouflage)
SRP: $51.00
Whisker Biscuit Deluxe QS (Black)
SRP: $64.50

Replacement Biscuits

When your biscuit goes and starts to show a widened oval, it's time to change. Four styles are available. Fits all models on Whisker Biscuit rests.
SRP: $12.00

CAVALIER EQUIPMENT
Avalanche Extreme

The Avalanche Extreme cord activated fall-away arrow rest by Cavalier Equipment provides micro vertical and horizontal adjustments. The Avalanche Extreme's cord can be placed at variable activation positions to ensure trouble-free operation. The enhanced arrow launcher is wider and an arrow holder is optional. Several mounting brackets are offered to accommodate various risers from several major bow manufacturers.
SRP: beginning at $29.95

Badger

Designed for easy set up and a drop-designed bracket provides superior arrow and fletching clearance. The prongs are covered with Teflon sleeves. An adjustment knob on the side of the bracket is easy to use.
SRP: $15.99

Stinger

Economically priced and a simple design with sturdy construction describes this rest. It has two metal prongs to hold the arrow and slotted mounting bracket provides a wide range of adjustment to fit any bow.
SRP: $11.99

COBRA
Frontiersman

A rest with a stainless steel shaft and prongs, plus independent windage, spring tension and elevation adjustments. The shaft rotates on a single bearing and Pronghorns—Cobra's exclusive sturdy prong coating—are included.
SRP: BLK $13.99
MY camo: $15.99

Pronghorns

Slick, self-lubricating low friction material to cover arrow rest prongs and silence the release and draw process. Fit most $1/8$-inch diameter prongs and outperforms heat shrink tubing.
SRP: per pair $2.64

ARROW RESTS

Arrow Rests

COBRA
WOODSMAN II

GOLDEN KEY
ARROW TRAP

GOLDEN KEY
MIRAGE

GOLDEN KEY
HUNTER ELITE

COPPER
JOHN ALLEYCAT

GOLDEN KEY
FREE FALL

GOLDEN KEY
FUNNEL

COPPER JOHN BOBCAT

Woodsman II
This arrow rest has durable Rylon construction, independent adjustments and dual bearings to support the shaft. Pronghorn rigid covers are included to cover the two stainless steel prongs.
SRP: $9.99

COPPER JOHN
AlleyCAT
The more advanced AlleyCAT delivers independent adjustment options. This rest has a larger mounting bracket and is more adjustable than the BobCAT.
SRP: $59.95

BobCAT
The entry-level BobCAT rest features rotary horizontal adjustment and horizontal slide adjustment. It's a drop-away string-activated rest with launchers that are shrink wrapped with a teflon coated polymer to reduce friction at the release and increase quietness.
SRP: $39.95

GOLDEN KEY-FUTURA
Arrow Trap
A new-style arrow rest with overhead tubing to hold the arrow on the rest at any angle. The prongs are spring loaded and this rest can be tuned with the Internal Tension Spring. The Speed Tune is similar in design with a camouflaged mounting bracket and gold axle sleeve but without the overhead channel found on the Arrow Trap.
SRP: $60

Free Fall and Mirage
Drop Away Rests
These Golden Key-Futura rests are designed to drop or fall when the arrow is released. The Drop Away model is mounted inside a large U-shaped bracket. The Fall Away models are two prongs mounted to a metal axle. All are cord activated when the bow is drawn and operate when the tension is released at the release of the arrow.
Mirage Drop Away
SRP: $105

Speed Drop
SRP: $45
Free Fall
SRP: $65
Premier Free Fall
SRP: $155

Funnel Rest
A rest where your arrow and fletching pass through a multi-tabbed flexible tunnel that's mounted on an axle at the side. The Launcher Cone holds your arrow when your bow is in any position.
SRP: $45

Hunter Elite
This premium drop-away rest has two silent launchers that are controlled by an arm that activates when the bow is drawn and a cable is pulled tight. Upon release the tension is relaxed and the prongs fall free. This rest is rugged and fully adjustable for vertical and horizontal positioning. It is available in left and right-hand models.
SRP: $160

GOLDEN KEY POWER DROP

GOLDEN KEY SHOOT OUT

GOLDEN KEY TM SILENT HUNTER

GOLDEN KEY ROYAL HUNTER

GOLDEN KEY SPEED SET HUNTER

Power Drop

Golden Key-Futura's Power Drop rest has a drop-away action that's triggered when the cables make contact with a plunger that protrudes from the back of the rest. Innovative! The cables make contact with a large, soft rubber, tip. The Power Drop can also be set as a solid convention style rest.

SRP:. $175

Royal Hunter

The Royal Hunter rest by Golden Key-Futura has a honest-to-goodness horseshoe shaped arrow launcher that drops away at the launch. It's operated by a 12-position adjustable tension spring. Other features are a quiet, click-free adjustment and a dropped mounting bracket to permit full arrow fletching clearance.

SRP: $126.50

Shoot Out Arrow Rest

Unlike any other rest, your arrow passes through a triangle and passes over three protruding coated posts. The triangle can be converted from top or side loaded positions and mounts between two plates on the rest's lower arm. Can be easily installed as a left or right-hand model.

SRP:. $65

Speed Set Hunter

A rest with a dropped mounting bracket to ensure arrow and fletching clearance. The metal prongs of the rest are attached to a steel axle. Easy to grip adjustment knobs assist with set up and finetuning. The Hunter model has Teflon Hush tubes on the two prongs and the standard model has steel prongs only.

SRP: coated prongs. $36
    steel prongs $28

TM Hunter Series

These rests are simple and affordable. Styles include the Hunter with Teflon Hush tubes on the prongs, A Basic with bare steel prongs and Silent Hunter with sturdy and adjustable curved prongs to cradle the arrow. The Hunter Ultimate model has adjustable controls and marked calibrations to assist with adjustments.

SRP: TM Hunter. $24.59
    Basic. $19.00
    Silent Hunter. $32.00
    Ultimate Hunter $65.00

One way to improve your shooting accuracy is properly aligning your broadheads. To do this, spin your arrows on an arrow straightener and align the broadheads so they don't wobble. The truer the broadheads are aligned, the better your groups with broadheads will be.

ARROW RESTS

Arrow Rests

**MUZZY
ZERO EFFECT**

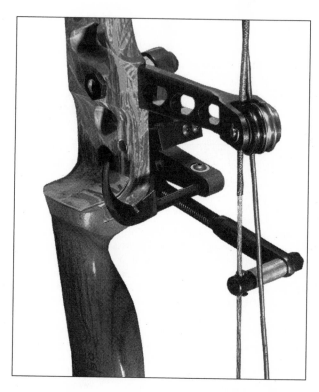

**MUZZY ZERO
EFFECT LEGACY**

MUZZY
Zero Effect Arrow Rest

This odd looking rest opened the door for fall-away rests. One arm attaches to the cable and another arm cradles the arrow, until the release and then the arm drops down and the arrow floats free for the launch. Muzzy also heard from "Leftys" who howled that the earlier versions of the Zero Effect rest were offered only in right-hand versions and has introduced three left hand models. Available in left and right hand models.

SRP: **$116.65**

Zero Effect for Hoyt and Legacy Bows

Muzzy also heard from Mathews Legacy and Icon owners, and quickly discovered that those bow owners also wanted to try a Zero Effect Arrowrest. After listening, Muzzy is introducing two new Zero Effect rests—one for the Mathews bows and another model to fit the protruding spine on the newer Hoyt risers.

SRP: **$92.99**

ARROW RESTS

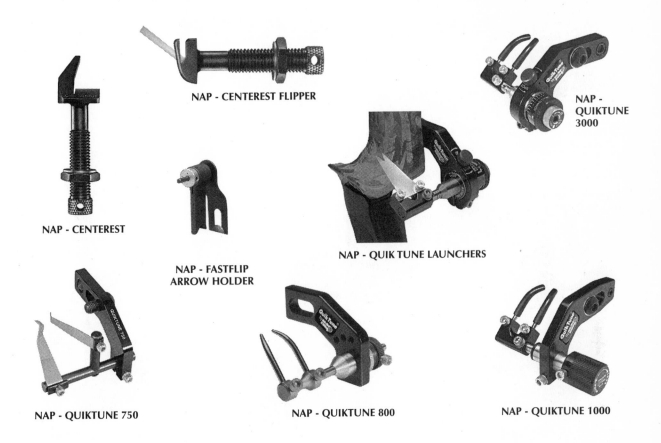

NAP - CENTEREST FLIPPER

NAP - QUIKTUNE 3000

NAP - CENTEREST

NAP - FASTFLIP ARROW HOLDER

NAP - QUIK TUNE LAUNCHERS

NAP - QUIKTUNE 750

NAP - QUIKTUNE 800

NAP - QUIKTUNE 1000

NEW ARCHERY PRODUCTS
Centerest Arrowrests

This NAP arrow rest has been around for years and enjoyed by many. They are known for durability, easy installation and adjustability. The standard arrowrest has a composite arrow rest and the flipper version incorporates a flipper arm to hold the arrow. Both models are available in left- and right-hand styles. Replacement centers permit exchange of the erst without affecting the alignment.

SRP standard arrowrest $13.99
    replacement center $6.99
Centerrest Flipper $22.99
    replacement center $13.99

FastFlip Arrow Holder

This unique arrow holder works with any QuikTune arrow rest and adjusts to any arrow diameter and for center-shot use. It fits left- and right-hand bows and quickly flips back out of the way upon drawing.
SRP: $15.99

QuikTune 750

This arrow rest is designed for use with al carbon and aluminum arrows and by release and finger shooters. It can be easily installed and adjusted with one wrench and it's vibration resistant. The QuikTune 750 fits both left- and right-hand bows. It has spring steel arms and Teflon silencers.
SRP: $22.99

QuikTune 800

This New Aprchery Products arrow rest features two steel prongs for the arrow to rest on. This rest can be set in high, medium and low fixed positions. It can be set with a wrench and is offered in left- and right-hand models.
SRP: $24.99

QuikTune 1000

This NAP rest features a patented triple bearing design, all-weather reliability and has Fork Tamer silencers installed. The rest is designed for hunting and archery competition applications and has a fully-independent micro-adjustable tension adjustment feature. This rest is offered in LH and RH models.
SRP: $41.99

QuikTune 3000 Micro-Adjustable

Precision adjustment without guesswork are the norm for this arrow rest that features micro-adjustment calibrations marked on the indicator knob Other features include a micro-adjust center-shot, two prong fork tamers silencers and a 3-D launcher. The prongs can be changed to a single rail system that is included with the arrow rest and RH and LH models are available.
SRP: $74.99

Quik Tune Launchers

These 3-D Lizard Tongues target launchers are designed for the tournament trail and built with stainless steel. Three sizes are included with each package: light (.008), medium (.010) and heavy (.012). These will fit on most QuikTune rests.
SRP: $19.99

ARROW RESTS

Arrow Rests

NAAG - BEAR HAIR

NAAG - BRAVE YOUTH BOW NO-FALL

NAAG - MARINER BOWFISHING REST

NAAG - CENTER SHOT

NAAG - BEAR SHOOT AROUND

NAAG - BEAR WEATHER

SAVAGE DERRINGER HUNTER

SAVAGE DERRINGER MICRO

NORTH AMERICAN ARCHERY GROUP

Bear Hair Rest
Designed for use on recurve and long-bows. It can be cut to fit any surface.
SRP: $3.49

Bear Shoot Around Rest
Same design as Weather Rest with an additional prong to position your arrow shafts away from the bow.
SRP: $2.49

Bear Weather Rest
Pliable rubber rest with flip out arm to hold arrow.
SRP: $1.99

Brave Youth Bow No-Fall Rest
This rest is designed to prevent arrows from falling off rest as young archers develop shooting skills. The rest fits the Brave bow.
SRP: $1.99

Center Shot Rest
Simple bracket attaches to your bow and two prongs hold arrow. Available for right-hand bows only.
SRP: $12.99

Mariner Bowfishing Rest
Round design permits use of heavier fiberglass fishing arrows while protecting bow.
SRP: $15.65

SAVAGE SYSTEMS
Derringer Hunter
Similar to the Deringer Micro with a ⅜-inch thick mounting bar. The axle will lock for fast set ups. Other features include a silent urethane return stop, stainless steel spring, and non-strip collar. Available in left and right hand models.
SRP: $29.95
steel and Teflon launchers . $34.99

Derringer Micro Rest
This Savage Systems rest is inertia activated and has a precision micro-drive for fast adjustments that you can make with your fingers. A setscrew can then be tightened to lock the rest's axle in place while you make any other necessary adjustments. Other features on this rest include a laser engraved reference scale, lifetime play-free bushings and steel launchers with tubing or Teflon coating. Other options include left- or right-hand models.
SRP: black $52.95
Camouflaged $57.95

Arrow Rests

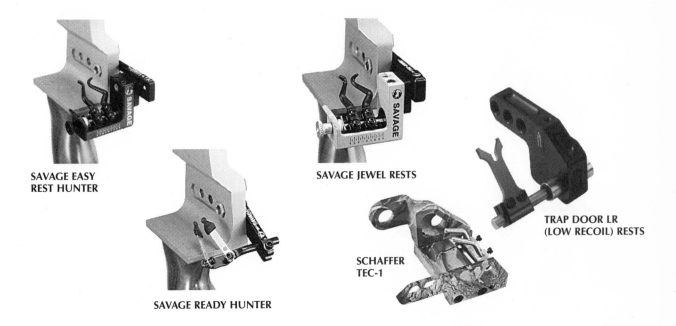

SAVAGE EASY REST HUNTER

SAVAGE JEWEL RESTS

SAVAGE READY HUNTER

SCHAFFER TEC-1

TRAP DOOR LR (LOW RECOIL) RESTS

Easy Rest Hunter Rest
This rest is micro adjustable and has Teflon launchers that act as an arrow holder when rotated to the up position. This rest is offered with coated or uncoated stainless steel prongs.
SRP: **$52.95**

Jewel Rests
These Savage System rests are adjustable in every possible direction and have a solid mounting bar and precision-machined aluminum body engraved with a Vernier scale. Arrows rest on two sturdy and adjustable prongs. Available finishes include: gold, platinum or black.
SRP: black **$62.96**
    platinum and gold **$67.95**

Ready Hunter Rests
Simple, strong and dependable describes these rests that feature a mounting bracket and U-axle for superior fletching clearance. It's available from Savage Systems with Teflon or stainless steel launchers.
SRP: **$15.95**

SCHAFFER PERFORMANCE ARCHERY
TEC-1
The TEC-1 is Schaffer Performance Archery's answer to demand for an arrow rest that will fit the riser on newer Hoyt bows. This rest is offered in Realtree Hardwoods HD Green, weighs 3 ounces and can be set up as a fall-away or conventional steady rest. Dual prongs or the interesting lizard tongue rest can be installed to hold or lick the arrow. Note: The company's MAT-1, E-2 and CRS rests are similar in design with the shelf platform and two protruding steel prongs. These can be set as a conventional or fall-away rest and are similar in price to the TEC-1.
SRP: **$99.99**

SPECIALTY ARCHERY PRODUCTS
Back Drop Arrow Rest
The activation string attaches to a bow cable with a specially designed clamp. Upon activation, the rest action moves backward, not forward. A spring and brass timing adjustment knob make timing and height adjustments simple.

This rest also goes through the standard arrow rest-mounting hole found on most bow risers so installation is basic and solid. During use, the arrow rests in a durable Delrin roller that ensures silent operation. The rest can easily be converted from right- to left-hand use.
SRP: **$77**

TRAP DOOR
Trap Door LR (Low Recoil) Rests
The standard LR (Low Recoil) model is designed to work on bows with low recoil vibration and will accommodate bows with 30- to 100-pound draw weights. The mounting and internal detection system for the inertia triggered activation are housed in a light 6061-T6 machined aluminum unit that's pre-drilled to fit all standard bows. A cover plate protects the internal controls from weather, abuse and dirt. Dampening bumpers inside the housing and a Delrin launcher assures quiet performance. The launcher attaches to a stainless steel rod that's pre-marked for adjustments.
SRP: **$86.95**

ARROW RESTS

Arrow Rests

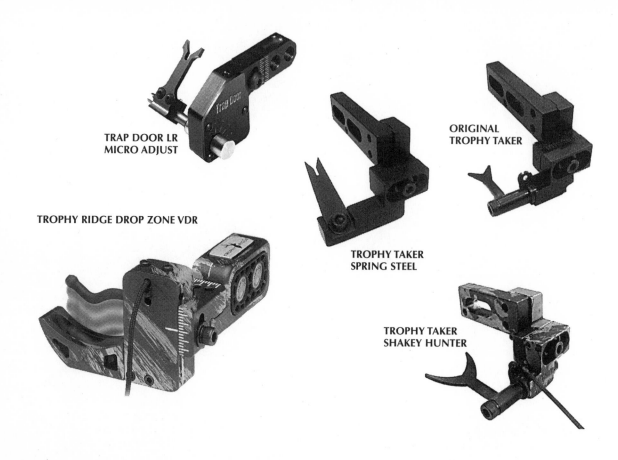

TRAP DOOR LR
MICRO ADJUST

TROPHY RIDGE DROP ZONE VDR

TROPHY TAKER
SPRING STEEL

ORIGINAL
TROPHY TAKER

TROPHY TAKER
SHAKEY HUNTER

Trap Door LR Micro Adjust
keyed and calibrated horizontal shaft
for left and right adjustments independent of vertical adjustments.
SRP: $102.50

Trophy Ridge
Drop Zone VDR
(Vertical Drop Rest)
The Drop Zone VDR (Vertical Drop
Rest) has a vertical arm launcher that
raises the arrow as you draw with a
NO-Stretch cable that tugs to activate
the arm. Until you are ready to use the
rest and release, the arrow is securely
held in a pre-launch position on the
bow's shelf with a closed-cell foam
VDR rack system. The rest's V-Notched
launcher arm permits you to hold the
bow at extreme angles without the
arrow falling off. Upon release the
arm falls into a lower housing shell
that also acts as a broadhead guard.
This rest is available in anodized
Match-Tek black, green and brown.
SRP:. $125

Trophy Taker
Original Trophy Taker
This rest is available for left and right
hand bows and with a long and short
mounting bar made from durable
machined aluminum. Machined hash
marks help ensure precision windage
and elevation adjustments and a
$^{10}/_{32}$-inch hex bolt helps anchor the
selection in place. Two threaded
windage and elevation holes maximize adjustment options and a set
screw on the mounting bar prevents
any rotation. The strong stainless steel
launcher is cushioned by a completely
enclosed spring. These rests—12
models are available—are available
in black, silver and camouflage.
SRP: $74.99

Shakey Hunter
Similar to the Original Trophy Taker
with a durable non-stretch and stretchable cord that can be attached to
cables or the bow's cable slide. Also
features a one-piece stainless steel
launcher with 1⅛-inch wide tip.
Available in left- and right-hand models.
SRP: $74.99
    camouflaged $79.99

Spring Steel
Similar to the Shakey Hunter and
Original models, the Spring Steel
model comes with two widths of
launchers for large or small arrows.
Three spring steel launchers of various
stiffness are included with each rest.
These provide perfect arrow tuning
capabilities and are easily changed.
SRP: $64.99

ARROW RESTS

HUNTING & SHOOTING ACCESSORIES

Archer's Gloves and Tabs

N-CST

N-MT TAB

FG-2

FG-25C

NEET

Comfort Spacer Tab N-CST
A finger tab with a molded finger spacer, suede leather backing and leather front overlay. RH or LH available.
SRP: Starting at **$5.25**

Glove FG-2
A high quality tan suede glover with hook and loop fastners and an elstic back for a comfortable fit. This glove has three fingers with smooth leather or hair calf tips.
SRP: hair **$10.30**
   Leather **$6.75**

Glove FG-2SC
Advantage Timber or Mossy Oak Break Up camouflage.
SRP: hair **$10.00**
   Leather **$8.75**

Monster Tab N-MT
A tab designed for shooting three fingers under first, this tab has no finger cut out. Its' offered in LH and RH models and sizes S, M and L. Your choiceof leather or hair calf finish.
SRP: **$5.15**

If you shoot with a new glove or tab, remember that it may require some breaking in before you go hunting or shoot in a tourament. Use the glove or tab when practicing for a few days to get it "grooved" and broken in.

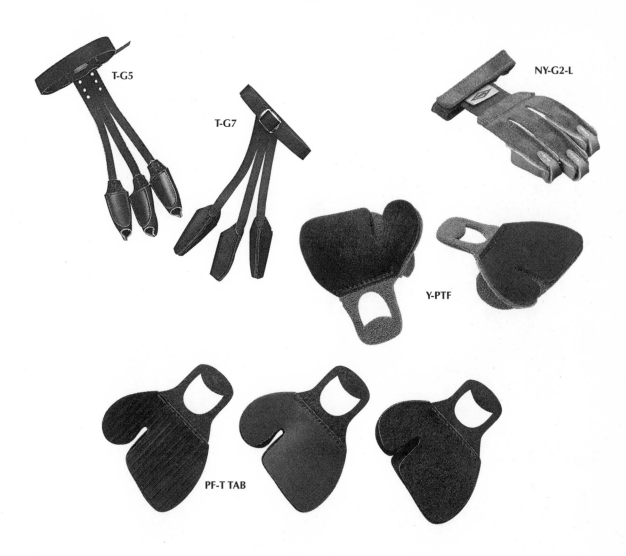

T-G5

T-G7

NY-G2-L

Y-PTF

PF-T TAB

Pinch Free Tab PF-T
A finger tab with a soft felt finger spacer and suede leather backing. Sizes offered include XS, S, M, L and XL. You choice of hair calf, super leather or Rib Tab facings. RH or LH models are available.
SRP: **$5.25**

Traditional Glove T-G5
A traditional glove with Cordovan leather tip overlays on the three fingers. This glove has a snap buckle wrist strap. Sizes S, M, L and XL and it's available in burgundy and honey brown.
SRP: **$12.55**

Traditional Glove T-G7
SRP: **$10.25**

Youth Glove NY-G2-L
This leather glove is made to fit small archer's hands and has a hook and loop fastener. It has smooth leather finger tips and is made of suede leather.
SRP: **$5.45**

Youth Tab Y-PTF
A small finger tab made by Neet with small young archers in mind. Left- and right-hand models are available.
SRP: . . . . **Starting at $4.85**

Archer's Gloves and Tabs

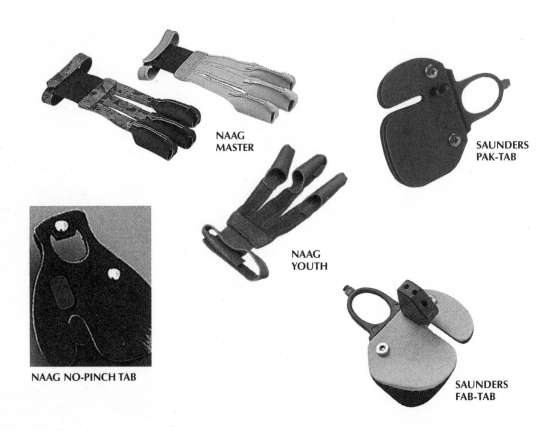

NAAG
MASTER

SAUNDERS
PAK-TAB

NAAG
YOUTH

NAAG NO-PINCH TAB

SAUNDERS
FAB-TAB

NORTH AMERICAN ARHCERY GROUP
Master
A three-finger leather glove with elastic adjustment section and leather/Velcro wrist strap. The Master is available in sizes medium and large.
SRP: $9.49

No-Pinch Tab
This tab is available in medium and large, features durable leather layers and sturdy rivets.
SRP: $6.49

Youth
Smaller version of Master glove designed for smaller fingers and hands.
SRP: $8.99

SAUNDERS ARCHERY
Pak Tab and Fab Tab
Finger tabs with felt string pads and leather backing. Offered in sizes small medium and large and the tabs can be changed to several options.
SRP: $10.95
    Fab Tab II $9.95

Archers who shoot with a glove will find cold-weather shooting more comfortable if they buy a larger size glove that will fit over a wool liner.

Arm Guards

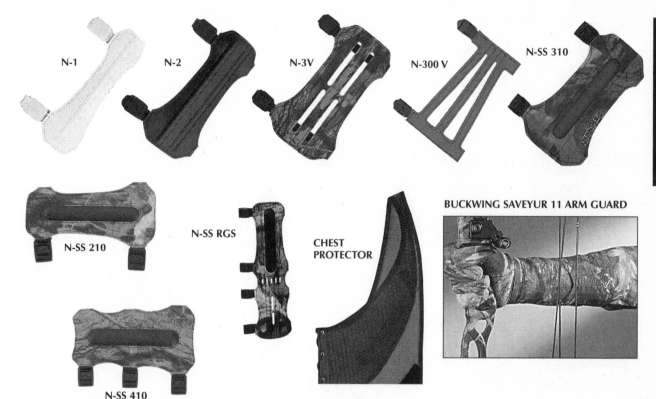

N-1 N-2 N-3V N-300 V N-SS 310

N-SS 210 N-SS RGS CHEST PROTECTOR BUCKWING SAVEYUR 11 ARM GUARD

N-SS 410

BUCKWING
Saveyur 11 Arm Guard
This stretch to fit arm guard keeps sleeves and bulky coats out of the way for a smooth release. It's now available in a larger men's size and in smaller sizes for women and youths.
SRP: $7.68

NEET
Armguard N-1
An armguard made for target shooters, this guard uses two adjustable straps and is made of vinyl. It's available in black and white.
SRP: $3.75

Armguard N-2
SRP: $4.00

Armguard N-3V
SRP: $7.00

Armguard N-300-V
Open guard that attaches with two straps. Available in black, white, red, blue and camouflage.
SRP: starting at $6.90
   more for camouflaged

Armguard N-SS-310
This adult sized guard in 6¾-inch long and nearly 4 inches wide. It is fastened in place with two straps and has an exposed stave in a window. Made of Saddle Cloth or Cordura.
SRP: $6.75

Armguard N-SS-210
   SRP: $5.95
Armguard N-SS-410
Three adjustable elastic straps.
   SRP: $6.85

Armguard N-SS-RGS
A full-length arm guard with staves in the lower section and rods in the upper. Available in Advantage and Break Up camouflage and with a Cordura or Saddle Cloth finish.
SRP: Starting at $9.95

Armguard N-SS-RGL
   SRP: $10.00
Armguard N-RGL
   SRP: $9.00

Chest Protector
An adjustable nylon mesh over-the-shoulder guard. A self-adjusting back strap with hook and loop front fastener. Interchangeable as left- or right-handed. Available in black and white and sizes XS, S, M, L and XL.
SRP: $11.50

Hunter Guard N-3H
An armguard that's designed for hunters, this guard is wide and 7 inches long and is held securely in place with three adjustable straps.
SRP: $6.85

Mini Guard NY-MG
An arm guard for young archers. The stave is exposed in a window on the cover of this guard and two straps hold the unit in place on the arm.
SRP: $4.65

Arm Guards

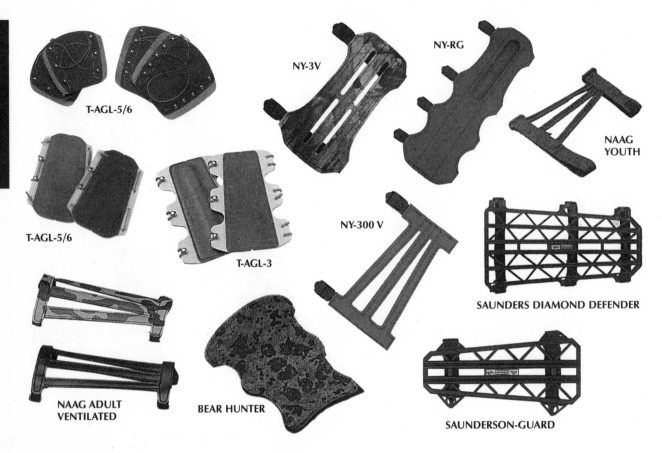

T-AGL-5/6

T-AGL-5/6

NY-3V

NY-RG

NAAG YOUTH

T-AGL-3

NY-300 V

SAUNDERS DIAMOND DEFENDER

NAAG ADULT VENTILATED

BEAR HUNTER

SAUNDERSON-GUARD

Traditional Armguards T-AGL-5/6
This Neet armguard is available in two sizes: 7½ x 8½-inch or 6⅜ x 7-inch for the 6 model. One size fits all and the elastic cord lacing fits into boot lace hooks along the edge. It's available in burgundy and brown.
SRP: Starting at $12.65

Traditional Armguards T-AGS/T-AGL
SRP: Starting at $10.50

Traditional Hunter Guard T-AGL-3
A leather armguard with 3-point hook up. It can be pre-laced to permit easy on/off with elastic cords.
SRP: $14.25

Ventilated Youth Guard NY-300V
This small arm guard is designed by Neet for you archers and has three staves, a Cordura outer layer and pull adjustable elastic straps. It's available in black, red, blue and camouflage.
SRP: $5.45

Ventilated Youth Guard NY-3V
SRP: $5.15

Youth Range Guard NY-RG
This full-length quiver gives protection to the full arm. The lower section has staves. It's held in place with adjustable pull elastic straps. Available in the same colors as the Ventilated Youth Guard.
SRP:. $7

NORTH AMERICAN ARHCERY GROUP
Adult Ventilated
This three-strap arm guard uses Velcro straps to securely hold it in place on you forearm. Available in camouflage and black.
SRP: camo. $7.49
    black. $6.49

Bear Hunter
This solid arm guard has a camo-printed leather surface and attached with three adjustable elastic bands.
SRP: $8.49

Youth
This three-strap guard is designed to fit young and small-framed archers. Color: black.
SRP: $5.99

SAUNDERS ARCHERY
Diamond Defender
This arm guard is 4x7.5-inches and is vented to be cool. Hooks latch easily and quietly. Adjustable elastic straps.
SRP: black. $10.95
    camouflaged $12.95

On Guard
These arm guards are cool, comfortable and an eye-catcher at the range! They are available in black, camo and purple, yellow, blue, green and white.
SRP: black and assorted colors $8.95
    camouflaged $10.95

Calls, Scents and Game Attractors

ACTIVE SCRAPE

BUCK FIRE

BUCK NIP

BULL RAGE

BOOT SCENT PADS

COON URINE

COYOTE URINE

DOE IN ESTRUS

EXCITE

NORTH AMERICAN ARCHERY GROUP RATTLE BAG

ELK FIRE

4X4 MULE DEER LURE

GRUNT'N LURE

North American Arhcery Group

Rattle Bag
Camouflaged cloth bag with solid components to simulate battling bucks. Has clip to secure unit to your belt or pack.
SRP: $11.99

Wildlife Research

Active Scrape (Mock scrape lure)
SRP: 1 oz. $5.99

Buck Fire (Doe-in-heat urine)
SRP: per 1 oz. $6.99

Buck Nip (Curiosity scent)
SRP: 1 oz. $5.99

Bull Rage (Elk lure)
SRP: 1 oz. $7.99

Boot Scent Pads
SRP: per pair $3.99

Coon Urine
SRP: 4 oz. $7.99

Coyote Urine (Cover up scent)
SRP: $7.99

Doe in Estrus (Buck lure)
SRP: 1 oz $5.99

Excite (white-tailed doe in heat estrus scent)
SRP: 1 oz. $9.99
4 oz. $24.99

Elk-Fire
Imitates a cow elk in heat and brings bulls in looking for the cow.
SRP:1 oz $7.99
4 oz $17.99

4X4 Mule Deer Lure
A full strength doe in heat urine with natural pheromones from mule deer.
SRP: $7.99

Grunt-N-Lure
Use this scent when calling bucks. It is loaded with doe in estrus, buck in rut and tarsal gland smells.
SRP: 1 oz $7.99

Calls, Scents and Game Attractors

HOT MUSK

HOT SCRAPE

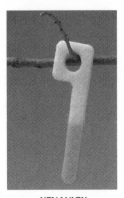

KEY WICK

SELECT DOE URINE

SUPER WICK

MASKING SCENTS

PRO DRAG

PRO WICK

RED FOX URINE

SELECT BUCK URINE

Hot-Musk
A unique blend of musks to create a lure effective on bucks and does.
SRP: 1 oz. $7.99

Hot Scrape
Use this doe in heat secretion at mock and natural scrapes to attract deer.
SRP: 1 oz. $4.99

Key Wick
A long think felt wick pad that's used to create a scent station near your stand.
SRP: $3.49

Masking Scents
These scents help hide the human odor and can be used in specific hunting terrains. Available in vanilla, pine, sage, cedar, earth, acorn, apple, persimmon and corn.
SRP: $5.99

Pro-Drag
A 7-inch synthetic felt pad with two tails to disperse scent and lay out a scent trail.
SRP: $4.99

Pro Wick
A small scent pad that can be tied to a limb and then have scent applied.
SRP: $3.49

Red Fox Urine
A masking scent that will not alarm deer. Arrives in a spray bottle.
SRP: 4 oz. $6.99

Select Buck Urine
This is a great territorial intrusion scent and brings bucks close when they smell it.
SRP: 1oz. $7.99

Select Doe Urine
A natural odor of deer scent that has territorial non-threatening appeal.
SRP: $5.99

Super Wick
A scent station that you create. The container has a screw on cap for storage and a wick that drops down when the container is hung up on a limb.
SRP: $5.99

Calls, Scents and Game Attractors

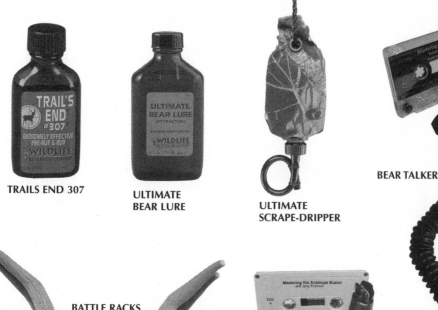

TRAILS END 307

ULTIMATE
BEAR LURE

ULTIMATE
SCRAPE-DRIPPER

BEAR BLASTER

BEAR TALKER

BATTLE RACKS

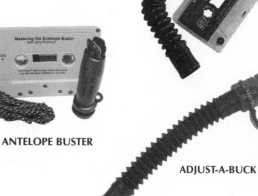

ANTELOPE BUSTER

ADJUST-A-BUCK

Trails End 307
A lure that's a proven top performer. When deer smell it they'll come to investigate.

SRP: 1oz. **$7.99**
4oz. **$17.99**

Ultimate Bear Lure
An intense smell with a sweet aroma that attracts bears.

SRP: 4 oz. **$12.99**
16 oz. **$29.99**

Ultimate Scrape-Dripper
This soft container can be hung over a real or mock scrape to drip scents. The dripper shuts down at night and can last up to 7 days when full.

SRP: **$12.99**

WOODS WISE
Woods Wise creates calls for nearly every critter found afield and in the forests and has an assortment of instructional tapes and videos

Adjust-A-Buck
This adjustable reed based call makes grunts and bleats—it's six calls in one. The expansion tube helps vary the tones. Simple O-ring slides to make adjustments.

SRP: **$11.99**

Antelope Buster
Use this call to imitate buck snort chuckles and to stop running prong-horns with a bark. Works well with decoys and will capture and hold any pronghorn's attention.

SRP: **$12.99**

Battle Racks
A set of full-contact antlers that are held in the middle for better balance and to avoid finger pinch while rat-tling. The bone Core hollow air cells help create realistic sounds.

SRP: **$19.99**

Bear Blaster
A call that produces variable pitches for loud distress cries to bring hungry and curious bears to your location. Take cover and be prepared when using it.

SRP: **$15.99**

Bear Talker
A dual-reed inhale/exhale call that imitates female and male bears. The call comes with an instructional tape and lanyard.

SRP: **$17.99**

Calls, Scents and Game Attractors

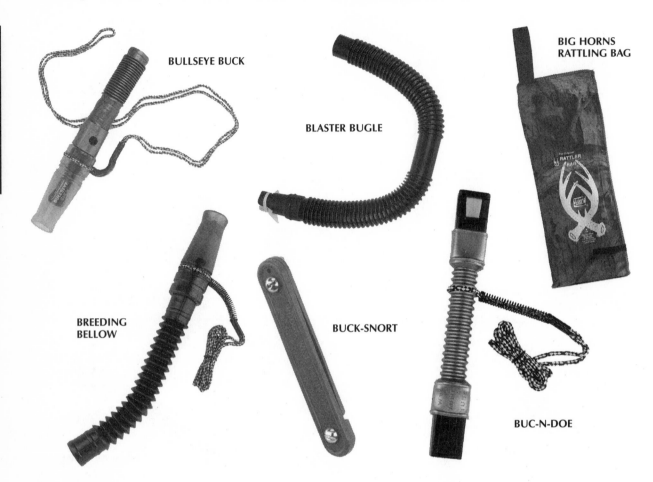

BULLSEYE BUCK

BLASTER BUGLE

BIG HORNS RATTLING BAG

BREEDING BELLOW

BUCK-SNORT

BUC-N-DOE

Big Horns Rattling Bag
This larger rattling bag can be used to imitate large bucks and trophy bulls. It can be hung from the belt and an elastic band wraps around it to keep it quiet when necessary.
SRP: $15.99

Blaster Bugle
An elk call that makes shrill notes and deep tones when used. It comes with an audio instructional tape, camo cover and lanyard.
SRP: $26.99

Blue Doe
The lost contact call is made with this innovative call. It has a sanded reed and won't freeze and plays while wet. The expansion tube changes it from a buck to doe voice.
SRP: $11.99

Breeding Bellow
This call mimics a ready to breed doe and is simple to use. A how to audiotape and lanyard are included.
SRP: $14.99

Buc-N-Doe
This original call has removable hands-free grunt and doe bleat calls. It can be hands free, pushbutton or a tube call. It makes an assortment of calls including plain buck grunts, Contac calls, aggressive grunts, hot doe bleats and tending grunts. If a deer is near, this call will bring it closer. Includes an instructional tape.
SRP: $14.99

Buck-Snort
This call is realistic and easy to use, and should create action when used with rattling and calling.
SRP: $9.99

Bullseye Buck
A deer call that makes all vocalizations and snorts. You inhale to make bleats and exhale to make grunts with this call. Instructional audio and lanyard are included.
SRP: $14.99

Callmasters Buck-n-Doe
Make buck hyper grunts and doe bleats with this call. It has 12 adjustments and a 2-reed system that's operated by inhaling and exhaling.
SRP: $12.99

EZY Cow
A call that's great for herd talk and it calls cows, calves and lovesick bulls.
SRP: $9.99

Calls, Scents and Game Attractors

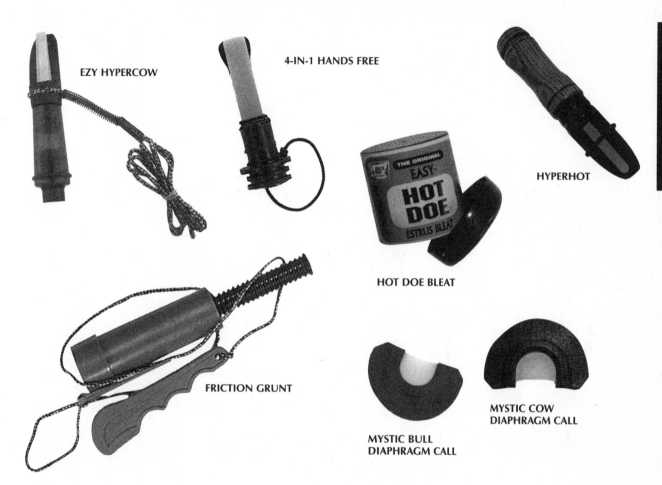

EZY HYPERCOW

4-IN-1 HANDS FREE

THE ORIGINAL EASY. HOT DOE ESTRUS BLEAT

HYPERHOT

HOT DOE BLEAT

FRICTION GRUNT

MYSTIC COW DIAPHRAGM CALL

MYSTIC BULL DIAPHRAGM CALL

EZY Hypercow
A mouth blown call that imitates a cow in heat breeding call to drive bulls wild. It's easy to use and versatile and can be muted for softer tones.
SRP: $9.99

4-In-1 Hands Free
This adjustable call fits in your mouth and makes grunts of bucks and does, plus doe and fawn bleats. An elastic lanyard is included.
SRP: $6.99

Friction Grunt
An adjustable twist tone tip and striker paddle helps make the buck's clicking courtship grunts and doe social grunts, plus rutting buck grunts and aggressive grunts.
SRP: $14.99

Hands Free Real Cow
A call designed for bowhunters and it is held in the mouth and blown. It calls cows, bulls and calves. This call will easily fit into a shirt pocket.
SRP: $8.99

Hot Doe Bleat
It's like have a deer in a container when you turn this cylinder over to imitate a hot estrus doe bleat.
SRP: $9.99

Hyperhot
The cow-in-heat elk call that makes five calls including mews and spike squeals. The call comes with a lanyard and audio instructional tape.
SRP: $14.99

Kodiak Western Doe & Fawn Bleat
Call trophy mule deer, blacktails and Coues deer with these mews and bleats. The call operates with hands free bite and blow design.
SRP: $8.99

Moose Blaster
A call that has an expansion megaphone and a red-hot XL-15 reed inside. This call makes estrus cow moans and cow protest whine and grunts. It's very compact and easy to use. For more details and to experience the thrill of a moose hunt watch the Moose Talk video with Jerry Peterson—a 70-minute VHS tape with live moose calling for $14.99.
SRP: $14.99

Mystic Bull Diaphragm Call
An in-the-mouth call with two reeds and a small frame designed to make aggressive bugles and growling chuckles.
SRP: $4.99

Mystic Cow Diaphragm Call
A call that's easy to master and it makes cow and calf calls and bugles.
SRP: $4.99

Calls, Scents and Game Attractors

RATTLER BAG

SCREAMER BUGLE

TENDING CLUNK

RATTLING ANTLERS

SEXY COW-N-CALF

SCREAMING FAWN

SCREAMIN' RODENT

Rattling Antlers
Premium antlers made with polymer for strength and uses the Bone Core technology to create air core cells like real antlers to produce a more realistic sound and bring bucks close. This set is perfect for sparing or all-out fights.
SRP: **$13.99**

Rattler Bag
This bag can be worn on your belt and tingled with one hand to imitate sparring bucks. It will bring aggressive and curious bucks to your location. An elastic strap helps keep it quiet when not in use and the camouflaged exterior bag helps prevent movement detection while in use.
SRP: **$14.99**

Screamer Bugle
This elk call has an expansion tube and exclusive triple reed that permits call adjustment. Includes an instructional tape, camo cover and additional latex for over the reed controlled tuning. This call uses the EZY# triple reed system that includes a pre-tuned diaphragm with Peel-n-Stick tape mounting.
SRP: **$29.99**

Screaming Fawn
This call brings whitetails, mule deer and blacktails to you with loud distress calls. It will also lure in coyotes, foxes, bears and other predators.
SRP: **$19.99**

Screamin' Rodent
Makes a rodent in distress shrill squeal and brings all predators running for the action.
SRP: **$9.99**

Sexy Cow-N-Calf
A call that makes all herd talk and it's easy to use and has automatic reed alignment pins. It has a wooden barrel.
SRP: **$12.99**

Super Howler
A freeze-proof reed in this loud long-range call can make locator howls and female invitation howls to bring coyotes close. The call includes two reeds to make various calls.
SRP: **$14.99**

Tending Clunk
A call that reproduces the hollow plunks and clunks of a rutting bull. To operate slap your hand over the call's opening.
SRP: **$9.99**

Targets & Range Equipment

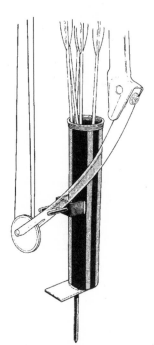

C.W. ERICKSON'S
ARROW STAND WITH BOW REST

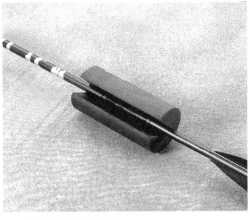

GOLDEN KEY-FUTURA
SUPER ARROW GRIP

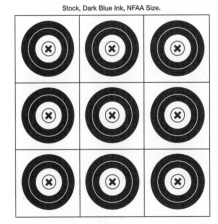

Stock, Dark Blue Ink, NFAA Size.

MANNEY'S ARCHERY
TIC TAC TOE TARGET

C.W. ERICKSON'S MFG.
Arrow Stand With Bow Rest
This tube-type stand spikes into the ground. Great for backyard use. The foam-lined cylinder protects arrows. The spike base has a foot ledge for easy installation.
SRP: $30.49

GLOBAL RESOURCE INCORPORATED
Ground Spike Bow Rest
This bow holder is secured to the ground with a spike and can be easily moved to any location. Holds all types of bows and can be used in a backyard range or while turkey hunting. Weighs 16 ounces and is 15 inches long.
SRP: $15.69

Handy Stand Deluxe Bow and Arrow Stand
This stand spikes into the ground and will hold two bows and lots of arrows in two separate tubes. The vinyl-covered rest protects a bow's finish. Cylinders have foam-lined bottoms and rims to protect arrows.
SRP: $71.49

GOLDEN KEY-FUTURA
Super Arrow Grip
The soft rubber cylinder has a deep groove that securely and firmly grips arrows when you're ready to pull them from a target. It fits comfortably in your hand and can pull all types and sizes of arrow shafts, including smaller diameter carbon shafts.
SRP:. $9

MANNEY'S ARCHERY TARGETS
1-Spot CM 40Tic Tac Toe
(per 100 targets, small quantities available) SRP: $23
3-Spot 4-Color Vegas Round
(per 100 targets) SRP: $33
4-Color Super 10 Ring
(per 100 targets) SRP: $33
5-Spot 300 Round (per 100 targets, small quantities available) SRP: $23

Indoor 600 Animal Size
This assortment of animal targets printed on heavy paper. The animals include marked kill zones. Critters depicted include: prairie dog, rabbit, turkey, ruffed grouse, fox, pheasant, bobcat, skunk, raccoon and javelina. The scoring rings are not visible past 20 yards which adds to the challenge.
SRP: . . . . $20 per 100

Targets & Range Equipment

EXOTIC SERIES CORSICAN RAM, BLACK BUCK, ALLIGATOR

EXOTIC SERIES FALLOW DEER

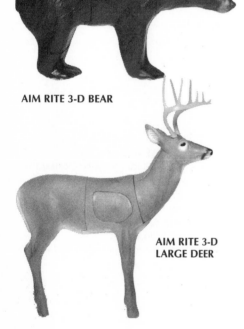

AIM RITE 3-D BEAR

CARBON BUCK

AIM RITE 3-D
LARGE DEER

MCKENZIE CARBON BLOCKS

MCKENZIE TARGETS
McKenzie Aim Rite 3-D Targets
This series of targets provide bowhunters with realistic and durable targets at an affordable price.

Medium Aim Rite Deer SRP: . $99.95
Medium Bear SRP: $124.95
Carbon Buck SRP: $149.95
Large Deer SRP: $124.95
Tuff Buck SRP: $72.99

McKenzie Carbon Blocks
These McKenzie targets are designed for carbon arrows and have non-bonded layered foam with a unique four-corner cable system to keep the target together. Two sizes are available: 18x18x16-inch and 18x24x16-inches.

SRP: small $89.95
Large $99.95

Carbon Buck
This life-like 3-D target has a super flex foam midsection for easy arrow removal and has painted 3-D vitals to help archers learn about deadly arrow placement. The target can be shot with broadheads, field points and expandables. This target will easily release carbon arrows and will last for thousands of shots.

SRP: $149.95

McKenzie Exotic Series
These full-size lifelike 3-D foam targets cover many of the species you'd encounter in Africa and at other hunting grounds around the globe.

Alligator SRP: $240.95
Black Buck SRP: $213.95
Corsican Ram SRP: $248.95
Fallow Deer SRP: $228.95

Targets & Range Equipment

HANDIBLOCK

HD SERIES ELK

HD SERIES BIGHORN SHEEP

HD SERIES BISON

HandiBlock

This compact 16x18x12-inch block can be shot on four sides and is constructed with layered foam. The Handiblock by McKenzie works well for compound bows and carbon arrows. It provides easy arrow retrieval and is designed to last for years of use.
SRP: **$69.95**

McKenzie HD Series

This series of life-like, full size 3-D targets feature high density foam and most targets can be easily and quickly disassembled for easy transporting and storage.

Bear SRP:
Bighorn Sheep SRP: **$328.95**
Bison SRP: **$849.95**
Bedded Deer SRP: **$250.95**
Large Deer SRP: **$261.95**
Medium Deer SRP: **$228.95**
Caribou SRP: **$632.95**
Elk SRP: **$684.9**
Mountain Goat SRP: **$328.95**
Wolf SRP: **$222.95**

Targets & Range Equipment

SHOOTING ACCESSORIES

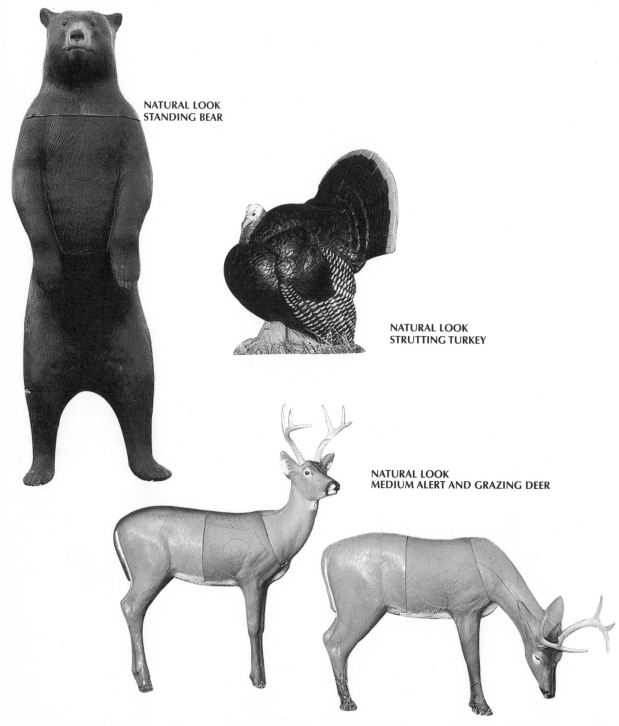

NATURAL LOOK
STANDING BEAR

NATURAL LOOK
STRUTTING TURKEY

NATURAL LOOK
MEDIUM ALERT AND GRAZING DEER

McKenzie Natural Look Targets
These tournament series targets have Super Flex foam centers for extra durability and easy arrow removal. The body is completely painted to protect the foam from harmful ultra-violet sunlight.

Medium Bear SRP:	$217.95
Standing Black Bear SRP:	$302.95
Coyote SRP:	$154.95
Mountain Lion SRP:	$229.95
Pronghorn Antelope SRP:	$217.95
Large Alert Deer SRP:	$198.95
Large Sneak Deer SRP:	$198.95
Medium Alert Deer SRP:	$152.95

Medium Grazing Deer SRP:	$152.95
Mule Deer SRP:	$254.95
Quartering Deer SRP:	$180.95
Javelina SRP:	$132.95
Turkey SRP:	$116.95
Strutting Turkey SRP:	$217.95
Wild Boar SRP:	$228.95

Targets & Range Equipment

ROCK RASCALS
WOOD CHUCK, FOX, RACCOON AND BOBCAT

ROCK RASCALS BEAVER

SAFARI SERIES LION

SAFARI WARTHOG

McKenzie Rock Rascals
This small game series by McKenzie includes seven species that are painted with great detail and posed in life-like positions. All targets have IBO approved scoring rings and use a tournament proven re-bar stand system.

Beaver SRP: **$115.95**
Bobcat SRP: **$99.95**

Fox SRP: $108.00
Raccoon SRP: $99.95
Wolverine SRP: $114.95
Woodchuck SRP: $99.95

McKenzie Safari Series
These 3-D targets will make you think that you're hunting in Africa when you spot them on a range near you or in your backyard.

African Blesbok SRP: $276.95
Chamois SRP: $223.95
African Hyena SRP: $221.95
African Impala SRP: $244.95
African Leopard SRP: $274.95
African Lion SRP: $443.95
Warthog SRP: $242.95

Targets & Range Equipment

HANDIBLOCK CROSSBOW TARGET

TUFF SHOT STOP BAG

CARBON BLOCK

VITAL ZONE BLACK BEAR

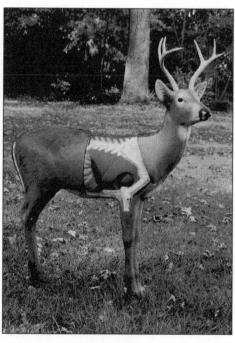

VITAL ZONE DEER

McKenzie Tuff Shot Series

These block targets by McKenzie meet the needs of archers everywhere and will hold countless arrows. They are lightweight, portable and accept shooting with flied points or broadheads.

Carbon Blocks
(small) SRP: $89.95
(large) SRP: $99.95

HandiBlock Crossbow
Target SRP: $79.95
Practice Target SRP: $34.95

Tuff Stop Bag Target
SRP: . . . . Starting at $63.95

Vital Zone Black Bear

This target accurately resembles a black bear on all fours and shows the organs on one side in vivid color and details. This target was created in cooperation with the National Bowhunter Education Foundation and is scaled to represent a 140-pound animal. It can be easily and steadily secured in the ground with two metal stakes that are provided. This target is a great training aid for beginning archers or anyone planning to go on a black bear hunt in the future.
SRP: $129.95

Vital Zone Deer

This three-dimensional foam target depicts a white-tailed deer buck while revealing the vital organs. It was designed in cooperation with the National Bowhunter Education Foundation as a training aid but can help all archers discover whether their arrows are accurately entering the kill zone.
SRP: $129.95

Targets & Range Equipment

CARBON SIX SHOOTER

ECONO

HUMONGO

50,000 PLUS

3-D SERIES

OUTDOOR RANGE

MORRELL MANUFACTURING
3-D Series
These Morrell targets include an alert white-tailed buck, a black bear and a rutting buck. These targets feature easy one-finger arrow removal and the mid-section can be recovered for $10. The chest cavities are wrapped with a unique fiber and burlap cover that stops arrows.
SRP: . . . . $139 to $169

Carbon Six Shooter
This six-sided Morrell cube has targets on all sides and can be shot on all sides. The target is freestanding and four sides will stop broadheads. A handle permits easy carrying of this 22x22x22-inch target.
SRP: $49.99

Econo
This target has a durable polypropylene cover with NFAA style 5-spot target dots on one side and five spots on the other side. The target is stuffed with high-compressed quality fiber and will last for thousands of shots. The Econo measures 23x23x10-inches.
SRP: $29.99

50,000 Plus
It is 28x28x16 and has a patented floating center and overstuffed to grade quality fibers. This target is 100% waterproof and will stop both carbon and aluminum arrows with ease. The 50,000 Plus is covered with a two-year warranty.
SRP: $59.99

Humongo
The Humongo is made from a special multi-layered foam and is designed so it will easily stop carbon, wood and aluminum arrows regardless of the broadhead or the speed, yet arrow removal is easy. It is a large 30x30x10-inch target and now features a 100% waterproof cover. It's designed for long life and fairly impervious to the weather.
SRP: $34.99

Indoor Range Cube
Similar to the Outdoor Range Target but designed for indoor use. This target will stop all arrows and has flat surfaces to pin paper targets onto.
SRP: $70.00

Outdoor Range Target
This cube-type target is covered with a polymer sack with grommets to permit easy hanging. The exterior has 16 dots to aid with precision practice.
SRP: $89.99

Super Super
This 24x24x12-inch target is stuffed with high-grade fiber then wrapped with space age netting. One side depicts a deer's chest and vitals and the other side of the target has five dots for practice. It is suspended on a metal frame.
SRP: $49.99

Targets & Range Equipment

EZ-SHOT

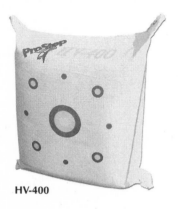

HV-400

RANGE TARGET KIT

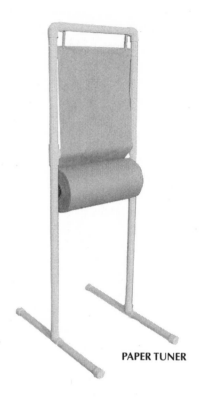

PAPER TUNER

P&P Outdoors

ProStop Targets and Pittman Game Calls have combined forces and are based in Louisville, Mississippi. The companies can be reached at 800-526-4868. The company manufactures a wide assortment of deer and turkey calls, plus numerous targets and bow tuning aids.

The Blob

This cube target is made for broadheads and will also work with field tips and all types of arrows. The unique, colorfully printed sides represent turkey and deer vital regions in a life-sized scale. All arrows can be easily removed. Size is 18x18x18-inches.
SRP: $69.95

EZ-Shot

This economical target is hand-packed with recycled polyester bonded fiber and will stop arrows traveling at up to 260 fps. Arrows can be easily removed and two faces of the target can be shot. Size is 23x28x13-inches.
SRP: $32.95

HV-400

This target is designed for today's high velocity carbon arrows and has 160 layers of synthetic fibers. The target can be shot from two sides and measures 24x24x15-inches.
SRP: $69.95

Mini-Mag

This small target is portable and durable and can take up to 4000 shots on each side. It measures 22x22x10 inches and will stop arrows traveling up to 250 fps
SRP: $26.95

Paper Tuner

Accurate arrow flight depends upon proper tuning and this stand will securely hold a roll of paper for the process. The stand is lightweight, portable and easily transported and stored.
SRP: $39.95

Paper Roll

This roll of paper fits the Paper Tuner stand and is 450 yards long and 20 inches wide.
SRP: $54.95

ProStop Magnum

This target was designed in 1986 and has withstood the test of time. It is hand-packed and can stop arrows zipping along at 300 fps. The ProStop Magnum can be shot from two sides and will last thousands of arrows. Size is 24x26x13-inches.
SRP: $46.00

Range Target Kit

This versatile and sturdy target is sent as a ready-to-assemble kit and can be used in backyards or at professional ranges. Sturdy legs keep the target in place and above ground to prevent water damage.
SRP: $190.00

Super Range

This 33x34x15-inch bag is filled with high-density synthetic fiber and has a thick power pad in the rear to stop arrows with absolutely no pass through.
SRP: $116.95

Targets & Range Equipment

RINEHART MOOSE TARGET

PACIFIC BOW BUTTS
BIGBUTT TARGET

PACIFIC BOW BUTTS
BigButt Target
Designed for pro shops and clubs, this target backstop by Pacific Bow Butts is 44 inches wide, 21 inches high and 20 inches thick. These targets can easily be stacked three high and rotated to provide years of dependable and carefree use. The targets are constructed with compressed, biodegradable straw and wrapped with burlap. The package is secured with ½-inch galvanized bands. Arrows are easily removed after a shot and the backstop can easily withstand more than 75,000 penetrations.
SRP: **$69.96**

RINEHART
Moose Target
When you want a big target or to prepare for a moose-oriented bowhunt, this target will serve the purpose. It is constructed of dense foam and stands nearly 5-foot tall at the shoulder.
SRP: **$1,393.25**

Targets & Range Equipment

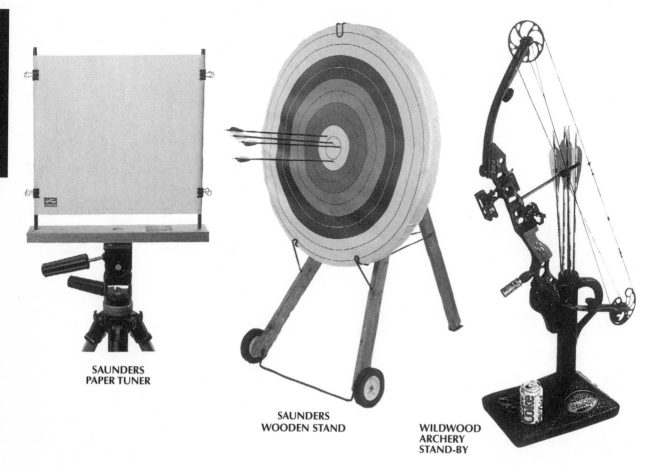

SAUNDERS
PAPER TUNER

SAUNDERS
WOODEN STAND

WILDWOOD
ARCHERY
STAND-BY

SAUNDERS ARCHERY
100# Stock Faces
These heavy weight paper targets have four rings in four colors, or blue and white circles with five spots or huge 40cm circle.

26x26-inch target
SRP: . . . . from $2.45
50x50-inch target
SRP: . . . . to $11.95

Indian Cord Mats
These machine wound targets have a durable prairie grass Indian-Cord inner layer that's covered with resilient natural burlap. The unit is economical and has a traditional appeal.

Several sizes are available and numerous stand options are available to hold the mats.

SRP: 25-inch $74.95
30-inch $84.95
36-inch $98.95
48-inch $126.95

Mat Stands
These stands will hold the Indian Cord mats and targets securely. Numerous sizes are available and you can select from a wheeled stand to an on-the-ground easel.
Wooden stand that holds 36- and 48-inch mats above waist level
SRP: $51.95
Metal stand that holds 36- to 48-inch targets at ground level
SRP: $98.95
Metal easel stand
SRP: $35.95
Dual support target stand
SRP: $19.95

Paper Tuner
This sturdy and wide stand by Saunders Archery helps you paper tune arrows. The compact 11x114-inch finished oak frame can be clamped or mounted onto a tripod in

seconds. A 17x17-inch four-color target is included along with instructions.
SRP: $24.95

Toughenized Faces
These faces have hundreds of nylon threads criss-crossing between two layers of heavy stock. They are available as squared or skirted and will cover the Indian Cord Mats.
48-inch face
SRP: . . . . From $10.95 to $24.95

WILDWOOD INNOVATIONS
Archery Stand-By
A unique bow and arrow stand that can be used in the backyard or at the range. A wide 10x14-inch base that's filled with sand securely supports the load and a tube holds the arrows. A bracket holds the bow and will not damage limbs or cams.
SRP: $39.95

BABY GRAND

LEGACY

BOWHUNTER EXTREME

MAGNUM EXTREME

API OUTDOORS
Baby Grand
This fixed position stand has a large 24x30-inch platform and will hold up to 350 pounds. The seat folds up out of the way when you need more room. The stand attaches to the tree with webbing. The Baby Grand weighs a light 16 pounds.
SRP: **$149.99**

Extreme Bowhunter
A climbing stand made with bow-hunters in mind. The stand adjusts easily, has lots of padding and is lightweight to backpack. It includes shoulder straps and a body harness. The stand weighs 20 pounds and will hold 300 pounds.
SRP: **$219.99**

Legacy
This climbing stand has a wire mesh 20x29-inch platform, weighs 29 pounds and is made with rugged steel. A cable secures the stand to the tree.
SRP: **$179.99**

Magnum Extreme
A climbing tree stand that will hold up to 350 pounds and has triple padding cushions. The stand uses a sure-grip chain to grip the tree. Comes with a full body safety harness.
SRP: **$329.99**

Tree Stands

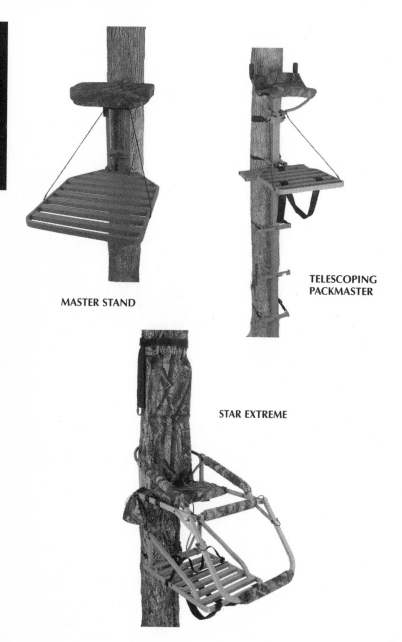

MASTER STAND

TELESCOPING
PACKMASTER

STAR EXTREME

V-LOCK
LADDER STAND

Master Stand
A fixed position stand with a detachable seat and 23x30-inch platform. The stand weighs 13 pounds and will support up to 300 pounds.
SRP: $129.99

Star Extreme
This climbing stand weighs 23 pounds, will hold 300pounds and has a roomy 20x29-inch platform. The climbing seat opens and swings out of the way for bowhunters.
SRP: $269.99

Telescoping Packmaster
This unique tree stand is a mobile ladder stand, fixed position stand or a telescoping ladder all in one. The package weighs 24 pounds and the ladder extends to 17-feet. It can be set up in 5 minutes and will hold up to 300 pounds.
SRP: $279.99

V-lock Ladder Stand
This ladder stand has a 17-feet high seat and an 18x18-inch platform. It weighs 64 pounds, will hold 300 pounds and can be disassembled into three sections for transporting.
SRP: $199.99

EZY CLIMB DELUXE TREE STEP

EZY CLIMB ROD TREE STEP

EZY CLIMB ROPE TREE STEP

EZY MIDGET T-SCREW

EZY CLIMB FOLDING TREE STEP

SUMMIT BROADHEAD BACKPACKER
CLIMBING TREE STAND

SUMMIT BUCKSTEPS

EZY T TREE STEP

CRANFORD MANUFACTURING COMPANY

Cranford makes tree steps that screw into the tree or that can be hung on the tree with a rope. Visit www.ezy-climb.com for more details. Cranford is located in Mocksville, North Carolina. All steps feature the EZY Climb screw that taps its way in the tree as you turn it.

EZY Climb Original Tree Step

This step is small, sturdy and easy to transport and place into the tree.
SRP: $3.75

EZY Climb Deluxe Tree Step
SRP: $3.25

EZY Climb Folding Step
SRP: . . . . $3.95 each

EZY Climb Rod Tree Step
SRP: $3.68

EZY T Step
SRP: $3.68

EZY Climb Folding Rope Tree Step

This step ties to a tree and can be used in areas where screw-in steps are illegal. The step folds conveniently and has a one-piece solid steel stainless steel hook.
SRP: $6.49

Midget T-Screw

This screw is used to place your stand on a tree.
SRP: $5.49

SUMMIT

Broadhead Backpacker Climbing Tree stand

Here's a stand that won't weight you down and was built with bowhunters in mind. It has a 20X28-inch platform, weighs 20 pounds and holds 300 pounds.
SRP: $239

Bucksteps

A set of individual steps that attach to the tree with cam buckles and webbing. The sections are 20 inches long, weigh 10 pounds for 4 steps and will hold up to 260 pounds.
SRP: $89

Tree Stands

GOLIATH TREE STAND

HEADHUNTER MINI

HEADHUNTER MAX

Goliath Tree stand
A Summit climbing stand that will support up to 350 pounds. The stand has a 20X28-inch platform and a wide top frame.
SRP:..................... **$279**

Headhunter Max
A large version of the Headhunter hang-on stand with a 21x24-inch platform. This stand will hold 260 pounds and weighs 17 pounds. Backpacking straps are included.
SRP:..................... **$89**
Headhunter Mini
SRP:..................... **$79**

Tree Stands

**REVOLUTION
CLIMBING TREE STAND**

**SEAT-O-THE-PANTS
4-POINT BODY HARNESS**

Revolution Climbing Tree Stand

A stand with an open front and the climbing bar doubles as a two-position footrest. This stand has a large cushy seat and it weighs 24 pounds. It has a weight limit of 300 pounds.

SRP:. $299

Seat-O-the-Pants 4-Point Body Harness

This harness is camouflaged and fits into a small pouch for transporting. It goes over the shoulders, between the legs and around the waist to hold you from all directions. It has a shock-absorbing tether to act as a brake if you fall. The webbing is rated to hold 6,000 pounds. Adult and youth models are available.

SRP: . . . . Starting at $59.99

Tree Stands

VIPER ULTRA CLIMBING STAND
FOOTREST AND SUPER SOFT SEAT

SWIFTREE CLIMBING POLE

VIPER XLS CLIMBING TREE STAND

As hunting season nears, it's a good idea to practice shooting your hunting bow while wearing the same hunting clothes you will use in the field.

Swiftree Climbing Pole

These pole sections strap to a tree's trunk and will place you more than 17 feet above ground. The system weighs 18 pounds and will hold up to 260 pounds.

SRP:. $50

Viper XLS Climbing Tree stand

The Viper XLS has cushioned bars to rest your bow on and a super sized platform to give lots of room to

maneuver. The unique cable system requires no fumbling with pins or knobs. This stand weighs 20 pounds and will climb trees from 8 to 20 inches in diameter. The weight limit is 300 pounds.

SRP:. $229

Viper Ultra Climbing Stand Footrest and super soft seat

SRP:. $259

Other Accessories

BUZZ BUSTER

BOHNING CAMO KIT

BOHNING WIND CHECK

BEN PEARSON ARCHERY
Buzz Buster

This small arm mounts on any cable guard with the turn of a hex wrench. Align the pad with the string and its ready to go, it's that simple. How does it work? When your string moves forward at the release to propel the arrow, it reaches a point in line with bow's axles. The string continues beyond this point, pulled by the arrow, and works to slow the arrow down. When the arrow nock breaks free of the string, you'll frequently hear a slight buss or twang as the string oscillates back in line with the axles. The buzz buster stops the string in line with the axles and the arrow breaks free under maximum power.
SRP: **$15.95**

BOHNING

This company manufacturers numerous items to upgrade your arrows and to build them.

The Bohning Company is based in Lake City, Michigan, and can be reached at 800-253-0136 or visit www.bohning.com.

Camo Kit

This easy to use kit is in a camouflaged case with a mirror included. Colors inlcude: shadow gray, flat black, bark brown and forest green.
SRP: **$5.76**
Skin Camo Crème
SRP: **$5.37**

Wind Check

This small bottle of odorless powder will help you determine the most fickle wind at your stand.
SRP: **$4.14**

Other Accessories

C.W. ERICKSON'S
SPORTSMEN'S UTILITY BELT

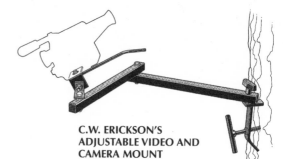

C.W. ERICKSON'S
ADJUSTABLE VIDEO AND
CAMERA MOUNT

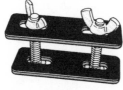

C.W. ERICKSON'S
TREESTAND ACCESSORY CLAMP

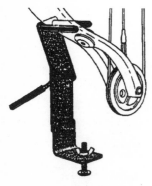

C.W. ERICKSON'S
TREE STAND BOW REST

C.W. ERICKSON'S
TREE STAND PROTECTOR

C.W. ERICKSON'S
HIGH RISER BOW REST

C.W. ERICKSON'S MFG.
Adjustable Video and Camera Mount
This adjustable swing arm is what the pros use to mount their cameras and video recorder to the tree to capture frame-by-frame and second by second details and action. Weighs 3 pounds and ins constructed of flat black tubing.
SRP: $63.99

High Riser Bow Rest
Similar to the standard tree stand bow rest but an extension raises the bow 6 to 7 inches above the stand. It's fully adjustable to accommodate all tree-stand situations. Allows hands to be free but keeps the bow close and ready.
SRP: $17.10

Sportsman's Utility Belt
Use this belt to secure loads to your pack, items to your treestand or around your waist to hold a bow holder, packs, knives etc. The belt is 1½-inch

wide webbing and fits waists up to 50-inches. Has a quick release buckle.
SRP: $8.39

Tree stand Accessory Clamp
This useful clamp can be used to secure many items to your treestand, plus to attach brush for concealment.
SRP: $5.59

Tree Stand Bow Rest
This handy prong can be used to securely and quietly hold your bow at the edge of your tree stand. Fits on almost all stands without drilling and vinyl cover holders secure your bow.
SRP: $9.79

Tree Stand Protector
The Protector is a 6½-foot long flexible cable to prevent theft. This item can double as a game drag.
SRP: $7.70

**HUNTER'S SPECIALTIES
MAG LIMB LIGHTS**

**HUNTER'S SPECIALTIES
HOT MELT STICK**

**HUNTER'S SPECIALTIES
SCENT ELIMINATION KIT**

**HUNTER'S SPECIALTIES
LIMB LIGHTS**

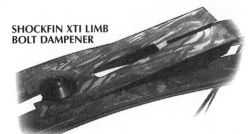

**SHOCKFIN XTI LIMB
BOLT DAMPENER**

**HUNTER'S SPECIALTIES
UTILITY ROPE**

**HUNTER'S SPECIALTIES
TRAIL MARKER TAPE**

HUGHES PRODUCTS COMPANY
EZ-Fold Gambrel
When space is at a premium, such as a remote camp that you backpack in to, this folding gambrel is the ticket to properly and safely handling game. It has a 350-pound weight capacity and will hang medium size game like deer and pronghorns. The extended arms reach out 22 inches and it's only 11½-inches long when folded. A pull rope is included.
SRP: **$15.95**

HPX5 Broadhead Sharpener and Wrench
A neat tool that is both a broadhead wrench and blade sharpener. This unit will sharpen all styles of broadheads and knife blades with either a tungsten carbide or ceramic sharpening system, plus it has slots to accommodate 3-, 4- and 5-blade broadheads. Yhis item is blaze orange so you will not loose it and it will fit in a shirt pocket!
SRP: **$5.95**

One-Man Hoist
Use this pulley system to hoist your deer or game animal up for skining and processing. This item can also be used for camp chores.
SRP: **$29.95**

HUNTER'S SPECIALTIES
Hunter's Specialties manufactures calls, scents and a very large assortment of archery and bowhunting oriented gear. The company is based in Cedar Rapids, Iowa.

Limb Lights
The twist type strips are reflective and wrap easily around small limbs and treesteps. They can be seen for approximately 100 yards.
SRP: **$4.45**
Mag Limb Lights
SRP: **$4.67**

Mag Hot Melt Stick
This glue stick is used to glue points and inserts to arrow shafts. It can also repair fishing rods and camp gear.
SRP: **$2.58**

Scent Elimination Kit
This kit includes Scent-Away soap, laundry detergent, dryer sheets and bar soap. Other items includes antiperspirant and a scent safe storage bag.
SRP: **$29.70**
Scent Away Dryer Sheets
SRP: **$4.90**
Scent Safe Deluxe Travel Bag
SRP: **$52.00**
Scent Away Spray Combo
SRP: **$18.31**
Trail Marker Tape
This non-adhesive safety orange tape is photodegradable and perfect for marking trails and while tracking. It breaks down in sunlight and is waterproof and easy to tear. The roll is 150 feet long.
SRP: **$2.52**

Utility Rope
A strong 20-foot long rope that is safe, quiet and washable. Use it to haul gear up to your treestand.
SRP: **$3.20**

Other Accessories

JIM FLETCHER'S FIELD TOOL

LANSKY CROCKSTICK
MULTI-SHARPENER

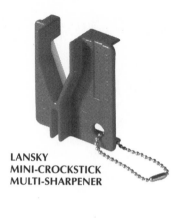

LANSKY
MINI-CROCKSTICK
MULTI-SHARPENER

HIP BOW HOLDER

SQUARE DEER STAND BOW HOLDER

JIM FLETCHER ARCHERY AIDS

This company is based in Bodfish, California, and can be reached at 760-379-2589.

Fletcher's Field Tool

This compact and foldable tool has the following Allen wrenches: $3/16$, $5/32$, $9/64$, $1/8$, $7/64$, $3/32$, $5/64$, and $1/16$-inch. It also has a slot and a #1 Phillips head screwdriver head. In addition the unit has an open-end adjustable wrench and a three-blade broadhead wrench. It is truly a toolbox in your hand.
SRP:. $25

LANSKY SHARPENERS
Crock Stick Multi-Sharpener

This small ceramic stick will fit in a shirt pocket and can be used to sharpen knives and broadheads. It has a triangular design and easy to grip safety end caps.
SRP: $8.00

Mini Crock Stick Sharpener

A small knife and fishhook sharpener with two removable ceramic sharpening stones. It can be used as a key ring.
SRP: $5.00

MOUNTTEK
Hip Bow Holder

An innovative hanger that permits you to hang your bow at your waist. The kit includes a bow mount, hip holder and the hardware.
SRP: $29.95

Round Stand Bow Holder

This holder permits you to secure your bow on the front or side of your tree stand so it's ready for action and nearby. The unique holder securely holds the bow until you lift it out of the bracket.
SRP: $26.95

Square Deer Stand Bow Holder

Similar to the Round Stand bow holder, but the attachment is made to fit square-edged stands.
SRP: $24.95

Other Accessories

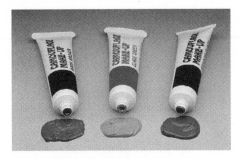

**NORTH AMERICAN ARCHERY GROUP
CAMO MAKE-UP CREAM**

**SHED HUNTER COMPANY
VIDEO HUNTER**

**NORTH AMERICAN
ARCHERY GROUP
SILENT BOW HANGER**

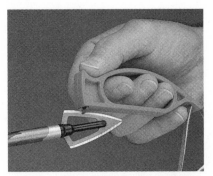

**NORTH AMERICAN ARCHERY GROUP
ARCHER'S EDGE BROADHEAD SHARPENER**

**NORTH AMERICAN ARCHERY GROUP
HOOK AND LINE KIT**

**SIMMONS SYSTEM ARCHERY
2ND CHANCE ARROW HOLDERS**

NORTH AMERICAN ARCHERY GROUP

The following items are available from the North American Archery Group in Gainesville, Florida. These items will work with their Bear and Jennings bows and for any hunter.

Archer's Edge Broadhead Sharpener

This compact hand-held unit can be used to sharpen broadheads for hunting.Compact enough to fit in shirt pocket. A must have item for hunters on the go!
SRP: $4.49

Camo Make-Up Cream

These items are sold as a kit or in bulk. Apply to face and hands to camouflage areas and increase concealment while hunting. Easily removed. Colors: green, black and brown.
SRP:. . . . . $3.49.

Hook and Line Kit

Perfect set-up for hoisting bow and hunting gear up to your treestand after you're safely secured into position. Rope is 20-foot long and has a sturdy clip on each end. Can also be used to secure unwanted brush out of shooting lanes. Two screw-in hooks are included in the kit for securing your gear and bow in the tree.
SRP: $3.49

Silent Bow Hanger

This sturdy, rubber-coated hook can be easily screwed into a tree to hang your bow while hunting.
SRP: 3-pack. $3.49
6-pack $3.99

SHED HUNTER COMPANY Video Hunter

A unique bracket that lets you mount a camcorder on the front of your bow to film you hunt as the action takes place. The bracket is lightweight, quiet, stable and easy to use. The bracket can also be used off the bow.
SRP: $29.99

SIMMONS SYSTEM ARCHERY 2nd Chance Arrow Holders

When you need a second chance without making unnecessary game spooking movement, these rubber coated screw-in arrow clips by Simmons System Archery will help hold a second arrow in a convenient and within reach location. Simply screw the holder into the tree trunk and pop an arrow between the prongs. Arrows can be removed quickly and quietly.
SRP:. . . . . $12.95 per three pack

Other Accessories

BREEZE DETECTOR

CARBO WASH

SCENT KILLER ANTI-PERSPIRANT DEODORANT

SCENT KILLER BAR SOAP

SCENT KILLER CLOTHING WASH

SCENT KILLER LIQUID SOAP

SCENT KILLER SPRAY

WILDLIFE RESEARCH
Breeze Detector Powder
A bottle of odorless powder that floats in the air to reveal wind currents.
SRP: **$4.99**

Carbo Wash
Recommended for washing carbon-activated clothing.
SRP: 16 oz. **$11.99**
32 oz. **$19.99**

Scent Killer Anti-Perspirant Deodorant
A stick deodorant that's odorless and helps keep you dry and odor free all day.
SRP: **$5.99**

Scent Killer Bar Soap
A 5-ounce bar that's nonscented and kills human odor.
SRP: 5 oz. **$4.99**

Scent Killer Clothing Wash
A laundry detergent that removes odors from clothes in the wash and leaves them odorless. This product contains no UV brighteners.
SRP: Starting at 16 oz. **$6.99**

Scent Killer Liquid Soap
This soap is gentle on the skin and has an antibacterial formula that attacks human odor.
SRP: 8 oz. **$5.99**
12 oz. **$6.99**
32 oz. **$14.99**

Scent Killer Spray
This product kills odors upon contact and is available in 4-, 8- and 24-ounce sizes.
SRP: 4 oz. **$4.99**
8 oz. **$6.99**
24 oz. **$12.99**

BOWHUNTING CLOTHING

CLOTHING

Bowhunting Clothing

HYRDO-FLEECE CLASSIC
INSULATED BIB

HYRDO-FLEECE CLASSIC
4-IN-1 PARKA

HYRDO-FLEECE
CLASSIC
INSULATED PANT

HYRDO-FLEECE
CLASSIC JACKET

BROWNING

Many Browning garments utilize Gore-Tex fabric technology, such as Supprescent. The Supprescent fabric provides 100 percent waterproof protection and breathable comfort, along with an added benefit of permanent odor barrier with carbon that is permanently embedded into the fabric. It requires no reactivation with heat and does not require sprays or re-applications.

Hydro-Fleece Classic 4-in-1 Parka with Supprescent

This Browning parka permits layering with an inner jacket that zips in and out. Other features include two zippered pockets, and inside security pocket and hood. The shell is quiet and soft Hydro Fleece and offered in Mossy Oak camo.
SRP: S-XL $300
XXL and larger $337

Hydro-Fleece Classic Insulated Bib with Supprescent

The perfect companion garment for the Classic parka. The bibs have front zipper, leg zippers and pockets. They are insulated and available in Mossy Oak camouflage.
SRP: S-XL $200
XXL and larger $233

Hydro-Fleece Classic Jacket with Supprescent

This lightweight hunting jacket has Gore's Supprescent technology to eliminate human odors. The jacket has a soft fleece exterior and is available in Mossy Oak Break Up camouflage.
SRP: S-XL $225
XXL and larger $250

Hydro Fleece Classic Pant with Supprescent

These pants are the companion to the jacket above and feature a draw cord with belt loops, a rear pocket and zippered legs for easy on and off.
SRP: S-XL $155
XXL and larger $171

Hydro-Fleece Pro Series 4-in-1 Parka with Supprescent

This garment has a coat within a coat that can be zipped in or out to meet changing temperatures and weather conditions. The outer shell is made of Cordura and is quiet and rugged. It has an archer sleeve that can be adjusted for sung fit to stay out of the way of the bowstring. The parka features a detachable hood, two-zippered bellows pockets, and inside security pocket and rear storage pocket. This coat is water- and windproof. It is made scent proof with Supprescent technology and waterproof with a Gore-Tex laminate. It's offered in Mossy Oak Break-Up.
SRP: S-XL $400
2XL and Larger $440

Bowhunting Clothing

HYRDO-FLEECE
INSULATED JACKET

HYRDO-FLEECE PANT

BUG-OUT COVER-UP PACKS

Hydro-Fleece Pro Series Insulated Bib with Supprescent

These bibs match the 4-in-1 parka above and are similar in design and construction. The bibs are insulated with Dupont Themolite and have an inner lining, two front pockets, a heavy duty full length front zipper and the leg zippers are full-length to permit easy on and off. It's available in Mossy Oak camouflage.

SRP: S-L $268
XXL or larger $298

Hydro-Fleece Pro Series Jacket with Supprescent

This feature packed jacket is not insulated and has similar construction and features as the parka. The jacket is lined with Gore-Tex Supprescent to eliminate odors reaching wary game species while hunting. The jacket is wind and waterproof, and has a soft and quiet Micro Fleece exterior. This jacket is designed to provide years of dependable service. The jacket is X-Change system compatible and available in Mossy Oak camo.

SRP: S-XL $260
XXL and larger $299

Hydro-Fleece Pro Series Pants with Supprescent

These pants are the companion to the above jacket and are great for bowhunting wear during normal hunting conditions. This garment has Supprescent technology. The pants have zippered legs, belt loops and a drawstring. They are available in Mossy Oak Break-Up.

SRP: S-XL $212
XXL and larger $233

BUG-OUT OUTDOORWEAR

Bug-Out manufacturers innovative bug suits to keep biting bugs away from your skin.

Bug Out Bug Packs

These handy bags contain a jacket, pants and headnet. The jacket has a full-length zipper and the pants have an elastic waistband. These garments are made of no-see-um mesh with micro fibers. The fiber will stop biting bugs and ticks and is colored olive drab.

SRP: olive . . . . $35.99 to $54.99

Bug Out Cover-Up Packs

These inexpensive suits come in a handy pack bag and include a jacket, pant and face mask. The jacket has a high collar, extra long sleeves and relaxed fit to permit movement. It has a full-length front zipper. The pants are cut oversized and have an elastic waistband. You can pull these on over standard clothing or other hunting garments to provide quick concealment or to better blend in under any cover. Available colors include Realtree Hardwoods, Advantage Timber, Realtree Hardwoods Blaze, Realtree Hardwoods Snow, Blaze solid and white. Sizes S-4XL large.

SRP: . . . . $39.95 to 54.99

CLOTHING

Bowhunting Clothing

CONTAIN MAXIMUM

ROBINSON OUTDOORS
DISCOVERY JACKET

ROBINSON OUTDOORS
DISCOVERY PANTS

CONTAIN SOLID

CONTAIN

Contain Maximum

The fibers of these Coolmax blend garments have built in deodorant. Contain helps prevent the formation of body odor. These items are designed to be worn next to the skin. All garments except the socks are available in Mossy Oak camouflage.

Long Sleeve T-Shirt
  SPR:. $46
Long John Bottoms
  SRP:. $46
Boxer Shorts
  SRP:. $34
Camouflaged Head Cover
  SRP:. $28
Gloves
  SRP: $11.99
Hiking Socks
  SRP: $16.99
Tube Socks
  SRP: $12.99

Contain Solid

These undergarments actually prevent the formation of body odor thanks to deodorant fibers. The gray garments are made from an acrylic/polyester blend and can be machine-washed.
Contain Solid Long Sleeve T-Shirt
  SRP: $32.99
Contain Solid Long John Bottoms
  SRP: $32.99

ROBINSON OUTDOORS

Discovery Jacket

A scent control jacket by Robinson Outdoors with a zip-out removable liner and two-piece hood. The jacket has 10 pockets, a chill-out ventilation system and non-slip shoulder pad. The specially designed arm permits movement. Available in Mossy Oak Break Up and Hardwoods camouflage.
SRP: . . . . **Starting at $269**

Discovery Pants

The companion garment to the Discovery jacket. The pant has a reinforced seat, 2 large cargo pockets, two front pockets, and 20-inch water repellent leg zippers.
SRP: . . . . **Starting at 229**

SCENT-LOK

Scent-Lok is the original creator of carbon fabric odor elimination technology and continues to improve, develop and expand the technology. These carbon fabrics actually trap gas particles released by the body during normal perspiration.

Bowhunting Clothing

SAVANNA MOCK-TURTLENECK

DAKOTA BOMBER JACKET

DAKOTA 6-POCKET PANT

SAVANNAH COVERALLS

SAVANNA BOMBER JACKET

SAVANNAH LONG SLEEVE MOCK-T

SAVANNAH 6-POCKET PANT

SAVANNAH STALKER JACKET

DAKOTA HEADCOVER

SCENT-LOK SAVANNA HEADCOVER

SCENT-LOK SAVANNA T-SHIRT

CLOTHING

SCENT-LOK DAKOTA SERIES

This single-layer Microsuede fabric is light, burr-proof, and repels moisture. It is colorfast so camouflage patterns will not fade. The Dakota series uses Climaflex fabric that is also extremely breathable and helps keep hunters dry inside and out. Available camouflage patterns are Advantage Timber and Mossy Oak.

Dakota Six-Pocket Pants
   SRP: $129.95
Dakota Single Layer Microsuede Bib Overalls
   SRP: $169.95

Dakota Single layer Microsuede Mock Turtleneck
   SRP: $99.95
Dakota Single Layer Microsuede Premium Bomber Jacket
   SRP: $129.95
Dakota Headcover
   SRP: $34.95
Scent-Lok Savanna Series
Savanna Bomber Jacket
   SRP: $99.95
Savanna BDU Pants
   SRP: $99.95
Savanna Lightweight Shirts
   SRP: $89.95

Savanna Stalker Jacket
   SRP: $114.95
Savanna Packable Coveralls
   SRP: $169.95
Savanna Ultra-Light T-Shirt
   SRP:. $59
Savanna Long Sleeve Mock T-Shirt
   SRP: $79.95, $87.94
Scent-Lok Savanna Headcover
   SRP: $21.95
Scent-Lok Facemask
   SRP: $21.95
Scent-Lok Hunting Caps
   SRP: $34.95

Bowhunting Clothing

CLOTHING

SCENT-LOK SUPREME 3-IN-1 SIX-POCKET PANT

SCENT-LOK SUPREME 3-IN-1 PARKA

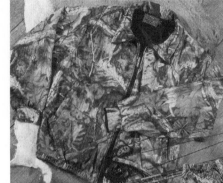

WHITEWATER WINDSTOPPER SUPPRESCENT JACKET

SCENT-LOK INSULATED GLOVES

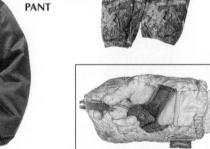

WHITEWATER WINDSTOPPER SUPPRESCENT PANT

SCENT-LOK CLASSIC GREEN HEADCOVER

CLASSIC GREEN SCENT-LOK PULL ON PANT LINER

SCENT-LOK CLASSIC GREEN JACKET LINER

SHERWOOD ARCHERY BOW HUNTER'S RELEASE MITT

SCENT-LOK SUPREME SERIES

These bomber and pants offer two-layer protection with an inner light-weight garment and a touch—but quiet—outer layer that repels water and the elements.

Scent-Lok Supreme 3-in-1 Parka Length Jacket
SRP: $189.95
2XL and larger $208.95

Scent-Lok Supreme 3-in-1 Six-Pocket Pant
SRP: up to XL $189.95
2XL and larger. $208.95

Scent Lok Gloves

Wear these to eliminate odors as you travel to your stand or while hunting.
SRP: $34.95
insulated $39.95

Classic Green Scent-Lok Liner Wear

These are the garments that got the entire human scent industry up and running. The original liners can be effectively worn under standard hunting clothing as a layering system. The Classic series are olive green in color.

Classic Jacket Liner
SRP: $75.95

Classic Headcover
SRP: $19.95

Classic Pull On Pant Liner
SRP: up to XL $75.95
XXL and larger $83.55

SHERWOOD ARCHERY
Bowhunter's Release Mitt

Protects release hand with quiet, warm fleece and 150-gram Thinsulate insulation. Innovative design allows for a smooth draw and release without fumbling with gloves, mittens or muffs. Slide hand inside and position release through the slot. Elastic cuff keeps cold out. Ambidextrous design. Mossy Oak Break-Up.
SRP: $29.95

WHITEWATERS OUTDOORS
Whitewater Windstopper Supprescent Jacket

A jacket made of ultra-soft and quiet 100% polyester Micro Fleece to eliminate fabric scratch. The jacket is lined with Gore's Windstopper membrane with active carbon permanently embedded in. Other features include two hand warmer pockets, stretch cuffs and a stand-up collar. This jacket is available in Realtree Hardwoods and Advantage Timber. It's offered in sizes Medium through 3XL.
SRP: . . . . $140 to $160

Whitewater Windstopper Supprescent Pant

A pant similar to the Whitewater jacket in construction and fabric, and this garment has a full elastic waistband and cuffs. It is also offered in the two Jordan Enterprises camouflaged patterns.
SRP: . . . . $130 to $150

Bow Fishing Gear

AMS SAFETY SLIDE

REEL SEAT

EVER CLEAN

BOW FISHING STARTER KIT

CLASSIC ARROW WITH GAR POINT

ECONOMY RIVER POINT

BLUE FIBERGLASS SHAFT

MUZZY BOW FISHING LINES

MUZZY
AMS Safety Slide
This innovative slide helps keep the line safely away from your arrow rest when at full draw and slides down the shaft when reeling in. End those frustrating arrow verses line launch problems with this AMS slide. Two diameters are available: 5/16 and 22/64.
SRP: . . . . **$3.25 each.**

Anchor Reel Seat and Rod
The anchor reel seat screws into your bow's stabilizer hole for quick mounting of the Zebco bowfishing reel. The Rod mounts in the reel seat to keep your line clear of the bow and arrow rest.
SRP: . . . . **$18 reel seat**
rod **$9.93**

Bowfishing Lines
Muzzy is your source for sturdy lines to reel in the big ones. Our inventory includes: Brownell Fast Flite, Muzzy Extreme, Brownell Gator Cord, Muzzy Tournament line, BCY 175# and 300# test lines. Lengths range from 75- to 300-feet and weight ranges span from 175-pound to the 600-pound Gator Cord.
SRP: Ranges from . . . . **$9.65 to $40**

Bowfishing Arrow Rests
Here are two rests designed to handle bowfishing arrows and the strain caused upon release.
Wheel of Fortune II: Incorporates a brass wheel on a stainless steel shaft for smooth corrosion free operation.
SRP: **$11.65**
Tri-Loop Rest: a shoot-through metal triangle designed to accommodate unfletched arrows.
SRP: . . . . **$11.65 each**

Bowfishing Starter Kit
This package includes everything you need to grab your bow and start hunting fish! Includes a Zbeco reel filled with 150-pound test Spectra line, a reel seat, Muzzy's Tri-Loop arrow rest, an a Muzzy Classic arrow with a carp point installed. All you need is water and fish for hot bow action.
SRP: **$69.95**

Classic Arrow With Gar Point
A solid fiberglass arrow with a quick-release gar point installed. The arrow includes a nock and a hole for a cable or string attachment.
SRP: **$11.00**
Classic Arrow With Carp Point
SRP: **$11.00**

Economy River Point
This Muzzy bowfishing arrow has a solid blue fiberglass shaft with a nock, predrilled hole and is unfletched.
SRP: **$7.17**

Ever Kleen Bow Holder
This leather loop-style bow holder keeps your bow at waist level and permits faster access and quicker shots. A sturdy belt loop ensures years of dependable service.
SRP: **$9.08**

Fiberglass Shaft
Solid premium fiberglass shafts for custom finishing with any Muzzy point. 32-inches long, tapered for nocks with predrilled holes.
Blue Fiberglass Shaft
SRP: **$2.67**
White Fiberglass Shaft
SRP: **$2.67**

Bow Fishing Gear

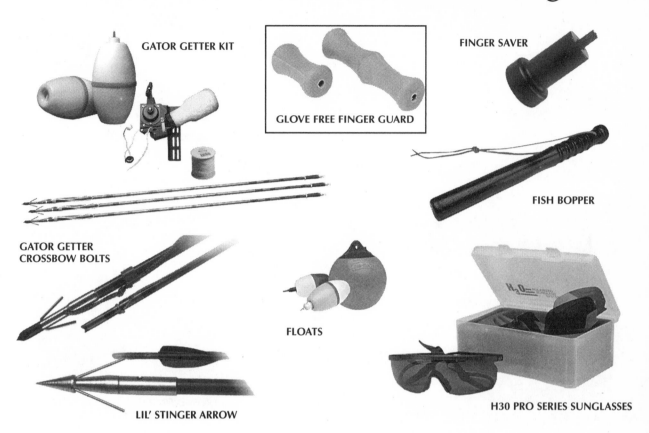

GATOR GETTER KIT

GLOVE FREE FINGER GUARD

FINGER SAVER

FISH BOPPER

GATOR GETTER CROSSBOW BOLTS

FLOATS

LIL' STINGER ARROW

H30 PRO SERIES SUNGLASSES

Finger Saver
This handy post screws into your bow's stabilizer hole and gives you something to wrap line around other than your fingers. The Finger Saver assists with fighting fish and while removing arrows stuck on the bottom.
SRP: $8.50

Fish Bopper
Stop those annoying flopping fish in their scales with this black mini-club. The Bopper has a string attached to prevent loosing it in water. Great for gar.
SRP: $6.00

Floats
Larger fish and gators often need to be released when you reach the end of the line. You can track their movements with these floats that are designed to work with Muzzy's slotted retriever reel.
Small Game Float, blue and white
SRP: . . . . $17.77 each
Big Game Float, yellow and white
SRP: . . . . $25.38 each
Deep Sea Float - orange
SRP: . . . . $31.92 each

Gator Crossbow Bolts and Gator Getter Kit
You can hunt gators with your crossbow and these crossbow arrows are rigged for the hunt. The same kit as above with crossbow applications is also available and includes similar components.
SRP: Gator Crossbow Kit . . . $225.33
Crossbow bolts. $23

Gator Getter Kit
Gators can provide thrills and problems. You can overcome the problems with this kit that includes: a slotted retriever reel, 2 big game floats, 600-pound Gator cord, three gator getter arrows with gator points, one extra spool of gator cord. Note that Gator arrows and gator points are sold separately.
SRP: Gator kit standard $225.33
Gator arrows $23
Gator points $7.62

Glove Free Finger Guard
These rollers permit accurate shooting even when you have wet fingers. One roller accommodates two fingers and the other roller is designed for use with one finger.
SRP: three pack $4.17

H30 Pro Series Sunglasses
These sunglasses will help you see into the water to locate fish. Interchangeable lenses can be easily and quickly installed to help you meet changing water clarity and light conditions. The sunglasses are ultra light for all-day wear.
SRP: includes three lenses . . . $59.98

Lil' Stinger Arrow
A solid premium grade fiberglass arrow with a Lil' Stinger point attached. Includes a layafletch, nock, and hole for cable or string attachments.
SRP: $9.17

Bow Fishing Gear

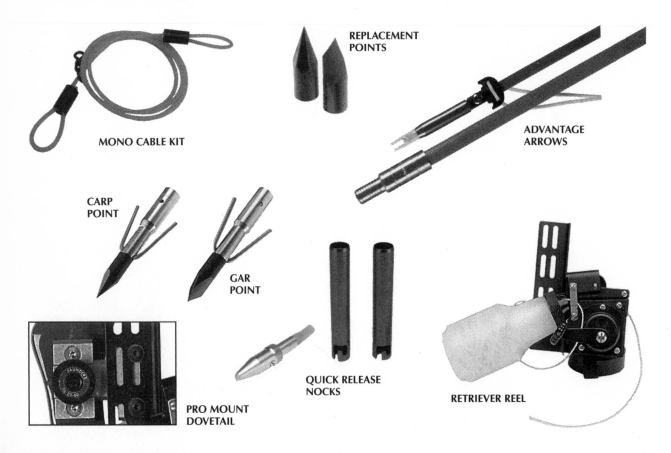

MONO CABLE KIT

REPLACEMENT POINTS

ADVANTAGE ARROWS

CARP POINT

GAR POINT

PRO MOUNT DOVETAIL

QUICK RELEASE NOCKS

RETRIEVER REEL

Mono Cable Kit
This bowfishing arrow kit includes a heavy 250-pound mono cable with swedges and swivels for complete installation.
SRP: **$3.75**

Premium Bowfishing Arrows
The Penetrator Arrow features a unique carbon/Glass and Aluminum composite with a Uni-nock system. This bowfishing arrow is fully cabled and collared. Various styles are available including: Penetrator with safety slide, Predator arrow for crossbows, and Predator arrows and Predator arrows with the newest safety slide feature and a unique Midnight camo finish. SRPs range from $17.69 to $22.69. The Advantage series of premium bowfishing arrows are fiberglass and have a full-length cable, and collar. Must install a point. The Advantage with safety slide has a Uni-nock and is Hi-Vis.
SRP: **$12.69**

Pro-Mount Dovetail
This bracket is per-drilled to fit preexisting riser holes and permits quick change over of components, such as the arrow rests listed above, to meet varying conditions.
SRP: **$17.25**

Quick Release Carp Point
Same as the Gar Point with longer tip and slightly longer barbs. Operates the same to release fish.
SRP: **$7.50**

Quick Release Gar Points
These points feature full stainless steel ferrules with the famous Muzzy Trocor point. A simple two turns of the point allows the barb to fold in the opposite direction and release fish. The short design aids in penetration.
SRP: **$7.50**

Quick Release Nock
This nock system permits removal of the nock for quick changes or fish removal on the water when quick removal counts, such as during bowfishing tournaments.
SRP: . . . . **$7.50 each**

Replacement Points
These points are designed to penetrate tough skinned fish and can be used to repleace the tips on any Muzzy fishing point. Screw on easily and quickly.
SRP: 2 to a card **$3.33**

Retriever Reels
These reels feature canisters to feed out heavy lines with no drag. The line cranks back into the canister with no tangles. The system comes loaded with Muzzy's 200-pound test Extreme line. Note; Slotted retriever reel is same as above but is designed to release a large float or ball at the end of the line. The floats can help you track large moving fish.
SRPS: standard **$57.32**
Slotted **$71.99**

Bow Fishing Gear

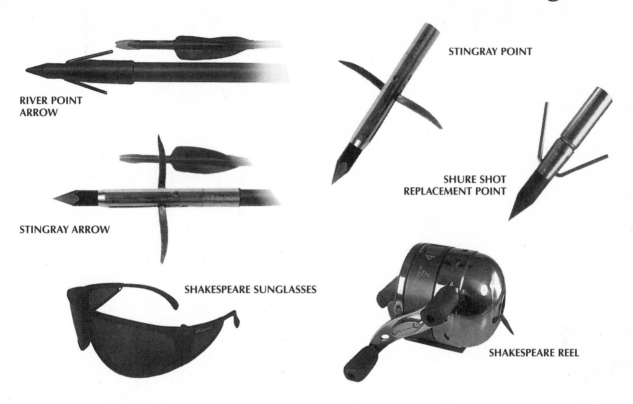

RIVER POINT
ARROW

STINGRAY POINT

STINGRAY ARROW

SHURE SHOT
REPLACEMENT POINT

SHAKESPEARE SUNGLASSES

SHAKESPEARE REEL

River Point Arrow
A fully assembled solid premium fiber-glass arrow with river point attached. Includes hole, nock and layafletch.
SRP: $7.58

Shakespeare Reel
This new reel has full brass and stain-less steel construction with special bearings and a high retrieve ratios resulting in faster landings. The reel can easily be converted from right or left-hand use and fits any anchor reel seat. Designed for seasons of depend-able performance.
SRP: $29.93

Shakespeare Sunglasses
These new wrap a rounds are designed with polarized lenses for visual acuity below the surface. They are lightweight and durable. A string can be attached to the arms to prevent loss.
SRP: $12.23

Shure Shot Point
This bowfishing point has a permanent tip and quick release barb. A twist of the tips permits the barbs to fold for-ward and release a fish.
SRP: $7.08

Shure Shot Replacement Tip
Replace worn or damaged tips on most bowfishing arrows.
SRP: $4.82

Stingray Arrow
A solid premium grade blue fiberglass arrow with a Stingray Point installed. The arrow includes a nock, layafletch (soft rubber vanes), and hole for a cable or string attachment.
SRP: $13.33

Stingray Point
This bowfishing point features a replaceable carp tip and extra-wide bite for a superior hold on large fish. Two twists release a fish. This is a rec-ommended tournament fishing point.
SRP: $8.83

BOW FISHING GEAR

Fletch interference often accounts for bad arrow flight. Some archers spray foot powder on the fletches before shooting to determine if this might be the problem. When the arrow is shot, a puff of powder shows if the fletch is hitting something it shouldn't.

Bow Fishing Gear

BOW FISHING GEAR

UNI-NOCKS

UNI-NOCK ADAPTERS

3-D CARP TARGET

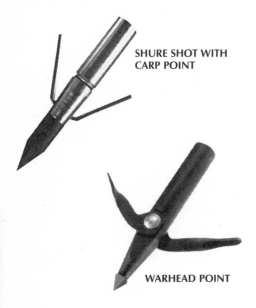

SHURE SHOT WITH CARP POINT

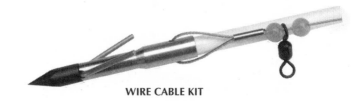

WIRE CABLE KIT

WARHEAD POINT

ZEBCO 808 BOWFISHING REEL

Shure Shot with Carp Point
This new muzzy point has a screw on replaceable carp tip for added convenience.
SRP: $8.83

3-D Carp Target
This 2-foot long carp target provides a fish when the real ones won't cooperate and is useful for practicing. It can swim underwater when rigged properly and provides realistic practice and hours of fun.
SRP: $53.77

Uni-Nocks And Adapters
These nocks allow easy replacement when using the Uni-Nock adapter system. These can replace the nocks on numerous bowfishing arrows listed above.
SRP: nocks $2.67
Adapters. $3.95

Warhead Point
This bowfishing point has twisted barbs that spin to improve in the water accuracy. The pyramid head positions the barbs close to the tip permitting holding power with only 2?-inch penetration.
SRP: $4.67

Wire Cable Kit
Includes all the items needed to cable any predrilled arrow, including a section of 300-pound test cable, swedges, swivel and orange beads.
SRP: . . . . $2.92 **each**

Zebco 808 Bowfishing Reel
Made for bowfishing, this reel has modified brass and stainless steel parts, plus a larger crank handle and lock-down drag. It arrives with 70-pound Dacron line.
SRP: $29.93

DIRECTORY OF MANUFACTURERS

AIM (Archery International Marketing)
95 Milk St.
Willimantic, CT 06226
888-246-8044
www.aimarchery.com

Alpine Archery
P.O. Box 319
Lewiston, ID 83501
208-746-4717
www.alpinearchery.com

APA Innovations
Box 1420
Biggar, Saskatchewan, Canada
S0K 0M0
866-353-REST
www.apaarchery.com

API Outdoors
Division of Outdoor Sports
4500 Doniphan Dr.
Neosho MO 64805
800-922-9034
www.apioutdoors.com

Archery Research
P.O. Box 5403
Tucson, Arizona 85703
800-385-5046
www.archeryresearch.com

Archery Shooter Systems
109 N. Wagner St.
Endeavor, WI 53930
866-823-7757
www.bowhanger.com

ArcticShield
905 S. 9th, Suite D
Broken Arrow, OK 74012
877-974-4353
www.arcticshield.com

Arizona Rim
6401 West Chandler Blvd., Suite A
Chandler, AZ 85226
800-635-6899
www.ezfletch.com

Arrow Dynamic Solutions
P.O. Box 806
Liberty Hill, Texas 78642
512-515-6299
www.arrow-dynamic-solutions.com

Barnett International
13447 Byrd Dr.
Odessa, FL 33556
800-237-4507

www.barnettcrossbows.com

Barrie Archery/Rocky Mountain Broadheads
P.O. Box 482
Waseca, MN 56093
507-835-3859
www.bowhunting.net/barrie

Bass Pro Shops
2500 E. Kearney
Springfield, MO 65898
800-BASS PRO
www.basspro.com

Beman U. S. A.
5040 West Harold Gatty Dr
Salt Lake City, UT 84116
801-539-1433
www.beman.com

Ben Pearson Archery Inc.
P.O. Box 327
734 Brewton Industrial Park
Brewton, AL 36427
251-867-8475
www.benpearson.com

Black Gold
34370 East Frontage Road
Bozeman, MT 59715
406-586-1117
www.montanablackgold.com

Blackhawk Archery Co.
P.O. Box 4240
Austintown, Ohio 44515
330-793-3314
www.blackhawkarchery.com

Black Widow Bows
P.O. Box 2100
1201 Eaglecrest
Nixa, MO 65714
417-725-3113
www.blackwidowbows.com

Blueridge
Division of Outland Sports, Inc.
4500 Doniphan Dr.
Neosho, MO 64850
800-922-9034
(no website)

Bodoodle
3301 US Highway 84 North
Coleman, TX 76834
800-467-8781
www.bodoodle.net

Bohning
7361 North Seven Mile Rd.

Lake City, MI 49651
800-253-0136
www.bohning.com/archery

Boonie Packer
Division of JFS, Inc.
P.O. Box 12517
Salem, OR 97309
800-477-3244
www.booniepackerslings.com

Bowhunting Traditions
385 Hendrickson School Rd.
Shell Knob, MO 65747
417-858-0522
(no website)

Browning Archery
One Browning Place
Morgan, UT 84050
800-333-3288
www.browning-archery.com

Bruin Custom Recurves
W9664 Highway D
Antigo, WI 54409
715-623-6537
www.bruinbows.com

Buck Stop Lure Co.
P.O. Box 636
3600 Grow Rd.
Stanton, MI 48888-0636
800-477-2368
www.buckstopscents.com

Buckmasters
4600 Southwest 41st Blvd.
Gainesville, FL 32608-4999
352-376-2327
www.beararch.com/buckmasters

BuckWing Products
2300 Eberhart Rd.
Whitehall, PA 18052
800-555-9908
www.buckwing.com

Bug-Out Outdoorwear
P.O. Box 185
Centerville, IA 52544
877-928-4688
www.bug-out-outdoorwear.com

C.W. Erickson's Manufacturing
P.O. Box 522
Buffalo, MN 55313
763-682-3665
www.archerhunter.com

Cabela's
One Cabela Dr.

Sidney, NE 69160
800-237-4444
www.cabelas.com

Carbon Express by Game Tracker
P.O. Box 380
3476 Eastman Dr.
Flushing, MI 48433
800-241-4833
www.carbonexpressarrows.com

Carbon Tech
4571 Pell Dr., Suite 3
Sacramento, CA 95838
800-951-8736
www.carbon-tech.com

Carolina Archery Products, Inc.
620 Valley Forge Rd.
Hillsboro, NC 27278
919-245-1400
www.carolinaarcheryprod.com

Cartel
AIM/Archery International
Marketing
95 Milk St.
Willimantic, CT 06226
888-246-8044

Carter Enterprises
P.O. Box 19
St. Anthony, ID 83445
208-624-3467
www.carterenterprises.com

Cavalier Archery Equipment Inc.
700 N. Nelly, #2
Gilbert, AZ 85233
480-497-2977
http://cavalier.safeshopper.com

Cobra Manufacturing
P.O. Box 667
Bixby, OK 74008
800-352-6272
www.cobraarchery.com

Code Blue
P.O. Box 1587
3601 Lind Rd.
Fort Smith, AR 72901
800-531-1201
www.codebluescents.com

Competition Electronics, Inc.
3469 Precision Dr.
Rockford, IL 61109
815-874-8001
www.competitionelectronics.com

DIRECTORY OF MANUFACTURERS

Contain Clothing
690 Industrial Circle
Shakopee, MN 55379
800-804-8588
www.containclothing.com

Copper John Corp.
173 State St.
Auburn, NY 13021
315-258-9269
www.copperjohn.com

Cranford Manufacturing
1927 Junction Rd.
Mocksville, NC 27028
336-284-2253
www.ezyclimb.com

Crimson Talon Broadheads
2XJ Enterprises, Inc.
320 Old Zion Rd.
North East, Maryland 21901
www.spintite.com

Custom Shooting Systems
5343 State Route 10
Salt Rock, WV 25701
304-736-3639
www.customshootingsystems.com

Darton Archery
P.O. Box 68
3540 Darton Rd.
Hale, MI 48739
989-728-4231
www.dartonarchery.com

DeerView Inc.
2618 15th Ave. East
North Saint Paul, MN 55109
651-773-1052
www.deerviewmirror.com

Doinker/Leven Industries
9025 Eton Ave., Unit D
Canoga Park, CA 91304
818-700-2899
www.doinker.com

DoskoSport
P.O. Box 1246
4300 Barnett Blvd.
Arlington, TX 76004
888-367-5624
www.doskosport.com

Double Bull Archery
P.O. Box 923
Monticello, MN 55362
763-295-3664
www.doublebullarchery.com

Easton
5040 Harold Gatty Dr.
Salt Lake City, UT 84116
801-539-1400
www.eastonarchery.com

Easy-Eye Archery Products
7196 Arkansaw Rd.
Allen, MI 49227
888-908-7446
www.eze-eye.com

Excalibur Crossbows
2335 Shirley Ave.
Kitchener, Ontario, Canada N2B
3X4
800-463-1817
www.excaliburcrossbow.com

Fedora Custom Bows
115 Wintersville Rd.
Richland, PA 17087
717-933-8862
www.fedoracustombows.com

Field Logic
101 Main St.
Superior, WI 54880
800-282-4868
http://fieldlogic.com/

Fine-Line
11304 Steele St.
Tacoma, WA 98499
800-445-0801
www.fine-linearchery.com

Firebrand Technologies
1546 Co. Rte. 45
Fulton, NY 13069
315-598-5348
www.discoverybowhunting.com

Flex-Fletch Products
1840 Chandler Ave.
Saint Paul, MN 55113
800-626-3844
www.flexfletch.com

Forge Bow Co.
2860 South 171st St.
New Berlin, WI 53151
414-732-7400
www.forgebow.com

Fred Bear Archery Co.
4600 Southwest 41st Blvd.
Gainesville, FL 32608-4999
352-376-2327
www.beararch.com

G5 Outdoors

P.O. Box 59
Memphis, TN 48041
810-392-8431
www.g5outdoors.com

Gateway Feathers
1015 West Lorenza Parkway
Douglas, AZ 85607
520-805-0863
www.gatewayfeathers.com

Gibbs Archery Gear
7781 Highway 167 South
Sheridan, AR 72150
870-942-4181
www.gagarchery.com

Global Resources Inc.
89 Lucas Dr.
Stoughton, MA 02072
781-341-2441
(no website)

Gold Tip Archery
352 South Industrial Dr
Orem, UT 84058
800-551-0541
www.goldtip.com

Golden Eagle
4600 Southwest 41st
Gainesville, FL 32608-4999
352-376-2327
www.beararch.com/goldeneagle

Golden Key Futura
14090-6100 Rd.
Montrose, CO 81402-1446
970-249-6700
www.goldenkeyarchery.com

Gorilla Tree Stands
P.O. Box 380
3476 Eastman Dr.
Flushing, MI 48433
800-241-4833
www.gorillatreestands.com

Great Lakes Crossbows
(see Darton Archery)

Great Plains Traditional Bow Co.
314 W. Foster Av.
Pampa, Texas 79065
806-665-5463
www.greatplains.pampa.com

Grim Reaper Broadheads
1250 North 1750 West
Provo, UT 84604-2955
801-377-6199
www.grimreaperbroadheads.com

H.S.Scents (Hunter's Specialties)
6000 Huntington Court NE
Cedar Rapids, IA 52402
319-395-0321
www.hunterspec.com

High Country Archery
P.O. Box 1269
312 Industrial Park Rd.
Dunlap, TN 37327
423-949-5000
www.highcountryarchery.com

Horne's Archery
P.O. Box 318
Boyd, TX 76023
940-433-3044
www.hornesarchery.com

Horton Manufacturing
484 Tacoma Ave.
Tallmadge, OH 44278
800-291-3649
www.crossbow.com

Hoyt USA
543 N. Neil Armstrong Rd
Salt Lake City, UT 84116
800-522-HOYT
www.hoytusa.com

Hughes Products Co.
P.O. Box 1066
112 Todd Court
Thomasville, NC 27360
336-475-0091
www.hughesproductsco.com

Hunter Safety System
8237 Danville Road
Danville, AL 35619
877-296-3528
www.deerhuntinggear.net

Hunter's Specialties
6600 Huntington Court
Northeast
Cedar Rapids, IA 52402
800-728-0321
www.hunterspec.com

Innerloc Broadheads
Sullivan Industries
1472 Camp Creek Rd.
Lakemont, GA 30552
706-782-5863
www.innerloc.com

interNature
AIM/ARCHERY International
Marketing
95 Milk St.

DIRECTORY OF MANUFACTURERS

Willimantic, CT 06226
888-246-8044
www.aimarchery.com

J.K. Chastain Archery
490 South Queen St.
Lakewood, CO 80226
303-989-1120
www.worldclassbows.com

Jennings Archery
4600 Southwest 41st Blvd.
Gainesville, FL 32608-4999
352-376-2327
www.beararch.com/jennings

Jim Fletcher Archery
(Fletchhunter)
P.O. Box 218
Bodfish, CA 93205
760-379-2589
www.fletcherarchery.com

Knight & Hale Calls
P.O. Box 1587
3601 Jenny Lind Rd.
Fort Smith, AR 72901
800-531-1201
www.knightandhale.com

Kolpin Outdoors Inc.
P.O. Box 107
205 DePot St.
Fox Lake, WI 53933
800-5KOLPIN
www.kolpin.com

Kwikee Kwiver Co.
P.O. Box 130
7972 Peaceful Valley Rd
800-346-7001
www.kwikeekwiver.com

Lansky Sharpeners
P.O. Box 50830
Las Vegas, NV 89016
702-361-7511
www.lansky.com

Lohman
4500 Doniphan Dr.
Neosho, MO 64850
800-922-9034
(no website)

Mag Sight Products
156 Middle Line Rd.
Ballston Spa, NY 12020
518-885-7199
www.magsightproducts.com

Mahaska Custom Bows

P.O. Box 452
Oskaloosa, IA 52577
641-673-5501
www.mahaskacustombows.com

Martin Archery
3134 W. Highway 12
Walla Walla, WA 99362-9483
800-541-8902
www.martinarchery.com

Mathews
P.O. Box 367
919 River Rd.
Sparta, WI 54656
608-269-2728
www.mathewsinc.com

McKenzie Targets
P.O. Box 480
Granite Quarry, NC 28072
888-279-7985
www.mckenzie3d.com

McPherson Archery Co.
P.O. Box 327
Brewton, AL 36427
251-867-8475
www.benpearson.com

Modoc Broadheads
33 South Pit Lane
Nampa, ID 83687
208-466-1827
www.modocbroadheads.com

Monarch Bows
P.O. Box 433
Darby, MT 59829
406-821-1948
www.monarch-bows.com

Montana Black Gold
34370 East Frontage Rd
Bozeman, MT 59715
800-336-0853
www.montanablackgold.com

Montana Decoy
P.O. Box 2377
Colstrip, MT 59323
406-748-3092
www.montanadecoy.com

Moosejaw Bows
P.O. Box 790
Cave Junction, OR 97523
541-592-6954
(no website)

Morrell Eternity Targets
1721 Hwy. 71 North

Alma, AR 72921
www.morrelltargets.com

MountTek Products
18700 Statesville Rd., #105
Cornelius, NC 28031
704-895-8649
(no website)

Muzzy Products Corp.
110 Beasley Rd.
Cartersville, GA 30120
800-222-7769
www.badtothebone.com

Neet
5875 Easy Highway 50
Sedalia, MO 65301
800-821-7196
www.neet.com

New Archery Products (NAP)
7500 Industrial Dr.
Forest Park, IL 60130
800-323-1279
www.newarchery.com

North American Archery Group
4600 S.W. 41st Blvd.
Gainesville, FL 32608
352-376-2327

Oneida Eagle Bow
20669 30th Ave.
Marion, MI 49665
231-743-2427
www.oneidaeaglebows.com

P & P Outdoors
330 Bond Rd.
Louisville, MS 39339
662-773-7956
(no website)

Pacific Bow Butts Target System
P.O. Box 108
Ilwaco, WA 98624
877-642-4989
www.pacificbowbutts.com

Palmer Bow Co.
408 North Center St.
Sabinal, TX 78881
830-988-2019
www.palmerbows.com

Parker Compound Bows
Route 11 South
Mint Spring, VA 24463
800-707-8149
www.parkerbows.com

Phantom Broadheads
6605 Rockmark Hwy. SE
Silver Creek, GA 30173
770-607-9922
(no website)

Plano Molding Co.
431 East South St.
Plano, IL 60545
800-874-6905
www.planomolding.com

Precision Designed Products (PDP)
3999 CR 5200 Archery Le
Independence, KS 67301
620-331-0333
www.pdparchery.com

Precision Shooting Equipment (PSE)
P.O. Box 5487
2727 North Fairview
Tucson, AZ 85703
520-884-9065
www.pse-archery.com

ProChrono
(see Competition Electronics)

Pro Releases
33551 Giftos St.
Clinton Township, MI 48054
800-845-8515

Pro Release Inc.
33551 Giftos
Clinton Twp., MS 48035
810-792-1410
www.bowhunting.net/prorelease

R.S. Archery Products
335 West John St.
Hicksville, NY 11801
800-444-9619
www.rsbowvise.com

Razor Caps
#6 Terrapin Lane
Mercerville, NJ 08619
609-890-2010
www.razorcaps.com

Reflex Inc.
543 North Neil Armstrong Rd
Salt Lake City, UT 84116
800-522-HOYT
www.reflexbow.com

Renegade Archery Co.
18706 County Highway Q
Bloomer, WI 54724

DIRECTORY OF MANUFACTURERS

715-568-2730
www.renegadebows.com

Revolution Archery
2783 Pueblo Road
Canton, KS 67428
800-293-2928
www.mpks.net/home-page/revarch

Rinehart 3-D Targets
1029 South Jackson St.
Janesville, WI 53546
608-757-8153
www.rinehart3-d.com

Robinson Outdoors Inc.
P.O. Box 18
110 North Park Dr.
Cannon Falls, MN
55009-0018
800-397-1927
www.robinsonoutdoors.com

Samick Sports Co.
AIM/Archery International
Marketing
95 Milk St.
Willimantic, CT 06226
888-246-8044
www.aimarchery.com

Satellite Archery
C/o North American
Archery Group
4600 Southwest 41st
Blvd. Gainesville, FL
32608-4999
352-376-2327

Saunders Archery USA
P.O. Box 476
1874 14th Ave.
Columbus, NE 68601
800-228-1408
www.sausa.com

Savage Systems
110 North Front St.
Oak Grove, LA 71263
800-545-4868
www.savagearchery.com

Scent-Lok
1731 Wierengo Dr.
Muskegon, MI 49442
800-315-5799
www.scentlok.com

**Schaffer Performance
Archery**
1403 East Cliff Rd.

Burnsville, MN 55337
952-894-6169
www.schafferarchery.com

Scorpion
(see New Archery Products)

Scorpyon Technologies
5603 E. Hop Toad Rd.
Kingman, AZ 86401
928-757-9328
www.scorpyon
tecnologies.com

**Scrape Juice Hunting
Products**
208 Lake Lillian Rd.
Perry GA 30169
478-988-4594
www.scrapejuice
products.com

Sherwood Archery
P.O. Box 421
Bellevue, NE 68005
888-228-1442
www.sherwoodarchery.com

Shooting Chrony Inc.
3840 East Robinson Rd.,
PMB # 298
Amherst, NY 14228
905-276-6292
http://chrony.ca

Simmons System Archery
157 Win-Dre Dr.
Jasper, AL 35504
205-387-7174
www.simmonssharks.com

SKB Cases
1607 N. O'Donnell Way
Orange, CA 92867
800-654-5992
www.skbcases.com

**Specialty Archery
Products**
P.O. Box 889
10510 265th St.
Clear Lake, IA 50428
641-424-5762
www.specialtyarch.com

**Sportsman's Outdoor
Products**
9352 South 670
Sandy, UT 84070
801-562-8712
www.gotarantula.com

Sports Sensors Inc.
P.O. Box 46198
Cincinnati, OH 45246
800-589-3805
www.archeryradar.com

Stacey Archery Sales
6866 Jennifer Lane
Idaho Falls, ID 83401
208-523-7278
(no website)

Starrflight
888-488-4712
www.starrflight.com

Steel Force Broadheads
P.O. Box 9
Rosemont, NJ 08556
609-397-1990
www.steelforce.com

Strawberry Wilderness
1031 Bridge St.
Prairie City, OR 97869
541-820-4346
www.strawberry
wilderness.com

Strong Case
by TnB Enterprises, Inc.
26563 Corporate Ave.
Hayward, CA 94545
510-732-6400
www.strongcasebytnb.com

Summit Specialties
715 Summit Dr. Southeast
Decatur, AL 35601
256-353-0634
www.summitstands.com

Sure-Loc Archery Products
C.S. Gibbs Corperation
100 Quality Lane
Versailles, IN 47042
812-689-9926
www.sureloc.com

T.R.U. Ball Release
P.O. Box 1180
131 Crennel Dr.
Madison Heights, VA
24572
800-724-4878
www.truball.com

TailorMaid Archery
Products
3627 11th St.
Wyandotte, MI 48192
734-246-3182

www.stringmaker.com

Toxonics Manufacturing
1324 Wilmer Rd.
Wentzville, MO 63385
636-639-8502
www.toxonics.com

Trap Door
34370 Frontage Rd.
Bozeman, MT 59715
406-586-1117
www.trapdoorrest.com

Trophy Ridge
732 Cruiser Lane,
Suite 200
Belgrade, MT 59714
406-388-7781
www.trophyridge.com

Trophy Taker
P.O. Box 1137
Plains, MT 59859
406-826-0600
www.trophytaker.com

**Trueflight
Manufacturing Co.**
P.O. Box 1000
Hwy. 51 S.
Manitowish Waters,
WI 54545
715-543-8410
www.trueflightfeathers.com

TRUGLO
P.O. Box 1612
13475 Neutron Rd.
McKinney, TX 75070
972-774-0300
www.truglosights.com

Vibracheck Stablilizers
10003 Raymar St.
Pensacola, FL 32534
850-857-0092
www.vibracheck.com

Walker's Game Ear
P.O. Box 1069
Media, PA 19063
800-424-1069
www.walkersgameear.com

Wasp Archery Products
707 Main St.
Plymouth, CT 06782
860-283-0246
www.wasparchery.com

Whitewater Outdoors
W4228 Church St.
Hingham, WI 53031
800-666-2674
www.whitewaterout-doors.com

Wildlife Research Center
1050 McKinley St.
Anoka, MN 55303
800-873-5873
www.wildlife.com

Wildwood Innovations
Route 4, Box 286
Ashland, WI 54806
715-685-0020
www.bowstands.com

Wing Archery Co.
227 Center Grove Rd.
Randolph, NJ 07869
973-989-8957
www.bobleearchery.com

Winn Archery Equip. Co.
13757 64th St.
South Haven, MI 49090
616-637-2658
www.winnarchery.com

**Wizard Outdoor
Products**
974 Home Place Road
Wetumpka, AL 36093
866-723-6899
www.wizardoutdoors.com

Woods Wise Products
P.O. Box 681552(W)
Franklin, TN 37068
800.735-8182
www.woodswise.com

Zwickey Archery
2571 East 12th Ave.
North St. Paul,
MN 55109
651-777-1965
(no website)

ARCHER'S BIBLE INDEX

ARCHER'S BIBLE INDEX

ARCHER'S BIBLE INDEX

ARCHER'S BIBLE INDEX

ARCHER'S BIBLE INDEX

INDEX